RUST BOOK

This is the ultimate auction book and the only guide you'll need when cruising the Internet in search of ancient iron. Auction guru Greg "Machinery Pete" Peterson has compiled over 8,000 auction prices covering all types of antique tractors, implements, and trucks. No estimates, guesses, or rules of thumb were used to arrive at these prices. This is real-time data – an accumulation of actual prices collectors have paid for antique machinery over the past five years.

And to assist in your search for old iron, we've also included the most complete listing of serial numbers by tractor make ever assembled, Nebraska Tractor Test results, and our exclusive club and publication list complete this, the first edition of *Rust Book*!

RUST BOOK

Rust Book by Greg Peterson
Successful Farming® Magazine
Senior Vice President: Doug Olson
Group Publisher, Men's Brands: Tom Davis
Publisher: Scott Mortimer
Editor In Chief: Loren Kruse
New Product Manager: Diana Willits
Consumer Marketing: Brenda Torsky

Ageless Iron Almanac™
Editor: Dave Mowitz
Art Director: Mark McManus
Managing Editor: P.D. Barbour
Designer: Ray Neubauer
Contributing Designer: Kathy Grove
Copy Editor: Steve Hakeman
Art Coordinator: Staci Bailey

It's worth HOW much?

A book just on old equipment prices?

Are you kidding me?

That would have been my reaction to such an idea 16 years ago, back in late 1989 when I got into the business of auction sale price data on farm equipment. My focus at the time was squarely on newer equipment. Sure, I tracked prices on all types of equipment, big stuff, small stuff, new, and old – but the big-ticket items were of utmost interest to me.

Old tractors and equipment were almost an afterthought on my part way back then. Guess I was young and stupid. Over the years I've been staggered by the response I've gotten to each and every "Machinery Pete" column I've written that has focused on antique tractors.

Back in 1990, in my first full year of tracking sale prices, John Deere Model B tractors sold for an average of $650 at auction. Flash forward to today and they are going for an average of $2,354 as I write this.

That represents a whopping jump in value of 362.2%!

Way back in 1990, Farmall Super MTAs sold for an average of $1,831 at auction. Now they are bringing an average of $5,273, up 288%.

Wow! Just a couple examples of the astounding growth in the antique tractor market over the past decade and a half. Quite honestly, tracking auction sale prices on these oldies but goodies has turned into one of my favorite endeavors. It's a rush to locate antique tractors at auction and then to see what they sell for.

Amazing!

That's why this project is so special to me because I know how deeply so many of you care about antique farm equipment. It's my hope that the information you find in this book, from the auction sale data to the average price data to the serial number info can be tremendously helpful, and you can utilize it as you continue pursuing your Ageless Iron passion.

Feel free to wear the cover off. It's our hope, indeed, that you'll use this book that much.

We've developed the book with an eye to the future of the antique farm equipment market, too. You'll find data on tractors from the 1920s, '30s, '40s, and '50s, yes, but also on tractors and other equipment from the '60s up through the mid-'70s as well. Maybe not quite in the antique category yet, but it will be someday soon. Enjoy!

Greg "Machinery Pete" Peterson

This is the real deal on prices

Rust Book isn't the first publication to track the value of antique farm machinery. In fact there are several books that attempt to *estimate* the value of old iron. Notice the emphasis I put on the word estimate.

Unlike these other efforts, the values you'll find in the following pages are *actual*. No guesstimates here, folks. These are real prices on recent purchases.

How recent? Try the last four years! Now that's up-to-date.

And if that doesn't put *Rust Book* at the top of any antique machinery reference list, consider that this guide is authored by THE expert in the world of farm machinery – Greg Peterson. Farmers, dealers, and ag bankers have depended on Greg's guidance to put a value on farm iron for over a decade.

So here it is – the first truly accurate price guide to Ageless Iron.

Dave Mowitz

contents

serial numbers

contents

nebraska tractor test results

abbreviations

AC = air conditioning

auto = automatic transmission

aux. = auxiliary

bkt. = bucket

bu. = bushel

cyl. = engine cylinders

GVWR = gross vehicle weight rating

hi-lo = high/low speed transmission

hp. = horsepower

hyd. = hydraulics

K = 1,000 miles

LP = liquefied petroleum

NF = narrow front

OD = overdrive

OH = engine overhaul

power adj. = power adjustable rear wheels

PS = power steering

pt = pull type

PTO = power take-off

ROPS = roll-over protective structures

sep = separator

SN = serial number

SP = self-propelled

spd. = speed

Std. = standard front axle

TA = torque amplifier

trans. = transmission

WF = wide front

1 hyd. = one hydraulic outlet

2 hyd. = two hydraulic outlets

1 pt. = one-point hitch

2 pt. = two-point hitch

3 pt. = three-point hitch

2WD = two-wheel drive

4WD = four-wheel drive

Area

The abbreviation under this column represents the region of a state in which the machinery sold. Example:

NEIA = northeast Iowa

Cond. = Condition

The following indicates the overall condition of the machinery as it sold at auction.

P = poor

F = fair

G = good

E = excellent

allis-chalmers

Allis-Chalmers traces its roots back to 1847 and the firm of Decker & Seville, which was known for its flour mills. In 1861 that firm was purchased by Edward Allis, who created a company that would become world famous for its flour mills, sawmills, and steam engines. Edward P. Allis & Company merged with Fraser & Chalmers in 1901 to create Allis-Chalmers Company. This new firm continued to expand its product line eventually offering a tractor, the Model 10-18, in 1914. Important acquisitions during Allis-Chalmer's history include Monarch Tractor in 1928, Advance-Rumely in 1931, and Gleaner Harvester in 1955. The Allis name lives on in today's farm machinery giant AGCO, which stands for Allis Gleaner Company.

allis-chalmers

Model	Year	Hours	Cond.	Price	Date	Area	Comments
160			F	$500	1/06	WCCA	Canopy, 1hyd
170		9,725	F	$2,400	2/05	WCOK	3 pt., PTO, 1 hyd., diesel, tires poor
170			G	$3,750	4/04	ECWI	
170			G	$4,600	4/04	SWPA	Gas
170			G	$5,900	3/04	SCMN	Loader
170	1968		G	$3,000	9/04	ECIA	Gas, WF, chains, 3 pt., late 1968 model
170			G	$4,100	9/05	SCON	Canadian sale, 2WD, diesel, 3 pt.
170			G	$4,750	3/05	ECMN	Gas
180			F	$3,600	1/04	NCIL	Gas, jumps out of 4th gear
180			G	$5,100	4/04	NEIN	Fresh OH
180			F	$5,600	12/04	WCIL	Gas, WF, with loader, new tires
180			G	$3,850	8/03	NWIL	AC, loader, diesel
180			G	$4,750	10/03	SCNE	Diesel
180			G	$5,700	8/03	WCIN	Original
180	1967	1,970	G	$5,750	3/03	NCOH	2 hyd., repainted, 18.4-28" tires
190			G	$0	12/04	ECMI	No sale at $1,750, gas, 2 pt.
190	1970		G	$4,250	11/05	NCIN	Series III
190XT			G	$6,500	1/06	ECIL	Series III, sold With Westendorf TA-26 loader & 6' bucket, cab
190XT			F	$3,100	12/05	WCMN	Series III, With koyker loader, 3 pt., PTO, 2 hyd.
190XT		3,092	F	$4,200	1/05	SWIL	
190XT		7,370	G	$5,000	1/05	ECNE	2 hyd.
190XT		4,105	F	$3,300	6/04	ECMN	Diesel, restored to new condition in looks only, smokes
190XT		3,557	G	$3,350	6/04	ECMN	Cab, diesel, unrestored, runs well, no smoke, 3 pt., PTO
190XT			F	$2,400	4/04	NEND	Diesel, 2 hyd., PTO, 18.4-34" dual tires
190XT			F	$4,500	4/04	NWPA	
190XT	1964	6,408	G	$2,000	2/04	NEIN	WF, console
190XT	1965	6,882	F	$3,300	2/04	WCMN	2 hyd., 3 pt., 540/1000 PTO, cab
190XT	1970		G	$3,200	11/05	NCIN	Series III, 2 hyd., 18.4-34
190XT	1972		G	$3,200	3/03	SWMI	Diesel, 18.4-34" tires
200		7,991	F	$3,600	3/05	SCMI	Canopy, 6 front weights, diesel
200		2,900	G	$5,900	2/05	NCIN	
200	1973		G	$5,800	2/05	NCIN	Diesel, cab, like new engine
200	1974		G	$6,200	4/05	SWMN	WF, diesel, year-round cab, 3 pt., 2 hyd., 16.9-38" tires
200			F	$2,250	5/04	NEPA	Diesel, platform 2 hyd., live PTO, needs trans. work
200		4,100	G	$6,600	4/04	SWPA	Cab
200	1974	2,585	G	$3,200	1/06	SCMI	WF, diesel, PTO, 3 pt., 6 front weights
200	1974	3,600	G	$5,500	9/04	NCIA	Factory cab, 18.4-38" tires
200			F	$3,000	7/03	SEMN	Diesel
200			P	$3,100	3/03	NCCO	2 speed was out
200	1974	2,185	G	$5,800	3/03	NCOK	Diesel, good rubber, 3 pt., PTO, 2 hyd., 8-speed
200	1975		G	$6,950	7/03	WCMN	2 hyd., 3 pt., PTO, cab, 18.4-38" tires, hub duals, rock box, 1 owner, diesel
B			G	$900	1/06	NEMO	
B			G	$1,400	11/05	WCIL	WF, hand start, overhaul
B			F	$550	9/05	NEIN	
B			G	$900	9/05	NENE	WF, steel wheels
B			F	$860	4/05	SEND	6' finish belly mower, WF
B			G	$1,075	3/05	SCIL	Electric start

allis-chalmers

Model	Year	Hours	Cond.	Price	Date	Area	Comments
B			E	$1,525	7/05	ECMN	Buyers premium 8% - final total = $1,647, NF, new paint, new tires
B			G	$2,200	6/05	ECIL	12-volt conversion, new paint
B			G	$1,525	4/04	ECWI	6' mounted mower
B			G	$1,600	12/04	ECNE	Clean, running
B	1939		G	$1,450	9/04	NECO	Restored, fair tires
B	1945		F	$500	3/04	SEWY	NF, PTO
B	1949		G	$2,200	9/04	SEND	PTO, 10-24" rears, 12-volt conversion, engine kit, turned crank
B			P	$325	9/03	SCMI	WF, did not run
B			G	$650	8/03	NWIL	Gas, 3 pt.
B			G	$1,550	10/03	ECMN	
B			F	$1,700	7/03	SEND	60" belly mower, WF
B			G	$1,800	8/03	SEMN	With cultivator
B			G	$1,950	7/03	SCMN	Woods mower
B			G	$2,000	3/03	ECND	WF, Sunmaster 5' belly mower
B	1941		F	$750	12/03	WCMI	4 cyl., gas, WF, PTO, 11-24" tires, saw, 30 hrs. on OH
C			G	$1,900	11/05	WCIL	WF, elect, converted to 12-volt, restored
C			G	$800	11/05	WCIL	NF, fenders, PTO, belt pully
C	1944		G	$1,125	8/05	NEIN	NF, sickle mower
C			F	$1,100	4/05	SCMI	NF, 5' belly sickle mower
C			G	$900	4/04	NWMN	Belly-mount mower
C			F	$1,200	9/04	WCMN	NF
C			F	$400	6/03	NCWI	Missing 2 tires
C			F	$750	5/03	WCIN	
C			F	$850	7/03	SEND	Prischmann 5' belly mower
C			G	$900	3/03	SEND	Belly mower, like new rubber, 9.5-24" tires
C			G	$1,100	7/03	SEND	Woods 5' belly mower
C			F	$1,150	8/03	SEPA	NF, cultivators, average rubber, good paint
C			G	$1,300	7/03	NEOH	
C			G	$2,050	3/03	ECND	Woods 60" belly mower, new paint
C	1945		E	$1,500	6/03	NEIL	Restored, NF, SN 33126
CA			G	$1,500	11/05	WCIL	NF
CA			G	$1,900	7/05	SESD	WF, planter, cult., plow and disk, runs
CA			G	$2,800	11/05	WCIA	WF
CA			F	$400	11/04	NWNY	
CA			G	$1,200	1/04	NEOH	
CA			G	$1,300	7/04	NWMN	
CA			G	$2,100	12/04	SEMN	Woods 5' belly mower
CA			F	$625	9/03	ECND	NF, PTO, Woods mower, bad water pump
CA			G	$1,600	9/03	NWIA	NF, fenders, Woods 6' belly mower
CA			G	$2,500	8/03	NWIA	NF, gas
CA	1952		G	$1,350	9/03	NEIN	Gas, NF
D10			G	$2,800	11/05	WCIL	Old restoration, repaint, 3pt
D10			G	$4,200	11/05	WCIL	WF, unrestored, front rock shaft
D12			G	$4,000	11/05	WCIL	WF, restored
D14			G	$1,700	10/05	WCIL	WF
D14			G	$2,500	11/05	SEND	
D14			G	$2,800	8/04	NCIA	Gas, NF, front pump, snow and manure bucket
D14			F	$3,000	10/04	SEPA	WF, good paint, rubber average

10

Model	Year	Hours	Cond.	Price	Date	Area	Comments
D14			G	$3,100	4/04	ECWI	WF
D14			F	$1,500	12/03	WCMI	Gas, loader, PTO, 2 pt.
D14			F	$1,900	8/03	NWIL	Diesel, Woods 5' mower
D15			G	$3,000	11/05	WCIL	WF, gas, old restoration, 3 pt.
D15			G	$5,600	9/05	NEIN	LP, series II
D15			G	$2,900	1/05	SWIL	Row crop, 2 pt.
D15			G	$3,200	3/05	WCIL	Gas, WF, PS
D15			G	$1,300	1/04	ECNE	WF, 2 pt.
D15			E	$3,100	2/03	NENE	WF, near new tires
D17			G	$1,050	12/05	WCOH	Duals
D17			F	$1,575	9/05	SEIA	
D17			G	$1,950	12/05	SEND	Farmhand loader
D17			G	$2,200	3/05	ECMN	Gas
D17			G	$2,300	11/05	WCIL	WF, gas, fenders
D17			G	$2,500	11/05	WCIL	WF, gas, PS, front weights
D17			G	$4,200	12/05	SEMN	WF
D17		5179	G	$5,000	11/05	ECIL	Series 4, 3 pt., WF, gas
D17	1962		G	$3,175	7/05	SESD	Series 4, WF, snap hitch
D17	1967		G	$5,700	11/05	SWMN	Series 4, gas, WF, cab, 3 pt., 2 hyd.
D17			G	$3,950	6/04	ECMN	Gas, WF, restored to new condition, runs great, loader
D17			P	$1,625	4/05	NCOH	Duals, cab, clutch sticks
D17			P	$1,625	4/05	NCOH	
D17			F	$2,000	3/05	NWIL	Loader, WF, gas
D17			F	$2,600	4/05	NCOH	Gas, WF, PS, wheel weights, 1 hyd.
D17		4,800	F	$2,600	4/05	SCMI	NF, AC, loader, LP
D17	1958		G	$1,300	1/05	NENE	Gas, WF, rock shaft, 540/1000 PTO, 14.9-28" rear tires
D17	1958		G	$3,000	2/05	NCIN	Diesel, 3 pt., WF
D17	1964	4,400	G	$4,900	6/05	ECIL	WF, power adj.
D17			G	$0	12/04	ECMI	No sale at $2,400, gas, WF, 3 pt.
D17			F	$750	3/04	SEIA	
D17			G	$1,350	12/04	NEND	3 pt., PTO
D17			F	$1,700	4/04	NEPA	
D17			G	$1,800	9/04	SEIA	
D17			G	$3,000	3/04	WCMN	Loader, separate hyd.
D17			G	$3,200	7/04	ECMN	Gas
D17			G	$3,650	5/04	NEPA	Gas
D17	1959		F	$1,550	2/04	NEIN	Gas, NF
D17			P	$975	7/03	SEMN	Gas
D17			G	$1,000	9/03	NEIN	Hi-crop
D17			G	$1,600	4/03	WCWI	Gas, WF
D17			F	$1,600	3/03	NENE	Gas
D17			F	$1,850	8/03	WCMN	Forklift mounted on rear of tractor, 10-12' lift
D17			G	$2,300	3/03	SEND	Series III, WF, 7' tilt bucket loader, gas
D17			G	$4,300	4/03	SEIN	Series IV, gas
D17			G	$5,100	3/03	NWIL	Series IV, WF
D17	1958		G	$2,100	6/03	NWIL	Gas, WF
D17	1958		G	$2,250	3/03	NESD	WF, PS, 3 pt., conversion, OH, very good tin
D17	1960		G	$2,250	9/03	SCMN	
D17	1964		G	$5,700	3/03	SEIA	Series IV, #400 loader
D17	1966	4,000	E	$8,500	3/03	NCOH	Series IV, Dunham loader, 3 pt., repainted, showroom condition
D19			F	$1,700	4/05	NCOH	WF, aux. fuel tank, snap coupler, 1 hyd., duals, weak fuel pump

allis-chalmers

Model	Year	Hours	Cond.	Price	Date	Area	Comments
D19			E	$2,300	4/05	NCOK	LP, snap-on duals, ran great, fresh OH
D19			G	$3,000	1/05	SWIL	3 pt.
D19			G	$2,100	12/04	SEMN	WF
D19			F	$3,500	4/04	NEPA	
D19			G	$1,300	9/03	NEIN	
D19	1962		G	$2,500	6/03	NWIL	Gas, cab, WF
D21			G	$6,000	3/03	SWWI	
D21	1966		F	$2,500	4/03	NWMN	Cab
G			G	$1,250	9/05	NWOR	Row crop, gas
G			G	$3,250	11/05	WCIL	Diesel, restored, hand start
G	1948		G	$1,300	6/05	ECIL	Elect. lift blade, new tires
G			G	$2,000	11/04	WCIL	Rebuilt engine, gas
G			G	$975	9/03	NEIN	
G			G	$2,400	6/03	WCMI	
G			G	$2,750	9/03	NEIN	
G	1948		F	$1,500	9/03	SCMI	With cultivator
RC			F	$1,100	11/05	SWMN	For restoration
RC			G	$800	9/03	NEIN	
U			G	$3,000	6/05	ECWI	
UC			G	$900	9/03	NEIN	
WC			F	$525	9/05	NENE	Drawbar, 13-24 tires
WC			F	$600	10/05	NEPA	
WC			G	$750	11/05	WCIL	
WC	1941		G	$850	12/05	NWIL	NF, good rubber
WC			G	$1,150	6/05	WCMN	NF, PTO
WC			E	$1,400	1/05	SWIL	Completely rebuilt, new tires
WC			E	$600	11/04	NCKS	NF, good rubber & paint
WC			G	$1,300	5/04	ECMN	Gas
WC			G	$1,350	9/04	ECMN	Gas, with loader
WC			G	$1,450	9/04	ECMN	Gas, factory WF
WC	1940		F	$350	5/04	NCKS	
WC	1941		F	$680	2/04	WCIL	Gas, WD motor, NF, fenders
WC	1943		F	$450	7/04	NCIA	Mechanical lift
WC	1947		G	$700	8/04	WCMN	New paint, good rubber
WC			P	$225	6/03	WCMI	For parts
WC			F	$750	10/03	ECNE	
WC			G	$800	9/03	SCMN	
WC			G	$800	9/03	NEIN	
WC			F	$1,650	4/03	WCMN	Blade, 7'
WC	1936		E	$2,000	6/03	NEIL	NF, fenders, clean
WC	1938		F	$725	12/03	NCOH	Round spoke rears, new rubber, 1 owner, original condition
WC	1939		P	$800	8/03	NCOH	Rough
WD			G	$1,200	2/06	ECMN	WF, good tin
WD			G	$1,075	7/05	SESD	
WD			G	$1,250	12/05	ECIN	With rotary mower, gas
WD	1951		F	$675	12/05	ECIL	
WD			G	$1,550	11/05	WCMN	WF
WD			P	$200	11/05	ECNE	Loader
WD			G	$2,100	11/05	SEND	WF, 3 pt., loader

Model	Year	Hours	Cond.	Price	Date	Area	Comments
WD			F	$450	10/05	NEPA	
WD	1954		G	$1,550	10/05	SWSD	2 pt., gas, good rear rubber, runs good
WD			G	$700	11/05	WCIL	NF, fenders
WD			G	$850	9/05	WCMN	NF, good paint & rubber
WD			G	$900	11/05	WCIL	
WD			F	$925	9/05	SEIA	Blade
WD	1949		G	$1,650	8/05	NEIN	Repainted, 3-bottom plow
WD	1949		G	$650	11/05	WCIL	NF, PTO, 3 pt.
WD			F	$475	3/05	NWIL	Gas, NF
WD			F	$900	2/05	NWWI	3 pt.
WD			G	$1,600	4/05	NCOH	Styled, loader and manure fork
WD			G	$2,100	6/05	WCMN	NF, PTO
WD	1947		G	$1,350	4/05	NCOK	Loader, bolt-on duals, PS, rebuilt WD-45 motor, WF
WD	1949		G	$625	4/05	NCOK	Gas, ran rough, WF
WD	1949		G	$1,400	4/05	NEIN	Gas, NF
WD	1950		G	$1,000	6/05	ECIL	6' side mount twin-belt sickle mower
WD	1951		G	$1,050	3/05	NCIA	Fenders, 12 volt
WD			P	$375	3/04	WCIL	Gas, loader
WD			P	$600	4/04	NEND	WF, PTO, doesn't run
WD			P	$800	10/04	NCOH	WF
WD			F	$1,000	4/04	NEPA	
WD			G	$1,600	7/04	ECMN	Gas
WD			G	$1,800	9/04	NECO	Restored, 3 pt.
WD			G	$1,900	12/04	SCMN	Reversed loader
WD			G	$2,000	8/04	NCIA	WF, sold, Stanhoist trip loader, gas
WD	1949		G	$1,100	2/04	ECNE	Loader
WD	1950		G	$925	11/04	WCMN	WF, 12-volt, 13.6-12.28" rubber
WD	1950		G	$1,700	9/04	NCIA	Woods 306 belly mower
WD			G	$275	9/03	NEIN	
WD			P	$425	7/03	SCMN	602 Ford, 2-row mounted corn picker, not running
WD			F	$550	2/03	SWOK	
WD			F	$600	3/03	ECND	Paulson loader, 2 pt.
WD			F	$600	12/03	NCIA	With loader
WD			F	$650	3/03	WCMI	PTO, gas
WD			F	$750	4/03	WCMN	
WD			G	$950	6/03	WCWI	New paint
WD			F	$975	8/03	WCMN	Loader
WD			F	$1,125	6/03	WCMN	NF
WD			E	$1,450	6/03	SENE	Gas
WD			G	$1,650	8/03	SCNE	
WD			G	$2,000	10/03	ECMN	
WD	1948		F	$1,300	9/03	SCMI	
WD	1953		F	$600	9/03	NEIN	NF, gas
WD	1954		G	$925	9/03	NEIN	NF, gas
WD45			G	$1,350	1/06	SCMI	NF, gas
WD45			G	$1,000	11/05	WCIL	
WD45			G	$1,000	11/05	WCIL	NF
WD45			F	$1,350	8/05	NWIL	Gas
WD45			G	$1,600	11/05	SWMN	With loader

allis-chalmers

Model	Year	Hours	Cond.	Price	Date	Area	Comments
WD45			G	$1,900	11/05	WCMN	WF, 1 hyd., 12-volt
WD45			G	$3,100	11/05	WCIL	WF, gas, snap coupler
WD45			E	$4,000	11/05	WCIA	New rubber, WF
WD45			G	$4,700	10/05	SWSD	WF, PS, loader & attachments
WD45			F	$750	8/05	SCMI	NF, rear blade
WD45	1955		G	$950	11/05	ECNE	
WD45	1957		G	$2,550	8/05	NEIN	WF, loader
WD45			F	$1,800	4/05	NCOH	Gas, WF, PS, trip loader, 1 hyd.
WD45			G	$2,200	6/05	SEND	WF, gas, PTO, wheel weights, PS
WD45			G	$4,100	2/05	SCMN	PS
WD45	1954		G	$700	6/05	ECIL	NF, power adj.
WD45	1957		G	$1,800	6/05	ECIL	WF, 3 pt., rear weights, 12-volt conversion
WD45			E	$640	11/04	NCKS	Repainted
WD45			E	$640	11/04	NCKS	Repainted
WD45			E	$700	11/04	NCKS	NF, fair rubber, good paint
WD45			E	$750	11/04	NCKS	NF, fair rubber, good paint
WD45			G	$750	11/04	NCKS	Good rubber & paint, NF
WD45			G	$875	11/04	WCIL	1 owner, gas
WD45			G	$1,000	4/04	ECWI	WF
WD45			E	$1,000	11/04	NCKS	WF, good rubber & paint
WD45			G	$1,050	1/04	NEOH	
WD45			G	$1,250	7/04	SEIN	Gas, NF
WD45			G	$1,300	4/04	ECWI	WF
WD45			G	$1,500	3/04	NEWI	WF, hyd.
WD45			G	$1,600	7/04	ECMN	Gas
WD45			G	$1,650	12/04	WCIL	Gas, WF
WD45			G	$1,800	11/04	NCKS	Good rubber & paint, NF
WD45			E	$4,000	11/04	NCKS	LP, very few made, NF, fair rubber, good paint
WD45	1954		G	$3,000	9/04	NECO	Runs, WF, new tires, single front, OH
WD45	1957		E	$2,400	11/04	NEKS	1 owner, WF, good rubber & paint, gas, snap coupler
WD45			G	$450	9/03	NEIN	Gas
WD45			F	$625	8/03	NEKS	
WD45			F	$800	12/03	SCNE	
WD45			G	$875	10/03	NWMN	2 pt., PTO
WD45			G	$900	7/03	WCSK	
WD45			G	$900	7/03	ECND	Aftermarket WF, 2 pt.
WD45			F	$1,000	10/03	ECNE	
WD45			G	$1,200	7/03	SCMN	Single-wheel front, running when parked
WD45			G	$4,000	9/03	NEIN	Diesel
WD45	1954		G	$2,150	1/03	SEIL	Snap coupler, 10-hp. elec. tractor
WD45	1954		E	$3,000	3/03	NCOH	Repainted, very nice
WD45	1955		F	$4,650	10/03	ECIN	Diesel
21B	1970		G	$11,000	11/03	ECND	Crawler, winch, blade, diesel
7G	1950		G	$3,500	3/04	SEWY	Diesel, extra tracks, crawler loader
FP80	1970		G	$4,500	7/04	NWMN	Forklift, gas, 8000 lbs., dual drive, 12' ht
HD 21	1966		P	$2,000	11/03	ECND	Crawler, diesel, rear plow, engine bad
HD 21	1967		F	$5,000	11/03	ECND	Crawler, diesel
HD 5	1950		F	$1,250	9/04	NECO	Runs, bucket
HD 7	1947		F	$7,000	3/04	NWMN	Crawler, high-lift hyd. dozer, live hyd., 12-volt, 1 owner

This line of tractors traces its roots back to B.F. Avery & Sons founded in 1825. By the 1940s the Louisville, Kentucky-based firm had grown into a full-fledged manufacturer of farm implements. The company bought the General GC tractor from Cleveland Tractor in 1943, which spawned the B.F. Avery tractor line.

b.f. avery

Model	Year	Hours	Cond.	Price	Date	Area	Comments
BF			G	$1,900	6/05	ECWI	
BF			G	$2,700	4/03	WCMN	Nice
BF			G	$1,400	11/05	WCIL	WF, Hercules, restored, fenders, new manifold & paint
N/A			G	$,2000	11/05	WCIL	V, WF, gas, rear wheel weights

caterpillar

In 1925 two of the fiercest competitors in the tractor industry, Holt Manufacturing and C.F. Best Gas Traction, merged to create the now world-famous Caterpillar crawler line. The newly formed company moved its headquarters to Peoria, Illinois, and set out to expand, eventually offering hundreds of models of earthmoving, construction, and material handling equipment.

Model	Year	Hours	Cond.	Price	Date	Area	Comments
W7	1970	2,895	G	$5,500	8/05	NCMI	1¼ yard bucket, 75 hp.
112	1961		G	$8,600	5/03	SWOK	Road grader, 10' blade, cab, good rubber
12	1945		G	$1,550	3/03	ECNE	4-cyl. diesel, pony motor, cab, 12' blade, 10-24" tires
120	1970	2,050	G	$13,000	5/04	ECNE	Motor grader, 6-cyl. diesel, cab, heat, 14' hyd. lift & tilt blade

Model	Year	Hours	Cond.	Price	Date	Area	Comments
30	1927		P	$500	4/04	SEND	With loader, needs magneto, engine is stuck
922B	1960		G	$4,100	4/04	WCNE	Diesel, pay loader, new paint, grapple mounts
930	1973		G	$16,500	6/05	ECNE	Loader, cab
933	1966		F	$2,200	1/04	WCIL	933c Traxcavator track loader, good diesel turbo engine, 1st gear out
950	1970		G	$18,250	2/05	NWKS	Wheel loader, 3-yard bucket
950	1971		G	$16,500	6/05	ECNE	Loader, cab
950	1975		F	$21,000	3/03	NCCO	4WD, loader
955H	1961	12,927	G	$6,800	6/03	ECNE	Crawler loader, Cat. diesel, PS, ROPS, 7' bucket with teeth
955K	1969		G	$8,100	3/03	ECNE	Crawler, 71 Series, street pads, 2½-yard bucket, canopy
D4	1961		G	$14,000	3/03	NWIL	Dozer, shuttle shift and hyd. tilt
D6B	1963		G	$9,000	3/03	SEIA	Dozer
D7E	1968		G	$14,000	6/03	ECND	Crawler dozer, 12' hyd. angle blade, ROPS, canopy, 24" tracks
D7E	1969		E	$20,750	8/03	WCIN	Completely rebuilt, spent $30K, 500 hours since rebuild
D7G	1975	2,232	F	$32,000	2/04	ECNE	Crawler dozer, Cat 3126 diesel, PS, canopy, 4-way blade, 28" pads, heavy-duty rear winch
D8	1958		G	$8,900	6/04	SENE	Diesel, hyd. tilt blade
D8	1972		P	$2,250	11/03	ECND	Crawler, winch, diesel
D8	1972		G	$25,000	4/03	NCKS	Dozer, 400 hours on new tracks, PS, rollers
D8H	1963		G	$8,000	3/03	ECNE	Crawler, 12' blade, cable dozer, canopy
D8H	1967		G	$9,500	6/03	ECND	Crawler, hyd. angle dozer & ROPS, canopy
D8H	1970		G	$18,000	3/03	ECNE	Crawler, less than 2,000 hours on OH, 12'6" hyd. blade, hyd. tilt, 1,000 hours on trans. & torque converter OH, bolt-together track, canopy & tree guard

The Canadian-based Cockshutt Corporation left an indelible mark on agriculture by offering farmers reliable yet sleek-styled horse-power. Besides making tractors for themselves, Cockshutt also fabricated machines for Co-op and Gambles. The firm, first founded in 1877, merged into the Oliver conglomerate in 1962.

cockshutt

Model	Year	Hours	Cond.	Price	Date	Area	Comments
1350			G	$1,600	9/03	NEIN	Gas
1350			F	$3,600	4/03	WCMN	44 hp., original, gas
1650			G	$3,000	9/03	NEIN	

Model	Year	Hours	Cond.	Price	Date	Area	Comments
1850			G	$4,000	6/04	WCWI	Std., Wheatland
2050			G	$7,250	6/04	WCWI	Front-wheel-assist drive, restored, new manifold, runs great
20			G	$3,300	11/05	WCIL	WF, unrestored, front/rear wheel weights, fenders, hyd, 3 pt.
20	1952		F	$3,000	11/05	WCIL	WF, fenders
30			G	$1,500	10/05	ECMN	Gas, saw rig
30			G	$2,400	9/05	NENE	Factory WF, live pump, PTO, drawbar, 13.6-38 tires
30	1948		F	$400	9/04	NECO	Runs, fair tires, good tin, no grill, cracked block
30	1949		G	$2,200	5/04	SCPA	3 pt., restored
30			G	$325	4/03	WCSK	Canadian sale, loader & bucket
30			G	$800	4/03	WCSK	Canadian sale, blade
40	1950		F	$900	8/03	NCIA	Gas
570			G	$3,700	2/03	WCMN	LP booster, tin good
60			G	$1,400	7/04	WCIL	Std., gas
70			G	$1,300	7/04	WCIL	Std., gas, new tires
770			G	$2,700	7/04	WCIL	Gas, row crop, fender extensions, adjustable WF
770			F	$1,100	10/04	SEPA	Co-op, gas, WF, good rubber

The Co-op tractor was originally engineered by the famous tractor designer Dent Parrett and then manufactured by the Duplex Machinery Company of Battle Creek, Michigan, for sale by an association of farmers' co-ops located throughout the Midwest. Over time, Huber, Cockshutt, and Custom would all build Co-op tractors.

Co-op

Model	Year	Cond.	Price	Date	Area	Comments
N/A		F	$1,100	10/04	SEPA	Gas, WF, good rubber
3		G	$1,600	8/05	SEND	
3	1942	G	$3,200	11/05	WCIL	WF, gas, restored
E3		G	$1,900	11/05	WCIL	NF, live PTO
E3		G	$800	8/05	WCMN	Very good 12.4-38 tires, good rubber & tin
E3		G	$0	12/04	ECMI	No sale at $900, 12-volt, repainted, runs good
E3	1947	G	$1,025	9/03	NEIN	Gas, NF
E4		G	$1,100	9/03	NEIN	
#2	1937	G	$2,650	8/03	NCIA	WF & NF, belt pulley, original book

david brown

Model	Year	Hours	Cond.	Price	Date	Area	Comments
1210			G	$4,000	12/05	SCIA	Westendorf WL-21 loader
1210			F	$450	4/04	NEPA	
1210		6,212	F	$4,400	6/04	SCMI	Case 65 loader, diesel, 18.4-30" tires, 540/1000 PTO
1210	1985		F	$4,700	4/03	NCND	3 pt.
1212			G	$3,900	2/04	WCWI	Dunham Lehr loader
1212	1973		F	$1,650	9/03	NEIN	WF
885		3,034	G	$2,400	8/05	NEIN	WF, diesel
990	1964		G	$950	9/04	NECO	Runs, good tires, 3 pt.
990			G	$2,600	5/03	SWOK	53 hp., Waldon 6' dozer blade, 3 pt., PTO, 50% rubber
995			G	$4,500	8/03	NWIL	#55 loader, diesel

ferguson

The Ferguson tractor's creator, Harry Ferguson, is better known for his creation of the three-point hitch and live hydraulic system on tractors. That invention originally appeared on Ford Model 9N tractors. Harry eventually broke away from Ford, building his own tractor under the Ferugson name beginning in 1947. Ferguson tractors were an instant hit, particularly in England and northern Europe.

Model	Year	Hours	Cond.	Price	Date	Area	Comments
20			G	$1,500	9/03	NEIN	
30			G	$1,700	11/05	WCIL	WF, gas, PTO
30		1,954	G	$3,600	2/04	WCIL	Davis Hi-lift loader, gas, utility tractor, 3 pt., over/under drive
30			F	$1,375	10/03	NWIL	
TE-20			G	$2,350	2/05	NEIN	With loader, gas
TO 20			G	$1,500	11/05	WCIL	
TO 20			F	$1,600	3/05	WCIL	Gas, cab, front blade
TO 20			E	$3,000	4/05	NCCO	New tires, 3 pt., PTO, new rims, strong engine, great paint job
TO 20			G	$1,700	8/04	NCOH	With loader
TO 20	1951		G	$1,700	1/04	WCIL	Gas, new tires
TO 30	1953		G	$1,300	8/05	NEIN	
TO 30			G	$1,425	6/05	NCIA	3 pt., like Ford 8N
TO 30			F	$975	8/03	NWIL	Gas
TO 30			F	$1,400	8/03	NWIL	Davis loader, gas
TO 30			F	$1,750	9/03	SCMI	
TO 30			G	$2,300	2/03	SWOK	
TO 30			G	$2,500	5/03	SWOK	

18

Ageless Iron® olympics

By Roger Welsch

The notion of "athletics" and "sports" has experienced an inflation not unlike me every year between Thanksgiving and Christmas. Now, right there with running, jumping, lifting, and throwing, are sports like competitive tap dancing and interior decorating. And I think that's fine. The only problem is that those of us who love old tractors have fallen out of the loop. I am, therefore, proposing to the International Olympic Committee that they consider adding the following events to the international competition as soon as possible.

● Rusty Rear Wheel Lug, 24-Inch Breaker Bar Speed Competition: From a standing start, contestants break loose and remove four of five rear, 1-inch wheel lugs. One lug will be welded in place; one lug will be loose and coated with graphite. Style points will be deducted for hernias and broken noses.

● 2-pound Wrench Throw: A consolation follow-up for the previous event. Contestants who incur hernias or broken noses will be able to gain lost style points by throwing the offending wrench for distance. Additional style points can be obtained if the athlete's ensuing curses continue through the entire flight of the wrench, including its bounces to a final rest somewhere close to the back fence lilac bushes.

● Drecko-Slimin' Transmission Wrestling and Cross-Country Run: Contestants will remove a thoroughly greased transmission from a tractor and squat-carry it 15 feet across a shop, around an engine stand, and between two floor jacks, stepping over a variety of ball bearings, 12-point sockets, and broken bolts scattered at random on the floor.

● Three-Man Engine Timing: Clearly, a team event. National squads will approach a four-cylinder machine. While a bottom man opens the flywheel vent and turns it to top-center fire position, the other two team members will open the magneto and timing gear case. All three will at all times scream contradictory instructions at each other. At least one member of the team during the competition will get a finger caught in the timing gear; at least one second member will clearly show judges he has finger-tested the magneto by a display of standing hair, flaring nostrils, and glowing eyeballs.

● Lock Washer Polo: The contestant has seven minutes to shuffle a ½-inch lock washer around a shop floor, keeping it well out of the reach of three opponents trying to pick the blasted thing up. The goal is to deposit the washer down a crack behind a shop cabinet where it will remain for the next 50 years, until the building burns down, or until it simply disappears mysteriously forever.

● Individual Crank Starts and Flywheel Spins: Contestants attempt to start, one after the other for a timed result, six tractors, three with flywheel starts, three with cranks, and one with a defective impulse. Survivors will be cleaned up, carried to a whirlpool tub, and given three weeks free physical therapy or a full body cast, depending.

● Cross-Country Woodlot Scanning: Teams of three drive through heavily worked agricultural land in a pickup truck. Without scanners, metal detectors, or binoculars, the teams find, negotiate for, and load as many pre-1950 tractors, implements, or parts as possible. Style points deducted for poison ivy, barbed-wire cuts, and imbedded shotgun pellets.

● Synchronized Dolly Floor Exercise: Teams of five, eight, and 12 mechanics perform prechoreographed routines on floor dollies to one (1) country-western tune, one (1) classical piece, and one (1) rock-and-roll song while completely lubing and changing the oil in an antique tractor selected by the Ageless Iron Olympic Committee. Awards based on the most torn ligaments, strained muscles, bruises, and stitches.

● 10-Item Checkbook Balance: This is a mixed-gender, team competition between a husband and wife. The spouse most deeply involved in tractor collecting, restoration, parts or tool buying purchases 10 items and conceals the purchases in a checkbook record in such a way that his/her spouse cannot find more than five of the expenditures in a 10-minute period.

Mine a treasure trove of Roger Welsch's musings and talk to the master of tractor mayhem in person at agelessiron.com.

ford

It took very little time for Ford Motor Company to dominate the tractor industry as they had automobile manufacturing. In 1917 they introduced their first tractor, the Fordson, which became the number one selling tractor in the U.S. within a year. And then in 1939 they introduced the Model 9N with its revolutionary Ferguson three-point hitch and built-in hydraulic system. This introduction solidified Ford's position as a tractor manufacturer. By the time the Long Blue Line was introduced in the mid-1950s, Ford had become the dominant tractor manufacturer in the world. Ford Motor eventually stepped out of farm power selling its tractor line to Fiat, which sold the tractor through its New Holland division. The Ford name was later dropped entirely. However, the Big Blue color is still in use on New Holland horsepower.

Model	Year	Hours	Cond.	Price	Date	Area	Comments
Fordson	1919		F	$3,000	7/03	WCSK	Canadian sale, restored, not painted
Fordson Major			G	$3,800	3/05	WCNE	Diesel, 3 pt., 14-30 rear tires, 7.50-16" front tires, PTO
Fordson Major			P	$350	3/04	WCMN	Does not run, 3 pt., PTO
Fordson Major			F	$1,200	9/04	NECO	Diesel, runs, 2 pt., fair tires
Fordson Major R			G	$1,500	6/03	WCWI	3 pt., diesel
Fordson			F	$700	6/05	ECWI	
Fordson	1930		G	$1,800	12/04	WCIL	Gas
2000			F	$3,000	4/05	SWPA	
2000			G	$3,500	9/05	SCON	Canadian sale, gas, ROPS
2000			G	$4,600	9/05	NEIN	With loader
2000			F	$1,600	2/05	NWKS	3 pt., PTO, gas
2000	1963	960	G	$2,600	1/05	SWOH	
2000	1969		G	$2,650	1/05	SWOH	Fresh OH
2000	1974	3,899	G	$3,200	1/05	SWOH	
2000			G	$1,200	11/04	NWNY	Select-O-Speed, 3 pt.
2000			F	$2,350	11/04	NWSC	Commercial tractor, forks, average
2000			F	$3,250	4/04	NEPA	
2000	1964		G	$2,550	3/04	SEIA	1 owner
2000		3,062	E	$3,400	4/03	WCIL	Utility
2000		2,411	G	$4,000	4/03	NCWI	Diesel
2000			F	$4,100	6/03	NEIA	Gas
2000			F	$5,000	7/03	WCSK	Canadian sale
2N			G	$1,600	9/05	SCON	Canadian sale
2N			F	$850	10/05	NEPA	
2N	1943		G	$700	8/05	NCIL	100 hrs on engine overhaul
2N	1944		G	$1,000	8/05	NEIN	12v
2N	1946		G	$3,000	9/05	ECMN	Gas
2N	1946		G	$1,400	8/04	ECIL	Step-up transmission, totally restored
2N			G	$1,700	12/03	NCIA	
2N			F	$3,200	5/03	WCIN	3 pt., loader
2N	1942		G	$1,500	3/03	SEIA	Restored 5 yrs. ago
3000			G	$1,300	12/05	SWMS	Diesel, 3 pt.
3000			G	$2,500	12/05	ECIN	Gas, 3 pt.
3000			G	$2,700	9/05	NCTN	Front mounted broom
3000			G	$3,000	10/05	WCTN	
3000			G	$4,000	10/05	WCTN	
3000	1971	3,000	G	$4,400	11/05	WCIL	40 hp., 8 speed trans, live PTO
3000			G	$1,700	1/05	NWGA	3 pt., PTO
3000			F	$3,950	3/05	SWIN	PS, gas
3000		2,900	G	$4,150	1/05	SWOH	
3000		1,845	G	$5,300	1/05	SWOH	
3000			G	$2,950	3/04	SEMN	3 pt., 540 PTO, hi/low
3000		1,200	G	$4,450	6/03	WCMI	Loader, 3-speed
3000			F	$5,850	8/03	SWOH	Gas, loader, 3 pt. didn't work
3000			G	$6,100	9/03	NEIN	Loader
3000	1973		G	$6,900	3/03	NCOH	Gas, loader, hi/lo, PS, front pump, 1 hyd., tire chains & weights, nice
3400			G	$4,700	8/05	SCMI	Recent overhaul, rebuilt hyd, bucket, 3pt
3400	1969		F	$2,310	11/04	WCMS	Gas, WF, 12.4-24" tires, 3 pt., 540 PTO
3500	1966	1,286	F	$3,800	3/04	SEWY	Loader, box blade, gas
3500			G	$6,500	1/03	SEMN	735 loader and 753 backhoe, 2 buckets, pallet fork

ford

Model	Year	Hours	Cond.	Price	Date	Area	Comments
4000	1968	3,864	G	$4,500	1/06	WCNE	WF, new paint
4000			G	$1,500	10/05	WCTN	Select-o-Speed
4000			F	$1,900	11/05	NWIL	Diesel, Select-o-Speed, with loader
4000		5,880	P	$3,200	8/05	NCOH	With loader, diesel
4000			G	$5,200	3/05	ECMN	Gas
4000			G	$5,500	12/05	SWMS	Diesel, 3 pt.
4000			G	$800	12/05	SWMS	Diesel
4000			P	$800	7/05	SESD	NF, Select-o-Speed, gas
4000			F	$2,000	1/05	NWOH	Utility, superior loader, 3 pt., Select-O-Speed
4000			G	$6,100	5/05	SWIN	Gas, 4 speed, PS, Farmhand #22 front-end loader
4000			G	$6,400	8/05	NCIA	Utility, Select-O-Matic, sold with Ford 727 loader, WF, 3 pt., new tires & rims, fenders
4000			G	$6,900	7/05	SEND	Woods dual loader, PS, 3 pt., PTO, hyd., bucket
4000	1975		G	$2,450	2/05	NEIN	Gas, WF, Select-O-Speed
4000		3,405	G	$3,400	9/04	NWSD	Utility, 3 pt., 2 hyd., gas
4000			G	$5,600	2/04	WCWI	Koyker Quick-Tach 210 loader, joystick, diesel
4000	1964	3,198	G	$1,800	3/04	SEWY	3 pt., PTO, rear fenders, gas
4000	1964		G	$3,700	11/04	WCOH	NF, hyd. loader and fork bucket, 5-speed, 3 pt.
4000	1965		G	$2,500	7/04	SEND	Utility
4000	1965		F	$2,500	7/04	NWMN	Utility, gas
4000			G	$3,200	9/03	SEIA	Utility, new paint and rubber
4000		4,100	G	$3,400	3/03	NEIN	Gas, platform, NF
4000			G	$3,550	9/03	NEIN	Diesel, Select-O-Speed
4000			G	$4,000	3/03	SWWI	
4000			G	$4,100	6/03	ECNE	3-cyl. diesel, 8-spd., 3 pt. boom
4000			G	$4,250	6/03	WCWI	Ford loader, 2 buckets
4000			G	$4,450	3/03	NCWI	3 pt., gas
4000	1970		G	$3,800	9/03	SEIL	New tires
4100	1973	2,624	G	$6,000	3/04	SEWY	WF, 3 pt., Ford loader, diesel
4110			F	$1,500	4/04	NEPA	
4110			P	$2,500	3/03	NCIL	1 hyd., 3 pt., 18.4-16.1" turf tires, diesel
4110			G	$4,600	3/03	NCIL	1 hyd., 3 pt., PTO, 18.4-16.1" turf tires, diesel
4500			G	$6,600	9/05	SCON	Canadian sale, loader, backhoe
4500			G	$2,600	3/04	ECMI	Industrial loader, no 3 pt., diesel
4500	1968		G	$0	12/04	ECMI	No sale at $7,000, tractor/loader/backhoe, complete engine rebuild, new clutch, pressure plate & radiator, tight machine
4500			G	$4,000	8/03	SEMN	Industrial loader, 3 pt., canopy
5000			G	$3,150	8/05	NEIN	Diesel
5000		3,186	G	$4,150	11/05	SCMI	Ford 727 loader, diesel
5000			F	$4,650	10/05	NEPA	
5000	1974	6,696	G	$5,700	5/04	ECMN	Cab, diesel, restored to new in looks, engine didn't start easily and smoked a bit, 3 pt., PTO
5000			G	$5,000	2/05	SCMN	ROPS, 3 pt., 540 PTO, 2 hyd., gas, 16.9-34" tires
5000		3,394	G	$6,100	4/05	ECND	Diesel, cab, 3 pt., PTO, 2 hyd., 15.5-38" tires, clean
5000			F	$6,750	5/05	SWIN	Diesel, 6-speed, PS
5000	1962		G	$3,750	2/05	NEIN	Gas, NF
5000	1972		F	$3,400	6/05	NESD	2WD, cab, 1 hyd., 3 pt., 18.4-30" tires
5000			F	$1,050	3/04	NWMN	Shift transmission
5000			F	$1,650	1/04	WCMI	Broken grill

Model	Year	Hours	Cond.	Price	Date	Area	Comments
5000			F	$2,900	1/04	WCMI	Drops broken grill
5000			F	$3,000	1/04	WCMI	With bucket loader
5000			F	$3,000	12/03	WCMI	Diesel, WF, 16.5x34" tires
5000			P	$3,200	4/03	NWPA	Diesel
5000			G	$4,350	3/03	SWWI	Loader, no PS
5000	1963		G	$4,800	4/03	WCSK	Canadian sale, 2WD, 3 pt, PTO, bucket, bale fork
5000	1965		F	$2,450	9/03	NEIN	WF, diesel
5000	1965		G	$2,800	3/03	ECSD	Selective speed transmission, WF
5000	1975	8,200	G	$6,550	4/03	WCSK	Canadian sale, 2WD, 18.4x30" tires, new rear, rebuilt PTO
5000	1979	3,750	E	$7,300	4/03	SWMN	Like new, hi/low, 16.9-34" tires
600			G	$1,500	12/05	ECIN	Gas, 3 pt.
600			G	$4,300	11/05	WCIL	WF, gas, 134 cu. in.
600			F	$1,400	2/05	WCIN	Industrial, 3 pt., PTO, hyd. front loader, no hood
600			G	$2,250	11/04	NWNY	Repainted
600			F	$1,950	3/03	NWIL	Utility, rear tile trencher
6000	1963		F	$1,300	9/03	NEIN	Diesel, WF
601			G	$2,000	11/05	WCIL	One arm loader
601			G	$4,400	9/05	NEIN	With new Kelly loader
601			G	$2,800	3/03	ECTN	Workmaster
601			F	$3,450	3/03	WCMI	PS, live PTO, weights
601	1960		G	$2,650	8/03	SENE	Gas
640			G	$2,050	12/04	ECMI	
641	1958		G	$2,300	8/05	NEIN	Gas
641		2,500	G	$2,975	12/03	WCIL	Workmaster gas utility tractor, loader
650	1954		E	$2,700	4/04	WCNE	3 pt., WF, gas
650	1956		G	$2,650	9/03	NEIN	WF, gas
655			G	$12,500	5/04	WCWA	4WD, backhoe, diesel
661			G	$2,850	1/05	SWOH	Live power
7000		4,614	F	$6,750	4/04	NWPA	
7000			G	$9,550	4/04	ECWI	WF
7000			F	$4,600	3/03	NCTN	
7000	1975	1,950	G	$5,900	1/03	NCOH	Diesel, open station, hi-clearance, 1 hyd., dual power, 540/1000 PTO
800			F	$2,200	5/05	SEPA	Gas, WF, rubber 50%
800			G	$2,900	12/05	SWMS	Gas, 3pt
800			G	$3,800	8/05	WCIL	With loader
800			F	$1,750	8/04	NCOH	Gas
800			F	$3,500	10/04	SEPA	Gas, WF, new paint, average rubber
800	1957		G	$4,300	2/04	NECO	1 owner, 3 pt., PTO, hyd.
800			G	$2,600	6/03	WCWI	
8000			G	$3,400	4/05	SEMN	Diesel, 3 pt., 23.1-34" tires
8000			G	$6,000	2/05	NCIN	Diesel, WF, OH
8000	1969	7,149	G	$3,500	3/04	NWMN	Cab, 8-speed, 3 pt, 540/1000 PTO, 2 hyd., 18.4×38" tires, band duals
8000			G	$2,200	9/03	WCMN	WF, diesel, 2 hyd., 540 PTO, 3 pt., front weights, 18.4-34" tires
8000	1969	4,500	G	$4,500	9/03	NEIN	Diesel, duals, no cab
801			G	$3,000	8/05	ECMI	5 speed, live PTO, good rubber, remote hyd., diesel
801			G	$5,500	12/05	NECO	Select-o-Speed, Ford step side loader, 3 pt., PTO, new rubber
801			G	$3,550	4/04	ECWI	Paulson hyd. loader
801			G	$300	3/03	NCWI	Gas, Select-O-Speed, loader

ford

Model	Year	Hours	Cond.	Price	Date	Area	Comments
801			G	$3,000	5/03	SWOK	
850			F	$2,000	12/03	WCMI	Gas, WF, 3 pt.
860			P	$1,900	8/04	NWIL	Loader, trip bucket
860	1954		E	$2,850	4/04	WCNE	Live PTO, rebuilt eng., WF, 33 hrs. on new tach
860			F	$2,000	3/03	SWWI	3 pt. did not work
8600			P	$2,600	4/05	NCOH	Did run, diesel, cab, 38" duals, weights, full power
8600		3,997	G	$6,400	5/04	ECWI	2 hyd.
8600			G	$6,600	4/04	ECWI	Hiniker cab, 800 hrs. on new engine
8600	1972		G	$7,500	12/04	SENE	Diesel
861			G	$2,200	2/05	NEIN	Gas, WF
861			G	$2,900	2/05	SCMN	5-speed
861			G	$3,100	1/04	NEOH	Diesel
861			G	$3,500	9/03	NEIN	
861			F	$4,250	11/03	NWIL	Ford loader, 3 pt., PS
8N			G	$2,800	2/06	SWNE	4 speed, side mount distributor, 3 pt., 540 PTO, 11.2-28 tires
8N	1947		G	$2,000	2/06	NCKS	3 pt., PTO
8N			G	$1,400	12/05	ECWA	4 cyl., flatbed, 4 speed, PTO, 3 pt.
8N			G	$1,400	9/05	SCON	Canadian sale, gas, loader, 3 pt.
8N			G	$1,800	9/05	NEIN	
8N			G	$2,000	4/05	ECMN	
8N			G	$3,000	12/05	NECO	3 pt., PTO, clean
8N			G	$3,000	12/05	NECO	3 pt., PTO, clean
8N			P	$335	10/05	WCIL	Parts tractor, bad
8N			P	$700	8/05	WCIL	Missing parts, bad
8N			F	$700	11/05	WCKS	3 pt.
8N	1950		G	$1,100	8/05	NEIN	Gas, repainted
8N	1951		G	$950	11/05	ECNE	
8N	1952		G	$2,100	11/05	WCIL	Side distributor running, 3 pt., front bumper
8N			P	$700	3/05	WCIL	Gas
8N			G	$1,000	1/05	NWGA	3 pt., PTO
8N			F	$1,100	2/05	SCCA	3 pt., PTO, 11.2-24" tires
8N			F	$1,100	1/05	SWOH	
8N			F	$1,200	1/05	SWOH	
8N			G	$1,250	1/05	SWOH	
8N			G	$1,325	1/05	SWOH	
8N			G	$1,350	1/05	SWOH	
8N			F	$1,550	2/05	NEIN	Gas, 12 volt, Sherman transmission
8N			G	$1,550	1/05	SWOH	
8N			F	$1,600	3/05	WCIL	Gas, new rear tires
8N			G	$1,800	4/05	NCIA	Ford side-mount sickle mower
8N			G	$1,900	3/05	WCIL	New tires, gas
8N			E	$2,000	4/05	NCOK	New paint, 12-volt system, runs excellent
8N			G	$2,050	1/05	SWOH	
8N			G	$2,500	2/05	NWKS	3 pt.
8N			G	$2,900	6/05	ECMN	Hi/lo
8N			G	$3,150	4/05	NWIL	Loader
8N	1948		G	$2,275	6/05	NEND	4 speed, 3 pt., PTO
8N	1951		G	$2,500	6/05	NEND	4 speed, 3 pt., PTO

Model	Year	Hours	Cond.	Price	Date	Area	Comments
8N	1959		G	$2,600	2/05	NECO	3 pt., PTO, 1 hyd., rubber 40%
8N			F	$650	5/04	NEPA	
8N			P	$750	3/04	WCIL	
8N			F	$1,200	5/04	NEPA	
8N			G	$1,400	12/04	NEND	3 pt., PTO
8N			F	$1,425	3/04	WCIL	Gas
8N			G	$1,550	1/04	SWOH	
8N			G	$1,550	3/04	NWIL	Gas
8N			G	$1,600	3/04	SWKS	3 pt., 3-pt. cement mixer
8N			P	$1,650	1/04	ECNE	Belly mower, as is
8N			G	$1,700	10/04	SCMN	3 pt.
8N			F	$1,750	9/04	NECO	Runs, 3 pt., fair tires
8N			F	$1,750	10/04	NCOH	Motor locked
8N			G	$1,850	12/04	WCIL	Gas, new tires, OD
8N			G	$1,950	3/04	SEIA	Loader
8N			G	$2,100	3/04	SEMN	3 pt.
8N			E	$2,300	3/04	NEKS	
8N			G	$3,200	3/04	SWDE	
8N	1948		G	$1,700	9/04	SEND	4-speed, 3 pt., PTO, 12-28" tires, engine kit, crank turned
8N	1949		E	$2,600	4/04	WCNE	Gas, new paint, engine rebuilt
8N	1951		G	$1,900	9/04	NECO	Runs, 2 pt., crane, good tires
8N			F	$675	7/03	NWIL	Power unit on steel wheel cart
8N			F	$1,100	12/03	WCMI	WF, gas, 4 cyl.
8N			F	$1,125	12/03	WCMI	4 cyl. gas, 3 pt., PTO
8N			G	$1,200	12/03	SCNE	
8N			F	$1,375	10/03	NWIL	
8N			F	$1,400	8/03	NWIL	
8N			G	$1,400	9/03	NEIN	
8N			G	$1,500	8/03	SEMN	3 pt., good rubber
8N			F	$1,500	9/03	NCSD	
8N			G	$1,500	10/03	SWWI	Gas
8N			F	$1,600	9/03	SCMI	
8N			F	$1,675	3/03	NCCO	
8N			F	$1,800	8/03	SEPA	Average rubber & paint
8N			F	$1,800	9/03	SCMI	
8N			F	$1,825	11/03	SWOH	
8N			G	$1,850	10/03	SWWI	Gas, new paint
8N			F	$1,900	12/03	WCMI	WF, 11.2x28" tires
8N			F	$1,950	7/03	SWOH	
8N			G	$2,000	4/03	WCSK	Canadian sale, 23 hp., PTO, 3 pt., blade, new starter, battery, new ring gear, new tires
8N			G	$2,000	9/03	NEIN	Loader
8N			G	$2,050	10/03	NWIL	
8N			G	$2,100	10/03	WCWI	Gas
8N			G	$2,100	2/03	SWOK	
8N			G	$2,200	6/03	WCSK	Canadian sale, dozer blade
8N			G	$2,200	12/03	SWMI	Gas, 3 pt., PTO, 12.4x28" tires
8N			G	$2,250	6/03	WCSK	Canadian sale, 2 new tires, 3 pt.
8N			G	$2,500	9/03	NEIN	
8N			G	$3,150	10/03	WCSK	Canadian sale, gas, 12.4x28" rear tires, new front tires
8N	1947		G	$2,050	8/03	NCIA	3 pt., new rear tires, OH, restored

ford

Model	Year	Hours	Cond.	Price	Date	Area	Comments
8N	1948		G	$1,800	11/03	WCKS	PTO, 3 pt., good paint
8N	1949		F	$1,370	7/03	NWIL	Industrial motor, 2-speed, 3 pt.
8N	1950		G	$1,300	3/03	NESD	3 pt.
8N	1951		F	$1,800	6/03	NEIL	WF
8N	1952		F	$2,000	6/03	NEIL	WF, power meter
900			G	$1,700	8/05	ECMN	NF
900			G	$3,800	12/04	WCIL	Gas, NF, new tires
900			F	$2,400	3/03	NENE	Gas, WF, Select-O-Speed
9000			G	$6,000	11/04	SEPA	
9000			F	$3,800	12/03	NCIN	
901			F	$1,150	7/05	SESD	NF, Select-o-Speed
901			G	$2,200	6/04	ECMN	WF, gas, back blade
901	1960		G	$2,650	9/04	NECO	Runs good, Select-O-Speed, 2 pt., good tires & tin
901			P	$275	8/03	WCMN	Loader, gas
901			F	$1,650	2/03	SWOK	
901			F	$2,200	6/03	NEIL	Power master
960	1954	1,700	G	$5,250	8/04	ECIL	NF, live power, PS, 3 pt., restored
960			F	$2,900	3/03	NCCO	
960	1955		E	$2,850	2/03	SWIA	NF, new rubber, reconditioned, looks like new
9600		5,061	F	$5,000	11/05	SCMI	Overhauled in '94, cab, 3 pt., 2 hyd., 10 front weights, snap-on duals
9600		7,313	G	$5,500	2/05	WCOH	ROPS, 540/1000 PTO, 2 hyd., 3 pt., duals
9600	1974	10,174	G	$4,400	2/05	NEIN	Cab, diesel
9600	1976		F	$3,800	4/04	WCMI	Open station, diesel
9600	1976		G	$7,300	3/04	NWMN	Cab, 3 pt., 540/1000 PTO, 2 hyd., duals, power speed, 20.8x38" tires & hub duals, rear wheel weights
9600			G	$4,700	10/03	WCWI	Dual power, 2 hyd., PTO, PS, rims
9600		8,000	G	$5,000	4/03	WCSK	Canadian sale, 150 hp., 3 pt., live PTO
961			G	$2,900	10/04	SCMN	3 pt.
961			G	$3,400	3/04	NCIL	Power master, NF, 3 pt., PTO
971	1962	7,085	G	$1,750	3/03	ECNE	Diesel, glow plug start, electric start, NF, PS, 3 pt., 12.4-28", 1 hyd., front/rear weights
9N			G	$2,100	1/06	SESD	WIith 3 pt.
9N			G	$1,400	12/05	NENE	
9N			F	$1,600	8/05	ECTN	Made in the 1940s, new paint
9N			F	$800	8/05	NEIN	Gas
9N	1942		G	$1,400	9/05	NECO	3 pt., gas
9N	1943		F	$1,300	9/05	WCNE	Gas, 3 pt., runs good, tin work bent badly
9N			F	$900	3/05	NWIL	Gas
9N			G	$1,125	1/05	SWOH	
9N			G	$1,150	1/05	SWOH	
9N			G	$1,350	4/05	NWIL	3 pt., PTO
9N			G	$1,450	1/05	SWOH	
9N			E	$1,600	4/05	NCOK	New paint, 12-volt system, runs great, with 5' mower
9N			G	$1,850	7/05	SEND	3 pt., hyd., PTO
9N			G	$2,000	6/05	NWMN	2-speed OD, 3 pt., PTO
9N	1940		F	$950	6/05	NEND	3-speed, 3 pt., PTO
9N	1940		G	$1,600	6/05	NEND	3-speed, 3 pt., PTO
9N	1940		G	$2,500	6/05	NEND	3-speed, 3 pt., PTO, turf tires

Model	Year	Hours	Cond.	Price	Date	Area	Comments
9N	1943		G	$1,700	3/05	NECO	3 pt., PTO, rebuilt, new tires
9N			F	$900	12/04	ECMI	
9N			F	$1,100	12/04	NCWI	Utility, step-down transmission, gas
9N			F	$1,150	4/04	NEPA	
9N			F	$1,300	6/04	ECMT	Runs good
9N			G	$1,575	7/04	NEND	3 pt., PTO, new tires
9N			G	$1,850	7/04	NWMN	3 pt., new paint & tires
9N			G	$2,100	9/04	NECO	Runs, loader & blade, 3 pt.
9N	1939		F	$700	12/04	WCIL	Gas
9N	1939		G	$1,800	9/04	WCWI	Gas, new rubber
9N	1940		E	$2,650	4/04	WCNE	New paint, gas, eng. weak
9N	1942		G	$1,500	9/04	SEND	3-speed, 3 pt., PTO, 12-28" tires
9N	1947		G	$2,550	3/04	WCWI	Gas, 3 pt.
9N			F	$900	2/03	WCMN	3 pt.
9N			F	$1,000	5/03	SWOK	
9N			G	$1,050	8/03	NCIA	3 pt.
9N			G	$1,200	7/03	SEND	3 pt., PTO, 11.2-28" tires
9N			F	$1,200	3/03	NWIL	Gas
9N			F	$1,300	5/03	SWOK	
9N			G	$1,300	3/03	SEIA	
9N			G	$1,375	3/03	SWWI	
9N			G	$1,400	7/03	SCMN	
9N			F	$1,500	3/03	WCMI	Gas, 3 pt., WF, new rubber, hi/lo range
9N			F	$1,600	10/03	NWIL	
9N			F	$1,700	10/03	ECNE	3 pt., new rubber
9N			F	$1,850	8/03	SEPA	WF, recent OH, new rubber & paint
9N			E	$3,150	6/03	WCWI	New rubber
9N	1940		G	$1,025	9/03	NEIN	New paint, gas
9N	1941		F	$1,100	9/03	NEIN	Gas
9N	1941		G	$1,300	9/03	SEIL	
Jubliee			G	$3,000	8/05	ECMI	Rebuilt engine, new gauges & wiring, new paint, good rubber
Jubliee	1953		F	$1,700	9/05	WCNE	Gas, 3 pt.
Jubliee	1953		G	$2,600	9/05	WCNE	Gas, 3 pt. blade, new tires
NAA	1953		G	$3,600	12/05	NECO	Golden Jubilee, 3 pt., PTO, nice
NAA			G	$1,100	1/05	NWGA	3 pt., PTO
NAA			F	$1,950	1/05	SWOH	
NAA			G	$2,300	6/05	ECMN	
NAA			G	$2,800	1/05	SWOH	
NAA			G	$2,900	1/05	NEMO	Utility, Ford loader
NAA	1953		G	$3,400	6/05	ECIL	New tires, 3 pt., 1 hyd. outlet, restored
NAA			F	$1,350	3/04	WCIL	
NAA			G	$1,750	7/04	NWMN	
NAA			G	$2,700	2/04	NEIN	WF
NAA			G	$3,525	12/04	WCIL	Gas, new tires
NAA	1953		G	$2,650	9/04	NECO	Runs, 2 pt., good tires & tin
NAA	1953		G	$3,850	10/04	NCOH	1 owner
NAA			G	$2,700	6/03	WCSK	Canadian sale, 3 pt.
NAA			F	$2,750	12/03	WCMI	Gas, 3 pt., PTO, loader
NAA	1953		G	$3,200	1/03	SCNE	Very straight and in good condition
NAA	1953		G	$3,600	6/03	NEIL	WF
NAA	1953		F	$2,200	7/03	SCMN	3 pt., live power, not running

international harvester

International Harvester's roots go back to the 1902 merger of two equipment industry leaders – McCormick and Deering. From that start the new firm instantly came to dominate the farm machinery industry building threshers, steam traction engines, stationary engines, and eventually tractors. In 1924 IHC introduced what would become one of the most popular lines of tractors ever built, the Farmall. The Farmall Regular is noted as being the first successful row-crop tractor in U.S. history. The International Harvester name and Big Red color lives on today as Case IH, the result of the merger of Case Corporation and IHC in 1984.

Model	Year	Hours	Cond.	Price	Date	Area	Comments
100	1974	9,571	G	$7,250	1/06	WCNE	Diesel, cab, with dozer
100			F	$900	6/05	WCMN	Farmall, original
100			G	$4,200	6/05	WCMN	Restored, fast hitch, WF, fenders
100	1956		E	$4,000	6/04	ECND	21 hp..
100			G	$1,550	1/03	SWOH	Utility, 48" belly mower
1066		8,000	F	$5,500	2/06	NENE	Cab
1066		5,981	F	$7,600	2/06	NENE	2 hyd., without cab
1066		3500	G	$9,100	1/06	NEIN	Black stripe, front fenders, nice
1066	1973	5,668	G	$7,750	2/06	SWOH	2 hyd., 18.4-38, duals, 12 front weights, 2 rear weights
1066	1974		F	$6,000	1/06	NWKY	No cab, turbo, average
1066	1974	6,981	F	$7,500	2/06	SCNY	2WD, open, 2 hyd., no weights
1066	1975	3,230	E	$14,250	1/06	WCIL	CAH, 2 hyd., weights
1066	1977	2,736	G	$9,300	2/06	SEIA	Cab, 2 hyd., duals
1066			G	$6,900	7/05	SESD	3 pt., diesel
1066			F	$7,300	4/05	SEPA	Cab, WF, good TA, rubber 40%
1066			G	$8,500	9/05	NEIN	Original
1066			G	$8,500	8/05	SEMN	Duals
1066		6,935	G	$4,300	1/05	ECNE	
1066			F	$4,900	4/05	SCSD	
1066		10,035	G	$5,600	2/05	NEIN	Diesel, cab, no doors
1066			G	$6,700	3/05	NENE	
1066		9,045	G	$6,800	2/05	NWKS	1466 engine, 18.4-38" tires, clamp-on duals, 2 hyd., dual PTO, cab, IHC 2350 loader, 6' bucket w/ grapple
1066			G	$7,400	6/05	SWMN	2,484 hours on tach, diesel, cozy cab, WF, 2 hyd., 3 pt.
1066		5,693	G	$7,400	4/05	NCOH	2 hyd., 2 PTOs, full weights, axle duals
1066		4,400	F	$8,000	3/05	SCIL	Cab, AC, slick tires
1066			G	$9,100	1/05	NENE	Diesel, Koyker K5 Quick-Tach loader, 3 pt., WF, 18.4-38"
1066	1972		G	$5,750	1/05	NEIA	Cab, diesel, 38" tires, 9-bolt axle duals, rock box
1066	1972		G	$8,100	8/05	ECNE	2,000 hours on OH, 3 pt., 2 hyd., 540/1000 PTO, ROPS canopy, fenders, 18.4-34", rear weights
1066	1973	7,250	G	$8,000	1/05	ECIA	Diesel, WF, 3 pt., 2 hyd., good 18.4-38"
1066	1973	3,400	G	$8,500	1/05	ECIA	Diesel, WF, 3 pt., 2 hyd., 3,400 hours on engine, new paint
1066	1974		G	$7,200	3/05	ECNE	1,117 hours on OH, 20.8-38" duals, 3 pt., 2 hyd., 540/1000 PTO
1066	1974		G	$10,780	3/05	SWIN	1 owner, tach shows 4,061 hours but not working, approx. 8,000-9,000 total hours, Hiniker cab, AC, turbo, 8/4 hi/lo, 540/1000 PTO, 2 hyd., 18.4-38", hub duals, quick hitch
1066	1975	6,250	E	$8,800	1/05	SENE	Diesel, weights, duals
1066	1975	3,934	G	$9,300	2/05	WCIL	Diesel, cab, weights, extra fuel tank, fast hitch, 18.4-38"
1066	1975	1,988	E	$9,500	4/05	NEIN	Diesel, black stripe, no cab
1066	1974	5,065	G	$7,350	11/04	NWIL	No cab, new tires, 2 hyd., dual PTO, 3 pt., axle duals, 12 front weights
1066	1976	5,990	G	$6,750	6/05	NEND	2 hyd., 3 pt., 540/1000 PTO, 18.4-38" duals, 80% rubber
1066	1976	5,900	G	$8,000	2/05	NCIN	Black stripe
1066			G	$4,600	3/04	WCMN	3 pt., PTO, 2 hyd., diesel, 18.4-38"
1066			G	$4,800	3/04	ECMI	2WD, cab, 3 pt., 2 hyd., dual PTO, 18.4-38" duals, diesel
1066			G	$5,600	6/04	SEMN	Duals
1066			F	$5,700	10/04	SEPA	Turbo, cab, TA out, good rubber
1066			G	$6,600	9/04	SEIA	
1066			G	$6,700	1/04	NWIA	Open station
1066			F	$7,250	1/04	NEOH	Needs brakes
1066			G	$8,100	11/04	SEPA	

international harvester

Model	Year	Hours	Cond.	Price	Date	Area	Comments
1066		7,613	G	$9,100	10/04	SWWI	No cab, black stripe
1066		4,120	E	$9,800	8/04	NCOH	1 owner, no cab
1066			G	$10,200	1/04	ECIL	Restored, 200 hours on complete engine OH, new paint
1066		3,500	G	$10,800	3/04	SEIL	No cab, no weights, no duals
1066			F	$13,100	3/04	SEPA	3-year-old rebuild, 120 hp., turbo
1066	1971	5,326	G	$6,750	3/04	NCIA	WF, no cab, 18.4-38"
1066	1972	4,500	G	$6,300	4/04	SCIA	Turbo, factory cab, new clutch & brakes, diesel, 18.4-38" newer rubber
1066	1972	6,004	G	$8,000	9/04	NCIA	White cab, AC, 2 hyd., OH, 2 PTOs
1066	1972		G	$9,000	2/04	ECIA	2,937 hours on major OH, 1,700 hours on mechanical TA, diesel, 38" rubber, factory cab
1066	1972	7,559	G	$11,000	8/04	SEIA	Hydro, 18.4-38" & 1l-15" tires, new paint, new tires
1066	1973	3,225	G	$5,900	9/04	WCMN	Turbo, diesel, cab
1066	1973	5,930	G	$6,250	1/04	NEIN	Cab, 2 hyd., 18.4-38", hub duals
1066	1973	3,016	E	$11,100	9/04	SCMN	Turbo, diesel, 1 owner, Hiniker cab, 18.4-38" band duals, 540/1000 PTO, AC, rock box, radio, very clean
1066	1974	5,200	G	$0	10/04	NEIA	No sale at $9,100, wanted $10,000, new paint, last OH in '89
1066	1974	6,045	F	$3,500	11/04	SEND	2 hyd., 3 pt., 540/1000 PTO, front fuel tank, 18.4-38"
1066	1974	7,900	G	$4,800	3/04	SWWI	Diesel, 4 hyd.
1066	1974	5,065	G	$7,350	11/04	NWIL	No cab, new tires, 2 hyd., dual PTO, 3 pt., axle duals, 12 front weights
1066	1974	4,550	G	$7,400	2/04	NWIL	WF, 3 pt., 630 hours on major engine OH, diesel, 18.4-38"
1066	1974	3,782	G	$11,800	1/04	WCIL	Year-round cab, 3 pt., PTO, 2 hyd., front & rear weights, duals & hubs
1066	1975	6,220	F	$3,400	2/04	NWKS	Cab, 2 hyd., 3 pt., 540/1000 PTO
1066	1975		G	$4,300	8/04	ECKS	
1066	1975	4,600	G	$7,600	2/04	NWIL	Cab, 132 air, heat, duals, 540/1000 PTO, 4 hyd.
1066	1975	4,192	G	$8,300	7/04	NCIA	Red cab, 2 hyd., 2 PTOs, new battery
1066	1975		G	$9,600	9/04	NCIA	Red cab, AC, front tank weights, 2 PTOs, 2 hyd., quick coupler, duals
1066	1975	891	E	$31,000	8/04	SEIA	20.8x38" & 11.00x16" tires, front weights, duals, 891 actual 1-owner hours
1066	1976	4,300	G	$6,200	8/04	WCIL	Black stripe, factory cab, 3 pt., 2 hyd., no duals, TA weak, recently installed, injection pump and alternator, diesel
1066			F	$2,900	4/03	ECVT	
1066			F	$3,500	7/03	SCMN	Cab, AC
1066		9,713	F	$3,500	9/03	ECND	Farmall, 3 pt., 540/1000 PTO, 2 hyd., 18.4x38" rear tires
1066			F	$3,600	2/03	NCMI	116 hp., Hiniker cab, dual PTO, 2 hyd., diesel
1066		10,000	G	$4,175	12/03	SCNE	Diesel, cab, 2 hyd., front & rear weights, 18.4-38", duals
1066			F	$4,250	4/03	NCND	Dual PTO
1066			G	$4,400	1/03	SWOH	Turbo
1066		4,378	G	$4,600	1/03	SCMI	Diesel, duals, inside rubber 90%, duals 50%
1066		6,720	F	$5,100	3/03	NCCO	
1066		5,930	G	$5,500	12/03	SCIA	Year-round cab, front weights, duals
1066		7,900	G	$5,500	3/03	WCMN	Turbo, 18.4-38", 540/1000 PTO, 3 pt., 2 hyd., cab, heat, runs good
1066			G	$5,900	3/03	NCWI	Cab, diesel
1066		4,042	E	$5,900	2/03	NENE	Complete OH

Model	Year	Hours	Cond.	Price	Date	Area	Comments
1066			F	$6,500	8/03	SEPA	Turbo, WF, average rubber
1066			G	$6,950	12/03	WCMN	WF, 3 pt., 2 hyd., duals, front weights, year-round cab, 2 PTOs
1066			G	$8,500	11/03	SWWI	75 hours on major OH
1066		2,757	G	$9,100	10/03	NWSD	Cab, 3 pt., 540/1000 PTO
1066			G	$9,100	1/03	SEIN	Cab, 2 hyd., duals
1066		6,300	G	$9,500	4/03	WCMN	Diesel, 18.4x38" rubber, original paint, duals
1066	1970	3,099	F	$4,100	9/03	SEIL	Duals
1066	1971	7,700	F	$3,900	3/03	NCCO	
1066	1972	7,700	F	$4,200	3/03	NCCO	
1066	1972	13,000	G	$6,200	6/03	WCSK	Canadian sale, 23.1x34" good rubber, dual PTO, dual hyd., hydro trans., 116 PTO hp.
1066	1973		G	$4,600	6/03	SWMN	Diesel, dual hyd., 3 pt., 18x38", IHC cab
1066	1973		G	$6,000	11/03	ECND	Hydro, cab, 3 pt., 540/1000 PTO, 18.4-38" (60%), loader w/ grapple
1066	1973	4,563	G	$7,200	8/03	SENE	Diesel
1066	1973	5,234	G	$7,900	3/03	SEIA	Cab, front weights, PTO, hub-mount duals, 1 owner
1066	1973		E	$8,500	11/03	SEIL	New tires, sharp
1066	1974		G	$6,550	8/03	NCIA	
1066	1974	5,637	G	$8,200	8/03	ECNE	Cab, 2 hyd., 3 pt.
1066	1975	7,000	F	$3,900	11/03	WCIN	2 hyd., 540/1000 PTO, axle-mount duals, cab
1066	1975	4,100	F	$7,100	4/03	NWPA	Black stripe, weights, 42" bolt-on duals, cab
1066	1975	4,100	G	$7,100	4/03	NWPA	Black stripe, 125 hp., cab, 18.4-42", axle-mount 18.4-38" duals, 10 front weights
1066	1975	4,895	E	$8,000	2/03	SEIA	No cab, WF , duals
1066	1976		F	$4,000	11/03	WCIN	Black stripe, 2 hyd., 540/1000 PTO, axle-mount duals, cab
1066	1976		F	$6,000	4/03	NCMD	Cab
1066	1976		F	$8,000	7/03	WCSK	Canadian sale, 2WD, duals
1066	1976	3,876	G	$9,900	1/03	ECIL	AC, 2 hyd., full weights, 18.4-38"
1066	1976	6,300	E	$10,900	2/03	NEIN	Cab, 2 hyd., 1 owner, black stripe, 20.8-38" duals
1206			G	$4,900	7/05	ECND	2hyd, 3pt, 540/1000 PTO, fenders, diesel
1206	1966		G	$8,800	8/05	SEIA	Diesel, 18.4-38, 56 shifter
1206			P	$555	3/05	WCIL	Diesel
1206			F	$3,000	2/05	WCIN	"Mechanic's special," 18.4-34" tires, bad TA, clutch, 3rd gear, noise in rear end, does run
1206			G	$5,600	2/05	NWKS	3 pt., dual PTO, rear weights, 18.4-34", newer 10:00-16.4" rib-front tires, 2 hyd.
1206		8,716	G	$8,100	4/05	NWIL	3 pt., PTO, 18.4-38", duals, TA is out
1206	1966	8,242	G	$2,200	6/05	NWMN	Wheatland, diesel, cab, PTO, 2 hyd.
1206	1967	4,018	G	$9,300	1/05	NWIL	WF, 2 hyd., 3 pt., 12 front weights, 18.4-38", clamp duals
1206			G	$6,250	1/04	SCNE	
1206			G	$7,000	1/04	WCIA	Dual PTO, WF, good tin
1206	1965	2,472	G	$7,200	8/04	SEIA	Wheatland, rare, 23.1-30" & 10:00-16" tires
1206			G	$3,600	2/03	SWOH	WF, no cab
1206	1969		G	$11,100	4/03	NCIA	Restored, 18.4-38", duals, new motor & paint
1256			F	$5,700	4/04	NEPA	
1256	1968		G	$5,800	2/04	NCIN	Diesel, WF, no cab, 20.8-38"
1256	1968	6,050	G	$6,000	12/04	SEPA	ROPS w/ canopy, new tires, 540/1000 PTO, 2 hyd., bad TA/clutch
1256	1969	5,700	G	$6,250	12/04	SEPA	Cab, turbo, 540/1000 PTO, 2 hyd.
1256			G	$4,500	9/03	WCSD	Cab, 2 hyd., 540/1000 PTO, TA, diesel

international harvester

Model	Year	Hours	Cond.	Price	Date	Area	Comments
1256			G	$4,800	11/03	NEND	Std., 2 hyd., 540/1000 PTO, 24.5-32" singles
1256		7,000	G	$7,000	3/03	NCWI	Diesel, 18.4-38R", WF, 3 pt.
1256	1967	7,839	F	$3,850	7/03	NWIL	WF, 3 pt., dual PTO, diesel
1256	1969		G	$6,100	3/03	NWIL	Diesel, WF, 3 pt., 2 hyd., new 18.4-38" tires, new fronts, front weights, 300 hours on major engine OH
130	1957		E	$4,000	6/04	ECND	21 hp.
130	1957		E	$4,400	6/04	ECND	New tires, 21 hp.
140			E		12/05	SWWI	No sale at $2,100, new paint
140			G	$1,800	9/05	SCON	Canadian sale, gas
140			G	$3,000	9/05	NEIN	Low houred with 1-pt. hitch
140			E	$2,300	3/05	WCMN	With belly-mount 6' sickle mower
140	1959		G	$4,000	6/05	NEND	WF, PS, 4-speed, 2 pt., fast hitch, PTO
140			E	$3,000	12/04	SWKY	With plows
140	1959		E	$4,200	6/04	ECND	New tires, 1-pt. hitch, new seat, 24 hp.
140	1960		G	$2,200	6/04	ECND	Poor tires, 24 hp.
140	1961		G	$2,325	9/04	NECO	Runs, lift hitch belly mower, cultivator, post hole digger, blade, good tires & tin
140			G	$1,950	4/03	SCND	Gas, WF, midmount sickle mower
140			G	$5,350	10/03	ECMN	Low hours, cultivator
140	1966		G	$2,000	3/03	ECTN	Cultivator
140	1974		G	$2,500	3/03	ECTN	Cultivator & sidedresser
140	1976		G	$3,000	3/03	ECIL	Attached Woods 42" deck, gas, WF, fenders, 11.2-24" tires
1456	1971	6,470	P	$1,450	9/05	NECO	3 pt., exc. tires on rear, cab, front weights, for parts
1456			F	$3,000	7/04	NWMN	2 hyd., 3 pt., dual PTO, weak TA
1456			G	$5,900	1/04	NWIA	Open station
1456			G	$9,500	9/04	ECWI	OH
1456	1971	3,763	F	$6,000	8/04	SEIA	18.4-38" & 12.5-15" tires, TA out
1456			F	$6,550	8/03	NWIL	Diesel, duals, weights
1456			G	$6,750	4/03	WCMN	Turbo
1466	1972		G	$10,000	1/06	WCIL	With loader & rear fork lift, black stripe, 3 pt., 2 hyd.
1466	1973		G	$7,500	2/06	WCKS	3 pt., PTO, IHC hyd. loader
1466			G	$10,700	3/05	ECMN	Cab, diesel
1466			F	$8,900	9/05	NENE	High hours, torque out
1466			P	$2,400	4/05	SCSD	Rough
1466		6,173	G	$8,200	1/05	WCOH	2 hyd., 540/1000 PTO, 3 pt., front weights
1466	1971		G	$3,900	6/05	NEND	Turbo, 2 hyd., 1000 PTO, 18.4x38" duals
1466			P	$2,900	6/04	NWMN	Cab heat, 3 pt., PTO, 2 hyd.
1466		6,382	G	$5,200	3/04	SCKS	3 pt., PTO, 2 hyd., 18.4-38", duals
1466		7,226	G	$5,400	1/04	ECIL	Front/rear weights, duals, 3 pt., 540/1000 PTO
1466			G	$5,800	6/04	ECWI	300 hours on engine OH
1466			G	$6,700	4/04	ECWI	1,500 hours on new engine
1466		5,900	F	$6,700	3/04	SEPA	WF, ROPS, turbo, 20.8-38R", rubber fair
1466			G	$9,000	3/04	NWIL	Diesel, loader, open
1466		5,620	G	$12,400	1/04	ECIA	900 hours on complete OH, cab, 18.4-38", duals, 3 pt., 2 hyd., diesel
1466	1971	4,500	G	$13,000	12/04	SEPA	Year-round cab, 540/1000 PTO, 1 owner
1466	1973	4,100	G	$4,800	4/04	NWIA	WF, cab, dual axles, 2 hyd., 3 pt., TA is good, diesel
1466	1973	5,997	G	$11,000	2/04	WCIL	1300 hours on OH, diesel, open station, dual PTO, 2 hyd., 3 pt., front & rear weights, 18.4-38, dual axles

Model	Year	Hours	Cond.	Price	Date	Area	Comments
1466			F	$3,600	8/03	WCMN	
1466			F	$3,900	3/03	SEIA	Duals
1466			G	$6,000	4/03	WCMN	No 3 pt.
1466			G	$6,250	9/03	WCSD	Turbo, 3 pt., 2 hyd., cab, AC, TA
1466			F	$6,700	4/03	NCND	TA OH, cab
1466	1973	8,075	G	$6,000	7/03	ECND	913 hours on new engine, 18.4-38", duals, rubber 90%
1466	1973		G	$8,500	1/03	ECIL	795 hours on new factory engine & TA, cab, AC, 2 hyd., weights, 18.4-38, axle duals
1466	1974		G	$6,500	12/03	ECWI	Cab
1466	1975	6,200	G	$6,250	6/03	WCSK	Canadian sale, 18.4x38" rubber, duals, dual hyd., 133 PTO hp.
1544			G	$2,500	2/03	ECIL	Cub Lo-boy 60" mower
1566	1975	3,695	G	$5,700	2/06	WCIL	CAH, duals
1566	1975		G	$9,500	1/06	WCNE	WF, 3 pt., 2 hyd., 1000 PTO, duals, 1000 hrs on OH, diesel
1566	1976		G	$5,400	2/06	WCIL	Black stripe, CAH, duals, new TA and clutch
1566	1975	7,500	G	$6,400	7/05	ECND	CAH, 3pt, 540/1000 PTO, duals, front fuel tank
1566	1975	7,800	G	$7,500	4/05	ECND	Factory cab, 3 pt., PTO, 2 hyd., 18.4-38R", duals, good rubber, clean
1566	1976		G	$6,200	3/05	NWMN	Factory cab, 3 pt., PTO, 2 hyd., black stripe
1566			F	$2,900	2/04	SEMN	Cab, PTO, duals, 3 pt.
1566			F	$5,100	10/04	SEPA	Cab, duals, average rubber
1566			G	$6,500	5/04	ECWI	Black stripe, dual PTO
1566			G	$6,500	4/04	ECWI	Cab, clamp-on duals
1566		3,900	G	$9,100	12/04	ECNE	Diesel
1566	1975		F	$4,300	3/04	SEIA	Cab
1566	1976	2,901	G	$6,000	8/04	SEIA	Black stripe, cab, front fuel tank, 20.8-38" & 11:00-16" tires
1566	1976	4,000	G	$11,250	12/04	SEPA	Bad TA, cab, 540/1000 PTO, 1 owner
1566	1976	1,326	E	$25,000	8/04	SEIA	Black stripe, 1 owner, front weights, 20.8-38" & 11:00-16" tires
1566		4,994	G	$3,800	6/03	ECND	Factory cab, recent TA, 1000 PTO, 2 hyd., 20.8x38" duals, clutch & starter
1566			F	$4,100	2/03	NCMI	161 hp., factory cab, AC, 1000 PTO, 2 hyd., 20.8-38", snap-on duals, diesel
1566			F	$4,500	7/03	WCSK	Canadian sale, 180 hp.
200			F	$800	1/06	NCCO	With cultivator
200			G	$3,100	2/05	ECMI	Farmall, fast hitch, gas
200			G	$6,500	6/05	WCMN	All restored, fast hitch, WF, fenders
200			G	$1,800	6/04	SEMN	
200			F	$2,700	9/04	WCMN	Gas, WF
200			G	$3,400	12/04	ECNE	
200	1955		G	$2,550	6/04	ECND	2 pt., 24 hp.
200			G	$2,100	6/03	NCWI	Gas, NF, 2 pt.
200			F	$3,100	11/03	NWIL	Gas, NF, fast hitch
230			G	$2,600	7/05	SESD	2pt hitch
230			G	$3,400	9/05	WCMN	Fast hitch, WF
230			G	$3,700	11/05	WCIA	NF, with continental mower, good
230	1957		G	$4,000	6/05	NEND	NF, 4 speed, 2 pt., PTO, belt pulley, hyd. front weights, band duals
230	1957		G	$3,300	6/04	ECND	New duals, side weights, 2-pt. pallet carrier
230	1957		G	$4,500	6/04	ECND	27 hp., motor OH, fresh paint
230	1957		E	$4,600	6/04	ECND	WF, 27 hp., one owner
230			G	$4,750	8/03	ECMN	NF, new paint
240	1959		G	$4,600	11/05	NWIL	Gas, with loader, no PS, good tires

international harvester

Model	Year	Hours	Cond.	Price	Date	Area	Comments
240		2,214	E	$5,350	2/05	NEIA	With rear blade, fast hitch
240		1,958	E	$5,100	6/04	ECND	New tires, new axle & seals
240			F	$2,875	8/03	SEPA	Utility, WF, average rubber, PS
300			G	$2,150	1/06	SESD	NF, 3 pt.
300			G	$4,075	1/06	SCMN	Vaughn loader (48" & 80" buckets), gas, 1 owner
300			G	$4,500	1/06	SCMN	Utility, gas, fast hitch, 1 owner
300			F	$1,800	9/05	SEIA	Farmall
300			G	$1,900	8/05	NEIN	WF, TA
300		3,687	G	$2,000	12/05	ECMI	Gas, NF, fast hitch
300			F	$950	8/05	ECMI	Utility tractor, new rubber and paint
300			F	$1,150	2/05	NCIN	
300			F	$1,300	2/05	WCIN	Gas, NF, 6 volt, belt pulley
300			F	$1,700	3/05	SCMI	Gas, NF
300			G	$2,600	3/05	NENE	
300			G	$2,700	6/05	ECMN	Farmall, fast hitch, PTO
300			G	$2,800	3/05	WCIL	Industrial, gas, utility tractor with loader
300			G	$2,900	6/05	WCMN	Restored, fast hitch, WF, fenders
300			G	$3,400	6/05	WCMN	Farmall, WF, original
300	1955	8,804	F	$950	2/05	WCNE	Gas, 2 pt., live PTO
300	1955	2,769	G	$2,400	3/05	SEWY	Gas, 3 pt., double front
300	1959		G	$3,500	7/05	NCMN	4 cyl., gas, 3 pt., PTO, PS, loader, blade & sickle mower
300	1959		G	$3,500	7/05	NCMN	4 cyl., gas, 3 pt., PTO, PS, loader
300			G	$1,100	2/04	NCWI	Gas, NF
300			G	$1,650	3/04	WCMI	NF, reconditioned w/ paint, gas
300			E	$2,450	3/04	SENE	Gas, new tires, NF
300			G	$2,550	7/04	SEND	WF, open station, 2 pt., PTO, new brakes
300		1,900	G	$2,550	7/04	NWMN	WF, open station, 2 pt., PTO, new brakes on both sides
300			G	$3,300	1/04	SCNE	Utility, 4 cyl., gas
300	1955		G	$1,800	8/04	NCIA	Farmall
300	1955	2,675	G	$1,900	3/04	SEWY	Utility, 3 pt., PTO
300	1955		G	$2,000	5/04	NCKS	Utility, 3 hyd., 2 pt. quick hitch, PTO
300	1955		G	$2,300	6/04	ECND	New tires
300	1955		G	$2,400	9/04	SEND	WF, Std. trans., TA, PTO, belt pulley, PS, 1 hyd., fenders, custom shop-built hyd., 3 pt., 14-38" rears, engine kit
300	1955		G	$2,900	12/04	WCIL	Gas, fast hitch
300	1955		E	$2,950	6/04	ECND	New tires, WF, 38 hp.
300	1955		G	$3,000	9/04	ECIA	Trip loader, snow and manure buckets
300			G	$950	9/03	NEIN	
300			F	$1,300	12/03	SCIA	Farmall, TA out, Stanhoist loader with trip bucket
300			G	$1,350	9/03	NEIN	
300			G	$1,700	3/03	ECND	Dual loader, looks sharp
300			P	$1,900	7/03	SWOH	Rough
300			G	$2,550	9/03	NEIN	
300			G	$4,000	1/03	ECNE	Utility, WF, 4-cyl. gas engine, TA, 5 speed, 13.6-28", 2 pt., lift assist
330			F	$1,025	11/04	NCOH	Utility, rough but running
340			G	$2,750	1/04	NENE	
340	1958	583	E	$5,700	6/04	ECND	NF, WF, fenders, new seat
340			G	$1,700	5/03	ECWI	TA, 3 hyd., gas

Model	Year	Hours	Cond.	Price	Date	Area	Comments
340			G	$2,800	12/03	ECIL	Utility, 3 extra hyd. remotes, 2000 loader, new 6' bucket
350			F	$1,400	9/05	NWOR	Diesel
350			G	$1,800	11/05	WCIL	NF, PTO, PS, fast hitch
350		4,000	G	$1,900	11/05	SCNE	Farmall, TA, 2 pt.
350			G	$6,500	6/05	ECMN	Farmall, gas, tricycle, new paint, rebuilt
350	1957	1,672	G	$2,100	2/05	WCIA	Gas, utility, total restoration, paint, rubber
350			G	$1,350	3/04	NCOH	Not running, NF
350			F	$1,500	4/04	NEPA	Loader
350			G	$1,950	6/04	NCWI	Tandem axle, WF, fast hitch
350			F	$2,350	10/04	SEPA	Diesel, TA, rubber fair
350			G	$2,400	2/04	NWIL	Hi-utility, gas, loader, 2 pt., new clutch & brakes
350			G	$3,700	3/04	SEND	Utility, WF, 3 pt., PTO
350	1957		G	$2,600	9/04	NECO	Runs, 2 pt., fair tires, power adjust wheels, excellent tin, gas
350	1957		E	$5,800	6/04	ECND	New tires
350	1957		G	$5,800	12/04	WCIL	Diesel
350	1958		G	$4,900	2/04	ECIA	Diesel, decent paint, WF
350			F	$950	3/03	SEIA	Loader
350			G	$1,100	9/03	NEIN	Diesel
350			P	$1,300	9/03	NEIN	Stuck
350			G	$1,750	8/03	NCIA	Fenders, fast hitch
350			G	$1,900	4/03	NCIA	Utility, gas, fast hitch, 16.9-28"
350			F	$2,200	3/03	ECND	NF, 2 hyd., diesel
350			F	$2,475	9/03	NWIL	Utility, not running, diesel
350			G	$2,500	2/03	WCIA	Farmall, just restored, new paint, new front rubber, NF, gas
350			F	$4,100	3/03	SWPA	Gas, superior loader
350			G	$10,400	9/03	NEIN	Hi-crop
350	1958		G	$2,500	3/03	NCCO	
400	1955		F	$3,800	2/06	NWIA	NF
400			G	$1,800	11/05	WCIL	NF, gas, torque amplifier, rebuilt radiators, oil pump & front end
400			G	$2,150	7/05	SESD	WF, gas
400			G	$3,300	12/05	NCCO	1955 model, Farmall, dual 325 loader, WF, 2 pt.
400	1956		G	$1,600	9/05	NCIL	LP, gas
400	1956		G	$1,600	9/05	NCIL	LP, gas
400			F	$3,500	3/05	NWMN	WF, PS, Cornhusker 3 pt., hyd., IH Model 2000 hyd. loader
400			G	$4,000	6/05	WCMN	Restored, fast hitch, WF, fenders
400			G	$4,250	6/05	ECMN	Engine OH, TA rebuilt, front weight set, new paint
400			G	$4,500	6/05	ECMN	Farmall, gas, row crop, WF, new tires, fast hitch, rebuilt
400	1955		F	$2,350	3/05	ECND	WF, TA, single hyd., Cornhusker, 3 pt., PTO
400	1955		G	$3,400	4/05	NCIA	3 pt., WF, Stanhoist loader with hyd. bucket
400			G	$1,100	5/04	ECWI	Gas/diesel, NF
400			F	$1,500	12/04	ECMI	WF, fast hitch
400			G	$1,600	6/04	NCND	Gas
400			G	$1,850	9/04	NCIA	Farmall, PS
400			G	$2,300	3/04	SEND	WF, 2 hyd., new rubber
400			G	$3,700	12/04	ECMN	WF, Kelly 600 hydraulic loader, good rubber, very clean
400	1955		G	$1,200	3/04	SEWY	Gas, 3 pt., WF
400	1955		F	$1,900	2/04	NWIL	NF, PS, IHC Model 33 loader, hyd. bucket, cracked block
400	1955		E	$2,000	6/04	ECND	Hyd., PS, 48 hp.
400	1955		G	$2,650	12/04	WCIL	Gas
400	1955		G	$3,100	6/04	ECND	48 hp., recent OH
400	1956		F	$1,550	1/04	WCIL	Gas, NF, new tires & paint

international harvester

Model	Year	Hours	Cond.	Price	Date	Area	Comments
400	1956		G	$2,200	4/04	WCNE	Gas, F11 loader, WF
400			P	$925	7/03	NWIL	Gas, NF, fenders
400			F	$1,000	4/03	SEMN	Fast hitch, good rubber
400			F	$1,100	9/03	SCMN	
400			F	$1,300	11/03	WCIN	Straight drawbar, belt pulley
400			G	$1,450	4/03	SEMN	Farmall, very good sheet metal
400			G	$2,500	12/03	ECIL	Row crop front
400			G	$2,800	9/03	WCSD	Gas, Farmhand F10 loader, grapple, PS, truck front end
400			E	$5,300	9/03	SEIN	With IHC 234 mounted picker
400	1954		G	$2,150	4/03	SEMN	
400	1955		P	$975	7/03	NWIL	Farmall, as is, diesel
400	1955		G	$2,200	12/03	SCNE	NF, 1 hyd., TA, Std. hitch, 13.6-38" tires, good paint
404			P	$950	1/06	SESD	Utility, salvage
404		2,127	G	$3,200	11/05	SCMI	IHC 2000 loader
404			G	$3,350	3/05	NECO	WF, 3 pt., PTO, hyd., 6-row front-mounted cultivator
404			G	$4,650	4/04	ECWI	Utility, Freeman hyd. loader
404			F	$2,250	12/03	WCMI	Gas, 14.9x24" tires
404	1963		G	$1,500	4/03	SCND	Midmount 6.5' sickle mower
404	1963		F	$1,750	12/03	NCIN	IHC 2000 loader, 3 pt.
4166			F	$6,100	12/05	SEMN	4WD, with blade
4166		2,339	P	$1,600	4/05	SCSD	4WD, for parts
424	1966		G	$2,500	8/05	NEIN	Gas, WF, loader
424		2,617	G	$2,700	1/05	SWOH	
424	1967	3,020	G	$4,750	4/05	NCKS	Gas, 38 hp., PTO, 3 pt., Schwartz 300 loader
424			G	$1,850	5/04	WCWA	4 cyl. diesel, 4-speed
424			G	$4,000	12/04	SEPA	Diesel, 155 mower
424	1964	10,504	E	$4,600	2/04	NEIN	Diesel, utility, restored
434			F	$3,850	3/03	WCMI	Utility, diesel, WF, 3 pt., PTO, loader
4366	1974	7,900	G	$1,400	9/05	NECO	Cab, duals, turbo, diesel
4366			G	$5,500	1/05	ECIL	4WD
4366		6,069	G	$7,250	7/05	ECND	4WD, 4 hyd., duals, new batteries, alternator, clutch assembly, center pins and bushings, steering ends, seat and floor mat
4366	1974	5,100	G	$5,700	4/03	NCIA	4WD, 3 pt., 30.5-32"
4366	1976	10,140	G	$4,000	7/03	ECND	6 cyl., 3 hyd., 10 speed, 18.4x38" tires & duals, completely rebuilt injector pump, housing at 10,139 hours, all new filters, rebuilt transfer case, oiler kit at 7,200 hours, AC freon changed from R12 to 134A
444			F	$1,825	1/05	SWOH	
444	1969		G	$4,500	3/05	NESD	2 hyd., gas, PTO, 3 pt.
450			G	$2,000	2/06	WCIL	Farmall, NF, gas
450	1957		G	$5,000	2/06	WCIL	NF
450			G	$2,600	7/05	SESD	NF, good TA with 3 pt.
450			P	$900	7/05	NCMN	Diesel, not running
450			F	$975	7/05	SEIA	Gas, straight bar, hyd., loader sold separate for $10
450			G	$3,300	4/05	NCCO	Farmhand F11 loader
450			G	$7,000	6/05	ECMN	Farmall, tricycle, fast hitch, new paint, restored, wheel weights
450			G	$1,150	4/04	ECWI	Farmall, WF
450			G	$2,000	4/04	SEND	Gas, WF, Schwartz front end, PTO, 2 pt., 3 hyd.
450			P	$2,000	10/04	NEIA	Rough
450			G	$3,700	2/04	NWIL	NF, 2 pt., fenders, 395 hours on OH, parade ready

Model	Year	Hours	Cond.	Price	Date	Area	Comments
450			E	$6,900	12/04	WCIL	Diesel, new tires, pro paint
450			E	$7,000	3/04	SWDE	1 owner, super nice
450	1957		G	$2,500	3/04	NWIA	Fast hitch
450	1957		G	$3,700	8/04	WCIL	PS, 2 pt., 540 PTO, gas
450	1957		G	$3,900	12/04	WCIL	Gas, PS
450	1957		E	$8,400	6/04	ECND	NF, WF, new seat, recent OH
450	1958		G	$2,500	6/04	WCND	
450			G	$1,500	4/03	SEIN	
450			G	$2,050	2/03	WCIA	Farmall, gas, NF
450			G	$2,350	9/03	NEIN	
450			E	$2,800	8/03	NEKS	Farmall, TA, 2 pt., restored
450	1957		G	$1,400	9/03	NWIL	Farmall, PS, diesel
454	1972		F	$4,250	4/03	NCMD	
460			P	$1,550	12/05	NWIL	Gas, WF, 2 pt.
460			F	$2,500	12/05	SEMN	With loader
460	1959		F	$1,600	11/05	ECNE	2 pt., PTO, utility, 14.9-28 tires
460			G	$2,050	8/05	ECNE	LP, NF, 2 pt., 1 hyd. w/ front port, 15.5-38" tires, cast weights
460			G	$2,800	6/05	SWMN	Utility tractor, gas, 3 pt.
460			G	$3,250	4/05	WCWI	Farmall, IH 2000 hyd. loader, 6' bucket
460	1960		G	$1,800	2/05	NEIN	Gas, NF, TA works
460			F	$1,500	9/04	ECIA	Fast hitch, gas
460			F	$1,550	4/04	NEPA	
460			G	$2,100	2/04	WCWI	NF, Westendorf loader
460		1,829	F	$2,100	9/04	SCMI	Gas, NF, fast hitch
460			G	$2,500	7/04	ECMN	Gas, with trip bucket loader
460			G	$3,000	8/04	NWIA	Gas, WF
460			F	$3,500	12/04	WCIL	Utility, gas, with loader
460			G	$4,900	12/04	SCNH	WF, Farmhand F11 loader w/ grapple fork
460	1958		E	$3,700	6/04	ECND	New tires, hyd., PS, 50 hp.
460	1960	4,316	G	$3,000	9/04	ECIA	Gas, NF, fast hitch
460	1961		G	$3,800	11/04	NCKS	Farmhand F11 loader
460	1963	4,993	G	$5,000	2/04	SCIA	Fast hitch, restored, gas, 15.5-38"
460			P	$1,100	7/03	NWIL	NF, gas
460			F	$1,150	3/03	WCMI	WF , gas, 3 pt., 15.5x38" tires
460			F	$1,475	8/03	NCIA	NF, gas
460			G	$1,750	4/03	WCWI	Gas, NF, fast hitch
460			G	$2,000	12/03	SCNE	Gas, WF
460			G	$2,050	2/03	NCIA	NF, Std., drawbar, gas
460			G	$2,150	4/03	WCWI	WF
460			G	$2,500	6/03	WCWI	WF, loader
460			G	$2,500	7/03	NWIA	Westendorf I30 loader, gas
460			G	$2,600	3/03	NCWI	Gas, utility tractor, PS, 14.9x28"
460			G	$2,750	9/03	SCMN	Loader
460			G	$3,400	9/03	NEIN	Farmall
460			G	$3,800	8/03	SCNE	
460			G	$4,100	9/03	NEIN	Hi-crop
460			E	$6,200	5/03	NEKS	IHC 2000 loader, 5' bucket, gas, WF, PS
460	1963		G	$2,200	8/03	ECNE	LP, NF, 3 pt., 2,100 hours on tach, 2-pt. fast hitch, 14.9-38" tires, rear wheel weights
464			G	$5,900	9/05	ECMN	Utility
464		2,388	E	$6,200	12/05	ECIL	Loader, gas, WF, PS, 3 pt., new 13.6-28 tires

international harvester

Model	Year	Hours	Cond.	Price	Date	Area	Comments
464			E	$8,800	3/03	ECWI	3 pt., hi/lo, water filter
464	1977		G	$2,600	6/03	NCIA	Gas, WF
504	1962		G	$2,200	11/05	NCIN	WF
504	1964		G	$1,600	8/05	NEIN	WF
504			G	$2,050	1/05	ECNE	
504			G	$6,000	8/05	ECIL	Utility tractor sold with IHC 1709 loader w/ 5' bucket, new 13.6-28" tires
504	1962		G	$3,900	3/05	ECMI	TA, 1 hyd., 540 PTO
504			F	$1,750	9/04	SEIA	
504			F	$2,200	12/04	NEIL	Gas, Ag Leader, 4 cyl., stick trans, 3 pt., 1 hyd.
504			G	$2,950	3/04	NCOH	Gas, NF
504	1962		E	$4,200	6/04	ECND	New tires
504	1965		G	$3,650	8/04	WCMN	Gas, WF
504	1967		G	$3,900	3/04	WCMI	WF , TA, 1 hyd., fast hitch, gas, new 13.6-38" tires
504	1968		G	$4,150	11/04	SENE	Diesel, WF
504			F	$1,600	8/03	NWIL	Gas, WF
504			G	$2,000	9/03	NEIN	High-clearance
504			G	$2,250	2/03	WCIA	German diesel, utility
504			G	$4,100	4/03	SEIN	Utility, Freeman loader, gas
504			G	$4,900	1/03	SWOH	IHC 2001 front loader
504			G	$5,000	9/03	WCSD	5-speed, TA, 2 IHC 9' mowers, 1 mounted
504	1965	1,042	G	$3,500	1/03	SWIA	Gas, WF, 1 hyd., 3 pt., 14.9-28" tires, radio
544			G	$3,500	4/04	NCWI	Gas, WF
544		6,347	G	$3,900	3/04	WCMN	Gas, WF, 1 hyd., 2 pt., PTO, 15.5-38"
544	1968	4,918	G	$4,350	2/04	ECNE	Hydro, gas, 15.5-38" tires, 2 hyd., 3 pt., WF
544		2,857	P	$2,000	4/03	SEPA	Rough, diesel, needs OH, no cab, good tires
544			G	$3,600	11/03	NWKS	Belly mower, new style, gas
544		2,207	G	$4,950	10/03	WCMN	WF, cab, hyd. Schwartz loader, gas
544	1968		E	$3,900	12/03	NWKS	3 pt., PTO, gas, 15.5-38"
544	1969		F	$4,050	3/03	NCCO	
560			F	$2,200	2/06	ECNE	
560			F	$1,065	9/05	SEIA	With loader
560			F	$1,550	9/05	SCMN	
560	1958		F	$2,500	9/05	ECIA	Row crop, gas, high hours
560	1962	2,689	G	$3,300	8/05	NEIN	Diesel, NF
560	1962		G	$3,950	8/05	ECMI	Farmall with NI loader and extra manure bucket
560			F	$800	4/05	SEND	Wheatland, diesel
560			P	$1,425	4/05	NCOH	Salvage, diesel
560			G	$1,750	1/05	ECNE	WF
560		4,300	G	$2,050	1/05	NENE	Propane
560			G	$2,075	2/05	NEIN	Diesel, turbo, WF, TA out
560			G	$2,100	6/05	SWMN	Diesel
560			G	$3,300	4/05	WCWI	Farmall w/ turbo
560			G	$4,100	2/05	SCMN	
560	1959		G	$2,950	8/05	NCIA	NF, Std., drawbar, diesel
560	1959		G	$3,500	6/05	NEND	WF, TA, PTO, 1 hyd. w/ IHC 2000 hyd. loader
560	1960	4,567	F	$1,700	2/05	NWKS	Diesel, 2 pt., 15.5-38", 1 hyd.
560	1961		G	$3,200	1/05	NEIA	Diesel, WF, fast hitch, fenders
560	1962		G	$3,800	8/05	NCIA	NF, fast hitch, repainted, diesel

Model	Year	Hours	Cond.	Price	Date	Area	Comments
560			P	$900	6/04	NWMN	Diesel, WF, 1 hyd., PTO, quick coupler
560			P	$1,200	3/04	NWMN	Needs work
560			F	$1,600	3/04	SEMN	Gas
560		6,898	G	$2,050	1/04	ECIL	Gas, tricycle
560			G	$2,100	3/04	WCMN	2 pt., 1 hyd., PTO, diesel
560			F	$2,100	1/04	ECNE	NF
560			F	$2,100	9/04	ECSD	Diesel
560			F	$2,250	3/04	WCMN	Diesel, WF, 14x34" duals
560			G	$2,300	9/04	SEIA	NF, fast hitch
560			G	$2,600	3/04	NWIL	Diesel, WF
560		3,500	G	$2,700	12/04	WCIL	Gas, fast hitch
560			G	$2,750	3/04	WCKS	Diesel
560			G	$2,800	3/04	WCIA	Gas tractor, NF, rebuilt for unleaded fuel
560			G	$2,850	12/04	WCIL	Gas, WF
560		3,105	F	$3,000	9/04	WCMN	With loader, diesel
560			G	$3,100	3/04	NWIL	NF, gas
560			G	$3,400	11/04	NEIA	Farmhand 233 loader, diesel, WF
560			G	$3,400	7/04	NCIA	Gas, 2 pt., NF
560			G	$3,600	3/04	NEKS	TA, gas, WF, new tires
560			G	$3,600	1/04	NWIA	Gas
560			G	$4,000	12/04	SEMN	Gas, Farmhand loader
560			G	$4,000	5/04	WCWA	4-390 diesel, PS, ROPS
560			G	$4,800	12/04	SEPA	Diesel
560	1959		G	$3,000	9/04	NCIA	3 pt. added, WF
560	1959	6,140	G	$3,250	9/04	ECIA	Gas, 1 owner, NF, fast hitch
560	1959		E	$4,500	6/04	ECND	New tires, 62 hp., recent OH, new seat
560	1960	9,369	G	$2,000	12/04	ECNE	LP gas, WF, 1 hyd., 3 pt., 15.5-38" tires, Farmhand F11 hyd. front loader with bale fork attachment & snow bucket
560	1960		G	$2,550	2/04	NWIL	NF, good rubber, gas
560	1960		G	$3,000	2/04	SENE	Diesel, complete engine OH, NF, new 15.5-38" tires, 2 pt., rear wheel weights
560	1961		G	$2,850	8/04	WCIL	540 PTO, PS, Std. drawbar, 2500 hours on engine/TA/clutch OH, gas
560	1961	8,800	G	$3,200	1/04	NEIN	Gas, WF, TA, fast hitch
560	1962		G	$2,250	9/04	SEIA	Gas, fast hitch, NF, with IHC 2-row ear corn picker
560	1962		G	$2,300	5/04	NCKS	PS, good rubber, 3 hyd., PTO
560	1962		G	$3,900	12/04	ECNE	Diesel, 15.5-38", WF, 2 hyd., 2 pt., rear weights
560	1962		G	$4,100	2/04	NCIA	Gas, 2 pt., fenders, NF
560	1962		G	$5,000	2/04	NECO	Dual loader, diesel, 2 pt., PTO, hyd., 1 owner
560	1962		G	$5,750	3/04	SWMN	2 hyd., PTO, WF, diesel, 16.9-34"
560	1963	4,938	G	$4,000	2/04	NCIN	WF, diesel, no cab, 312 direct inj. motor
560			P	$125	6/03	NCIA	WF, fast hitch, 813 hours on engine OH, TA out, fenders
560			P	$975	4/03	WCMN	Diesel
560			P	$1,300	9/03	SCNE	NF, 2 pt.
560			G	$1,700	1/03	SWOH	
560			G	$1,700	2/03	ECIA	Gas
560			F	$1,800	7/03	SEND	3 pt., 2 hyd., 540 PTO, Farmhand F11 loader, 8' bucket
560			F	$2,000	7/03	WCSK	Canadian sale, clutch redone
560			G	$2,200	12/03	WCIN	LP
560			F	$2,200	8/03	NCIA	Stanhoist loader, trip bucket
560			F	$2,200	9/03	SCNE	NF, 2 pt.
560			G	$2,300	5/03	WCSD	Gas, add-on 3 pt., down pressure, WF, recent OH

international harvester

Model	Year	Hours	Cond.	Price	Date	Area	Comments
560			G	$2,650	9/03	NEIN	WF, fast hitch
560			G	$3,200	8/03	NCIA	Loader
560			F	$4,000	3/03	NCCO	Loader, diesel
560	1958	6,020	F	$1,250	4/03	WCWI	Diesel
560	1958		F	$3,500	3/03	NCCO	Gas
560	1959	4,155	G	$1,650	8/03	NCIA	NF, Std. drawbar
560	1959		G	$2,200	6/03	NCIA	Gas, WF, fast hitch
560	1960	5,505	F	$1,650	4/03	WCWI	Diesel
560	1960		G	$2,800	8/03	SENE	Diesel
560	1961		G	$3,100	3/03	SENE	Diesel, WF
560	1962		G	$2,500	2/03	NCIA	Diesel
574	1977	2,654	G	$5,000	1/06	NWIL	Utility
574		2,328	F	$3,250	10/05	NEPA	With bucket, good rubber
574	1976	2,581	G	$7,700	3/05	NWMN	Utility, ROPS, canopy, grill guard, 3 pt., PTO, 2 hyd. and IH 2250 loader
574			F	$2,600	4/04	NEPA	1850 loader
574			G	$3,500	1/04	NEOH	Loader
574			F	$5,000	3/04	WCIL	IHC 2050 loader, 2WD
574		5,100	F	$6,400	3/04	SEPA	Diesel, WF, 16.9-30" tires, average rubber
574		3,200	E	$7,000	2/04	SEPA	3 pt., front weights
574	1972		G	$3,600	2/04	NEIN	Gas, utility, original
574	1972	3,039	G	$6,300	5/04	NWND	Good rubber
574	1974	3,312	G	$4,750	2/04	WCWI	Utility, 3 pt.
574			G	$1,700	9/03	NEIN	
574			G	$5,700	3/03	NWIL	Loader, gas
574	1974	3,242	G	$6,000	12/03	ECMI	Utility, gas, Freeman hyd. loader, 2WD, 1 hyd., 3 pt., 540 PTO, fresh engine OH, 18.4-26"
574	1977	1,786	G	$5,500	3/03	SEIA	Bush Hog loader, 1 owner
574	1985		G	$5,500	3/03	WCMN	WF, hyd. loader & hay spear
600			F	$750	9/05	NEIN	Std.original
600			G	$2,300	9/03	NEIN	
606			F	$1,450	3/04	SCKS	3 pt., PTO, gas
606		3,870	F	$4,500	4/03	SCND	Utility, gas, 1 hyd., 3 pt., 540 PTO, TA, IHC 2000 hyd. loader & bucket
650			F	$1,475	8/05	SEMN	
650			G	$3,500	11/05	WCIL	Repaint, PTO
650			F	$600	9/05	NEIN	LP, std.
650			F	$850	9/05	NEIN	Std. original
650			G	$550	9/03	NEIN	Std.
650			G	$1,050	9/03	NEIN	
656			G	$4,000	1/06	SESD	WF, 2 pt., diesel
656			G	$4,800	1/06	WCIL	Gas, WF, IHC 2000 loader
656			F	$6,000	1/06	NEIA	Gas
656	1969		G	$5,700	2/06	NWIA	Unknown hours, diesel, hydro, NF, 2 pt., 2 hyd.
656	1973	6,631	G	$5,100	1/06	WCNE	WF, 3 pt., 2 hyd., gas
656		5,424	F	$1,950	9/05	SEIA	
656			F	$2,950	12/05	SEMN	Diesel
656		10,004	F	$3,000	11/05	NWIL	Gas, NF, 3 pt.
656			G	$3,200	7/05	ECND	WF, 3 pt., 540 PTO

Model	Year	Hours	Cond.	Price	Date	Area	Comments
656		8,854	F	$3,675	9/05	NEIA	Gas, hydro, NF
656			G	$3,750	11/05	WCIL	Gas, new paint, rings & bearings
656	1966	6,476	G	$2,500	8/05	NEIN	NF
656	1967	5,600	G	$3,200	12/05	SEND	With Dual loader, clutch replaced '04, head worked in '03
656	1968	6,161	F	$2,000	9/05	NECO	Duals, turbo
656			G	$0	4/05	NCOH	No sale at $3,750
656			F	$2,250	6/05	NESD	Open station, gas, 3 pt., PTO
656			G	$3,000	1/05	SCIL	NF, 3 pt., gas
656		5,700	F	$3,600	4/05	SEND	1,000 hours on OH, gas
656			G	$4,100	3/05	NENE	WF, 3 pt.
656	1965		G	$5,800	2/05	NEIN	Loader, WF, diesel
656	1968		F	$2,600	6/05	NESD	Gas, 2WD, 540 PTO, 3 pt.
656	1970		G	$6,900	3/05	ECMI	TA, new tires, 2 hyd., 540 PTO, 3 pt.
656	1972		G	$6,000	1/05	WCIL	
656			F	$1,800	11/04	WCIL	Hydro, NF, diesel
656			F	$2,250	11/04	SEPA	NF
656			G	$3,150	1/04	ECIA	Gas, NF, 3 pt., 2 hyd.
656		3,879	G	$3,700	8/04	NESD	Cab, 3 pt., gas
656			G	$3,900	4/04	NCWI	WF, gas
656			F	$4,100	4/04	NEPA	
656			G	$4,100	12/04	ECNE	Diesel
656			G	$4,200	3/04	WCMN	Gas
656			G	$4,300	9/04	NWIA	WF, gas
656			G	$4,500	9/04	ECIA	Gas, hydro, WF
656			G	$4,500	9/04	WCMN	Loader, cab, WF, gas
656			F	$4,600	10/04	SEPA	Gas, WF, rubber fair
656			G	$5,100	2/04	WCWI	Hydro, NF, 3 pt., gas
656			G	$5,300	3/04	SWKS	3 pt., PTO, Excel cab, front end loader and bucket
656		3,800	G	$6,800	7/04	NCIA	Gas, Lundeen cab, 2 pt., Schwartz WF, Stanhoist loader w/ 7' hyd. bucket
656	1962	4,210	G	$5,700	3/04	WCMN	Diesel, open station, 2 hyd., 3 pt., 540 PTO, 16.9-34" hub duals
656	1964		G	$2,500	2/04	ECIA	NF, new front tires, gas, 15.5-38"
656	1968	5,677	F	$3,700	2/04	NWIL	NF, gas, 16.9-34", TA out
656	1968	8,000	G	$7,100	12/04	NWIL	Bush Hog loader & forks, hydro trans., diesel
656	1970		G	$6,500	9/04	ECNE	Dual 320 front-mounted loader w/ grapple, gas, 2 hyd. 15.5-38"
656	1971	3,868	G	$3,200	8/04	WCIL	Open station, gas, NF, Std. drawbar, 2 hyd., fenders
656			F	$800	2/03	SEMN	Farmall, NF, bareback
656			F	$1,000	3/03	WCMI	Farmall, NF, 3 pt., gas, live power
656			G	$1,200	9/03	NEIN	
656			F	$2,100	4/03	NCND	Diesel, row crop
656			F	$2,200	3/03	NWIL	Hydro, gas
656			G	$2,500	8/03	WCIL	Gas, NF, fenders
656			F	$2,600	4/03	NEPA	Gas, WF, hydro shift, 2 hyd.
656			F	$2,800	2/03	SEIA	Utility, WF, needs engine work
656			G	$3,300	5/03	SWOK	Gas, WF, 3 pt., PTO, 63 hp.
656		6,941	G	$4,100	2/03	ECNE	2 hyd., WF, 2 pt., Farmhand F11 loader, black stripe, bucket and grapple
656			E	$4,300	11/03	NENE	Diesel, WF, 2 pt., new rear rubber, sharp
656			G	$4,300	2/03	SCMN	Hydro, open station, WF, 3 pt., flat-top fenders, diesel
656			G	$4,500	8/03	SEMN	WF, fast hitch, fenders

international harvester

Model	Year	Hours	Cond.	Price	Date	Area	Comments
656		3,764	E	$4,750	11/03	NCWI	Hydro
656			G	$4,750	9/03	SEMN	Open station, fenders, 3 pt. with fully hyd. loader
656			F	$5,800	3/03	SWPA	Gas, WF, ROPS canopy
656			F	$6,000	4/03	NCMD	WF
656			G	$6,000	3/03	NWIL	Loader, gas
656		1,847	G	$6,900	4/03	SEMN	Hydrostatic drive, WF, 3 pt., 2 hyd.
656			G	$7,250	9/03	NEIN	Hydro
656			G	$9,000	9/03	WCSD	5 speed, cab, AC, Farmhand F25 loader with grapple and bucket
656	1965		G	$3,900	2/03	ECNE	Clean for age, gas, TA, 2 hyd., 3 pt., ROPS roll bar, square fenders, Snowco umbrella, 15.5-38"
656	1967		G	$3,500	3/03	NWIL	Gas, WF, 3 pt.
656	1967	4,599	G	$5,900	9/03	ECNE	1 hyd., fast hitch, WF, heavy-duty hyd. loader w/ large bucket, gas
656	1968	8,936	G	$4,700	12/03	SEND	Hydro, 3 pt., 1 hyd., 540 PTO, rear fenders, gas, 16.9-34"
656	1968		G	$5,700	3/03	SEIA	Hydro, WF, new rubber, 2 pt., Quick-Tach, ROPS
656	1968		G	$7,100	4/03	NCIA	Hydro, restored, diesel, new 16.9-38, 3 pt., new paint
656	1969	6,500	G	$5,100	8/03	NEKS	Diesel, WF
656	1970		F	$4,500	3/03	ECND	Open station, 2 hyd., 3 pt., PTO, new glow plugs, new meter and batteries
656	1972		G	$6,000	1/03	NENE	Recent major OH, new clutches, rebuilt hydro, good rubber, sharp
656	1973	3,110	G	$13,100	1/03	NWIL	Loader, utility, gas, 3 pt., 540 PTO, fenders
660	1959		F	$2,000	6/05	NEND	Diesel, hyd., PTO, PS, 16.9-34" tires, 1 owner
660	1963	3,958	G	$2,800	2/05	NEIN	Diesel, WF
660			F	$1,300	12/04	SEMN	New engine
666			F	$4,100	12/05	SEMN	
666			G	$5,300	11/05	SCIL	Canopy, 2 pt. hitch, TA
666			G	$5,700	12/05	SCMN	Gas
666			F	$3,200	4/05	SCSD	Gas
666		7,762	G	$7,000	3/05	NEOH	Completely restored but never an OH, looks like new, diesel, WF, 2 hyd., 3 pt., TA good, 1 owner
666		2,700	G	$5,500	5/04	ECWI	NF
666		3,552	G	$10,600	8/04	NESD	Cab, heater, 3 pt., dual 3100 Quick-Tach loader, gas, 3,552 hours
666	1975		F	$4,700	1/04	SCIA	Ran rough, gas, WF, 3 pt., PTO, new paint
666	1976		G	$5,600	4/04	WCMI	3 pt., live hyd., gas
666			G	$4,500	12/03	ECWI	
666		3,342	G	$4,900	4/03	NCWI	New paint, 3 pt.
666	1973	4,467	G	$6,100	12/03	NCIA	Factory WF, 3 pt., 1 hyd. (flow control), gas
666	1973	3,576	G	$8,000	11/03	ECNE	
666	1975	5,535	F	$3,500	4/03	WCWI	Diesel, WF, front weights
674			G	$4,600	9/05	SCON	Canadian sale, 2WD, 3 pt., hyd
674		4,834	G	$5,100	3/05	NEOH	Gas, 2 hyd., good paint, 3 pt., PS, 18.4-30" rear tires, 1 owner
674		3,280	G	$9,500	12/04	SEMN	IHC 2250 loader
674	1976	4,750	G	$8,500	12/04	SEPA	Diesel, row crop, 1 owner
674			F	$3,700	10/03	SEMN	Loader
674			G	$4,900	7/03	SCMN	Gas
674			G	$6,200	4/03	SWMN	IHC 2250 loader, utility, diesel

42

Model	Year	Hours	Cond.	Price	Date	Area	Comments
674		2,400	G	$9,100	8/03	WCIL	IHC 2250 loader, diesel, 18.4-30" tires
674	1977		G	$7,000	4/03	NCOH	Westendorf WL-21 loader, diesel, material bucket & bale spear
674	1977	2,512	F	$7,700	9/03	NWIL	Utility, diesel, IHC 2250 loader, 7' bucket, 16.9-30"
706			G	$6,000	2/06	WCIL	WF, gas
706	1964	5,400	F	$1,850	2/06	SCMI	Gas, NF, 3 pt., new 18.4-34 tires, 1 owner
706	1965	5,527	G	$5,500	1/06	WCNE	WF, dual 340 loader
706	1966	5,572	F	$3,400	2/06	NWIA	NF, 2 pt., 2 hyd., 5572 hours
706			F	$1,800	7/05	ECND	No 3 pt., 2 hyd., PTO, gas
706			F	$2,200	8/05	NWIL	NF
706			F	$2,600	12/05	SEMN	
706			G	$2,600	12/05	ECMI	Gas, NF, tach shows 1619
706		6,341	G	$2,800	9/05	NCIA	Cab, gas, WF, fast hitch
706			G	$3,500	8/05	SEMN	
706			G	$3,550	7/05	SESD	German diesel, WF
706			G	$5,500	12/05	SEND	Cab, heat with filtered air inlet, 3 pt., quick hitch, low hours
706			G	$5,900	6/05	ECMN	Gas, loader
706		3,524	G	$6,600	11/05	SCNE	Farmall, WF, 2 pt.
706			F	$2,200	2/05	NWKS	Diesel, engine knocks, Farmhand F11 loader, dual PTO, 2 hyd., 18.4-38"
706		8,360	F	$2,800	8/05	WCMN	German diesel, 3 pt., PTO, band duals, engine oil leak
706			G	$3,800	3/05	NENE	
706			G	$4,000	3/05	WCIL	Diesel, restored, fenders
706		10,000	G	$4,500	8/05	WCMN	German diesel, Farmall, band duals
706		4,682	F	$4,500	1/05	WCOH	Farmall, WF, 3 pt., diesel, older model
706	1965	8,647	G	$1,750	4/05	NEIN	NF, gas
706	1967		G	$3,200	4/05	SENE	Diesel, WF, new tires
706			F	$1,250	4/04	NEPA	Farmall
706			F	$1,750	11/04	SEPA	No brakes
706			F	$2,100	12/04	ECND	Gas, no cab, PTO, 2 hyd., rock box, like-new 16.9-38" tires
706			G	$2,100	12/04	ECND	Gas, no cab, PTO, rock box
706		3,064	G	$2,200	11/04	SCCA	70 hp., diesel
706		7,300	G	$2,600	3/04	NENE	Diesel, NF
706			G	$2,700	3/04	SCMN	Diesel
706			F	$2,900	4/04	NEPA	Loader
706			G	$3,100	4/04	ECWI	Farmall, cab
706			G	$3,150	1/04	NWIA	Gas
706		4,440	G	$3,400	3/04	NCIL	Gas, NF, recent OH, 3 pt., 2 hyd., new tires
706		4,300	G	$3,400	12/04	WCMN	WF, 3 pt., PTO, 1 owner, diesel
706		5,760	G	$3,450	1/04	ECIL	Gas, tricycle
706			F	$3,500	10/04	SEPA	Diesel, WF, fair rubber
706		7,285	F	$4,300	4/04	NWPA	Cab
706			G	$5,250	8/04	NCIA	Diesel, 2 pt., repainted, WL-21 Westendorf loader
706	1964	3,973	G	$1,800	3/04	WCMI	NF, fast hitch, 1 hyd., PTO, TA, gas, 18.4-34"
706	1965		G	$3,400	11/04	NWIL	Gas, WF, rear weights
706	1966	3,584	G	$2,800	3/04	NEIA	Gas, no cab, NF, less than 1400 hours on OH, 3 pt., PS, fenders, 15.5x38" tires, triple hyd.
706	1967		G	$2,900	5/04	NCKS	F10 Farmhand loader w/ 4 attachments, PTO, 2 hyd., TA works
706			P	$1,300	5/03	WCIN	WF, fast hitch, bad motor, for parts
706			P	$1,650	12/03	SCNE	Rough, diesel, 2 hyd., duals, poor rubber, 16.9-34"
706			G	$2,250	9/03	NEIN	
706			G	$2,250	9/03	NEIN	Farmall

international harvester

Model	Year	Hours	Cond.	Price	Date	Area	Comments
706			G	$2,500	8/03	NWIL	Gas, NF
706			G	$2,900	7/03	SCMN	WF, fast hitch, diesel
706		6,624	G	$3,000	7/03	ECND	Gas, WF, 2 hyd., PTO
706			F	$3,250	3/03	WCMN	Hyd., 3 pt., PTO, diesel
706			F	$3,300	5/03	ECWI	3 pt., diesel, high hours
706			G	$3,300	2/03	WCIA	No cab, WF, 2 hyd., 2 pt., top link, gas
706			F	$3,500	11/03	NWIL	Gas, WF, 3 pt.
706		1,000	G	$3,500	3/03	NCWI	Farmall, gas, WF, 16.9x38", recent eng. OH
706			G	$3,600	2/03	WCMN	Fast hitch, hyd. loader
706			F	$3,700	8/03	NWIL	Gas, WF, loader
706			G	$4,700	3/03	WCMN	Miller heavy-duty loader, 3 pt., 540/1000 PTO, new 18.4-34" rear tires, gas, greason valve
706			G	$4,900	4/03	ECMN	Diesel
706	1964		G	$2,750	8/03	ECNE	LP, NF, fenders, 16.9-34"
706	1964		F	$5,100	4/03	NCMD	NF
706	1965	6,943	G	$2,500	6/03	ECND	Wheatland gas, cab, 540/1000 PTO, 2 hyd., 18.4x38" rear tires, loader
706	1966	3,273	G	$3,700	9/03	NWIL	NF, 3 pt., diesel, 15.5-38"
706	1967	5,078	G	$3,600	1/03	NWIL	Year-round cab, WF, dual PTO, hyd., 2 pt., 10 front weights, fewer than 500 hours on OH
756		6,918	G	$4,700	2/06	ECIL	Fenders, 2 hyd., front & rear weights, good TA, overhaul engine
756	1967	8,566	G	$5,200	1/06	ECNE	WF, 2 pt., 2 hyd., 15.5-38
756			F	$2,600	4/05	SEPA	Gas, WF, 30% rubber
756			F	$2,800	9/05	SEIA	Gas
756			E	$7,300	3/05	WCWI	WF, 3 pt., 2 hyd.
756			G	$4,000	4/04	ECWI	Hyd. loader
756			F	$4,500	10/04	SEMN	Sold with IHC 2000 loader, 3 pt., WF, gas
756			G	$4,600	2/04	ECNE	NF, diesel, 16.9-38" very good tires, 2 hyd., dual PTO, fenders
756		8,500	F	$5,000	3/04	SEPA	Diesel, WF, rubber fair, 18.4-38R"
756	1971	6,200	G	$4,800	3/04	WCMI	Gas, TA, fast hitch, PTO, 1 hyd., WF, 18.4-34"
756			F	$3,500	3/03	NEND	Diesel, 540/1000 PTO, 3 pt.
756			F	$4,100	10/03	NWIL	Gas
756			F	$4,550	12/03	WCMI	Diesel, WF, PTO, 3 pt., single hyd.
756			G	$8,500	2/03	WCOH	Dunham loader
756	1967	8,000	F	$5,200	7/03	WCSK	Canadian sale, diesel, new rear tires, dual hyd., 77 PTO hp., heads & crank rebuilt
756	1969		G	$3,700	4/03	SCMN	Cozy cab, 3 pt., 2 hyd., F series
766	1975	3,833	G	$4,500	1/06	NWIA	WF, 3 pt., 2 hyd. and PTO, cab
766			F	$4,050	5/05	SEPA	Diesel, WF, no TA, 40% rubber
766		5,600	F	$9,000	4/05	SEPA	WF, black stripe, 60% rubber
766		500	F	$1,350	2/05	SCMN	New engine, 18.4-34" duals, 3 pt. , 540/1000 PTO, 2 hyd.
766			E	$5,200	3/05	NECO	Diesel, 3 pt., PTO, hyd.
766			G	$6,825	1/04	ECNE	WF, 3 pt., 2 hyd., Farmhand 235 loader, bale spear & bucket
766			G	$7,000	3/04	WCMN	Cab
766	1971	4,970	G	$5,100	8/04	WCIL	Open station, gas, WF, 3 pt., 2 hyd., PTO, 150 hours on engine OH and new clutch, no cab
766	1972		G	$3,700	4/04	NCND	Row crop, TA, engine & clutch OH in 2002
766			G	$3,300	3/03	SENE	Gas
766			F	$6,000	3/03	SWPA	Diesel, WF, 4 hyd., 3 pt., year-round cab, good rubber
766	1972		G	$3,650	9/03	NEIN	Gas, WF

Model	Year	Hours	Cond.	Price	Date	Area	Comments
766	1973		G	$6,500	3/03	NWIL	200 hours on engine, WF, 1 owner, weights, diesel
766	1974	3,893	G	$7,100	2/03	NCIA	2 hyd., NF, no cab, diesel, new 16.9-38
806	1964		F	$3,700	1/06	NWIL	Diesel, WF, 2 pt., 18.4-34
806	1967	9,611	G	$4,850	1/06	NEMO	
806			F	$2,400	7/05	ECND	Row crop, diesel, no 3.pt., deluxe fenders, dual hyd
806			F	$2,700	7/05	SESD	WF, cab, 2 pt., good TA
806		9,143	F	$2,900	11/05	SCMI	Gas, WF
806			P	$4,400	9/05	NEIA	Rough
806			G	$5,700	7/05	ECND	Year-round cab, diesel, 3 pt., PTO
806			G	$8,000	11/05	SEND	
806	1963	5,300	F	$3,300	9/05	WCNE	Diesel, 3 pt., cab
806	1966	6,914	P	$2,100	9/05	NECO	Diesel, cab, cracked block, 3 pt.
806			P	$0	2/05	WCOK	No sale at $1,400, wanted $3,500, LP, 3 pt., 1 hyd., tires poor, PTO
806			P	$750	2/05	WCIL	For salvage, diesel
806			F	$1,700	2/05	NCOK	Wheatland
806			G	$3,500	4/05	SEMN	Diesel, 3 pt., 18.4-38"
806			F	$3,900	6/05	WCMN	Cab, diesel, WF, 2 hyd., 2 PTOs
806			G	$4,250	2/05	WCIN	2-pt. hitch, 18.4-34" tires & duals, 2 hyd.
806			G	$5,600	4/05	NWIL	WF, year-round cab, 2 hyd., good TA, diesel
806	1967	6,815	F	$4,700	1/05	NWIL	WF, dual PTO, 2 hyd., 3 pt., TA out, 18.4-34"
806			G	$4,250	4/04	ECWI	Farmall, year-round cab
806			G	$6,700	12/04	SCNH	WF, cab
806		6,500	F	$7,700	10/04	SEPA	Diesel, weights, rubber good
806	1963		F	$2,650	12/04	ECNE	962 hours on tach, LP gas, 2 hyd., 3 pt., 15.5-38, NF, fenders
806	1964		G	$5,100	9/04	SCMN	Diesel, new clutch, new paint, rock box, 540/1000 PTO, 2 hyd., open station
806	1965		G	$6,000	1/04	NWOH	WF, 2 hyd., dual PTO
806	1967		F	$4,700	3/04	NEMN	Diesel, cab
806	1967		G	$5,600	2/04	NECO	Diesel, 1 owner, cab, 3 pt. , PTO, hyd., 12.4-42"
806			F	$1,450	9/03	NEIN	
806			F	$2,750	1/03	ECWI	WF, TA, head reconditioned, Freeman trip bucket loader with snow bucket
806			G	$3,100	9/03	WCSD	Wheatland, cab, 2 hyd., 540/1000 PTO, diesel
806			G	$3,150	6/03	WCSD	Diesel, 3 pt., cab, Farmhand 228 loader w/ grapple
806			G	$3,250	3/03	NWIL	Diesel, NF
806		3,300	G	$3,700	7/03	SCMN	Hub duals, 3 pt., single hyd., dual PTO, year-round cab
806			F	$3,700	12/03	SCNE	Cab, 2 hyd., 18.4-34", duals, rubber 50%, diesel
806			F	$3,900	9/03	SCNE	WF, cab, 2 hyd.
806			G	$4,000	11/03	NEIA	Diesel, cab, WF, 3 pt., 18.4-38", duals
806		5,331	G	$4,600	7/03	SCMN	Cab, PTO, hub duals
806	1964		G	$3,300	8/03	ECNE	LP, WF, fenders, 18.4-34", front weights, 3 pt.
806	1967		G	$4,100	8/03	ECNE	Diesel, new 18.4-38" rice tires, fenders, NF
806	1967	7,330	G	$5,000	11/03	WCIL	3 pt., WF
806	1967		G	$5,500	1/03	NWIL	Diesel, WF, 2 hyd., 18.4-38"
826	1971	4,505	G	$6,800	1/06	WCIL	
826			G	$12,500	12/05	SWWI	$7K recently spent on engine
826	1970		G	$6,250	9/05	ECIA	German diesel, WF, high hours, cab
826			G	$5,750	2/05	NEIA	
826		4,771	G	$7,000	4/05	NCOH	WF, 3 pt.
826	1970	5,495	F	$5,400	2/05	NWKS	Diesel, 15.5-38", 2 pt., 1 hyd.
826			G	$5,500	3/04	WCMI	3 pt., dual PTO, 2 hyd., TA, diesel

international harvester

Model	Year	Hours	Cond.	Price	Date	Area	Comments
826			G	$5,900	3/04	SEND	Hydro, cab, hyd, 3 pt., PTO, dual 3100 hyd. loader
826			G	$6,000	6/04	SEMN	Loader
826	1970	5,175	F	$4,700	2/04	NWIL	WF, 320 hours on major engine OH, diesel, TA out, 3 pt. broke, 18.4-34"
826	1970	6,418	G	$5,000	9/04	ECND	Cozy cab, TA manual trans, rock box, 2 hyd., 540/1000 PTO, 18.4-34" hub duals
826		3,288	F	$7,500	10/04	SWWI	
826	1971	6,500	F	$2,300	7/04	NEND	Cab, Std. trans, 540/1000 PTO, 2 hyd., 18.4-34"
826			G	$2,700	3/03	NCCO	Diesel
826		3,800	F	$6,100	8/03	SEPA	WF, average rubber
826	1971	5,900	F	$3,800	4/03	NCIA	3 pt., duals
856			F	$5,300	2/06	ECNE	2 hyd., 3 pt., 7800 hours
856	1971		G	$6,500	2/06	WCMN	Hiniker cab, tilt steering wheel, 18.4-30, 9 bolt hubs, no duals
856	1973	8,614	G	$7,100	2/06	SEIA	WF, flat top fenders, 800 hrs on OH
856			P	$2,500	12/05	SEMN	Rough
856	1969	3,504	F	$2,300	9/05	NECO	Cab, 3 pt.
856	1970		G	$5,100	12/05	WCMN	
856	1968	5,855	G	$7,300	3/05	SCMI	Diesel, 12 front weights, 150-gal. saddle tanks, duals
856	1968	6,220	E	$11,000	1/05	NEMO	
856	1969		F	$5,900	2/05	WCIL	Diesel, cab
856	1969	4,859	G	$6,600	6/05	NCIA	Factory wide front, fast hitch, year-round cab, diesel, 18.4-38"
856	1969	4,019	G	$6,700	8/05	SWOH	Diesel
856	1969	5,222	G	$7,900	6/05	SEND	Cozy cab, 3 pt., 540/1000 PTO, 18.4-38" hub duals, diesel
856			G	$4,550	1/04	NENE	Diesel
856			G	$4,700	3/04	SEND	Hiniker cab, 3 pt. , PTO, band duals, tank heater
856			G	$4,900	3/04	NEKS	WF
856	1968		G	$7,000	7/04	SEND	
856	1968		G	$7,000	7/04	NWMN	
856	1968		G	$7,000	7/04	SEND	
856	1968	4,233	G	$7,650	8/04	NWIA	WF, 3 pt., diesel
856	1969	7,736	G	$4,400	5/04	NWND	Diesel, cab, 3 pt., hyd., PTO
856	1969	8,412	G	$5,500	2/04	NEIN	Diesel, WF
856	1969		G	$5,500	11/04	SENE	Diesel, WF, cab, 2 hyd., good mechanically, appearance fair, 18.4-38"
856	1969		G	$6,300	2/04	ECNE	Diesel, new 18.4-38" Firestone tires, 10:00-16" 4-rib front tires, 3 pt., 2 hyd., dual PTO, fenders
856	1970		F	$3,400	9/04	ECND	Cab, no 3 pt., 18.4-34"
856	1970	7,132	G	$7,100	2/04	NCIA	Diesel, cab, WF, 3 pt., 2 hyd., front weights, fewer than 500 hours on $9,000 new engine in 1991, hubs & duals
856	1971		G	$4,500	3/04	NENE	Diesel, cab, 2 pt.
856	1971	7,800	F	$4,500	6/04	ECMT	Leon loader, 3 pt.
856	1972		G	$6,200	4/04	NWIA	150 hours on engine OH, fast hitch, fenders, diesel
856			G	$2,500	9/03	NEIN	High-crop
856			F	$4,100	2/03	NCMI	3 pt., dual PTO, 2 hyd., diesel
856		7,600	F	$4,300	3/03	NCCO	
856			P	$4,500	10/03	NCSD	Rough, diesel, cab, AC
856			G	$4,600	12/03	SCMN	WF
856		3,800	F	$5,000	8/03	SEPA	WF, average rubber
856			G	$5,500	12/03	SEIA	Diesel, WF, 18.4-38"
856	1967	9,713	G	$2,350	6/03	ECND	Wheatland diesel, 540/1000 PTO, 2 hyd., 18.4x38" tires

Model	Year	Hours	Cond.	Price	Date	Area	Comments
856	1967		G	$5,000	6/03	SWOH	WF, cab
856	1969		F	$3,400	9/03	ECND	Wheatland diesel, 540/1000 PTO, 2 hyd.
856	1970	4,875	G	$8,500	1/03	NWIL	Year-round cab, 2 pt., WF, dual PTO, hyd., 10 front weights, less than 400 hours on OH
856	1973		F	$3,500	3/03	NEND	3 pt.
966		7,800	F	$12,000	1/06	NEIA	
966	1972	1,200	G	$10,200	2/06	NEIA	Cab, bought on Aug. '05 consign. sale for $6,800
966	1972	6,625	F	$5,100	2/06	WCNE	Diesel, year-round cab, 3 pt., Dual 3000 loader & grapple
966			F	$3,975	9/05	NENE	Year-round cab, 540/1000 PTO, 2 hyd.
966			F	$4,000	9/05	NENE	
966			F	$5,600	8/05	SEMN	NI 319 corn picker
966			G	$8,000	8/05	NWIA	Recent engine overhaul, WF
966	1975	3,500	G	$9,500	12/05	SCIA	Cab, 1 owner
966			P	$2,500	6/05	WCMN	Rough, 3 pt., PTO, 2 hyd.
966			P	$3,400	3/05	WCIL	Diesel
966		3,900	F	$7,150	1/05	WCOH	Duals, 540 PTO, White cab, AC
966		4,049	G	$10,000	4/05	WCWI	Front weights
966	1975	1,026	E	$14,500	4/05	SCMN	Hiniker cab, 1 hyd., band duals
966	1976	7,010	F	$5,000	2/05	WCOK	New paint, 3 pt., PTO, 2 hyd., diesel, cab interior & tires fair
966			F	$3,700	3/04	NEKS	Diesel, hydro, motor needs work, good paint & tires
966			F	$4,000	12/04	NWIA	
966		4,960	G	$5,300	12/04	WCMN	Duals, 3 pt., PTO, year-round cab, diesel
966			G	$7,000	6/04	SEMN	
966		4,500	G	$9,000	3/04	SEIL	No cab, black stripe, no weights or duals
966		4,500	G	$9,000	3/04	SEIL	No cab, no weights, no duals
966	1971	5,737	G	$5,600	2/04	NEIN	Cab
966	1972	5,306	G	$6,000	3/04	NEIA	Diesel, Hiniker cab w/ radio, major OH w/ less than 1,000 hours, 3 pt., single hyd., new batteries, 18.4x34" tires w/ fluid, rear weights, axle-mount duals, rock box
966	1974	4,581	E	$6,900	9/04	ECIA	Hub duals, 3 pt., diesel
966	1974		E	$8,000	11/04	NWOH	Open station, WF, hub duals, 2 hyd., 3 pt., renewed engine, 12 IH front weights
966	1976		G	$5,950	8/04	NENE	
966	1976	5,888	G	$9,100	2/04	ECIA	2 hyd., 3 pt., WF, 800 hours remanufactured motor, 18.4-38"
966			G	$5,000	8/03	SEMN	Cab, AC, 3 pt., 200 hours on OH
966			G	$5,500	9/03	NEIN	
966			F	$5,600	8/03	SEPA	WF, average rubber, new clutch
966			G	$6,100	11/03	NENE	Clean, WF, 2 pt., diesel, weights, good rubber
966			F	$6,700	3/03	SWPA	Diesel, WF, 3 pt., decent rubber
966			E	$7,000	11/03	NENE	Sharp, WF, diesel, 2 pt., new paint, excellent rubber
966	1973	4,626	G	$5,850	6/03	NCIA	Cab, 3 pt., 2 hyd., 2 PTO, 18.4-34", duals
966	1975	4,680	G	$7,700	12/03	ECMI	Cab, TA, new 16.9-38" tires & axle duals, 2 PTO, 2 hyd.
966	1976	5,538	G	$5,300	3/03	ECNE	Diesel, year-round cab, 2 pt., 2 hyd., 18.4-38"
A	1941		G	$450	1/06	WCNE	WF, PTO
A	1942		G	$875	1/06	WCNE	WF
A	1942		G	$900	1/06	WCNE	WF
A			G	$1,150	9/05	NENE	Farmall cultivision A tractor, WF, PTO, 9-24 tires
A			G	$1,400	10/05	NEPA	Farmall
A	1940		G	$800	8/05	NEIN	Gas, WF
A			F	$1,000	3/05	WCNY	Farmall, original paint
A			G	$1,300	2/05	NEIN	Farmall, gas, WF
A			F	$2,600	3/05	NESD	Farmall, WF, Woods belly mower
A	1940		G	$2,900	6/05	NEND	Farmall, WF, 4 speed, belt pulley, PTO, rear weights, fenders

international harvester

Model	Year	Hours	Cond.	Price	Date	Area	Comments
A	1942		F	$1,400	7/05	NCMN	Farmall, WF
A	1945		G	$1,975	1/05	WCIL	Farmall, Woods 42' belly mower
A			P	$575	4/04	WCMI	Farmall, needs work
A			F	$750	4/04	NEPA	
A			F	$800	4/04	NEPA	Front blade
A			G	$1,200	6/04	NCND	Farmall, Woods mower
A			F	$1,200	6/04	NWMN	Farmall, WF, cultivator, Lindsey belly mower
A			G	$1,500	6/04	SEMN	Farmall
A			G	$1,650	7/04	ECMN	5' mower deck
A			G	$2,850	8/04	NESD	Farmall, WF, 5' Woods belly mower
A	1939		F	$2,000	9/04	WCMN	Farmall
A	1940		F	$700	9/04	NECO	Farmall, runs, fair tin, good tires
A	1940		G	$2,900	6/04	ECND	Magneto shutoff, 16 hp.
A	1940		G	$3,250	6/04	ECND	Belly mower, new paint, 16.1 hp.
A	1941		G	$2,900	9/04	NWMN	McCormick Farmall, rear pulley, PTO, new tires and rims, rear weights
A	1941		G	$3,100	6/04	ECND	16 hp.
A	1946		G	$2,800	6/04	ECND	New tires, triples
A	1946		G	$4,500	9/04	WCMN	Farmall, good rubber & paint, PTO, with Artsway 6' belly mower
A	1947		G	$2,450	12/04	WCIL	Farmall, gas
A	1954		G	$5,100	6/04	ECND	New hyd., 43.6 hp.
A			G	$900	7/03	NEOH	Belly blade
A			G	$1,100	9/03	NEIN	Farmall
A			F	$1,150	12/03	WCMI	Farmall, blade, WF, 11.2x24" rears
A			G	$1,450	10/03	ECMN	Farmall
A			G	$1,700	9/03	WCMI	Farmall, 4 cyl., gas, WF
A			F	$1,800	8/03	NCSD	Farmall, hyd.
A			G	$1,900	2/03	WCIA	Farmall
A	1949		G	$1,900	7/03	SEND	Farmall, new tires and paint
A	1972		G	$1,800	3/03	NWIL	Farmall, Woods 4' belly mower, gas
B			G	$1,500	11/05	WCIL	NF, fenders, PTO
B			P	$450	8/05	ECMN	Farmall, single front wheel, engine stuck
B			G	$1,000	7/05	ECND	Winco 7500-watt generator
B			G	$1,200	7/05	ECND	Woods 5' belly mower
B			G	$1,450	3/05	ECNE	Farmall, 50 hours on OH
B			G	$600	4/04	ECWI	Farmall
B			F	$725	1/04	NEIN	Farmall, wheel weights
B			F	$800	1/04	NENE	Farmall, not running
B			G	$900	4/04	NCWI	Farmall, set up for ginseng
B			G	$1,400	9/04	SEND	Farmall, cultivision, single front, rear pulley, PTO, 10-24" rears
B			E	$1,700	6/04	NEKS	Farmall, restored, clean
B			G	$2,300	3/04	NEIA	9.5×24" tires, new battery, less than 200 hours on OH, around 1946-48
B			G	$2,450	6/04	ECND	New paint & tires
B	1945		G	$1,700	6/04	ECND	Rotary belly mower, 16 hp.
B	1945		G	$2,800	12/04	WCIL	Farmall, gas, NF
B	1946		G	$2,300	6/04	ECND	Rotary belly mower, manifold valve, 16 hp.
B	1946		G	$2,900	6/04	ECND	New paint

48

Model	Year	Hours	Cond.	Price	Date	Area	Comments
B	1947		G	$1,850	6/04	ECND	WF, 16 hp.
B	1947		G	$2,200	6/04	ECND	16 hp., single wheel, mower
B			F	$450	4/03	WCSD	Farmall, collectible
B			F	$500	7/03	ECND	Farmall
B			F	$975	12/03	ECIL	Farmall, Woods belly mower
B			G	$1,000	4/03	SEMN	Farmall
B			G	$1,500	4/03	SEMN	Farmall
B			G	$1,500	3/03	NCIA	Farmall, rear & front spray booms, 5 valves & tank
B			F	$1,700	8/03	NCSD	Farmall, new paint
B			G	$1,700	6/03	NCIA	Farmall, Woods 59" belly mower
B			F	$2,000	8/03	NCSD	Farmall, with mounted buzz saw
B	1946		G	$1,900	7/03	NWMN	Cultivision, single wheel, PTO, Woods 60" mower
BN			F	$850	3/04	SWPA	Farmall
BN			F	$1,050	11/04	NCOH	Farmall, rough but running
BN	1946		G	$3,600	6/04	ECND	16 hp.
BN			F	$700	2/03	SWOH	Farmall
C	1950		G	$2,000	2/06	WCMN	Farmall, demo
C	1950		G	$750	1/06	WCNE	Gas, WF, new tires & paint
C			F	$1,000	8/05	SEMN	With cultivator
C			G	$1,500	8/05	NCIA	Farmall, belly mower
C			G	$2,000	6/05	ECMN	Farmall, belly mower
C			G	$2,700	12/05	SCMN	Farmall
C			G	$2,900	9/05	NENE	Farmall, fenders, PTO, drawbar, new paint, tires & rims
C	1948		F	$450	11/05	ECNE	Farmall, PTO, 12.4-36 tires
C			G	$1,600	6/05	ECMN	Tricycle, belt pully
C			E	$1,700	3/05	WCWI	Farmall, cultivator
C			G	$1,700	3/05	WCNY	Farmall, repainted but average
C			G	$1,800	8/05	NEIN	Farmall, Woods belly mower, fenders and new rear rubber
C	1948		G	$2,075	7/05	NCMN	WF, new tires all around, electric start
C			G	$1,700	2/04	SWMN	Farmall, 2-row cultivator, NF
C			G	$2,050	6/04	SEMN	Farmall
C			G	$2,100	8/04	WCMN	Farmall, 6' Woods belly mower
C	1947		G	$2,400	6/04	ECND	Motor OH
C	1948		G	$1,400	9/04	NWMN	Farmall, WF, std. trans, 1 hyd., PTO, fenders, rear weights
C	1948		G	$1,700	8/04	SEIA	Farmall, tear drop fenders
C	1948		E	$2,000	6/04	ECND	WF, 21 hp.
C	1948		E	$2,100	6/04	ECND	New tires
C	1948		G	$2,300	9/04	NECO	Farmall, restored, good tires
C	1950		G	$1,600	9/04	NECO	Farmall, runs, 6' mower, good tires & tin
C	1950		G	$3,200	12/04	WCIL	Farmall, gas, demo, white, new tires
C			G	$700	4/03	SEIN	Farmall
C			F	$1,000	12/03	SCNE	Farmall, NF
C			G	$1,150	7/03	NEOH	Farmall
C			F	$1,350	7/03	NEOH	Woods belly mower
C			G	$1,600	8/03	SWMN	Farmall, NF, Woods 562 belly mower
C			G	$1,750	3/03	ECND	Farmall, Woods 5' mower
C			G	$1,800	3/03	SENE	Farmall, gas
C			G	$2,000	7/03	NWMN	Belt pulley, PTO, hyd.
C	1948		G	$2,900	6/03	NCIA	Farmall, Woods 59 belly mower, 12-volt system

international harvester

Model	Year	Hours	Cond.	Price	Date	Area	Comments
C	1949		G	$1,650	1/03	ECNE	Farmall, NF, 4 cyl. gas, 4-speed, 10-36" tires, 12-volt system electric start, IHC 5' belly mower
C	1949		G	$2,500	7/03	ECND	Farmall, 60" Woods belly mower
C	1950		G	$1,975	6/03	NWIL	Farmall, gas, NF, rear sickle mower, good tires
Cub			P	$100	1/06	WCCA	4-cyl. gas
Cub			F	$500	1/06	WCCA	4-cyl. gas
Cub	1974		G	$2,000	2/06	WCIL	60" mower, new paint
Cub			G	$1,350	9/05	SCON	Canadian sale, Farmall, blade
Cub			G	$1,700	11/05	WCIL	WF, restored, Brush Hog mower
Cub			G	$2,000	9/05	SCON	Canadian sale, Farmall, blade/plow
Cub			F	$2,350	12/05	NWIL	With Woods 60" deck, rusty
Cub	1947		G	$3,150	9/05	ECMN	Farmall, gas, 1-bottom plow and 4' sickle mower
Cub			G	$1,100	6/05	ECMN	Needs OH, belly-mount grader
Cub			G	$1,250	8/05	SWOH	Farmall, with belly mower
Cub			G	$1,300	1/05	SWOH	Farmall
Cub			G	$1,500	3/05	SCMI	Restored
Cub			G	$1,575	1/05	ECNE	Farmall
Cub			G	$1,600	6/05	ECMN	Farmall, engine OH
Cub			G	$2,600	6/05	ECMN	Farmall, swept back WF, new paint
Cub	1947		G	$2,600	6/05	NEND	Farmall, WF, 3 pt., PTO
Cub			G	$0	12/04	ECMI	No sale at $1,450, WF, front blade & flail mower, runs excellent
Cub			G	$1,000	11/04	NWNY	Farmall, engine OH, new rear tires, 3 pt.
Cub			G	$1,000	11/04	NWNY	Farmall, plow attach
Cub			F	$1,200	10/04	SEPA	Farmall, with mower, fair rubber
Cub			G	$2,000	7/04	NWMN	Mower deck
Cub			G	$2,000	12/04	WCIL	Farmall, sickle mower
Cub	1946		G	$1,350	8/04	NCOH	With belly mower
Cub	1948		G	$3,400	6/04	ECND	Belly mower, 1-bottom plow, 11 hp.
Cub	1950		E	$7,100	6/04	ECND	New tires, 11 hp.
Cub	1952		G	$2,900	6/04	ECND	New seat, 11 hp.
Cub	1961		G	$1,800	2/04	NEIN	Belly mower
Cub	1969		G	$3,300	6/04	ECND	1-row cultivator, 10.8 hp.
Cub			P	$700	5/03	WCIN	Farmall, not running
Cub			P	$800	5/03	WCIN	Farmall, belly mower, not running
Cub			G	$1,400	5/03	NEKS	Farmall, WF, belly blade
Cub			G	$1,425	5/03	NEKS	Farmall, WF, 1-bottom plow
Cub			G	$1,500	3/03	NCIL	WF, fenders, wheel weights
Cub			G	$2,000	10/03	SWWI	Farmall, gas
Cub			G	$2,100	10/03	SEMN	Farmall, with mower
Cub			G	$2,500	4/03	WCWI	Farmall, Woods 59" mower
Cub			G	$2,750	9/03	SEIA	Farmall
Cub			F	$2,800	8/03	SEPA	Farmall, WF, Woods belly mower, good rubber
Cub	1949		E	$4,700	7/03	WCSK	Canadian sale, fully restored & painted
Cub	1953		E	$1,950	8/03	NCCO	Farmall, restored, new paint & tires, 6' dozer blade, new engine OH, WF
Cub	1957		F	$1,450	9/03	SCMI	Farmall, WF, belly mower
Cub 154			G	$1,550	3/03	NWIL	LoBoy, Woods 60" belly mower
Cub LoBoy			G	$1,750	11/05	NCCA	With mower
Cub LoBoy			G	$1,800	11/05	WCIL	WF, restored, fenders

Model	Year	Hours	Cond.	Price	Date	Area	Comments
Cub LoBoy	1966		G	$1,400	6/05	ECIL	Auburn trencher & blade
Cub LoBoy			F	$900	3/04	WCIL	Gas, deck
Cub LoBoy	1956		F	$1,550	11/04	NWIL	5' Woods mower
Cub LoBoy	1959		G	$3,350	7/04	NWMN	2 incomplete mower decks, new turf tires, repainted
Cub LoBoy			F	$900	12/03	WCMI	4 cyl., gas
Cub LoBoy			G	$1,550	3/03	NWIL	Mower, gas
Cub LoBoy			G	$2,700	9/03	NEIN	Deck
Cub LoBoy			G	$5,200	8/03	NCIA	WF, fenders, sold with 5' belly mower
Cub LoBoy	1961		G	$1,825	9/03	ECNE	Farmall, gas, WF, turf tires, 60" belly mower, SN #15017
F12			G	$1,700	4/05	ECMN	Farmall
F12			P	$800	9/05	NENE	Farmall, for parts
F12			F	$875	9/05	SEIA	
F12	1937		G	$700	4/05	NCOH	Farmall on rubber, restored
F12			G	$700	1/04	WCIL	Farmall, gas
F12			F	$1,600	10/04	SEPA	Farmall, unrestored, average rubber
F12			F	$600	7/03	ECND	Farmall, on steel, set up w/ generator
F12			G	$950	3/03	SEIA	Farmall, on full steel
F12	1935		G	$2,200	6/03	NEIL	Farmall
F14			G	$2,250	4/05	ECMN	Farmall
F14			F	$1,100	10/04	SEPA	Farmall, unrestored, average rubber
F14	1938		F	$650	9/04	NWMN	McCormick, specialty, JD engine, NF, custom
F20			P	$200	11/05	SWMN	Farmall
F20			P	$225	11/05	SWMN	Farmall
F20	1939		P	$250	9/05	NCIA	Farmall, motor stuck
F20	1939		F	$700	9/05	NENE	Farmall, factory cast wheels, 11.2-36 tires
F20			P	$25	6/05	WCMN	To be restored
F20			P	$25	6/05	WCMN	To be restored
F20			F	$400	6/05	WCMN	Farmall, loader
F20			P	$75	10/04	SEMN	Farmall, for parts
F20			G	$900	1/04	SCIA	Farmall
F20			G	$950	1/04	SCIA	Farmall
F20			G	$1,700	6/04	SEMN	Farmall, WF
F20			G	$1,800	8/04	ECMI	Farmall, gas, NF, new rubber, restored
F20	1935		F	$650	9/04	NECO	Farmall, runs, new tires, OH
F20	1935		G	$750	12/04	WCIL	Farmall, gas
F20	1936		G	$950	12/04	WCIL	Farmall, gas, road gear
F20	1937		F	$650	1/04	NEIN	Farmall, with sickle mower, NF, regular
F20	1938		G	$1,200	5/04	NCKS	Farmall, repainted
F20	1938		G	$1,600	12/04	WCIL	Farmall, gas
F20	1939		G	$1,600	12/04	WCIL	Farmall, gas, road gear
F20	1940		G	$1,800	9/04	NECO	Farmall, restored, poor tires
F20			P	$250	9/03	NCIA	Needs restoration
F20			F	$450	7/03	NEOH	
F20			G	$750	1/03	ECNE	NF, 4 cyl. gas, 11-36" tires, 4-speed trans, new 6:00-16" front tires, belt pulley, completely restored
F20			G	$800	8/03	SEMN	Farmall, on low rubber
F20	1937		F	$400	4/03	SEMN	Farmall
F20	1938		G	$1,400	6/03	NEIL	Farmall
F20	1939		F	$450	4/03	SEMN	Farmall, good rubber
F30			G	$1,500	9/05	NENE	Farmall, road gear, 13.6-38 tires
F30	1930		G	$3,250	2/05	NWOH	Farmall, wide tread, older restore
F30			P	$100	2/04	NWIL	For parts

international harvester

Model	Year	Hours	Cond.	Price	Date	Area	Comments
F30			P	$350	9/04	NCKS	Farmall, rough, stuck
F30	1937		G	$1,050	9/04	NECO	Farmall, runs good, good tires, new oils, completely gone through
H			G	$1,000	1/06	NEMO	
H			G	$1,800	2/06	WCIL	Farmall, NF
H	1944		F	$1,300	2/06	SCMI	Farmall, gas, NF, good 12.4-38 rubber
H			G	$1,000	11/05	SEND	Farmall, factory WF
H			P	$1,025	11/05	NCOH	Farmall
H			G	$1,300	11/05	WCIL	
H			G	$1,400	11/05	WCIL	NF, restored, belt pulley, PTO
H			G	$1,750	4/05	ECMN	Farmall, with loader
H			P	$200	9/05	NENE	Farmall, for parts
H			F	$500	7/05	SESD	Farmall
H			F	$500	9/05	SEIA	With loader
H			F	$540	4/05	SEPA	Farmall, NF, 30% rubber
H			F	$600	5/05	SEPA	Farmall, NF, poor paint, 50% rubber
H			F	$670	7/05	SESD	Farmall
H			F	$850	10/05	ECMN	Farmall, gas, WF
H	1940		G	$800	9/05	NCIA	Farmall
H	1942		G	$2,000	11/05	WCIL	NF
H	1944		E	$1,700	8/05	NCIL	Farmall, restored, new rubber, front and rear
H	1945		G	$1,100	8/05	NCIL	Farmall, live PTO
H	1947		P	$375	11/05	ECNE	Farmall, new 11.2-38 tires
H	1947		P	$500	9/05	NCIA	Farmall, transmission bad
H	1948		G	$1,075	12/05	ECNE	Farmall, near new 11.2-38 tires
H	1948		F	$600	11/05	ECNE	Farmall, new 11.2-38 tires
H	1950		G	$1,500	8/05	NEIN	12 volt
H	1951		G	$725	8/05	NEIN	Gas, NF
H	1952		P	$220	11/05	ECNE	Farmall, for parts, on steel wheels
H			F	$600	3/05	ECCO	Not running
H			F	$650	3/05	SCMI	
H			F	$650	3/05	ECMI	Farmall
H			F	$675	4/05	SCMI	Farmall, NF, gas
H			F	$750	7/05	SCMN	Farmall, WF
H			G	$800	1/05	NEMO	Farmall
H			F	$800	2/05	WCOH	Farmall
H			F	$950	1/05	NENE	Farmall, with JD 7' mower
H			G	$975	1/05	ECNE	Farmall, loader
H			G	$1,200	6/05	WCMN	Farmall
H			G	$1,350	3/05	ECNE	Farmall
H			G	$1,600	7/05	ECIL	Farmall
H			H	$1,700	6/05	ECMN	Tricycle, fenders
H			G	$2,500	6/05	ECMN	WF, fenders
H	1940		G	$1,200	4/05	NCIA	Farmall, live pump, fenders
H	1940		G	$1,300	6/05	ECIL	6 volt, rear weights, hyd.
H	1945		F	$1,000	5/05	NCKS	Farmall, PTO, NF, Farmhand F10 loader
H	1945		E	$1,100	2/05	WCNE	Farmall, gas, rear weights
H	1945		G	$1,150	3/05	ECND	Farmall, Schwartz WF, PTO
H	1946		F	$700	3/05	NECO	Farmall, PTO

Model	Year	Hours	Cond.	Price	Date	Area	Comments
H	1947		E	$1,050	3/05	WCWI	Farmall
H	1947		G	$2,500	4/05	WCWI	Farmall, 1 owner, new paint, exc. rubber, duals
H	1949		P	$550	7/05	NCMN	Not running, missing tin, Farmall
H	1951		G	$2,400	4/05	SCNE	Farmall, PTO, rear weights, 11-38" tires, runs
H	1952		F	$800	2/05	NCKS	Farmall, runs
H	1952		G	$950	1/05	WCIL	Farmall
H			P	$385	6/04	ECMT	Farmall
H			F	$425	4/04	NEPA	Farmall
H			G	$500	3/04	SENE	Farmall, gas
H			F	$500	9/04	SEND	Farmall, NF, repainted, good rubber
H			F	$650	7/04	NWMN	Loader
H			F	$700	3/04	SEIL	Farmall
H			P	$760	3/04	SCMN	Farmall, not running
H			G	$800	7/04	ECND	540 PTO, complete with front end loader
H			F	$850	10/04	SEPA	Farmall, with loader, chains, rubber fair
H			G	$950	3/04	NWMN	Farmall
H			G	$950	11/04	ECNE	Farmall, fenders, Murphy gauges
H			G	$950	6/04	NCWI	Farmall, good rubber
H			G	$1,000	12/04	SEMN	Farmall
H			G	$1,100	2/04	ECMI	Farmall, NF
H			F	$1,150	8/04	NESD	NF
H			G	$1,200	1/04	NEOH	Farmall, with planter
H			E	$1,550	6/04	NEKS	Farmall, restored, clean
H			G	$1,700	1/04	SCIA	Farmall, factory, WF, new tires
H			G	$1,800	7/04	ECMN	
H			G	$2,200	1/04	ECNE	Farmall, with loader
H			G	$3,200	9/04	ECMN	Farmall, with loader, gas
H	1939		E	$2,000	6/04	ECND	New tires, original seat, 30.2 hp.
H	1940		G	$1,300	9/04	NWMN	Farmall, NF, std. trans, steel wheel rears with lugs, PTO
H	1940		G	$1,500	6/04	ECND	28 hp., new rear tires, spoke wheels
H	1940		G	$1,800	6/04	ECND	Toolbox, 28 hp.
H	1941		F	$500	9/04	NECO	Farmall, runs, fair tires, good tin, belt pulley, NF
H	1942		F	$450	9/04	NECO	Farmall, runs, fair tires, good tin, belt pulley
H	1942		F	$550	9/04	NECO	Farmall, runs, needs carburetor work, poor tires
H	1942		F	$600	9/04	NECO	Farmall, runs, good tin, fair tires
H	1942		F	$750	2/04	NEIN	Farmall
H	1943		E	$1,350	11/04	SENE	Farmall, gas, WF, 3 pt., 12 volt
H	1945		F	$700	9/04	NECO	Farmall, runs, good tin, poor tires
H	1945		G	$1,100	9/04	NECO	Farmall, restored, good tires
H	1945		G	$1,700	12/04	WCIL	Farmall, gas, all steel wheels
H	1946		G	$1,000	9/04	NECO	Farmall, older restoration, fair tires, good tin
H	1946		G	$1,400	9/04	NECO	Restored, WF, new tires, belt pulley
H	1946		G	$1,600	9/04	NECO	Farmall, restored, 3 pt., good tires, belt pulley
H	1946		G	$1,800	12/04	NCIA	Farmall, Woods L306 belly mower
H	1947		F	$850	4/04	WCMI	Farmall
H	1947		F	$1,050	6/04	ECND	30.2 hp.
H	1947		G	$1,225	2/04	ECIA	Farmall, gas, row crop
H	1947		G	$1,700	3/04	NCMI	Farmall, NF, good rubber, fender
H	1947		G	$2,300	6/04	ECND	WF, 28 hp.
H	1949		G	$900	2/04	NCOH	Farmall
H	1949		G	$1,650	2/04	ECIA	Farmall, gas, row crop
H	1949		G	$2,100	2/04	NCIA	Farmall

international harvester

Model	Year	Hours	Cond.	Price	Date	Area	Comments
H	1950		G	$950	9/04	NECO	Farmall, runs, 3 pt., NF, good tires & tin
H	1952		G	$2,100	12/04	WCIL	Farmall, gas
H			P	$150	9/03	NEIN	Parts
H			F	$325	6/03	NCWI	Farmall, NF
H			P	$450	10/03	NCSD	Farmall, rough, NF
H			P	$500	7/03	NWIL	Farmall, NF, Caswell loader
H			F	$650	8/03	SEMN	Farmall
H			G	$725	5/03	SWOK	Farmall, new paint
H			F	$725	4/03	WCMN	Farmall, NF, 6 volt
H			G	$750	7/03	WCMN	Farmall, NF, single hyd., PTO
H			F	$750	2/03	SCMN	Farmall
H			F	$775	6/03	NCWI	Farmall, NF
H			G	$850	4/03	WCMN	Farmall
H			G	$850	4/03	NWIA	Farmall, new paint
H			F	$875	1/03	ECIA	Farmall
H			G	$900	6/03	SWMN	Gas, NF & Schwartz hyd. loader, eng. stuck
H			F	$900	9/03	SCNE	Farmall, NF
H			G	$925	9/03	NEIN	Farmall
H			F	$975	3/03	NWSD	Farmall, NF, needs work
H			F	$1,000	10/03	NWIL	Farmall, with old loader
H			G	$1,025	11/03	SENE	Farmall, gas, loader
H			G	$1,100	10/03	SEMN	NF, Farmall
H			G	$1,150	12/03	NEIA	Farmall, fenders
H			G	$1,150	11/03	NEKS	Farmall, straight tin, good rubber, needs paint, local OH
H			G	$1,250	4/03	SEMN	Farmall
H			G	$1,400	9/03	NEIN	Farmall
H			F	$1,450	12/03	WCMI	Farmall, NF, PTO
H			G	$1,500	12/03	ECWI	Farmall, WF
H			G	$1,550	7/03	WCMN	Farmall, NF, 12 volt, Woods L306 belly mower
H			G	$1,600	3/03	WCMN	Farmall, NF, 12 volt
H			G	$2,000	9/03	NEIN	Farmall
H	1940		P	$400	6/03	NCIA	Farmall, not running, as is
H	1940		P	$550	6/03	NCIA	Farmall, as is, not running
H	1940		G	$750	9/03	SEIL	Farmall, new paint
H	1940		F	$850	9/03	SCMI	Farmall
H	1940		G	$1,400	12/03	NCIA	Farmall, Woods L306 belly mower
H	1941		G	$700	7/03	NWMN	PTO, hyd.
H	1942		G	$700	8/03	NCIA	Farmall
H	1942		G	$1,025	9/03	NCIA	Farmall, repainted, valves ground
H	1943		G	$800	6/03	NCIA	Farmall, straight arm loader
H	1944		F	$500	3/03	NWIL	Farmall
H	1945		G	$1,275	1/03	NWIL	Farmall, 540 PTO, good paint
H	1945		G	$1,700	3/03	NCCO	
H	1945		G	$2,100	7/03	WCIL	Farmall, NF, good tires, good tin, good paint, gas
H	1946		F	$550	3/03	ECNE	Farmall, all new tires
H	1947	3,100	F	$2,200	7/03	WCSK	Canadian sale, hyd., belt pully, 2 tanks, new rear tires, sieves, elevators, rotors, gear boxes
H	1948		G	$1,025	6/03	NCIA	Farmall
H	1948		G	$1,100	3/03	ECND	Farmall, WF, hyd., 1 owner

Model	Year	Hours	Cond.	Price	Date	Area	Comments
H	1948		G	$1,475	12/03	NWOH	Farmall, restored, fenders
H	1949		G	$1,550	3/03	NCMN	Farmall, NF, PTO, fenders, 12.4-38" singles, hyd. loader & hyd. bucket
H	1951		F	$700	9/03	SCMI	Farmall
H	1953		G	$2,300	3/03	NENE	Farmall, new paint, good tires
M			G	$1,550	1/06	SESD	Farmall, NF, runs
M			G	$1,675	2/06	SEIA	Farmall, WF
M	1944		E	$1,150	1/06	WCNE	WF, new paint
M	1950		F	$1,000	1/06	WCNE	WF, 12 volt
M	1952		F	$1,300	2/06	NENE	Farmall, NF
M			G	$1,100	7/05	SESD	Farmall, repainted
M			G	$1,150	9/05	SCON	Canadian sale
M			F	$1,200	9/05	WCMN	Farmall
M			F	$1,250	8/05	NWIL	Farmall, gas
M			G	$1,350	9/05	SCON	Canadian sale
M			P	$200	10/05	NCKS	Parts
M			G	$3,500	12/05	SCMN	Farmall, with loader
M			G	$650	12/05	SEMN	
M			F	$650	11/05	WCIL	NF, weights, PTO, hyd.
M			F	$900	8/05	SEMN	With mounted picker
M	1944		E	$1,600	9/05	NECO	Gas, WF, new tires
M	1946		G	$800	9/05	NECO	Double front, gas
M	1948		G	$1,800	8/05	NWIA	Farmall
M	1948		G	$2,000	11/05	WCIL	WF, gas, original, carb. overhaul, belt pulley
M	1950		G	$1,500	8/05	NCIL	Farmall, power steering, live PTO, hand clutch
M	1951		F	$725	12/05	NWIL	Farmall, gas
M	1952		P	$325	11/05	ECNE	Farmall, for parts
M			P	$400	1/05	NENE	Farmall, not running
M			P	$450	4/05	SCSD	Farmall, for parts
M			F	$650	2/05	NWKS	Farmall, WF, 3 pt.
M			G	$1,050	7/05	SEIA	Farmall, low hours
M			F	$1,100	3/05	SCMI	
M			G	$1,500	1/05	ECNE	Farmall, new tires & paint
M			G	$1,600	1/05	NENE	Farmall, with Farmhand F10 loader
M	1941		G	$1,750	3/05	WCIL	Good paint, NF, gas
M	1944		G	$1,425	8/05	ECNE	Farmall, gas, NF, m&w 4" pistons & governor, 13.6-38" tires, wheel weights
M	1944		E	$2,350	3/05	SCIL	Farmall, PS, live hyd.
M	1947		G	$825	4/05	SENE	Farmall, gas
M	1947		G	$1,550	4/05	NEIN	Farmall, gas, NF, belt pulley
M	1949		G	$2,500	4/05	NCOH	Farmall, Super M hyd. loader kit and IHC 2000 loader, PS
M	1950		G	$2,000	3/05	ECMI	Farmall, NF, PTO drawbar
M	1950		G	$2,200	8/05	NCIA	Farmall, 12 volt
M	1951		G	$1,200	1/05	SENE	Farmall, gas, NF, good paint
M	1951		E	$1,300	3/05	WCWI	Farmall, fenders, NF, wheel weights
M	1951		G	$2,375	3/05	NCIA	Farmall, live pump, PS, 12 volt
M	1952		G	$1,125	2/05	NEIN	Farmall, gas, NF
M	1953		P	$950	7/05	NCMN	Farmall, alternator, electric start
M	1953		G	$3,000	6/05	ECIL	Single hyd., 6 volt, rear weights
M			P	$475	6/04	ECMT	Farmall
M			P	$700	3/04	WCIL	NF, gas

international harvester

Model	Year	Hours	Cond.	Price	Date	Area	Comments
M			F	$700	4/04	NEIA	Farmall, with New Idea picker
M			F	$700	7/04	NWMN	Loader
M			F	$750	10/04	SEMN	Farmall, Hyster OD and loader
M			F	$825	7/04	ECMN	Farmall, Freeman bucket
M			F	$850	3/04	WCMN	Farmall, NF, 13.6-38"
M			P	$900	3/04	WCIL	Farmall, gas, NF
M			F	$900	1/04	SCIA	Farmall
M			F	$950	1/04	SCIA	Farmall
M			F	$950	9/04	SEND	Farmall, Schwartz WF
M			G	$950	3/04	NCOH	Farmall, NF
M			G	$1,000	3/04	ECMN	Farmall
M			E	$1,150	3/04	SENE	Farmall, gas
M			G	$1,200	12/04	SEMN	Farmall
M			F	$1,250	12/04	SEPA	Farmall, 2-row mounted corn picker
M			G	$1,450	12/04	WCIL	Farmall, gas, 9-speed
M			F	$1,600	12/04	SCNH	WF
M			G	$1,600	3/04	NWMN	Farmall
M			G	$1,850	3/04	SEIL	Farmall, live hyd.
M			G	$2,000	10/04	NEIA	Farmall
M			G	$2,400	3/04	WCKS	Farmall, Jayhawk loader & buckrake, NF
M			G	$3,000	3/04	NWIA	Farmall, PS, Artsway 72" belly mower
M	1939		G	$1,450	12/04	WCIL	Farmall, gas, single front wheel
M	1939		G	$1,600	12/04	WCIL	Farmall, gas
M	1939		G	$1,800	12/04	WCIL	Farmall, gas, steel rear
M	1939		E	$2,200	6/04	ECND	New front tires, 36 hp., 2-speed, spoke wheels, original seat
M	1940		G	$1,400	12/04	WCIL	Farmall, gas
M	1940		G	$1,800	11/04	SWOH	Farmall, WF
M	1940		G	$1,800	9/04	NECO	Farmall, restored, fair tires
M	1941		G	$1,400	12/04	WCIL	Farmall, gas
M	1941		G	$1,600	12/04	WCIL	Farmall, gas, PS
M	1942		G	$850	4/04	WCNE	Gas
M	1942		G	$1,400	12/04	WCIL	Farmall, gas
M	1942		G	$1,700	9/04	NECO	Farmall, runs, 3 pt., fenders, WF, good tires, excellent tin
M	1942		G	$2,100	12/04	WCIL	Farmall, all steel wheels, gas
M	1943		G	$1,750	6/04	ECND	36 hp.
M	1943		G	$1,950	12/04	WCIL	Farmall, gas
M	1944		F	$1,150	9/04	NECO	Farmall, runs, WF, fair tires, good tin
M	1944		G	$1,300	8/04	NWIL	Farmall, gas
M	1944		G	$1,400	12/04	WCIL	Farmall, gas
M	1944		G	$1,600	2/04	SENE	Farmall, 14.6-38" tires, 9-speed, newer engine, live hyd. pump, 3 pt., rear weights
M	1944		E	$1,600	6/04	ECND	36 hp.
M	1945		G	$1,700	6/04	ECND	NF tires, WF
M	1945		G	$1,750	12/04	WCIL	Farmall, gas, new tires
M	1946		F	$600	9/04	NWIA	Farmall, WF, 12-volt system
M	1946		G	$1,800	12/04	WCIL	Farmall, gas, PS
M	1947		F	$600	2/04	ECNE	Farmall, 13.6-38" tires, Duncan loader
M	1947		G	$1,400	12/04	WCIL	Farmall, gas
M	1947		G	$1,500	6/04	ECND	36 hp.

Model	Year	Hours	Cond.	Price	Date	Area	Comments
M	1947		G	$1,700	8/04	NWIA	Farmall
M	1947		G	$2,100	12/04	WCIL	Farmall, gas, new tires
M	1948		G	$1,500	12/04	WCIL	Farmall, gas
M	1948		G	$1,500	12/04	WCIL	Farmall, gas
M	1949		G	$1,050	9/04	SEND	Farmall, NF, 9-speed, OD, belt pulley, 13.4-38" rears, PTO
M	1949		G	$1,250	9/04	SEND	Farmall, NF, Std., belt pulley, PTO, 13-38" rears, new sleeves & pistons, engine kit, wheel seals
M	1949		G	$1,600	12/04	WCIL	Farmall, gas
M	1949		G	$1,750	4/04	WCNE	Older dual loader, double front, gas
M	1950		G	$1,200	8/04	ECIL	12 volt, repainted
M	1950		G	$1,500	12/04	WCIL	Farmall, gas
M	1950		G	$2,750	3/04	NCMI	Farmall, NF, belt pulley, hi/lo
M	1951		G	$1,500	2/04	NEIN	NF, 12 volt
M	1951		G	$1,700	2/04	NWIL	Farmall, NF, new paint, 12 volt, new seat, fenders, 38" tires
M			P	$150	2/03	WCIA	Farmall, no PS
M			F	$400	7/03	ECND	Farmall, NF
M			F	$500	3/03	NEKS	Farmall, runs
M			F	$650	7/03	WCSK	Canadian sale, Farmall, gas, dozer blade
M			F	$650	4/03	WCMN	
M			F	$650	7/03	SEND	Farmall, WF
M			G	$675	9/03	NEIN	
M			G	$800	6/03	WCSD	Farmall, NF, Farmhand F10 loader, starts up and sounds good
M			G	$800	8/03	SEMN	Farmall
M			F	$850	6/03	WCMN	Farmall, bad paint, poor rubber
M			G	$850	2/03	NEIA	Farmall
M			G	$900	5/03	SWOK	Farmall, new paint
M			G	$950	8/03	NWWI	Farmall, WF, 2-speed
M			G	$1,000	3/03	NESD	Farmall, WF, 12-volt system, PS
M			F	$1,100	10/03	ECMN	Farmall
M			G	$1,100	9/03	NWIL	Farmall
M			G	$1,100	2/03	ECIA	Farmall
M			G	$1,150	6/03	WCSK	Canadian sale, Farmall, row crop, 13.6x38" rubber
M			G	$1,150	7/03	SCMN	Farmall, WF, 12-volt system
M			G	$1,200	11/03	SENE	Farmall, NF, gas
M			G	$1,250	9/03	NWIL	Farmall
M			G	$1,250	9/03	WCSD	Farmall, PS, post hole digger
M			G	$1,350	1/03	SWOH	Farmall
M			G	$1,350	9/03	NEIN	
M			G	$1,400	9/03	NWIL	Farmall, PS
M			G	$1,500	9/03	NWIL	Farmall
M			G	$1,500	9/03	SWWI	Farmall, gas, NF
M			G	$1,500	9/03	NWIL	Farmall, PS, new tires, disc brakes
M			F	$1,500	3/03	NCCO	F11 loader
M			F	$1,600	3/03	SWPA	Farmall, gas, NF, live hyd., good running condition
M			G	$1,650	2/03	WCIA	Farmall, straight, PS
M			G	$1,650	9/03	SWWI	Farmall, gas, NF
M			G	$1,700	4/03	ECNE	Farmall, NF
M			F	$1,750	9/03	SCNE	Farmall, WF, Farmhand F10 loader with snow bucket, grapple, and sweep head
M			E	$3,200	1/03	NCCO	Farmhand F11 loader
M			P	$3,300	3/03	NCCO	F11 loader, live loader power

international harvester

Model	Year	Hours	Cond.	Price	Date	Area	Comments
M			G	$3,600	9/03	SEMN	Farmall, gas, NF, hyd., like new rubber
M	1939		G	$1,400	12/03	NCIA	Farmall, JD Roll-a-Matic front, live pump, over drive, 12 volt
M	1940		G	$2,700	7/03	NWIL	Farmall, with IHC 24 mounted corn picker
M	1941		F	$675	7/03	NWIL	Farmall
M	1941		G	$1,100	7/03	NWMN	Belt pulley, PTO, hyd.
M	1941		G	$2,200	1/03	ECIL	Farmall, 9-speed, 2-way hyd., new 13.6-38" tires
M	1942		F	$650	9/03	NEIN	Gas, Farmall, on steel, NF
M	1945		G	$1,100	9/03	NESD	Farmall, NF, Farmhand Hi-lift loader
M	1946		G	$1,500	7/03	ECND	Farmall, WF, hyd., PTO, hyd. loader
M	1946		G	$1,500	4/03	SEMN	Farmall, live hyd., NF, 100 hours on OH
M	1947		F	$400	9/03	SCMI	Farmall
M	1947		F	$750	7/03	ECND	Farmall, NF, belt pulley, 12.4-38" rubber
M	1948		F	$875	3/03	ECIL	Farmall, PS, weights, 13.6-38", attached loader
M	1948		G	$1,100	9/03	NESD	Farmall, Schwartz WF
M	1948		G	$3,000	6/03	NEIL	Farmall, 9-speed, live hyd.
M	1948		G	$3,200	3/03	NCCO	F11 loader
M	1949		G	$2,600	3/03	NCCO	
M	1949		G	$2,800	8/03	NWIA	Farmall, clam fenders, new tires, new paint, parade ready
M	1949		G	$4,600	11/03	ECNE	Farmall
M	1950		G	$1,375	7/03	NWIL	Farmall
M	1951		F	$1,125	7/03	NCND	Farmall, loader, NF
M	1951		G	$1,700	12/03	SCIA	Farmall, WF, good paint
M	1952		G	$1,180	12/03	WCIL	Farmall, row crop, 12-volt system, gas
M	1952		G	$1,475	7/03	NWIL	Farmall, 12-volt system, Stanhoist loader
MD	1941		F	$950	3/04	SEWY	Live hyd., no 3 pt., diesel
MD	1947		G	$3,800	12/04	WCIL	Farmall, diesel, 9-speed
MD	1948		G	$1,800	12/04	WCIL	Farmall, diesel
MD	1949		G	$1,900	12/04	WCIL	Farmall, diesel
MD	1950		G	$1,700	12/04	WCIL	Farmall, diesel
MD	1950		G	$2,000	12/04	WCIL	Farmall, diesel
MD	1950		G	$2,750	12/04	WCIL	Farmall, diesel, WF, hand clutch
MD	1950		G	$3,250	9/04	SEND	Schwartz WF, Std., PTO, fenders, rear weights, 13-38" rears, new starter drive
MD	1951		G	$2,050	12/04	WCIL	Farmall, diesel
MD	1951		G	$3,300	12/04	WCIL	Farmall
MD	1951		E	$4,400	6/04	ECND	New tires, OD, recent OH, 2-speed rear end
MD			G	$600	9/03	NEIN	Farmall
MD			G	$1,300	9/03	NWIL	Farmall, PS
MD			G	$1,500	9/03	NWIL	Farmall
MD			G	$2,375	1/03	ECIL	Diesel, PS, weights, Workmaster loader, 5' bucket
MTA			G	$4,000	10/04	NWPA	Farmall, WF, new paint
MTA	1954		G	$2,800	9/04	ECND	Farmall, factory WF, Farmhand F11 hyd. loader with snow bucket, PTO pump
MTA	1954		G	$3,600	12/04	WCIL	Farmall, gas, PS
MTA			G	$3,400	10/03	ECMN	Farmall, gas, WF
MTA	1954		F	$2,950	11/03	NEIN	Farmall, motor locked
OS4	1945		G	$2,050	5/04	SCPA	Restored
Regular	1928		G	$2,500	12/04	WCIL	Farmall, gas
Regular	1930		G	$1,500	12/04	WCIL	Farmall, gas

Model	Year	Hours	Cond.	Price	Date	Area	Comments
Regular	1931		G	$2,100	12/04	WCIL	Farmall, gas
Regular	1932		G	$1,400	9/04	SEND	Farmall McCormick Deering, downdraft carb., spoke wheels, 11.4-36" rears, belt pulley, engine OH
Regular			F	$1,175	7/03	NWIL	Farmall, round spoke wheels, original m&w knobby tires SN 129511
Super A			G	$2,250	8/05	ECMI	Farmall, restored, starter/generator & carb. rebuilt, new paint
Super A			G	$2,325	9/05	NCIL	Woods L59 mower
Super A			G	$2,325	9/05	NCIL	Farmall, Woods L59 mower
Super A			F	$2,400	9/05	SEIA	
Super A			G	$2,900	11/05	WCIL	WF, electric, valve job, belt pully
Super A			G	$3,000	10/05	SWSD	Farmall, WF, with Continental rotary belly mower, 5', rare
Super A			G	$5,200	11/05	WCIL	WF, electric
Super A	1950		G	$5,400	6/05	WCMN	Farmall, demonstrator, white, restored WF
Super A			G	$1,300	1/04	NEOH	Farmall
Super A	1950		G	$1,500	6/04	NCND	Farmall, new tires
Super A	1950		E	$5,900	6/04	ECND	New tires, recent OH, new seat
Super A	1953		G	$1,800	9/04	NECO	Farmall, runs, new tires
Super A	1953		G	$4,050	6/04	ECND	OH, 18 hp.
Super A			F	$1,075	8/03	SEPA	Farmall, WF, new paint, average rubber, cultivator & plow
Super A			F	$2,000	6/03	WCIA	Farmall, IHC 23 side-mounted mower, good rubber, rough appearance, runs good
Super A			G	$2,050	5/03	NEKS	Farmall, Woods 5' finish mower
Super A			G	$3,100	9/03	NEIN	
Super C	1952		G	$2,200	2/06	NECO	Farmall, single front, 2 pt., PTO
Super C			G	$1,200	11/05	WCIL	NF, gas, weights, fenders, belt pulley
Super C			G	$1,850	11/05	NWPA	Farmall, hyd. fast hitch
Super C			G	$4,100	9/05	NCND	Farmall, WF, 59" Woods mower, very clean unit
Super C	1953		F	$1,350	9/05	NENE	Farmall, belly mount mower, PTO, drawbar, 11-36 tires
Super C			G	$2,475	5/05	NEKY	Farmall, cultivator with 2-row side dressers, new rubber
Super C			G	$2,500	2/05	NCCO	Farmall
Super C	1953		F	$500	4/05	NCIA	Farmall, NF, fenders, 60" Artsway belly mower
Super C	1953		G	$4,900	8/05	NCIA	Farmall, factory WF, 12 volt
Super C			F	$700	10/04	SEPA	Farmall, cultivator, NF, fair rubber
Super C			G	$1,200	3/04	NWIL	
Super C			F	$1,250	3/04	WCMN	Farmall
Super C			G	$1,600	9/04	NCIA	Farmall
Super C	1948		G	$2,350	5/04	SCPA	Front weights, restored
Super C	1952		G	$1,800	9/04	WCMN	Farmall
Super C	1953		G	$2,300	6/04	ECND	24 hp.
Super C	1953		G	$4,800	2/04	NCIA	Farmall, fenders, WF
Super C	1954		E	$3,300	6/04	ECND	WF, 24 hp., wide axles
Super C			F	$1,000	8/03	SEPA	Farmall, NF, average rubber
Super C			G	$1,300	5/03	NEKS	Farmall, NF, drawbar hitch
Super C			G	$1,450	7/03	NEOH	
Super C			G	$1,500	5/03	NEKS	Farmall, NF, fast hitch
Super C			G	$1,800	1/03	ECNE	Farmall, NF, 4 cyl. gas, newer 9.5-36" tires, 2 pt., lift assist, 4 speed, PTO, 12-volt system, electric start
Super C			G	$2,700	8/03	NCIA	Farmall, Woods belly mower
Super C	1948		G	$1,100	9/03	NCIA	Farmall, NF, good paint & tin, with JD #5 sickle mower
Super C	1948		G	$1,200	9/03	SEIL	Farmall, new paint, 5' Rhino belly mower and belly blade
Super C	1951		F	$1,000	3/03	NCCO	WF
Super C	1951		G	$1,500	3/03	NWIL	Farmall, NF, tin work fair
Super C	1952		G	$1,500	9/03	SCMI	Farmall

international harvester

Model	Year	Hours	Cond.	Price	Date	Area	Comments
Super C	1952		E	$2,300	1/03	NCCO	Farmall
Super C	1952		F	$2,300	3/03	NCCO	WF
Super C	1952		G	$2,400	3/03	NWIL	Farmall, gas, good tires, good tin
Super C	1953		E	$1,650	3/03	SENE	Farmall, gas
Super C	1956		G	$1,650	2/03	NCOH	Farmall, 2 pt., NF, cultivator
Super H			F	$1,450	2/06	NENE	Farmall
Super H			G	$2,600	2/06	WCIL	Farmall, NF, fenders, restored and 1 owner
Super H			G	$1,650	11/05	SCNE	Live hyd., WF
Super H			G	$800	11/05	WCIL	
Super H	1954		G	$2,500	11/05	WCIA	Farmall
Super H			G	$1,650	3/05	NWMN	Cornhusker 3 pt., new rear tires
Super H			G	$2,700	6/05	ECMN	Tricycle, new tires, battery under seat, aftermarket 3-pt. hitch
Super H			G	$3,200	2/05	SCMN	Farmall, Woods mower
Super H			G	$3,300	2/05	WCIA	Farmall, International WF, paint faded, tires 50% and weather checked, tin straight as new
Super H	1953		F	$675	2/05	SCKS	Farmall
Super H	1953		G	$2,500	8/05	NCIA	Farmall, fenders, good tires
Super H	1953		G	$3,400	6/05	WCMN	Farmall, WF, restored, fenders
Super H	1954		E	$5,250	3/05	NESD	Farmall, NF
Super H			E	$1,850	3/04	SENE	Farmall, gas
Super H			G	$2,400	3/04	SEMN	Farmall
Super H			G	$2,650	6/04	SEMN	Farmall
Super H			G	$3,900	12/04	WCIL	Farmall, gas
Super H	1953		G	$1,650	9/04	NECO	Farmall, restored, good tires, belt pulley
Super H	1953		E	$4,150	8/04	WCMN	Farmall, mint condition, new tires
Super H	1953		E	$5,000	6/04	ECND	New tires, engine OH, toolbox & fenders
Super H	1954		G	$4,200	12/04	WCIL	Farmall, gas, new tires, fenders
Super H	1954		E	$4,900	6/04	ECND	New tires, fenders
Super H			F	$1,750	3/03	SWPA	Farmall, gas, NF, good running condition
Super H			F	$2,050	6/03	WCIA	Farmall, OK appearance, NF, 3 pt., PS, good rubber
Super H			G	$2,800	4/03	SEMN	Farmall
Super H			G	$3,000	10/03	ECMN	Farmall
Super H			G	$3,100	9/03	NEIN	
Super H			G	$3,600	3/03	NESD	Farmall, WF, 12-volt system
Super H	1951		G	$2,850	11/03	ECNE	Farmall
Super H	1953		G	$1,850	9/03	NESD	Farmall, Schwartz WF, very good rubber
Super H	1953		G	$2,200	12/03	ECMI	Farmall, NF, rare hand clutch
Super H	1953		G	$3,750	3/03	WCMI	Farmall
Super H	1954		F	$2,600	5/03	WCIN	Farmall
Super H	1954		G	$2,700	3/03	ECIL	Farmall
Super H	1954		G	$3,650	8/03	NCIA	Farmall, live pump, PS, sold with Woods L306 belly mower
Super M	1952		G	$4,900	2/06	NECO	Farmall, Farmhand F11 loader, WF, PS, PTO
Super M	1953		P	$900	1/06	WCNE	Farmall, gas, WF, not running, for parts
Super M			F	$1,100	12/05	NWIL	Farmall, gas
Super M			G	$2,000	12/05	WCIN	Farmall, PS, NF, restored and overhauled
Super M			P	$2,600	10/05	WCMN	Farmall, rough, WF, 3 pt. loader
Super M	1952		E	$6,600	9/05	NCIL	Farmall, puller tractor
Super M	1952		E	$6,600	9/05	NCIL	Puller tractor
Super M			G	$3,100	3/05	SCMI	Farmall

Model	Year	Hours	Cond.	Price	Date	Area	Comments
Super M			G	$3,500	3/05	ECND	Farmall, gas, WF, PTO, Farmhand F10 loader
Super M			G	$5,500	3/05	ECND	Farmall, gas, rollover diesel, WF, PTO
Super M	1952		G	$3,200	7/05	NWMN	Farmall, gas, factory WF, 1 hyd., PTO, PS, 2 hyd.,
Super M	1953		F	$2,000	3/05	SCIL	Farmall, fresh dealer OH, PS
Super M	1953		E	$3,900	3/05	WCNY	Farmall, repainted nicely
Super M	1953		G	$4,000	2/05	ECSD	Farmall
Super M			P	$975	9/04	NCIA	Farmall, rough
Super M			G	$1,225	4/04	ECWI	WF
Super M			G	$1,750	4/04	SEND	Farmall, gas, Schwartz WF, 14.9-38" tires
Super M			F	$1,850	12/04	WCIL	Farmall, gas
Super M			G	$2,150	12/04	SEMN	Farmall
Super M			F	$2,600	1/04	SCIA	Farmall, engine stuck, WF, new tires
Super M			G	$2,850	9/04	ECNE	Farmall, PS, live hyd., 15.6-38"
Super M			G	$3,100	1/04	NWIL	Farmall, gas, NF, good tin & tires, converted to 12 volt, 13.9-38" rears
Super M	1950		G	$1,500	6/04	NCND	Farmall, with loader
Super M	1952		E	$1,550	6/04	NEKS	Farmall, restored, clean
Super M	1952		G	$2,000	12/04	WCIL	Farmall, gas, single front wheel
Super M	1952		G	$2,200	6/04	ECND	New rear tires, 43.5 hp., NF
Super M	1952		G	$3,100	9/04	WCMN	Farmall, gas, new rubber, good paint & tin
Super M	1953		G	$1,700	12/04	WCIL	Farmall, gas
Super M	1953		G	$2,600	12/04	WCIL	Farmall, gas, PS
Super M	1953		G	$2,650	2/04	NCIA	Farmall
Super M	1953		E	$4,200	6/04	ECND	WF, 44 hp.
Super M	1954		G	$1,700	5/04	NCKS	Hyd., PTO, add-on PS, TA out
Super M			F	$900	3/03	NWSD	Farmall
Super M			F	$1,400	11/03	NEIA	Farmall, needed paint & front tires, PS, 12 volt
Super M			G	$1,400	6/03	WCSD	Farmall, WF, hyd., starts right up
Super M			G	$1,675	8/03	NCIA	Farmall, aux. hyd. to run auger
Super M			G	$1,800	9/03	WCSD	Farmall, truck front end, Farmhand F10 loader, hay basket, 9' teeth
Super M			F	$1,850	6/03	NCWI	Farmall, gas, WF, 12 volt
Super M			G	$1,950	9/03	SEMN	Farmall, gas, WF
Super M			G	$2,250	9/03	SEMN	Farmall
Super M			G	$2,350	9/03	NEIN	
Super M			G	$2,700	7/03	SEND	Farmall, gas
Super M	1951		F	$900	2/03	ECNE	Farmall
Super M	1951		G	$1,350	3/03	ECNE	Farmall, NF, live power, 12 volt
Super M	1952		G	$1,450	3/03	WCMN	Farmall, gas, WF, live hyd.
Super M	1952		G	$1,600	8/03	NCIA	Farmall, Stanhoist loader
Super M	1952		G	$1,650	2/03	WCIA	Farmall
Super M	1952		F	$1,700	3/03	NCCO	
Super M	1953		F	$1,100	3/03	NWIL	Farmall, NF, PS, 12 volt
Super M	1953		G	$1,800	12/03	ECIL	Farmall, LP conversion, Firestone 11.9-38" tires
Super M	1953		G	$3,900	3/03	WCMI	Farmall
Super M	1954		G	$4,350	1/03	NWIL	Farmall, WF, PS, IHC 2000 loader with 6' material bucket, 18.4-38" hub duals
Super MD			G	$1,750	6/05	NEND	Farmall, WF, 18.4-38" tires
Super MD	1953		G	$7,000	12/04	WCIL	Farmall, diesel
Super MD	1953		G	$9,250	12/04	WCIL	Farmall, diesel
Super MD	1953		E	$10,200	6/04	ECND	New tires, completely gone through
Super MD			G	$2,100	9/03	NWIL	Farmall, new tires
Super MD			G	$2,850	4/03	SEMN	Farmall, PS, new engine OH, good heads, NF, all original

international harvester

Model	Year	Hours	Cond.	Price	Date	Area	Comments
Super MTA			G	$4,450	1/06	ECIL	Farmall, row crop, 13.6-38, nice
Super MTA			G	$4,900	2/06	NEIA	Farmall
Super MTA	1954		F	$2,000	1/06	NECO	Farmall, Farmhand F11 loader, bent bucket
Super MTA			G	$2,000	11/05	WCIL	NF, gas, restored, PTO
Super MTA			G	$2,400	7/05	SESD	Farmall
IHC Super MTA			F	$2,900	9/05	NENE	Farmall, NF, PTO, new clutch & TA, new paint
IHC Super MTA			G	$5,100	12/05	WCIN	Farmall, PS, fenders, 3 pt., rebuilt torque, NF, chrome stack
IHC Super MTA	1954		G	$1,300	9/05	NCIL	NI horn loader
IHC Super MTA	1954		G	$1,300	9/05	NCIL	Farmall, NI horn loader
IHC Super MTA	1954		G	$2,900	9/05	NCIL	
IHC Super MTA	1954		G	$2,900	9/05	NCIL	Farmall
IHC Super MTA	1954		E	$8,900	3/05	WCMN	Farmall, 1 owner, 12 volt, wide and narrow front, very nice
IHC Super MTA			G	$3,400	6/04	SEMN	Farmall
IHC Super MTA			G	$3,600	7/04	WCIA	Farmall, new paint, straight tin, PS
IHC Super MTA	1954		G	$3,200	4/04	WCNE	Gas, older F11 loader
IHC Super MTA	1954		G	$3,700	12/04	WCIL	Farmall, gas, PS
IHC Super MTA	1954		G	$3,800	12/04	WCIL	Farmall, gas, full weights
IHC Super MTA	1954		G	$3,850	12/04	WCIL	Farmall, gas, WF
IHC Super MTA	1954		E	$4,300	6/04	ECND	
IHC Super MTA	1954		G	$4,800	2/04	ECIA	Farmall, row crop, gas, 14.9-38
IHC Super MTA	1954		G	$5,400	8/04	WCIL	Farmall, gas, PS, 2-way hyd., oversize sleeves and pistons
IHC Super MTA	1954		E	$5,700	6/04	ECND	New tires, hyd., 44 hp.
IHC Super MTA	1954		E	$7,500	6/04	ECND	New tires, hyd., OH motor, WF, 43.6 hp.
IHC Super MTA	1954		E	$8,800	6/04	ECND	New tires, recent OH
IHC Super MTA	1954		E	$10,500	6/04	ECND	New tires, 43.6 diesel
IHC Super MTA			F	$1,600	5/03	WCIN	Farmall, motor runs, transmission has a noise
IHC Super MTA			G	$2,200	5/03	ECWI	Farmall, WF, TA out, Schwartz front end
IHC Super MTA			G	$2,900	1/03	NENE	Farmall, Schwartz WF, 1 owner, original paint, very good tin work, good TA & tires
IHC Super MTA			E	$3,900	8/03	NWIL	Farmall, PS, gas
IHC Super MTA	1953		E	$6,000	3/03	ECWI	Farmall, PS, 12 volt, live hyd., good TA, museum ready, duals
IHC Super MTA	1954		G	$6,800	3/03	NESD	Farmall, WF, very good tin
IHC Super MTA	1954		G	$7,300	6/03	NEIL	Farmall, diesel, WF, SN 82448
IHC Super MTA	1954		E	$10,250	3/03	WCMI	Farmall, show ready!
IHC W4	1941		E	$4,150	9/05	NCIL	Farmall
IHC W4	1941		E	$4,150	9/05	NCIL	
IHC W4			G	$1,350	12/04	NWIA	Low hours
IHC W4			G	$1,500	12/04	SEMN	Farmall, Std.
W4	1941		G	$1,800	9/04	SEND	Std., PTO, new 14.9-24" rears, rings & bearings
W4	1941		G	$2,100	10/04	NEPA	All fuel, restored
W4	1951		G	$1,900	9/04	SEND	Std., 1 hyd., belt pulley, PTO, 14.9-26" rears, engine kit
W4			G	$1,400	6/03	ECND	Recent paint
W4	1951		G	$2,300	9/03	SEND	McCormick
W6			G	$1,400	9/05	NCIL	
W6			G	$1,400	9/05	NCIL	
W6	1952		F	$1,600	5/05	NCKS	Engine free but needs tuning, 540 PTO, 1 hyd.
W6			G	$1,500	1/04	SCIA	
W6			P	$250	9/03	NEIN	Parts
W6			G	$375	4/03	WCSK	Canadian sale

Model	Year	Hours	Cond.	Price	Date	Area	Comments
W6			G	$425	9/03	NEIN	
W6			G	$1,250	4/03	ECNE	WF, PTO, 1 hyd.
W9			G	$1,400	11/05	WCIL	Add on PS, gas, 4 cyl
W9	1951		F	$800	9/05	NECO	PTO
W9			P	$325	5/04	NWND	Not running
W9			G	$2,400	12/04	WCIL	Std., gas
W9	1947		G	$1,400	9/04	SEND	Std., 1 hyd., 18.4-34", transmission seals, 12 volt
W9			P	$200	4/03	SEMN	For parts, Farmall, gas, good fenders
W9			P	$600	9/03	NEIN	Parts
W9			G	$900	9/03	NEIN	
W9			G	$1,900	9/03	NEIN	Gas
W9			G	$2,250	10/03	WCSK	Canadian sale, 2WD, gas, 16.9x34" tires, Malco loader & bucket
W9	1949		F	$850	7/03	NWMN	Belt pulley
WD6			F	$900	11/05	ECNE	PTO, 14-30 tires
WD6	1941		G	$2,400	7/05	ECND	2-bottom plow
WD6			P	$650	4/03	SEMN	For parts only
WD6			G	$2,400	9/03	NEIN	
WD9			F	$850	4/03	SEMN	New injectors
TD15B	1965		G	$7,000	1/04	NEIN	Dozer, hyd. tilt 4-way blade, reverser
TD20	1968		G	$10,600	3/03	SEIA	Dozer, straight blade, PS, ROPS and sweeps

IHC's torque amplifier revolution

International Harvester Company's (IHC) introduction of a torque amplifier now seems like a minor improvement when considered in light of the advanced full power-shift transmissions offered on today's high-horsepower tractors. But when IHC's torque amplifier (often referred to as a TA) came out in 1954, it marked a revolution in transmission engineering. For the first time, farmers could shift a tractor between two gears, not only on-the-go, but under load, without having to use the clutch or throttle the engine down.

The advantages of this maneuver were huge, particularly when tilling. The torque amplifier gave farmers the ability to shift a tractor down, thereby generating more draft, an invaluable aid when encountering a tough spot in the field. So popular was this feature that within the decade, the torque amplifier was available on most high-horsepower tractors.

This IHC exclusive design was located in the tractor's clutch housing. The device consisted of a planetary drive operating off its own manually operated, single-disk clutch that drove the input shaft of the regular five-speed transmission.

In operation, when the torque amplifier's clutch was engaged, the planetary drive was locked up to deliver a 1-to-1 gear ratio to the transmission. When the tractor was shifted from direct drive to torque amplification, the clutch would release, and the travel speed of the tractor was reduced about 32%. This increased pulling ability by almost 48%, thanks to a gear ratio increase of 1.482-to-1.

The beauty of IHC's torque amplifier was that it doubled to 10 the number of available gears in a standard five-speed transmission. Plus the torque amplifier could be engaged and disengaged without using the tractor's clutch or regulating engine speed.

In some ways, the IHC design could be called the first power-shift transmission, since it allowed shifting between gear sets while under power.

IHC originally offered the torque amplifier on its Farmall Super M-TA, Super MD-TA (diesel), and the McCormick Super W6-TA. This planetary-type torque amplifier was to remain in production on some IHC tractors of less than 70-hp. until 1980.

By the way, the Super M-TA is also notable for being the first IHC tractor to come equipped with an independent or "live" power take-off, which continued to work even after the transmission was disengaged.

j.i. case

J.I. Case traces its roots back to 1842 when Jerome Increase Case started building threshers. Case was one of the first major competitors in the horsepower business; its first steam engine was built in 1869, first steam traction engine in 1876, and first tractor in 1911. Actually, Case had fabricated a prototype tractor as early as 1892 establishing the firm as a pioneer in the industry. Although best known for manufacturing reliable tractors, Case is also noted for building a luxury car in 1910. Today Case Corporation, which purchased IHC in 1985, is still headquartered in the city in which it was founded, Racine, Wisconsin, and is considered one of four largest farm machinery firms in the world.

Model	Year	Hours	Cond.	Price	Date	Area	Comments
1030			F	$2,400	6/05	SWMN	Diesel, WF, new PTO, 3 pt., new 18.4-34" tires
1030			F	$2,650	6/05	SEND	Cab, 2 hyd., 3 pt., 540 PTO, 18.4-34" singles
1030			F	$1,300	3/04	WCMN	Cab, 3 pt., 2 hyd., PTO diesel
1030			F	$1,900	6/04	NWMN	Cab, heat, 930 block, 2 hyd.
1030			F	$1,300	2/03	ECAR	Good tires, paint worn
1030			F	$2,300	6/03	WCMN	Diesel, WF
1030		5,522	G	$3,250	4/03	WCIL	Cab, new 20.8-34", duals
1030			G	$8,200	1/03	ECCO	Wheatland, cab
1070			F	$4,500	4/05	SCSD	Black Knight
1070			G	$5,100	1/05	NENE	Diesel, 3 pt., WF, 18.4-38"
1070		4,663	G	$6,200	8/05	SWOH	Cab
1070			G	$2,900	2/04	NCWI	Diesel, cab
1070		4,600	G	$3,000	9/04	NEKS	WF, 3 pt., 2 hyd., like new batteries & alternator, good tires, recent repair on PTO & hydraulic pump, good paint
1070			G	$3,600	2/04	WCIN	140 hours on OH, cab
1070			G	$3,850	12/04	SEMN	
1070			F	$4,650	3/04	NWIL	Cab, AC
1070			F	$4,650	3/04	NWIL	Diesel, WF
1070			F	$7,000	10/04	NWPA	With Case 830 loader, engine rebuilt
1070	1971	5,000	F	$3,950	1/04	NCIL	Black Night demonstrator
1070	1973		G	$4,000	2/04	NEIN	Cab
1070	1974	1,991	G	$8,300	3/04	WCMI	Agri King, no cab, 3 pt., PTO, 2 hyd., 18.4-34"
1070	1975	7,800	G	$4,100	11/04	SCKS	Transmission overhaul at 5,500 hrs., 3 pt., PTO
1070			G	$3,000	11/03	NWSD	3 pt., cab, 2 hyd.
1070			F	$3,100	7/03	WCSK	Canadian sale
1070		5,000	F	$3,900	2/03	SCNE	Cab, white, 2 hyd., 18.4-34"
1070			G	$4,200	3/03	NCWI	Cab, diesel, high hours
1070			F	$4,900	2/03	WCPA	Steel wheels
1070			G	$5,750	12/03	SCMN	
1070		5,600	F	$6,000	3/03	SEPA	Cab, AC, 540/1000 PTO, 2 hyd., 4 speed, PS
1070			G	$7,500	4/03	WCSK	Canadian sale
1070			G	$7,600	5/03	SWOK	Loader
1070	1973		F	$4,200	3/03	ECND	Cab, 8-speed, 2 hyd., 3 pt., PTO, 18.4-38R", duals
1070	1973		F	$6,000	3/03	NCMN	Cab, 12-speed, PS, 2 hyd., 3 pt., PTO, 18.4-38", front weights
1070	1974		F	$3,250	7/03	WCSK	Canadian sale, 2WD
1070	1974		G	$5,525	12/03	WCIL	Cab, PS, 3 pt., less than 500 hrs. on OH
1070	1978	5,242	G	$7,000	5/03	WCSK	Canadian sale, 2WD, 18.4x38" tires, 2 hyd., PTO, powershift, 100 hp.
1170	1970	5,362	G	$4,625	8/04	ECNE	451 turbo, 18.4-38", 2 hyd., 540/1000 PTO shafts, cab, AC, 4-speed 2-range trans., weight bracket
1175			G	$3,700	3/05	NWIL	Weights, diesel
1175	1973	6,610	G	$4,000	3/05	SEWY	Diesel, cab, 3 pt.
1175			F	$2,000	3/04	SCMN	
1175		8,000	G	$7,500	3/04	WCMI	2WD, cab, 3 pt., PTO, 2 hyd., 18.4-34" tires
1175	1977		G	$4,900	11/04	WCOK	Cab, 2 hyd., 3 pt., PTO, Degelman 9' dozer blade, good rubber
1175	1972		F	$4,850	10/03	NWIL	Cab
1175	1973		P	$2,200	10/03	NWIL	
1175	1974		P	$2,500	10/03	NWIL	2 hyd.
1175	1977	6,056	F	$4,500	11/03	NWIL	Cab
1175	1977	4,300	G	$14,750	4/03	WCSK	Canadian sale
1200		7,732	F	$3,400	6/03	SEND	4WD, Traction King, 2 hyd., 18.4-34" tires
Model	**Year**	**Hours**	**Cond.**	**Price**	**Date**	**Area**	**Comments**

j.i. case

Model	Year	Hours	Cond.	Price	Date	Area	Comments
1270		9,048	G	$4,200	4/05	SEND	451 turbo engine, recent clutch work, 3 pt., 2 hyd., PS, 1000 PTO
1270		5,000	F	$4,000	12/04	WCIL	Diesel
1270			G	$4,200	3/04	SCMN	
1270		3,433	E	$4,300	11/04	NCKS	3 speed, PS, 2 hyd., front & rear weights, cab
1270			G	$3,400	10/03	ECWI	PS
1270		6,300	G	$7,000	9/03	NCSD	Cab, AC, duals, PS, 3 pt., 6300 hrs.
1270	1973		F	$2,100	4/03	NCND	Cab
1270	1976		G	$3,600	3/03	SEIA	
1270	1978	6,934	G	$7,000	10/03	WCSK	Canadian sale, 2WD, 18.4-38" duals, PS, 2 hyd., 1000 PTO, 137 hp.
1370			P	$1,300	4/05	SCSD	Needs transmission work
1370		5,750	F	$4,700	6/05	SEND	2 hyd., 3 pt., 1000 PTO, 18.4-38" hub duals
1370	1972		G	$3,250	2/05	NEIN	Diesel, cab
1370	1972	6,100	F	$3,850	4/05	ECND	PS, 3 pt., PTO, 20.8-38" tires
1370	1974	3,809	G	$5,500	2/05	WCIL	Factory cab, PS, 1000 PTO, 3 pt., 2 hyd.
1370	1976	4,626	G	$4,000	1/05	NCIA	Cab, 2 hyd., quick coupler, clamp-on duals, front weights
1370			G	$3,400	3/04	ECMI	Cab, 3 pt., PTO, 2 hyd., diesel
1370			G	$4,000	12/04	ECMN	2WD, good rubber, field ready
1370			F	$4,600	3/04	NWIL	Cab
1370			F	$4,600	3/04	NWIL	Gas, duals, weights
1370			G	$5,000	10/04	NWPA	Engine rebuilt in 2001
1370			G	$7,100	3/04	ECMN	Diesel, loader
1370			G	$9,100	12/04	SEMN	
1370	1973		F	$5,200	2/04	SCIA	Cab, 1,600 hrs. on OH, weak PS, 18.4-38" tires
1370	1976	4,367	G	$5,300	12/04	ECND	Cab, PS, 3 pt., PTO, 2 hyd., 20.8-38" tires, clean
1370	1977	6,800	G	$4,400	2/04	SWIA	90% rubber
1370			F	$2,750	8/03	NWIL	Cab, AC, diesel, duals
1370			F	$3,950	8/03	NWIL	Diesel
1370			G	$4,400	8/03	NWIL	Diesel
1370		5,500	F	$6,500	3/03	SEPA	Cab, AC, 1000 PTO, 2 hyd., 4 speed, PS
1370			G	$8,000	4/03	WCMI	OH, loader
1370	1975	6,900	F	$3,000	11/03	ECND	Cab, 3 pt., PTO, 20.8-38" tires
1370	1975	3,809	G	$4,400	9/03	NWIA	WF, PS, cab, AC, 2 hyd., 3 pt., rock box, 18.4-38" tires, duals
1370	1976	2,565	G	$5,300	3/03	SEIA	Cab, hub mount duals
1370	1977	6,350	F	$8,400	3/03	NCMN	OH, cab, 12 speed, PS, 2 hyd., 3 pt., 1000 PTO, 18.4-38" tires, band duals, front weights
1370	1978	7,477	G	$5,600	2/03	NWIL	Cab, AC, 20.8-38" tires, clamp-on duals, diesel
1470			F	$1,800	3/05	NWMN	4WD
1470			F	$5,100	2/05	SCMN	4WD, OH, 3 pt., duals, no PTO
1470			G	$3,100	9/03	NEIN	
1470		3,518	G	$4,900	10/03	NWSD	Traction King, 540 PTO
300	1957		G	$3,700	6/05	SWMN	Gas, restored
311			G	$1,750	6/04	WCWA	4 cyl. gas, front loader bucket, 3 pt., rear PTO
400			F	$1,400	4/04	NEPA	
400			G	$1,900	8/04	WCMN	WF, 3 pt., PTO
400			F	$900	12/03	SCNE	NF
400			F	$950	10/03	NWMN	Std.
400	1956		F	$1,200	6/03	WCMN	NF, gas
400	1957		F	$1,850	6/03	WCMN	WF, gas

Model	Year	Hours	Cond.	Price	Date	Area	Comments
400	1958	8,756	G	$1,550	6/03	ECND	Row crop, WF, PTO, 2 hyd.
410			P	$1,200	3/04	NEKS	Rough, 18.4-30" tires, good rubber
500			P	$900	4/05	SCSD	Std., for parts
500			G	$2,200	3/04	SWKS	PTO, Hyd.
500			G	$1,450	9/03	NEIN	Std.
530	1964		G	$3,750	3/04	WCMI	Triple-range transmission, WF, 3 pt., PTO, gas, 14.9-28" tires
530			G	$4,250	1/03	ECCO	Factory loader, shuttle transmission, OH, new paint
600			P	$1,500	4/05	SCSD	Diesel
600			G	$2,850	9/03	NEIN	Std.
630			P	$1,900	4/05	SCSD	Stuck engine, for parts
630			G	$2,000	4/04	NCKS	Case-O-Matic transmission
630			G	$1,000	11/03	WCWI	Diesel
700			P	$950	4/05	SCSD	For parts
700	1959	6,271	G	$1,300	7/03	ECND	Gas, row crop, 540 PTO, 2 hyd., 14.9x38" tires
700	1959	6,271	G	$1,500	7/03	ECND	Gas, row crop, 540 PTO, 2 hyd.
730	1968		F	$3,500	1/04	NCOH	WF, PS, 3 pt., 1 hyd.
730	1968		G	$5,100	3/04	WCMI	Comfort King, WF, 3 pt., PTO, 2 hyd., 18.4-34" tires
730			G	$600	6/03	WCSK	Canadian sale, 2WD, 18.4x30" tires, gas, hyd. lift
730			G	$2,500	12/03	NEIA	Comfort King, NF, 3 pt., 2 hyd., gas
730			F	$3,400	3/03	SWPA	Gas, 3 pt.
800			P	$825	4/05	SCSD	LP, for parts
800			F	$1,100	9/04	NECO	Runs, Case-O-Matic transmission, OH, fair tires
800			G	$525	9/03	NEIN	WD6
830			P	$600	4/05	SCSD	Engine stuck, for parts
830			P	$1,000	4/05	SCSD	Standard, diesel, for parts
830			F	$1,550	2/05	NCIN	Gas
830			F	$1,925	2/05	SCMN	Gas, Comfort King, WF, 3 pt., orange post
830			G	$2,800	4/04	NEIN	Comfort King
830	1960	4,598	F	$1,100	3/04	SEWY	WF, PTO, 3 pt., LP
830	1967	5,709	G	$3,950	12/04	ECMI	Comfort King, Case-O-Matic, WF, 3 pt., 2 hyd.
830			F	$1,300	1/03	ECCO	LP, new paint
830			G	$1,450	9/03	NEIN	
830			F	$1,500	10/03	NWMN	Row crop, PTO
830			F	$1,900	8/03	NWIL	Diesel
830			F	$2,100	2/03	SWOK	
830			G	$2,950	6/03	SWMN	Dual range transmission, 3 pt.
830			G	$3,500	4/03	WCSK	Canadian sale, front end loader, diesel, PTO
830			G	$4,200	2/03	SWOK	
830	1965	6,900	G	$2,900	12/03	WCIL	Comfort King, WF, Draft-O-Matic, 3 pt.
830	1966		F	$2,050	7/03	WCSK	Canadian sale, hyd. belt pully, 64 PTO hp.
870			F	$2,050	10/04	SEMN	Needs engine work
870			G	$4,000	1/04	NEOH	3-speed, cab
870	1971	6,773	F	$4,800	3/04	SEWY	Cab, 3 pt., WF, diesel
870	1971	5,100	G	$5,500	2/04	NEIN	
870			F	$3,500	10/03	WCSD	PTO, no cab, 3 pt., diesel
870			G	$4,100	2/03	SWOK	
870	1971		G	$4,550	4/03	NWPA	200 hrs on major OH, clean, Agri King, diesel, 80 hp., 18.4-34" tires
900			P	$800	4/05	SCSD	For parts
900			G	$1,500	7/03	WCMN	WF, diesel, 2 hyd., 15.5-38" tires
900	1959		G	$1,550	6/03	ECND	Propane, 2 hyd., 18.4-38" rear tires
900	1959	2,518	F	$1,600	9/03	ECND	LP, 540 live PTO, 2 hyd., 18.4x34" tires

j.i. case

Model	Year	Hours	Cond.	Price	Date	Area	Comments
930			P	$800	4/05	SCSD	With blade, for parts
930			P	$900	4/05	SCSD	LP, 3 pt., no PTO, rough
930		5,114	G	$2,600	4/05	ECND	Comfort King, 2 hyd.
930	1966		G	$1,500	6/05	ECIL	8-speed, 3 pt.
930			F	$950	9/04	NECO	Runs, OH, standard, cab, good tires & tin
930			F	$2,600	11/04	NWIL	Diesel, WF
930			G	$3,100	3/04	WCMI	Comfort King 2WD tractor, clamp-on duals, WF, 3 pt., PS, 2 hyd., diesel, 18.4-34" tires
930			F	$4,600	4/04	NEPA	
930	1964		G	$2,850	11/04	SCKS	LP gas, PTO, hyd. pump
930	1966		G	$3,000	2/04	NEIN	3 pt., WF, diesel
930			F	$1,950	10/03	WCSD	Comfort King, 2 new tires, diesel, 2 hyd., cab
930		4,507	F	$3,000	12/03	ECIL	WF, PS, live pump PTO
930			G	$4,800	3/03	SWMN	Diesel, WF
930	1961	5,246	F	$1,700	9/03	ECND	Diesel, Std., 540 live PTO, 2 hyd.
930	1963	6,446	G	$1,400	6/03	ECND	Diesel, PS, Std., 540 PTO, 2 hyd., 18.4x34" tires
930	1967		F	$1,500	1/03	NWIL	Diesel, Comfort King, 3 pt., 2 hyd.
930	1967		F	$1,650	10/03	NWIL	Cab
930	1967		G	$2,100	11/03	WCKS	3 pt., PTO, cab, diesel
930	1968		F	$3,200	4/03	NWMN	Row crop, cab, 3 pt., PTO
930	1968		G	$3,300	7/03	ECND	Diesel, 540 PTO, 2 hyd.
930	1968		G	$3,300	7/03	ECND	Diesel, row crop, 3 pt., 540 PTO, 2 hyd., 13.6x38" rear tires
930	1968		G	$5,100	1/03	SWOK	2 hyd., 3 pt., 85-hp., rubber 85%
970			P	$1,300	4/05	SCSD	For parts
970	1975	4,447	G	$6,000	2/05	NWOH	18.4-34" tires
970			G	$3,400	6/04	SEMN	
970			G	$7,500	2/04	SEMN	Westendorf loader & grapple
970	1972	5,764	F	$3,900	3/04	SEWY	Diesel, cab, 3 pt., PTO
970	1978	5,600	F	$5,300	11/04	NWIL	1000 rpm, front weights
970		8,260	F	$2,300	4/03	NCWI	White cab, 3 pt.
970			G	$3,000	2/03	SCKS	
970			F	$4,100	3/03	WCWI	Open station
970			G	$4,250	3/03	WCWI	Cab
990	1979		G	$3,000	3/04	WCIL	
C			P	$950	4/05	SCSD	For parts
C			G	$700	10/04	NEPA	Restored
CC			G	$750	10/04	NEPA	Original
D			P	$750	4/05	SCSD	For parts
DC			P	$300	4/05	SCSD	For parts
DC			P	$400	4/05	SCSD	For parts
DC			G	$575	6/05	SEND	540 PTO, new rear tires
DC			P	$1,150	4/05	SCSD	Standard, for parts
DC	1952		G	$3,250	6/05	ECIL	Rear rims widened 3"
DC			P	$300	11/04	SCKS	Wheatland, for parts
DC			G	$1,450	9/04	ECNE	3 pt., 13.6-38" tires
DC	1950		G	$625	9/04	ECNE	Gas, 15.5-38" tires, NF
DC			G	$1,200	1/03	ECIL	Hyd. lift arms, new tires
DC			G	$1,450	7/03	NCIA	Repainted
DC	1946		E	$1,300	6/03	NEIL	Restored, NF, fenders

Model	Year	Hours	Cond.	Price	Date	Area	Comments
L	1937		G	$1,600	9/04	NECO	Runs, fair tires
LA			P	$275	4/05	SCSD	For parts
LA			P	$925	4/05	SCSD	For parts
LA	1948		F	$350	9/04	SEND	Standard, PTO, 18.4-30" tires, not running
LA	1949		G	$1,600	10/04	NEPA	LP, restored
LA			G	$850	9/03	NEIN	LP
LA	1940		F	$1,040	10/03	ECIN	
SC			P	$425	4/05	SCSD	For parts
SC			P	$550	4/05	SCSD	For parts
SC			G	$1,100	4/05	NENE	540 PTO, Duncan loader
SC	1941		G	$2,700	6/05	ECIL	New paint
SC	1943		G	$1,000	4/05	NEIN	Gas, NF
SC			F	$350	3/04	WCMN	With trip loader
SC			F	$600	10/04	NEPA	Restored
SC			G	$725	10/04	NCOH	
SC			G	$750	12/04	NWIA	Full steel wheels, rare
SC			G	$2,000	6/04	SEMN	
SC	1947		G	$700	2/04	NEIN	NF
SC	1950		G	$900	3/04	WCWI	WF, 3 pt., live power, gas
SC	1951		G	$600	9/04	ECNE	Loader, 11.2-38" tires, NF
SC	1951		G	$1,000	9/04	SEND	WF, belt pulley, PTO, 12.4-38" tires, rear weights
SC			G	$725	3/03	NWIL	Gas
SC			G	$1,400	9/03	NEIN	
SC			F	$2,600	7/03	WCSK	Canadian sale, original
SC	1950		F	$725	11/03	SENE	
SC	1950		F	$750	11/03	SENE	Single front wheel, motor stuck
SC	1950		G	$1,125	7/03	NWIL	Restored
SC	1954		G	$1,900	3/03	NCCO	Lyons loader
VA			G	$600	10/04	NEPA	
VAC	1949		F	$700	4/05	SCNE	Runs, 11-28" tires
VAC			P	$225	12/04	ECMI	For parts
VAC			P	$450	9/04	ECMT	NF, engine may be stuck
VAC			F	$750	4/04	NEPA	
VAC			G	$950	9/04	ECNE	New 13.6-28" tires
VAC			G	$975	9/04	ECNE	3 pt., 12.4-28" tires
VAC			G	$1,100	9/04	NECO	Restored, good tires
VAC			G	$1,300	12/04	ECMI	Repainted, runs good, PTO
VAC	1946		G	$925	8/04	WCMN	
VAC	1949		G	$900	9/04	SEND	NF, PTO, belt pulley, 11.2-28" tires
VAC	1951		G	$1,000	12/04	ECMI	PTO
VAC			F	$110	1/03	ECNE	Gas, NF, PTO, engine stuck
VAC			G	$600	9/03	NEIN	
VAC			G	$625	7/03	NCIA	Fenders
VAC			G	$800	1/03	ECIL	
VAC			G	$800	10/03	ECMN	
VAC			F	$1,100	8/03	SEPA	NF, fair rubber
VAI			F	$1,300	1/05	ECNE	Woods 59" mower
VAI	1948		G	$1,050	10/04	NEPA	
VC			P	$450	4/05	SCSD	For parts
VC			P	$390	7/03	NEOH	Did not run

john deere

Not in his wildest dreams could John Deere have imagined the impact the company he founded would have on American agriculture. During his life Deere gained fame for building plows. But he would die before the introduction of the company's first tractor. The machine, the All Wheel Drive, was highly innovative featuring all-wheel propulsion and a four-cylinder, high-speed engine. But it was the Model D, introduced in 1923, that helped catapult Deere as a horsepower contender. The D employed Deere's famous horizontally-operating two-cylinder engine, which would power hundreds of Deere models until the introduction of the New Generation tractors and their four-cylinder power plants in 1960. Today Deere & Company is a world supplier of farm machinery, construction equipment, and lawn and garden items.

Model	Year	Hours	Cond.	Price	Date	Area	Comments
1010			G	$3,700	6/05	ECWI	Remote
1010			G	$3,750	6/05	ECMN	3 pt., PS
1010			G	$5,750	6/05	ECMN	Std., gas, WF, 3 pt., new tires & paint
1010			G	$6,000	6/05	ECMN	Row crop, gas, WF, 3 pt., PTO, lever, new paint, restored
1010			G	$8,800	7/05	SCIA	Std., restored
1010	1962	764	G	$8,500	2/05	NWIL	WF, 3 pt.
1010			F	$2,600	12/04	SEPA	
1010	1961		G	$6,400	5/04	SCPA	PS, restored
1010			G	$3,500	1/03	ECKS	Gas, 3 pt.
1010			F	$3,600	8/03	NWIL	3 pt., PTO, gas
1010			E	$6,500	8/03	NCCO	Restored, gas, new tires & paint, WF, 3 pt.
1010			G	$7,700	3/03	NWIL	Shuttle gear, 8-way blade
1010	1960	2,500	E	$12,200	8/03	NWIL	Restored, diesel
1020			G	$3,200	1/05	NWGA	3 pt., PTO
1020			P	$5,250	3/04	SWPA	Diesel, loader
1020	1973	8,826	F	$2,250	3/04	SEWY	3 pt., PTO, rear fenders
1020			F	$7,200	4/03	WCMN	Deere loader
1020	1966	1,153	G	$5,800	2/03	SWIN	Utility, Deere 37 full front end loader, WF, 3 pt., PTO hyd.
1020	1971	1,283	G	$5,500	1/03	WCIL	Woods 5' belly mower, gas
1520	1971	2,040	G	$9,000	1/06	SCKS	Diesel, roll guard, canopy, 1 hyd, 14.9-28" tires, 46 hp.
1520		6,200	G	$3,750	4/05	WCWI	Utility, gas
1520			G	$5,500	3/03	NEIA	Deere 48 loader, tires shot
1530			G	$8,500	9/05	NEIN	Utility
1530	1974		F	$4,750	10/05	NCOH	1225 hours on replaced tach, diesel, JD front end loader
1530	1975	2,630	G	$10,100	3/05	ECND	8 forward/4 reverse, 1 hyd., diff. lock, 3 pt., quick hitch, PTO, Deere 143 loader
1530	1974		G	$6,550	9/04	WCWI	Freeman loader, diesel
1530	1975		G	$6,250	2/04	ECMI	New engine & pump
2010			F	$1,500	9/05	NWOR	Gas
2010			F	$3,500	10/05	NEPA	Diesel, open cab, good rubber
2010			F	$4,700	12/05	NCCO	With loader
2010	1961	7,320	P	$1,900	9/05	WCNE	Diesel, 3 pt., smokes
2010	1962		G	$4,200	9/05	NECO	Diesel, new paint, WF
2010	1962	6,636	G	$4,600	8/04	ECMN	WF, diesel, buyers premium 8% for total price of $4,968
2010			G	$2,500	6/05	ECWI	
2010			F	$3,500	4/05	SCSD	Deere 9' sickle bar mower
2010			G	$4,100	6/05	ECWI	Loader
2010		1,068	G	$10,900	7/05	SCIA	Row crop, NF, fenders, 1 owner
2010	1961		F	$1,950	2/05	NEIN	Gas, tach shows 1,782, WF, 3 pt.
2010	1964		G	$5,700	2/05	NCIN	New paint and good rubber, gas
2010			P	$1,550	11/04	WCIL	Rough shape, gas
2010			P	$2,300	11/04	WCIL	Rough shape, loader
2010			F	$2,300	12/04	WCIL	Gas, Deere 36 loader
2010			P	$3,500	9/04	NWIL	Utility, Deere 36 loader
2010			G	$4,600	8/04	NENE	
2010	1963		F	$3,000	2/04	NEIN	Gas, trip loader, WF
2010	1963		G	$3,000	7/04	ECMN	
2010	1964		G	$4,800	11/04	WCOH	WF, PS, power slide wheels
2010			F	$1,500	9/03	SCMI	Gas, WF
2010			F	$1,900	12/03	NCIN	
2010			G	$2,350	3/03	NCWI	Utility, gas
2010			F	$2,450	5/03	SWOK	
2010			F	$2,600	12/03	WCMI	Gas, NF

john deere

Model	Year	Hours	Cond.	Price	Date	Area	Comments
2010			F	$2,650	2/03	SWOK	
2010			F	$2,900	12/03	SCNE	Gas, NF
2010			F	$3,100	4/03	NCMD	Gas
2010			G	$4,500	9/03	NEIN	LP row crop
2010			G	$7,000	8/03	NCIA	Loader and backhoe, 24" bucket, shuttle syncro
2010	1962		P	$4,300	3/03	NCCO	Loader
2020			F	$3,200	12/05	NWIL	Gas, WF
2020			G	$7,000	10/05	WCMN	Diesel
2020		4,661	F	$2,500	8/05	SEIA	Loader, gas, 3 pt., PTO, 2 hyd.
2020			F	$4,500	2/05	WCOK	Loader, gas, 3 pt., PTO, 2 hyd., ran fair, tires fair
2020	1966	5,309	G	$5,600	8/05	SWOH	Diesel
2020			G	$5,700	8/04	NCIA	Utility, 3 pt., ROPS, cover
2020	1968	5,827	G	$6,600	2/04	SCIA	Restored, 500 hrs. on OH, gas, 16.9-28" tires, hi/lo
2020	1970	2,001	F	$4,800	3/04	SEWY	3 pt., WF, Farmhand 21 loader, bucket & grapple
2020	1971		G	$7,500	3/04	NCMI	Dunham hyd. loader, bucket and bale spear, 1 hyd, hi/lo, diesel, 1 owner, 15.5-38" tires
2020			G	$4,800	4/03	WCMN	Utility, gas
2020		6,966	P	$5,250	2/03	NCIL	Utility, Deere 48 hyd. loader, 3 pt., gas, 1 hyd., 16.9-28" tires, rough
2020			G	$5,500	4/03	NCMD	Loader
2020	1966	4,400	G	$7,100	7/03	SEND	Open station, hyd., 3 pt., PTO, PS, 1 owner
2020	1968		F	$3,200	4/03	NCMD	Diesel
2030		3,500	F	$3,400	9/05	SEIA	Brake problem, Koyker loader
2030		4,094	G	$6,900	12/05	NCOH	Utility, diesel, shuttle trans, hi lo, umbrella, front. wghts, 1 hyd
2030			P	$1,500	2/05	SCCA	For parts, WF
2030			G	$9,300	1/05	NWIL	30 hrs. on OH, Deere145 loader, diesel
2030	1978		F	$4,600	4/05	WCMN	55 hp., 2WD
2030			F	$2,950	11/04	NWNY	Original paint, fender rust
2030		3,000	F	$6,200	3/04	SEPA	Deere 145 loader, diesel, WF, poor rubber, rough appearance
2030	1973	4,800	G	$9,400	12/04	NCOH	Diesel, Deere 146 loader
2030	1974	4,366	G	$6,000	8/04	NCIA	Utility, gas, 16.9-28" tires
2030		5,500	G	$7,900	4/03	WCMN	Reverser, Deere 240 all-hyd. loader
2030		3,800	G	$8,200	12/03	SEIA	Deere 146 loader, diesel, roll guard canopy
2030	1974		G	$4,000	1/03	NCOH	50 Series 4-cyl. engine, diesel, 3 pt., 1 hyd., PS
2510		1,707	E	$10,000	9/05	WCMN	Diesel, sharp
2510			G	$6,000	12/05	NCOH	Diesel, NF, syncro, row crop, brush guards, wheel wghts
2510			G	$7,500	12/05	NCOH	Diesel, NF, row crop, brush guards, wheel wghts, PS
2510	1967		G	$7,000	8/05	WCIA	
2510	1968	6,961	G	$5,100	7/05	WCMN	Diesel, cab, WF
2510			F	$5,000	2/05	NCIN	Gas, loader
2510			G	$5,500	2/05	ECNE	NF, 1 hyd., 3 pt., diesel
2510	1966		G	$4,500	6/05	ECIL	Syncro, rock shaft
2510	1966		G	$5,700	7/05	NCIA	Gas, 15.5-38" tires, NF, 2 hyd.
2510	1967		G	$6,300	1/05	NEIA	NF, 3 pt., fenders
2510			F	$2,925	4/04	NEPA	Gas
2510			F	$3,750	5/04	NENE	Gas, NF, 3 pt., poor rubber
2510			F	$4,000	10/04	SEMN	
2510			F	$4,000	4/04	NEPA	
2510			G	$4,200	4/04	ECWI	Canopy
2510		2,586	G	$4,800	12/04	ECMI	Diesel, WF, 16.9-38" tires, 3 pt., sharp

Model	Year	Hours	Cond.	Price	Date	Area	Comments
2510		4,770	G	$5,000	8/04	NCOH	Gas, WF
2510			G	$5,200	12/04	NCWI	NF, remanufactured engine
2510		3,200	G	$6,300	4/04	NEIN	
2510			E	$6,600	3/04	NENE	Gas, WF, 3 pt., 2 hyd., new transmission, good rubber
2510	1966	6,850	G	$6,000	3/04	WCNE	No cab, syncro, WF, 3 pt., 420 hrs. on new engine, diesel
2510	1966	3,229	G	$6,100	4/04	WCNE	Gas, Koyker K5 loader
2510		7,220	F	$2,100	12/03	NWIL	Gas
2510		3,720	G	$3,850	3/03	SEIA	NF, 3 pt.
2510		3,900	E	$6,900	8/03	NWIL	PS, row crop, original, gas
2510			G	$9,900	9/03	SEMN	Deere 48 loader, WF, PS, 2 hyd., PTO, good rubber, OH, new clutch, ring gear, new starter and alternator
2510	1966		G	$3,750	4/03	NCIA	Gas, NF, syncro, 13.6-38" tires
2510	1966	6,336	G	$4,100	9/03	WCIA	Gas, NF, no cab, 3 pt., 1 hyd., good rear rubber
2510	1966	2,038	G	$4,200	1/03	SEIL	Row crop, 3 pt., PTO, diff. lock, rear rock shaft, 15.5-38" tires, new paint 2 yrs. ago
2510	1966		G	$5,250	8/03	NCIA	Gas, NF, front weights, 1 hyd.
2510	1966		G	$7,100	2/03	NCOH	New engine 1998, diesel, NF
2510	1967		G	$5,900	2/03	WCIA	Rollbar canopy, gas, WF, syncro, 15.5-38" tires
2510	1967	7,450	E	$6,400	3/03	ECNE	Gas, clean, WF, 3 pt., 1 hyd., 15.5-38" tires, sycnro, sharp
2510	1967		G	$7,500	3/03	NWPA	Gas, 50 hp.
2510	1968		G	$3,800	8/03	NWIA	2 hyd., PTO shield, NF
2520	1970	4,200	G	$8,900	12/05	SEMN	WF, cab, side console, 3 pt., 2 hyd., rock box
2520			G	$7,100	7/05	SCMN	Side console, WF, gas
2520			G	$9,500	7/05	SCIA	Syncro, original
2520	1972	9,516	G	$16,900	4/05	SENY	Side console, PS, 2 hyd., no weights, 15.5-38" tires, straight sheet metal, new engine 250 hours ago
2520			G	$0	8/04	NWIA	No sale at $4,950, wanted $5,500, gas, NF, 1 hyd., syncro
2520			F	$4,000	4/03	NEPA	Gas, WF, no reverse gear ($2k to fix)
2520			E	$10,500	8/03	NWIL	Diesel, restored, 3 pt., weights
2520			E	$14,600	8/03	NWIL	PS, restored, WF, 3 pt., weights, OH, diesel
2520	1970		G	$6,000	11/03	WCIA	Gas, syncro, WF, 300 hrs. on OH, 3 pt.
2520	1970		F	$11,900	3/03	NCIL	Gas, high crop, 2 hyd., side console, 18.4-38" tires
2520	1971		G	$11,750	6/03	SEMN	3 pt., flat fenders, great runner, SN 023138r
2520	1972	8,128	G	$10,100	10/03	SEMN	Syncro
2630	1974	3,828	G	$7,500	2/06	ECIL	ROPS, 3 pt., 2 hyd., hi/lo trans.
2630			F	$8,600	11/05	NEIA	With JD loader (rough)
2630			G	$8,900	12/05	NCCO	With JD loader & rear blade
2630			F	$4,750	12/04	SEPA	Good rubber
2630		5,866	G	$9,100	2/04	WCSD	60 hp., Deere 146 loader, bucket & fork
3010			G	$7,500	2/06	NEIA	
3010			G	$3,100	9/05	NENE	Gas, NF, Roll-o-Matic, 3 pt., drawbar, 13.6-38"
3010			G	$3,600	10/05	ECMN	Diesel, JD 46 loader
3010			G	$4,100	12/05	WCMN	Gas, WF, 3 pt., PTO, single hyd., rock box
3010			F	$4,400	12/05	WCMN	With JD 48 loader, gas, WF, syncro, 3 pt,. PTO, remotes
3010			F	$4,650	9/05	WCMN	Gas
3010	1961	5,106	G	$5,600	9/05	WCNE	Diesel, 3 pt., new rear tires
3010	1962		G	$8,300	9/05	SEMN	Utility, 3 pt., 2 hyd., front wghts
3010			G	$4,300	2/05	ECNE	WF, 1 hyd., 3 pt., diesel
3010	1962	2,979	G	$7,600	2/05	NWIL	Diesel, 3 pt., WF, new rear tires
3010	1963		F	$4,900	1/05	NENE	Syncro, NF, diesel, 1 owner, looked rough
3010	1963	1,368	G	$6,100	8/05	SWOH	Diesel, NF
3010	1963		G	$6,200	6/05	ECIL	WF, electric ignition, 46a loader
3010			F	$2,300	10/04	SEPA	Utility, loader, fair rubber

john deere

Model	Year	Hours	Cond.	Price	Date	Area	Comments
3010			F	$2,350	2/04	NEIN	Gas, NF
3010			F	$3,400	3/04	ECWI	Diesel
3010			F	$3,400	12/04	ECNE	Gas
3010			G	$3,650	11/04	WCIL	LP, original
3010			G	$5,050	3/04	WCIL	Diesel, NF, new paint, OH
3010			G	$5,800	11/04	WCIL	WF, restored, diesel
3010			G	$7,500	7/04	SEND	Diesel, cab, heat, gear, 2 hyd., 3 pt., Deere 48 loader & grapple
3010			G	$7,500	7/04	NWMN	Diesel, gear, 2 hyd., 3 pt., PTO, Deere 48 loader & grapple, OH in 1997
3010			F	$8,000	9/04	NCIN	1st orchard, 1 of 31, no fenders, gas
3010	1961		G	$3,600	5/04	SCPA	PS, restored
3010	1961		G	$6,300	3/04	NWIN	1 owner, new rubber, original paint
3010	1962		P	$1,900	9/04	ECSD	Bad transmission
3010	1962		G	$3,300	2/04	NEIN	Gas, NF
3010	1962		G	$4,000	3/04	SEWY	New tach, 3 pt., PTO
3010	1963		G	$4,500	9/04	ECNE	Syncro range transmission, 1 hyd., 3 pt., diesel, NF, 15.5-38" tires, 4 front weights, new paint
3010	1963		G	$6,250	3/04	NWIA	Diesel, WF, 3 pt., 2 hyd., syncro
3010			F	$2,125	5/03	SWOK	
3010			G	$2,750	11/03	NENE	Gas
3010			P	$3,000	10/03	NCSD	Diesel, Farmhand F25 loader, rough, 3 pt.
3010		4,522	G	$3,200	2/03	ECIL	Deere 35 loader, gas
3010			G	$3,200	9/03	NEIN	Gas, NF
3010			F	$3,300	12/03	WCMI	Diesel, NF, new clutch, foam front tires
3010		7,933	G	$4,000	3/03	ECMI	WF, 1 hyd., 3 pt., gas, 15.5-38" tires
3010			G	$4,500	6/03	SENE	Diesel
3010			G	$4,500	8/03	NCIA	
3010			F	$4,600	9/03	ECND	Gas, 250 dual loader, synchro shift, 16.9-38" rear tires, trans. rebuilt 1 yr. ago
3010			F	$5,500	9/03	NCSD	Gas, 3 pt., new rear tires, Deere 48 loader
3010			F	$6,300	3/03	WCMI	Diesel, 3 pt., PTO, 15.5-38" tires, WF
3010			E	$9,500	10/03	WCSK	Canadian sale, diesel, 146 fel
3010	1961		F	$2,800	4/03	NCND	Row crop, PTO, 3 pt., diesel
3010	1961		F	$5,000	1/03	SWNE	High hrs., 3 pt., PTO, hyd., diesel
3010	1961		F	$5,200	3/03	NENE	Farmhand F11 loader (rough), diesel, good rubber, poor tin
3010	1961		G	$5,400	11/03	NWIA	NF, Roll-a-Matic, 2,700 hrs. on engine & hyd. OH, 3 pt., 2 hyd., 15.5-38" tires, Cat II quick hitch
3010	1962	5,460	G	$4,500	12/03	WCIL	Open station, NF, fenders, 3 pt., diesel
3010	1962		F	$4,600	3/03	NCCO	
3010	1963	6,969	G	$3,300	8/03	NCIA	New motor in 1998, gas, 15.5-38" tires
3010	1963		G	$7,300	2/03	WCNE	Syncro, WF, Farmhand loader, 1 owner, fresh paint, new tires
3020	1966	6,981	G	$7,250	2/06	SCPA	PS, tach not working
3020	1968		G	$11,500	2/06	NECO	3 pt, PTO, 110 hrs on overhaul, diesel, 15.5-38" tires
3020	1971	2,105	E	$19,500	1/06	SCKS	Diesel, syncro, 2 hyd, 2,105 actual hours, complete engine overhaul at 2,057 hours, WF, R134A
3020			P	$1,900	12/05	NWIL	WF, diesel
3020		5,800	F	$2,950	8/05	WCIL	Gas, NF, syncro, 1hyd
3020			F	$3,050	7/05	SESD	WF, 3 pt., gas
3020			F	$3,600	12/05	WCWI	
3020			F	$4,600	12/05	NWIL	With JD 46A loader, diesel

Model	Year	Hours	Cond.	Price	Date	Area	Comments
3020			G	$5,000	12/05	ECIN	Narrow wheel
3020			G	$5,600	4/05	SWPA	Fresh overhaul, new paint, new tires
3020			F	$6,250	9/05	SEIA	Diesel
3020			G	$6,500	9/05	NEIN	Console
3020			G	$7,000	10/05	SWSD	Gas, cab, heater, WF, Farmhand 525 loader and grapple
3020	1964		G	$4,900	12/05	NENE	Syncro, 18.4-34" new tires, diesel, NF, 2 hyd., new paint
3020	1964	5,393	G	$8,700	7/05	WCMN	JD 148 loader, cab, diesel, 2 hyd., QR, average rubber
3020	1965		G	$5,900	9/05	NCOH	Diesel, WF, hours unknown, sharp but hood nose dented in
3020	1966	5,780	G	$4,200	11/05	NEIA	Gas, NF, 3 pt., like new 15.5-38" tires
3020	1967	11,500	F	$2,350	11/05	NEIA	Gas, NF, standard hitch, 15.5-38" tires
3020	1972		G	$9,400	8/05	WCMN	3,200 hours on overhaul, diesel, side console, 2 hyd., 3 pt., 540 & 1000 PTO, new clutch in 2001
3020			F	$3,300	6/05	ECWI	
3020			G	$5,500	3/05	WCMN	Diesel, new tires on rear, Quick-Tach
3020			G	$6,450	7/05	SCMN	WF, side console, gas
3020			G	$9,000	6/05	ECMN	Gas, 148 loader, new paint
3020			G	$10,250	3/05	NCAL	
3020	1964		G	$6,600	2/05	WCIL	Gas, PS
3020	1965	5,289	G	$5,250	4/05	NCIA	Gas, cab, syncro, Deere WF, 2 hyd., quick coupler
3020	1965	5,509	G	$6,750	8/05	SWOH	Diesel
3020	1965		G	$7,400	1/05	NENE	PS, 2 hyd., WF, 3 pt.
3020	1965		G	$7,900	3/05	SCMI	Diesel, WF, 2,071 hours after OH, 3 front weights
3020	1967		F	$4,700	3/05	NESD	Syncro range, gas, 16.9-34" tires, 1 hyd., PTO, 3 pt., no cab
3020	1968	6,787	G	$7,900	4/05	SCMI	WF, 1,000 hours on new engine, diesel, square manifold, new rubber, new pressure plate
3020	1968		G	$8,000	7/05	SENE	Diesel, 2 hyd., WF
3020	1969	6,850	G	$7,850	1/05	SCNE	2 hyd., 540/1000 PTO, gas, repainted 4 yrs. ago
3020	1969	8,543	P	$9,000	4/05	SENY	Side console, PS, 2 hyd., 15.5-38" tires, poor sheet metal, very dented, no weights
3020	1970	7,811	G	$9,800	3/05	WCNY	Open station, syncro, diesel, 16.9-34" tires, 2 hyd., 1 owner
3020	1970	3,706	E	$19,000	1/05	NENE	Console, diesel, WF, 15.5-38" tires, fenders, front weights, sold by stock auction company
3020			F	$4,000	12/04	SEMN	Gas
3020			G	$4,250	12/04	WCIL	Gas, PS, NF
3020			G	$4,400	12/04	ECMI	Diesel, WF, front weights, 2 pt.
3020			G	$4,500	2/04	WCWI	LP, WF, ROPS, 3 pt.
3020			F	$5,000	2/04	SEMN	WF, 3 pt., 2 hyd., diesel
3020		4,100	G	$5,650	12/04	WCIL	Gas, WF, new paint
3020		10,000	F	$6,900	3/04	NCWI	WF
3020			G	$8,600	3/04	NEIA	Diesel, 1,700 hrs. on OH, 3 pt., 2 hyd., foot throttle, syncro, 4 slab front weights, 3 rear weights, front fenders
3020		3,421	G	$8,800	9/04	ECNE	1 owner, NF, 2 hyd., ROPS, new 15.5-38" tires
3020	1964	6,800	E	$8,250	11/04	SENE	Diesel, WF, PS
3020	1964	100	G	$8,700	3/04	NCMI	1 hyd., engine reconditioned and ready for use, diesel, 16.9-34" tires
3020	1964		G	$16,000	6/04	WCWI	High crop, diesel, 3 pt.
3020	1966		G	$5,200	2/04	SCIA	WF, gas, 15.5-38" tires, syncro
3020	1966		G	$5,300	11/04	NCIA	Gas, factory WF, 2 hyd., syncro, quick coupler, 15.5-38" tires
3020	1966		G	$5,900	3/04	NEMI	Diesel, 3 pt., 1 hyd., with hyd. outlet multiplier
3020	1966		G	$6,250	12/04	ECMN	Fluid in rear tires, new paint, new tires, 1,100 hours on OH
3020	1966		G	$7,400	8/04	NCIA	Egging cab, 3 pt., Schwartz WF, 1 hyd. on rear and one on side, Deere 148 loader, 15.5-38" tires, gas
3020	1967	8,200	G	$5,100	9/04	SWIA	Diesel, WF, 1 hyd.

john deere

Model	Year	Hours	Cond.	Price	Date	Area	Comments
3020	1967		G	$6,500	8/04	NEKS	1 owner, WF, good paint & rubber, diesel, syncro, 2 hyd.
3020	1967	6,092	F	$6,500	12/04	NWOH	Diesel, WF, 15.5-38" tires
3020	1967	9,438	G	$7,850	11/04	WCIA	Controls on dash, no cab, OH at 4,500 hrs., 3 pt., NF
3020	1968		G	$4,975	9/04	WCWI	Diesel, park gear does not hold
3020	1968	5,387	G	$8,500	12/04	SENE	Deere 46a loader, gas
3020	1970		G	$6,500	11/04	WCIA	Diesel, WF
3020	1970	4,040	E	$7,000	4/04	WCNE	WF, gas, no cab
3020		5,150	G	$1,972	6/03	SWMN	Dual hyd., side console, engine needs work
3020		6,930	F	$2,700	12/03	NWIL	Gas
3020			F	$3,300	3/03	SEIA	Cab, PS, loader
3020			G	$3,900	12/03	SEMN	
3020			F	$3,900	9/03	WCSD	Gas, 3 pt., NF
3020			G	$4,000	12/03	NECO	PS, 3 pt., PTO, hyd., WF
3020			G	$4,150	3/03	NESD	WF, 3 pt., 1 hyd., gas
3020			F	$4,400	4/03	NEPA	Gas, NF, syncro, 2 PTOs, 1 hyd., 15.5-38" tires
3020		1,500	E	$5,200	8/03	NWIL	Original, NF, PS, gas
3020			G	$5,500	4/03	NCMD	
3020			G	$5,900	4/03	ECMN	Gas
3020		3,200	G	$6,500	9/03	NCSD	PS, 3 pt., gas, nice, 3,200 hrs.
3020			G	$6,750	12/03	NWIA	
3020			G	$6,900	3/03	SEMN	NF, no cab, 3 pt., 2 hyd.
3020		6,815	G	$7,000	2/03	ECNE	WF, 2 hyd.
3020			G	$7,000	9/03	NEIN	Console, Std.
3020		5,315	G	$7,400	8/03	SCNE	Syncro
3020		3,066	G	$7,900	6/03	NCWI	Gas, WF
3020		1,503	E	$8,700	8/03	NWIL	LP, original, NF
3020		6,200	G	$9,500	9/03	NCSD	Deere 148 loader, 3 pt.
3020			G	$9,800	4/03	NEPA	Diesel, cab, 3 front weights, console, 18.4-34" tires
3020	1963		F	$5,500	3/03	NENE	Good rubber, high hours, poor tin
3020	1964		G	$3,100	2/03	WCIL	Gas, 300 hrs. on OH, syncro, WF
3020	1964	5,492	F	$4,100	2/03	NWIL	Gas, WF, 2 hyd., 3 pt., 16.9-34" tires
3020	1964		F	$4,500	3/03	NEND	2 hyd., 3 pt., 540/1000 PTO, 15.5-38" tires
3020	1964	8,836	G	$5,300	3/03	ECNE	Diesel, clean, syncro, WF, 3 pt., 16.9-34" tires, 2 hyd., used 15 quarts of oil per day
3020	1964		G	$5,750	1/03	SCIL	Diesel, WF, 15.5-38" tires
3020	1964	4,600	G	$6,000	1/03	SEMI	Diesel, ROPS, WF, syncro, 1 hyd.
3020	1964	9,677	G	$7,750	11/03	WCMN	Diesel, PS, 1 hyd., 15.5-38" tires
3020	1964	3,363	G	$7,900	2/03	NWOH	WF, 2 hyd., 3 pt., diesel, 15.5-38" tires
3020	1965		G	$4,250	8/03	NWIA	Gas, 3 pt., PTO, shields, fenders
3020	1965		F	$5,650	3/03	NCCO	
3020	1966		G	$5,500	4/03	NCIA	Fresh OH, gas, WF, syncro, 18.4-34" tires
3020	1966		G	$5,500	9/03	NEIN	Diesel, WF
3020	1966	4,457	G	$5,600	2/03	SEND	Open station, syncro, 1 hyd., no 3 pt., PTO, 16.9-34" tires (70%)
3020	1966		G	$8,050	2/03	NWIL	Open station, WF, 3 pt., 2 hyd., syncro, Deere 46a loader & 5' bucket, approximately 1,500 hrs. on OH, gas
3020	1966	6,627	G	$9,200	3/03	NWIL	Syncro, WF, Deere 148 loader
3020	1967		F	$3,100	3/03	NESD	Propane, syncro, 3 pt., single hyd., hub duals
3020	1967		F	$4,750	2/03	SEMN	Gas, 3 pt.
3020	1967	8,200	F	$4,900	8/03	SENE	Diesel
3020	1967	6,720	G	$5,700	1/03	SCIL	Diesel, WF, 2 hyd., weights, diff. lock

Model	Year	Hours	Cond.	Price	Date	Area	Comments
3020	1967		G	$6,500	3/03	NENE	Very clean, diesel, WF, cab, good rubber
3020	1968	3,516	G	$1,500	7/03	ECND	WF, syncro, 2 hyd., 3 pt., quick hitch, PTO, band duals, gas
3020	1968	5,315	G	$2,300	8/03	NWIA	NF, 1 hyd., gas, fenders, 15.5-38" tires
3020	1968	5,146	G	$12,250	1/03	NWIL	Utility, Deere 46a loader, diesel
3020	1971		G	$9,700	11/03	NCOH	WF, diesel
320			G	$10,000	11/05	WCIL	Utility, PTO
320			G	$10,100	11/05	WCIL	WF, restored, 3 pt., belt pulley, PS
320			G	$9,250	11/05	WCIL	Std, restored, PTO, front weights
320	1958		G	$17,500	9/05	SEMN	Standard, 3 pt fenders, front and rear weights
320			G	$10,500	6/05	ECMN	Gas, WF, slant steer, 3 pt., new tires
320			G	$11,000	6/05	WCMN	3 pt., PTO, new tires, fully restored
320			E	$14,000	3/04	NEIA	Utility, 3 pt., no center link, fenders, WF, OH, new brakes and clutch
320			G	$6,600	8/03	SEPA	Restored, WF, new rubber & paint
320			G	$23,000	6/03	SEMN	Southern special, restored, runs, SN 325049
320S			E	$9,700	8/03	NWIL	Restored, WF, 3 pt., weights, gas
320U	1957		G	$11,900	5/04	SCPA	PTO, rockshaft, restored
330			G	$19,750	7/05	SCIA	Std., good tag, 1 of 844 built, restored
330			E	$15,500	8/03	NWIL	Std., 3 pt., new hood, rubber, engine, runs good, not tag, restored, gas
330	1959		E	$15,700	6/03	NEIL	WF, restored, 3 pt., SN 330210
330S			E	$14,000	8/03	NCCO	Restored, gas, new paint, good tires, WF, 3 pt.
330U			G	$28,500	7/05	NEIA	Restored, 1 of 247 built
330U			E	$19,000	8/03	NCCO	Restored, gas, new paint & tires, WF, 3 pt.
40			F	$1,450	1/06	SESD	WF, 3 pt.
40			G	$1,600	11/05	WCIL	3 pt., Model M grill
40			G	$2,650	11/05	SCMI	Gas, WF
40			F	$2,695	2/05	SCMN	WF, 3 pt.
40			G	$4,750	6/05	ECMN	WF, 3 pt., PTO
40			F	$1,800	1/04	SWOH	
40			F	$2,175	11/04	SEPA	NF
40	1953		G	$3,050	9/04	NECO	Restored, good tires, 3 pt., single front
40			G	$2,000	7/03	NWMN	Utility, loader
40			G	$3,000	9/03	NEIN	Std.
40			G	$4,100	4/03	ECMN	Gas
40	1955		G	$4,250	7/03	ECND	WF, 3 pt.
4000		5,527	G	$10,250	2/06	WCMN	Gas, syncro trans, 3 pt, PTO, 2 hyd, Allied 595 loader
4000	1972	8,911	G	$20,500	2/06	SCPA	PS, 1 of about 400 built
4000			F	$6,000	9/05	SESD	Diesel
4000	1971		G	$15,250	11/05	SCKY	
4000			G	$8,300	3/05	NWIL	WF, console, diesel
4000			G	$11,000	2/05	ECNE	WF, 1 hyd., 3 pt., diesel
4000	1971	6,100	G	$7,250	2/05	ECMI	Side console, diesel, 2 hyd., front weights, 1 owner
4000			F	$7,250	10/04	SEPA	WF, diesel, fair rubber
4000	1968		G	$8,750	2/04	SWIN	Diesel
4000	1970	6,487	G	$9,300	8/04	NCIA	Console, WF, front tank, 18.4-34" tires
4000	1971		G	$10,000	3/04	ECMI	Canopy, side console, 15.5-38" tires, axle duals, diesel
4000	1972		F	$7,750	10/04	SEPA	WF, clean, fair rubber, diesel
4000	1971	6,134	G	$8,100	2/03	ECNE	Syncro, 3 pt., Deere WF, fenders, 1,000 hrs. on OH, shedded
4000	1972	4,730	G	$10,500	6/03	WCIA	Clean, WF, 1 hyd., smooth rubber
4010	1961		G	$5,000	2/06	ECKS	
4010	1961		E	$6,750	1/06	WCNE	WF, no cab, rebuilt
4010	1963	3,365	G	$6,300	1/06	SCMI	WF, cab, 3 pt., 2 hyd., diesel

john deere

Model	Year	Hours	Cond.	Price	Date	Area	Comments
4010			G	$4,250	9/05	WCCO	Diesel, PTO, 3 pt.
4010			F	$4,400	12/05	WCWI	LP
4010			G	$6,100	10/05	ECMN	Diesel, extra fenders, cab, 3 pt.
4010			G	$8,000	12/05	WCIN	WF, syncro range, 1,000 hrs on overhaul
4010	1961		F	$3,600	7/05	ECND	1 hyd., 18.4-34"
4010	1961	4,642	F	$4,400	8/05	SEMI	1 hyd., quick hitch
4010	1962		F	$5,600	12/05	NWIL	WF, 3 pt., diesel
4010	1963	8,118	G	$6,700	12/05	ECMN	Diesel, cab, 2 hyd., 3 pt., quick hitch, band duals, 12-volt
4010	1963		G	$9,850	9/05	SEMN	FWA, hyd. level front, front weights, 3 pt.
4010			F	$3,000	7/05	SCMN	Loader, diesel
4010			F	$3,400	3/05	SEIA	Industrial, loader
4010			F	$3,750	1/05	NENE	Diesel, WF, 3 pt., weak clutch
4010			F	$3,900	2/05	NWWI	Diesel, early model, 3 pt., 540/1000 PTO, syncro range
4010			G	$4,100	3/05	ECMI	Gas, WF, syncro range, 2 hyd., 3 pt., PTO, 15.5-38" tires
4010			F	$4,500	4/05	SEND	500 hrs. on hyd. pumps, 2 hyd., 3 pt., syncro range
4010			F	$5,000	4/05	WCIN	High hours, diesel, NF, good rubber
4010			G	$5,600	4/05	WCWI	Cab, 4020 pistons, clamp-on duals, diesel
4010		3,700	G	$5,900	2/05	WCOK	1 owner, bareback, PTO, 1 hyd., tires good, diesel
4010			G	$6,200	2/05	WCIA	Diesel, WF, ROPS
4010		4,311	G	$9,200	1/05	SENE	1 hyd., front weights, syncro
4010			G	$20,000	7/05	SCIA	Hi crop, diesel, good tag, restored
4010	1962		F	$4,600	3/05	NECO	High hours, Deere 158 loader, grapple
4010	1962		G	$5,200	7/05	NEIA	Diesel, Schantz WF, 1 hyd.
4010	1962		G	$6,600	3/05	ECND	WF, syncro, 3 pt., PTO
4010			G	$2,700	11/04	SCCA	Utility, diesel, hyd., PTO, 3 pt., canopy
4010			G	$3,700	12/04	NEND	Dual loader
4010			F	$3,750	12/04	ECMI	2 hyd., repainted, diesel, 404 engine, hyd. works but lever is stuck
4010			G	$4,100	4/04	SEND	
4010			F	$4,200	3/04	NWIL	Gas, cab, loader
4010			F	$4,400	8/04	NWIA	Fresh paint, diesel
4010			G	$4,500	2/04	ECNE	LP
4010			G	$4,700	12/04	ECNE	Diesel
4010			F	$4,800	8/04	NWIA	Diesel, WF, 1 hyd.
4010			G	$4,900	6/04	ECWI	Deere 48 hyd. loader
4010			G	$5,000	3/04	NCWI	Diesel, NF, cab
4010			G	$5,000	3/04	NCMI	Cab, diesel, 15.5-38" tires, duals, PS, factory 3 pt., 1 hyd.
4010			F	$5,900	10/04	SEMN	NF, ROPS, owner said it had Deere 4230 motor, rear tires fair, hour meter did not work
4010			F	$6,250	10/04	SEPA	Diesel, WF, new paint, good rubber
4010			F	$6,400	4/04	NEPA	Loader
4010			G	$6,500	2/04	WCWI	NF, ROPS, 3 pt.
4010			G	$6,800	9/04	ECNE	Loader tractor
4010			G	$7,500	2/04	ECMO	1 owner, diesel
4010			G	$7,900	10/04	NCOH	1 owner, diesel, WF
4010			G	$11,200	1/04	SEMN	Open station, 2 hyd., less than 200 hrs. on complete OH, sold with newer Westendorf WL-42 loader
4010	1961	7,290	F	$3,775	12/04	ECNE	LP, syncro, 2 hyd., 3 pt., 15.5-38" tires" newer tires, NF
4010	1961		F	$4,200	2/04	WCMN	Diesel, leaking anti-freeze, 18.4-34" tires, 2 hyd., 2 PTO, 3 pt., syncro

Model	Year	Hours	Cond.	Price	Date	Area	Comments
4010	1961	4,511	F	$4,600	6/04	NWMN	Diesel, PTO, 2 hyd., syncro Levy live power front assist
4010	1961	6,800	F	$5,100	9/04	SCMI	Diesel, WF
4010	1961		G	$7,500	6/04	WCWI	Rare, diesel, Levy live power front assist, 3 pt., weights
4010	1961		G	$7,700	6/04	NCND	With blade, syncro
4010	1961		E	$8,200	9/04	WCMN	Diesel, syncro, new paint, good rubber
4010	1962	8,449	F	$4,700	3/04	NWMN	Row crop, 3 pt., 540/1000 PTO, 2 hyd., 15.5-38" tires & band duals, front weights
4010	1963		F	$3,400	8/04	ECNE	Propane, syncro, 18.4-34" tires
4010	1963		G	$3,900	4/04	NCND	No cab
4010	1963	5,376	G	$6,600	3/04	SEWY	3 pt., PTO, no cab, WF, diesel
4010	1963	5,815	G	$7,900	1/04	ECIA	Diesel, syncro, NF, 2 hyd., 3 pt.
4010	1963		G	$8,800	1/04	NECO	Deere 158 loader
4010	1964	9,000	F	$5,900	11/04	WCIA	Cozy cab, front and rear fenders, WF, new tach, 3 pt.
4010			P	$1,600	5/03	ECWI	Rough, gas, NF, year-round cab
4010		8,000	F	$3,100	4/03	WCMN	
4010			G	$3,150	3/03	SWWI	NF
4010			G	$3,600	12/03	SEMN	
4010			G	$4,000	9/03	NEIN	
4010			G	$4,300	3/03	NESD	WF, diesel
4010			G	$4,550	7/03	SCMN	WF, diesel
4010			G	$4,900	9/03	SCMN	
4010			G	$5,100	3/03	ECIN	WF, diesel
4010			F	$5,200	9/03	SCNE	Syncro range, 1 hyd., front weights
4010		2,613	G	$5,500	12/03	ECIL	WF, new rubber all around, 3 hyd.
4010			F	$5,500	4/03	WCMN	Diesel, WF
4010			G	$5,900	10/03	NWMN	Recent 20 Series engine, cab, 3 pt., PTO
4010			G	$6,600	9/03	NEIN	Diesel, WF
4010			G	$6,750	10/03	WCSK	Canadian sale, cab, dual hyd., std., OH at 5,000 hrs.
4010		9,424	G	$7,000	7/03	ECND	Syncro, 2 hyd., 3 pt., PTO, fenders
4010			F	$7,000	8/03	NWIL	WF, duals, diesel
4010		1,620	G	$7,700	11/03	NCKS	
4010			G	$8,400	9/03	SEMN	3 pt., hyd., PTO, wheel and front weights, good rubber, diesel
4010			F	$8,750	3/03	WCMI	4WD, 22 hp., diesel, ROPS, hydrostatic dr., 3 pt., PTO
4010			G	$16,000	9/03	NEIN	
4010	1961		F	$2,500	12/03	NEIL	1 hyd., 15.5-38" tires
4010	1961		G	$4,200	3/03	NWIL	NF, diesel
4010	1961		G	$4,500	1/03	WCIL	Gas, cab, fenders, WF, 1 hyd.
4010	1961	4,460	G	$5,600	1/03	NWIL	WF, diesel
4010	1961		G	$7,700	9/03	NWOH	WF, 2 hyd., new tires, duals
4010	1962	6,563	G	$3,300	4/03	WCIA	NF, diesel, new seat and battery
4010	1962		G	$3,300	4/03	WCIA	WF, no cab
4010	1962	6,322	G	$7,750	2/03	NWOH	Diesel, WF, 3 pt., 2 hyd., 400 hrs. on OH, 18.4-34" tires
4010	1962		G	$8,000	1/03	WCIL	Deere 145 loader, diesel
4010	1963	7,064	G	$2,550	3/03	ECNE	Propane, rear hyd. port, safety-guard custom 400 cab, front-mount hyd. loader, 7' bucket
4010	1963		F	$5,200	9/03	SCNE	Recent engine work, paint was bad, syncro, 1 hyd.
4010	1963	4,679	G	$5,500	12/03	NWIL	WF, 2 hyd., 1,000 hrs. on major engine OH, 15.5-38" tires
4010	1963		F	$6,750	5/03	WCIN	WF, turbo, weights
4010	1963		G	$7,050	11/03	SEIA	2 hyd., 1,615 hrs. on complete mechanical rebuild, Westendorf WL-21 loader, bale prong attach, ROPS and weights
4020			G	$10500	2/06	WCMN	Diesel, PS, side console, 3 pt., 2 hyd., diff. lock
4020			F	$11300	2/06	NEIA	High hours, recent OH
4020	1965	6,578	P	$3400	2/06	NCIL	2 hyd., needs clutch

john deere

Model	Year	Hours	Cond.	Price	Date	Area	Comments
4020	1966	4,500	F	$10,700	2/06	NCKS	JD 146 loader, dirt bucket, 3 pt., dual PTO, 1 hyd., no cab, used oil, tin bent, side panel missing, several oil leaks, loader welded, bucket bent
4020	1967	6,400	E	$6000	2/06	SEMI	Syncro shift, gas
4020	1969	6,628	G	$11700	2/06	WCIL	Side console
4020	1970	7,700	G	$9800	2/06	WCMN	2WD, side console
4020	1972	2,818	E	$21500	2/06	SWNY	PS, restored, 2 hyd., no rear weights, 4 front weights, 18.4-38" tires
4020	5300		E	$14400	11/05	SEMI	Duals, weights
4020		4,151	F	$2250	9/05	SEIA	Gets water in oil
4020			F	$5750	9/05	SCMN	
4020			F	$5800	8/05	WCIA	
4020			G	$7,250	12/05	WCMN	Diesel, side console, 2 hyd., 3 pt., PTO, roll guard cab, 18.4-38"
4020			G	$7,700	7/05	ECMN	Diesel
4020			G	$7,800	9/05	NENE	Diesel, WF, 3 pt., drawbar, 18.4-34"
4020			F	$8,000	10/05	NEPA	Open cab
4020			G	$9,500	9/05	NEIN	Console
4020	1964	8,517	G	$13,900	12/05	NWIL	Diesel, PS, WF, 2 hyd., Model 48 loader
4020	1964		G	$6,100	12/05	NENE	PS, 18.4-34" near new rear tires, WF, 2 hyd., fenders
4020	1964		G	$6,200	12/05	WCMN	Diesel, syncro, 2 hyd.
4020	1965		P	$2,400	12/05	NWIL	Parts tractor, diesel, 18.4-34"
4020	1965		G	$7,400	7/05	ECND	2 hyd., 3 pt,. engine majored recently
4020	1966	4,964	F	$4,300	8/05	SEMI	3 pt,. 1 hyd.
4020	1966		G	$5,500	9/05	WCIL	Gas, 2 hyd., fenders, WF, 3 pt.
4020	1966		E	$9,200	8/05	NCIL	1 hyd., restored, syncro, 18.4-34"
4020	1967		F	$3,900	12/05	NENE	Syncro, WF, 18.4-34"
4020	1967		F	$6,000	9/05	NCOH	Hours unknown, diesel, WF, looked fair
4020	1968		G	$7,300	11/05	NEIL	Diesel
4020	1969		G		12/05	NCCO	No sale at $10,900, PS, 1 owner, year-round cab, side console, axle duals, OH about 3,000 hours ago
4020	1969	7,048	F	$6,700	11/05	SCIA	Hiniker cab, WF, 2 hyd., 18.4-34"
4020	1969		G	$8,700	11/05	ECNE	Side console, CAH, 3 hyd.
4020	1970	10,250	F	$10,250	11/05	WCIL	New tires, side console
4020	1970		P	$6,600	8/05	NECO	Bad cab, smokes, console, rough
4020	1970		G	$9,900	12/05	WCMN	Console, factory cab, 1 owner, diesel
4020	1972	7,123	G	$12,000	12/05	NWIL	1 owner, sharp, 3 pt., 2 hyd., M&W turbo, new radiator, 18.4-38"
4020			F	$5,300	7/05	SCMN	PS, diesel
4020			G	$5,750	6/05	ECMN	Row crop, WF, synchro, fenders, 3 pt., PTO, rebuilt
4020			G	$5,900	3/05	NWIL	Diesel, NF
4020			G	$6,200	6/05	ECIL	3 pt., Deere WF, syncro, 500 hrs. since OH, good paint
4020			F	$6,750	2/05	WCWI	2 hyd., Hiniker cab, 3 pt., WF, diesel
4020		6,286	G	$7,100	8/05	SWMN	Diesel, 3 pt., PTO, 2 hyd., diff. lock, syncro, year-round cab
4020			G	$7,300	1/05	ECNE	2 hyd., WF
4020			G	$7,800	2/05	SWNE	Diesel
4020			G	$9,250	3/05	WCIL	Diesel, console, new paint
4020			G	$12,900	1/05	SCMN	Console, complete rebuild
4020			E	$28,000	7/05	NWIL	Hi crop, 1 of 121 made, diesel, restored, new tires, WF, side console PS (possibly the 1st side console PS off the line), deluxe seat, PTO
4020	1964		P	$3,700	8/05	NWIL	Rough, gas, WF, 2 hyd., good 15.5-38" tires
4020	1964	5,004	F	$4,100	4/05	SCMI	Cab, quick hitch, diesel, WF, good rear rubber, snap-on duals

Model	Year	Hours	Cond.	Price	Date	Area	Comments
4020	1965		G	$4,100	4/05	NEIN	2,896 on tach, NF, 18.4-34" like new tires
4020	1965		G	$7,750	2/05	NEMI	Diesel, syncro, 2 hyd., 3 pt., PTO, 18.4-34" tires
4020	1966		G	$3,750	6/05	ECIL	WF, 3 pt., 2 outlets, front & rear weights
4020	1966		F	$4,250	2/05	NWIL	NF, 3 pt., 2 hyd., gas, 15.5-38" tires
4020	1966	4,909	G	$6,400	8/05	NWIL	Gas, NF, open station
4020	1966	6,988	G	$8,000	4/05	SCMI	WF, diesel, 2 hyd., canopy, new 18.4-34" tires, new head, radiator, trans., pump & injectors, clean
4020	1966	12,200	E	$8,500	4/05	NCOK	Crown fenders, heavy-duty front axle, Deere 158 loader, 7' bucket & round bale spike attachment, PTO, no 3 pt., 1-family owned
4020	1966	6,000	E	$10,100	3/05	WCWI	2 hyd., WF, 3 pt., front weights, diff. lock, new paint
4020	1966		G	$11,200	2/05	NCIN	2 hyd., new paint and good rubber, PS, diesel
4020	1967		G	$5,000	2/05	NEIN	Diesel, NF, 500 hours on OH
4020	1967		G	$6,700	3/05	ECSD	Diesel, syncro, WF, 18.4-34" tires
4020	1967		G	$8,000	3/05	NCCO	ROPS canopy, 2 hyd., 3 pt., 540/1000 PTO, 1,600 hrs. on OH
4020	1967		G	$8,000	3/05	SENE	High hours, WF, diesel
4020	1967	6,603	G	$9,500	7/05	ECIL	
4020	1967	6,686	G	$10,000	3/05	NCIA	Factory WF, 2 hyd., quick coupler, hyd. pump OH, diesel, 18.4-34" tires
4020	1967	6,826	F	$12,100	4/05	SENY	PS, 2 hyd., 18.4-34" tires, good sheet metal
4020	1968	6,920	F	$4,400	7/05	NEIA	Gas, WF, 3 pt., 1 hyd.
4020	1968		G	$7,500	2/05	NENE	Synchro, 18.4-34" tires, 2 hyd., 3 pt. WF, new paint, bought new
4020	1968	6,600	G	$7,700	4/05	NCOH	Diesel, WF, syncro, 34" tires, 2 hyd., add-on tractor step & handrail
4020	1968	5,910	G	$8,300	8/05	SWOH	Cab, diesel
4020	1968		G	$11,750	2/05	ECIA	3 pt., 2 hyd., new PS and clutch, WF, 200 hrs. on complete OH, Farm-hand F258 high lift loader, bucket
4020	1968	15,000	G	$13,500	2/05	ECSD	
4020	1969		G	$5,700	2/05	NCIN	PS, shift console
4020	1964		G	$6,750	9/04	ECNE	Syncro, Ansel cab, 18.4-34" tires
4020	1964		G	$6,800	9/04	ECNE	2 hyd., 15.5-38" tires
4020	1964	6,400	G	$7,200	12/04	NCNE	PS, diesel, WF, 540 PTO, 3 pt., fenders, 18.4-34" tires
4020	1964		G	$7,900	3/04	NENE	Recent OH, WF, syncro
4020	1965		G	$6,100	2/04	SENE	LP, PS, 3 pt., NF, 18.4-38" tires
4020	1965	6,248	G	$6,500	3/04	NEND	Diesel, row crop, cab, 3 pt., 540/1000 PTO, 2 hyd, 14.9-38" rear tires, duals, front weights
4020	1965	4,171	G	$7,700	10/04	NWMN	WF, cab, syncro, 540/1000 PTO, 2 hyd., diesel, syncro
4020	1965		G	$8,400	3/04	SEIA	New tires
4020	1966		G	$5,000	7/04	SEND	Gas, 2 hyd., 48 loader & 4-tine grapple
4020	1966		F	$5,000	7/04	NWMN	Gas, 2 hyd., Deere 48 loader & 4-tine grapple
4020	1966		F	$5,100	4/04	NCND	Factory 3 pt., PS
4020	1966		G	$6,300	2/04	NWIL	Diesel, WF, 2 hyd., engine OH 3 yrs. ago, 18.4-34" tires
4020	1966	4,751	G	$8,200	4/04	WCNE	WF, diesel, no cab
4020	1966	7,400	E	$12,600	3/04	NWIN	38" rubber, axle duals, sharp
4020	1967		F	$5,300	5/04	NENE	Diesel, syncro, new clutches
4020	1967		F	$6,000	10/04	NWMN	Diesel, cab, 3 pt., PTO, syncro
4020	1967		G	$6,800	3/04	NEKS	Deere 58 loader, 7' bucket, 2 hyd., diesel
4020	1967		G	$7,100	9/04	WCWI	Year-round cab, diesel
4020	1967	8,294	G	$7,300	1/04	SENE	1 owner, 2 hyd., 18.4-34" tires, rubber 70%, new paint, OH at 6,000 hours, service records
4020	1967	5,115	G	$7,600	3/04	WCMN	Cab, diesel, 2 hyd., 16.9-38" tires, hub duals, rock box
4020	1967		G	$8,000	12/04	NCIA	Syncro, diesel, factory WF, been OH, 12 volt, 2 hyd., quick coupler, 18.4-34" tires, duals

john deere

Model	Year	Hours	Cond.	Price	Date	Area	Comments
4020	1967		G	$8,200	2/04	ECIA	Diesel, no cab, WF, 3 pt., PS, new 18.4-34" tires, 600 hrs. on pistons & sleeves, new rear high-velocity pump
4020	1967		G	$9,100	12/04	ECNE	Syncro, 2 hyd., fenders, 18.4-34" tires
4020	1968		G	$7,500	3/04	NENE	170 hours engine OH, diesel, syncro, 18.4-38" tires, new rubber, fenders, 3 pt.
4020	1968		G	$8,300	6/04	SEMN	
4020	1968		G	$8,300	3/04	NCMI	Cab, diesel, front weights, 12 volt, 1 hyd., 18.4-34" tires
4020	1968	9,000	G	$8,700	1/04	NWIL	2,000 hours on engine OH, diesel, WF, new 16.9-38" tires, clean, front weights, new paint
4020	1968	6,800	G	$9,100	12/04	NCWI	Diesel, A1 condition
4020	1968		G	$10,100	1/04	WCIL	2,000 hrs. on OH, open station, WF, fenders, ROPS, 3 pt., dual PTO, fresh paint, diesel
4020	1969	7,820	G	$6,400	8/04	ECNE	Syncro, 2 hyd., year-round cab, 18.4-34" tires
4020	1969		G	$8,000	5/04	ECND	Cab, side console, 3 hyd., 3 pt., PTO
4020	1969		G	$9,800	8/04	NCIA	PS, diesel, 18.4-34" tires
4020	1969	6,550	G	$12,300	9/04	NEIA	Hiniker cab, 2 hyd., 3 pt., side console, syncro, diesel, 18.4-34" tires
4020	1970		G	$7,900	3/04	ECMN	
4020	1970		G	$10,000	2/04	SENE	Console, syncro, 18.4-34" tires, 3 hyd., 3 pt., fenders, WF, front end weights, shedded
4020	1970		F	$10,300	3/04	ECNE	1,064 hrs. on second tach, diesel, syncro range, side hyd. controls, 2 hyd., 3 pt., 18.4x34" tires, rear wheel weights, 3 front weights, ROPS
4020	1970	5,462	G	$10,500	9/04	ECNE	Dual side console hyd., 18.4-34" tires, 1 owner
4020	1970	5,537	E	$14,600	1/04	NCIL	2 hyd., side console, 3 pt., Quick-Tach, PS, WF, sharp
4020	1971	16,061	F	$8,100	2/04	NWIL	Syncro, WF, diesel, new rear tires
4020	1971	6,110	G	$8,850	2/04	NEIN	Console, ROPS
4020	1971		G	$15,000	9/04	WCWI	1,300 hours on OH, side console, syncro, quad shift, factory 3 hyd., diff. lock, 18.4-34" tires
4020	1972	6,100	G	$7,400	8/04	ECKS	Syncro, 2 hyd., 3 pt., WF
4020	1972	10,000	G	$10,500	2/04	ECMO	1 owner, diesel
4020	1972		F	$12,000	8/04	NWIA	2,300 hrs. on OH, WF, little rough, PS, diesel, 1 owner
4020			F	$3,000	3/03	NWSD	Dual loader, PS, cab, 3 pt., 2 hyd., 2 PTOs
4020			F	$3,100	9/03	NWKS	Cab, 3 pt., PTO, syncro range, motor locked up
4020			P	$3,850	7/03	SCMN	Rough, WF
4020			G	$4,450	3/03	NCWI	Diesel, syncro, 2 hyd., 18.4-34" tires, diff. lock
4020		7,200	G	$4,750	3/03	NWIL	Hiniker cab, diesel, PS
4020			F	$4,800	12/03	WCMN	Std., PTO, 1 hyd.
4020		8,910	F	$4,825	12/03	NWIL	Gas, NF
4020			F	$4,900	8/03	WCMN	PS, 1 hyd., 3 pt., PTO, new clutch and injector pump
4020		6,400	F	$5,000	4/03	NCWI	Diesel, ROPS
4020			P	$5,100	4/03	SCOK	Rough
4020			F	$5,400	7/03	SEND	Diesel, 2 hyd., 3 pt., PTO
4020			F	$5,400	7/03	SEND	3 pt., PTO, gas, 18.4-34" tires, 70% rubber
4020		3,400	G	$5,400	7/03	NWOH	WF, 3 pt., new tires, duals, gas, repainted
4020		7,100	G	$5,500	2/03	NEIA	PS, cab
4020			F	$5,800	3/03	ECIN	PS
4020			F	$5,900	3/03	NCCO	
4020			F	$6,000	4/03	WCWI	Diesel, WF, cab, 3 pt.
4020			G	$6,100	9/03	NEIN	
4020			F	$6,300	4/03	WCMN	Diesel, OH

Model	Year	Hours	Cond.	Price	Date	Area	Comments
4020			G	$6,500	2/03	NCIA	Deere WF, syncro, 1 hyd., 3 pt., new paint, no cab, 15.5-38" tires
4020			G	$6,500	7/03	ECND	Snowblower
4020			F	$6,600	3/03	ECIN	Gas, OH, paint bad
4020		2,113	G	$6,800	4/03	SEPA	OH in '98, no cab, diesel, good tires
4020			G	$6,800	2/03	SWMN	PS, WF, 3 pt., earlier model, good rubber, bad PTO brake
4020			G	$6,900	12/03	SWIA	WF, cab, like new
4020			G	$7,000	4/03	WCWI	Diesel, 3 pt., dual hyd., console, recent OH, faded paint
4020			F	$7,000	9/03	NCSD	3 pt., PS, cab, high hours
4020			G	$7,000	9/03	NEIN	LP, console
4020			G	$7,100	7/03	SCMN	Side console, no cab
4020			G	$7,100	2/03	ECIL	Diesel, high hours
4020			G	$7,250	11/03	NWSD	Diesel, PS, 3 pt., under 3,200 hrs., FH-F25 loader, grapple and hay basket
4020			G	$7,300	2/03	SWMN	Syncro, WF, 3 pt., new rubber, square manifold
4020			G	$7,400	8/03	NENE	
4020		6,808	G	$7,400	3/03	ECNE	PS, diesel, Hiniker, 2 hyd., 3 pt., rebuilt motor
4020			G	$7,800	3/03	NWIL	Side console, WF, diesel
4020			E	$8,200	3/03	WCWI	
4020			G	$8,500	4/03	WCSK	Canadian sale, diesel, 18.4x34" tires, 8 spd. powershift, 12 volt, cab, 95 hp
4020		9,168	G	$10,000	2/03	WCMN	PS, side console, 2 hyd., diff. lock, rock box
4020			G	$10,000	10/03	SCKS	Deere 148 loader, 7' bucket, syncro range, 3 pt., PTO, 2 hyd., OH
4020		5,586	G	$10,000	11/03	NWKS	PS, 3 pt., 3 hyd., 18.4-34" tires, diesel
4020		6,382	G	$10,600	8/03	SCNE	Syncro
4020			G	$10,600	3/03	ECIN	Koyker K5 loader, console
4020			G	$10,700	4/03	WCMI	Side console, factory turbo & automatic transmission
4020			G	$10,900	4/03	WCMI	Side console
4020			G	$11,600	4/03	WCWI	Diesel, WF, PS, ROPS, recent OH
4020			E	$12,000	8/03	NWIL	Hi crop, side console, 3 pt., fenders, diesel
4020		6,740	E	$13,000	8/03	SCNE	Syncro range
4020			G	$14,900	9/03	NEIN	Hi crop
4020			E	$16,250	8/03	NWIL	Restored, hi crop, PS, diesel
4020			E	$18,500	8/03	NWIL	Hi crop, diesel, restored
4020	1964		F	$4,400	8/03	WCMN	PS, 3 pt., 2 hyd., PTO, dual loader & grapple
4020	1964		F	$5,700	1/03	ECIA	PS, 1 hyd., WF
4020	1964		F	$7,000	3/03	NCCO	PS
4020	1964		G	$8,000	3/03	NCOH	WF, 3 pt., PS
4020	1965		G	$6,500	9/03	SCMN	
4020	1965	9,840	F	$6,600	3/03	NWIL	Diesel, Case 40 loader, WF
4020	1965		G	$7,300	8/03	NCIA	PS, WF, diesel, 3 pt., 1 hyd., 18.4-34" tires
4020	1965		G	$7,900	2/03	ECNE	PS, Hiniker cab, 3 pt., Deere WF, $4,700 spent on transmission in spring of 2002, shedded
4020	1965		G	$10,000	11/03	NCOH	
4020	1965	7,179	G	$10,750	9/03	WCIA	No cab, diesel, 3 pt., WF, PS, 2 hyd.
4020	1966	5,613	G	$4,850	9/03	NCIA	LP, WF, 3 pt., diff. lock
4020	1966		F	$5,500	3/03	NESD	Cab, PS, 3 pt., dual hyd., 540/1000 PTO, needs some work
4020	1966		G	$7,500	9/03	NESD	Cab, heat, syncro, 3 pt., 2 hyd., diesel, 18.4-34" tires,
4020	1966	9,753	G	$8,000	2/03	WCIA	Diesel, no cab, WF
4020	1966	4,527	G	$8,400	4/03	NCIL	PS, 2 hyd., 1 owner, 18.4-34" tires
4020	1966	4,700	G	$8,500	2/03	WCIL	Turbo, syncro, diesel, WF, rear weights, 18.4-34" tires
4020	1966	8,150	G	$8,900	9/03	NCIA	Deere 48 loader, cozy cab, syncro range, OH at 6,950 hrs.
4020	1966	9,596	G	$9,500	3/03	SEIA	PS

john deere

Model	Year	Hours	Cond.	Price	Date	Area	Comments
4020	1966	4,700	G	$13,000	12/03	WCIL	Deere 148 loader, diesel, open station
4020	1967		G	$5,900	3/03	ECNE	WF, diesel, clean, syncro, 18.4-34" tires
4020	1967	7,575	G	$6,500	1/03	SWIA	Diesel, PS, WF, 2 hyd., 3 pt., new 18.4-34R" Firestone tires, front weights, ROPS
4020	1967		F	$6,900	3/03	NWIL	Diesel, WF, 2 hyd., 3 pt., PS, front weights, 18.4-34" tires, dmi clamp on duals, 3,379 hrs. on major OH
4020	1967	8,000	E	$8,400	3/03	ECNE	Clean, diesel, WF, 3 pt., 18.4-34" tires, 2 hyd., rear weights, syncro, year-round cab
4020	1967		G	$8,500	4/03	NWIA	WF, diesel, OH, 2 hyd., 3 pt., front weights, fenders
4020	1967	4,517	G	$9,050	4/03	NCIL	PS, 2 hyd., 1 owner, diesel, 15.5-38" tires
4020	1968		F	$3,500	2/03	WCIL	Lots of hours, gas
4020	1968		F	$6,000	3/03	NEKS	1,000 hrs. on OH & new clutch, diesel, Hiniker cab, syncro, 2 hyd.
4020	1968	8,138	G	$6,700	1/03	SEIL	Diesel, diff. lock, 2 hyd., weights
4020	1968		G	$6,750	6/03	WCSK	Canadian sale, diesel, cab, 85 hp, Deere 48 fel
4020	1968		G	$7,300	7/03	NCIA	Diesel, factory WF, 2 hyd., syncro
4020	1968	9,200	G	$7,800	2/03	WCIL	Diesel, syncro, 18.4-34" tires
4020	1968	7,715	G	$9,200	3/03	SEIA	PS
4020	1968		G	$9,800	3/03	SWMN	Deere 158 loader
4020	1968		G	$10,350	8/03	ECIL	Deere 148 loader, WF, 3 pt., 2 hyd., 900 hrs. on recent OH
4020	1968		G	$10,600	11/03	WCKS	3 pt., PTO, cab, syncro, Deere loader
4020	1969		G	$0	12/03	WCIA	No sale at $8,000, console, WF, 2 hyd., new paint, 18.4-38" tires
4020	1969		F	$5,500	11/03	WCKS	3 pt., PTO, Ansel cab, Deere 158 loader
4020	1969	7,022	G	$7,700	7/03	WCMN	Year-round cab, Deere fenders
4020	1969	8,900	F	$7,900	3/03	NCCO	Console
4020	1969	5,580	G	$9,000	8/03	NWWI	
4020	1969	7,162	G	$9,200	2/03	SEMN	1974 Deere 158 loader, side console, WF, 3 pt., 2 hyd., cab
4020	1969		G	$9,800	12/03	WCIA	Factory cab, recent OH, syncro
4020	1969		G	$12,300	9/03	SEMN	Side console, 3 pt., 2 hyd., PTO, like new front weights, diesel
4020	1970	9,742	G	$6,000	1/03	SEIL	Diesel, 2 hyd., weights, 1 owner
4020	1970	7,796	G	$8,800	2/03	NWIL	Diesel, factory cab, WF, 3 pt., dual PTO and hyd., diff lock, syncro, front & rear weights, aux. fuel tank
4020	1970		F	$9,100	2/03	NEKS	2 hyd., diesel, WF, syncro, 2,130 hrs. on complete OH
4020	1970	8,300	E	$9,300	3/03	SENE	800 hrs. on OH, diesel
4020	1970	3,818	G	$9,900	1/03	SWIA	PS, WF, 3 hyd., 3 pt.
4020	1970	6,100	G	$10,000	8/03	NEKS	No cab, diesel
4020	1970	6,720	G	$10,400	2/03	WCIL	Deere 148 loader, syncro, side console, diesel
4020	1970		G	$10,700	9/03	ECKS	1 owner, manual transmisssion, hour meter changed out
4020	1970	6,850	G	$11,000	3/03	NEKS	1 owner, 2 hyd., syncro, duals
4020	1970		G	$11,100	9/03	NCKS	
4020	1970	5,036	G	$11,300	6/03	NCIL	Diesel, syncro, side console, 2 hyd.
4020	1970		G	$12,000	3/03	ECNE	Average appearance, diesel, PS, WF, good rubber
4020	1970		G	$12,100	4/03	NCKS	1,000 hours on OH and clutch overhaul, loader, 3 pt., PTO
4020	1971	8,466	G	$6,700	3/03	SENE	Diesel
4020	1971	3,027	G	$18,000	3/03	NCIL	1 owner, syncro, 2 hyd., side console, quick hitch, WF
4020	1972	6,000	G	$9,200	7/03	NWMN	Factory cab, syncro, 2 hyd., 3 pt., band duals
4020	1972	6,200	G	$11,900	1/03	ECIL	Diesel, console, 18.4-34" tires, new rear end
4020	1972	4,680	G	$11,950	3/03	ECIL	Diesel, Deere cab, weights, diff. lock
4020	1972	3,401	G	$13,000	3/03	SCKS	Syncro, 3 pt., PS, 2 hyd.
4020	1972		E	$15,000	8/03	NWIL	Restored, diesel, WF, 1 owner

Model	Year	Hours	Cond.	Price	Date	Area	Comments
4030	1974	6,761	F	$7,300	2/06	SCPA	2 WD, 4 post
4030		4,695	E	$18,000	11/05	SWMN	2 WD, 540/1000 PTO, 3 pt, 2 hyd, 1 owner, 18.4-34"
4030			F	$5,000	4/05	WCWI	Front weights, diesel
4030	1973		G	$7,000	3/05	SCIL	Open station, 2 hyd.
4030		1,966	E	$18,500	1/05	NENE	WF, 3 pt., cab, shedded, new cab interior, not used in 4 yrs.
4030			P	$4,100	8/04	SWPA	Rubber 25%
4030			F	$4,500	8/04	NWPA	Cab
4030		15,000	G	$7,810	2/04	NCKY	4-post ROPS
4030	1974		G	$11,500	8/04	ECKS	
4030	1974		E	$12,000	5/04	SENE	3 hyd., diesel
4030	1975		G	$9,000	3/04	SCMN	
4030	1975	8,573	G	$11,900	3/04	WCNE	WF, 3 pt., rebuilt rear end
4030	1975	4,880	G	$14,000	8/04	NWIA	400 hrs. on OH, second owner, 18.4-34" tires
4030			G	$6,800	12/03	SCMN	Cab, gas
4030			E	$8,300	8/03	NWIL	Restored, WF, gas
4030		11,645	G	$10,100	7/03	ECND	3 pt., PTO, Deere 148 loader, 2 hyd.
4030			G	$10,100	2/03	SWOK	
4030	1974	6,818	G	$10,100	1/03	WCIL	
4030	1974		G	$17,000	9/03	NWND	Deere 148 loader, grab fork, cab, AC, 18.4-38" tires
4030	1975	4,656	G	$10,200	9/03	ECNE	ROPS canopy, 3 pt., 2 hyd.
4030	1975	5,304	G	$10,800	9/03	NCIA	Cab, AC, 3 pt., syncro
4030	1975	7,500	G	$12,500	3/03	SCNE	
4030	1976		G	$9,000	9/03	NEIN	Diesel, open station
40C	1953		G	$3,400	10/04	NEPA	Restored, rebuilt engine
40S	1953		G	$2,800	5/04	SCPA	Repainted, restored
40S	1953		G	$4,200	5/04	SCPA	Restored
40T			F	$1,700	8/05	ECMI	NF, 3 pt., no arms
40T	1953		G	$7,500	9/05	SEMN	WF, front and rear wtghs, fenders, 3 pt.
40T			G	$3,600	6/05	ECWI	New rubber
40T			P	$150	9/03	NEIN	Parts
40T			G	$175	9/03	NEIN	Parts
40T			P	$225	9/03	NEIN	Parts
40T			P	$225	9/03	NEIN	Parts
40U			G	$2,600	9/03	NEIN	
40U			F	$2,850	12/03	NEIL	WF, Woods 59 mower
40W	1955		G	$4,500	5/04	SCPA	Restored
40W			E	$13,750	8/03	NWIL	All fuel, 1 of 60 built, restored
420			G	$3,000	11/05	WCIL	WF, running, unrestored
420	1956		G	$4,400	6/05	SWOH	Gas, WF, utility, no 3 pt.
420	1957		G	$3,000	11/05	WCIL	
420			F	$2,800	6/05	ECMN	Gas
420			G	$4,000	6/05	ECMN	Row crop, WF, 3 pt., PTO, fenders, new tires, power adj. wheels
420			G	$7,000	6/05	ECMN	Std., gas, WF, new tires, 3 pt., PTO
420			G	$9,750	6/05	WCMN	3 pt., PTO, new tires, fully restored, WF
420			F	$2,700	10/04	SEPA	NF, average rubber
420			F	$4,450	10/04	SEPA	Slant steer, WF, new paint, average rubber
420			E	$5,200	3/04	NEIA	Tricycle, 3 pt., NF, dual Touch-O-Matic, fenders, 196 hrs. on OH
420	1956		F	$2,250	3/04	SEWY	Gas, 3 pt.
420			G	$450	9/03	NEIN	
420			E	$5,000	8/03	NCCO	Restored, gas, new tires, WF, 3 pt.
420			E	$5,500	8/03	NCCO	Restored, gas, good tires, WF, 3 pt.
420	1956		G	$5,400	8/03	WCMN	WF

john deere

Model	Year	Hours	Cond.	Price	Date	Area	Comments
420	1957		G	$2,300	7/03	SEND	Small cultivator
420C	1956		G	$2,550	10/04	NEPA	With blade, PTO
420C	1958		F	$1,575	9/04	NECO	Does not run, complete
420S			G	$23,500	7/03	ECCO	1 of 23, repainted
420T	1958		G	$4,700	6/05	ECIL	5 speed, 3 pt., new rears
420T			E	$6,000	8/03	NWIL	Restored, LP, single front wheel
420T			G	$6,000	9/03	NEIN	
420T			G	$7,000	6/03	SEMN	LP, nice old original tractor, SN 136510
420U	1958		G	$12,250	9/05	SEMN	5 speed, reverser, air stack, front and rear weights
4230		7,000	G	$16,750	2/06	NECO	QR, Koyker 565 loader, 3660 hrs on OH, 1977 model
4230	1976	7,350	E	$17,750	2/06	WCIL	2 hyd., PS, 197 hrs on a complete engine OH, 18.4-38"
4230	1976		F	$6,250	2/06	NWIN	Syncro
4230			G	$12,800	9/05	SCMN	
4230			G	$8,900	10/05	SWWI	
4230	1973		G	$15,000	9/05	SWOH	WF, cab, front weights, 1000 hrs on redpath OH
4230	1973		G	$7,000	4/05	SWPA	Cab, weights, 2 hyd.
4230			P	$3,000	2/05	SCCA	Front weights, canopy, syncro, 3 pt., PTO, 1 hyd., rear weights, 14.9R46" tires
4230		7,020	F	$8,900	4/05	SCMI	Cab, AC, heat, 3 pt., 2 hyd., 18.4-34" tires, snap-on duals
4230			G	$10,500	3/05	SWCA	Front weights, canopy, 3 pt., PTO
4230			G	$11,300	2/05	WCWI	2 hyd., cab, heat, AC
4230		2,600	G	$12,600	4/05	NWIL	PS, 2 hyd.
4230		6,700	G	$12,600	4/05	WCWI	Cab, clamp-on duals
4230			G	$13,000	1/05	ECNE	
4230			G	$15,500	4/05	SCSD	Deere 740 loader
4230	1973	8,187	G	$12,250	1/05	SCNE	3 hyd., 540/1000 PTO, 6 front weights, good mechanically, poor paint
4230	1975	7,025	G	$9,900	3/05	ECMI	105 hp., cab, AC, 2 hyd.
4230	1976	6,997	G	$12,500	7/05	ECIL	
4230	1976	3,846	G	$17,200	8/05	NCIA	Cab, AC, 2 hyd., front weights, quick coupler
4230	1977	9,013	G	$12,750	6/05	WCMN	Cab, PS, 2 hyd., 3 pt., PTO, duals, 1 owner
4230			G	$7,450	1/04	NEOH	
4230		3,275	G	$7,750	3/04	NWMN	Cab, 3 pt., 2 hyd., PTO
4230			G	$8,500	12/04	SEMN	
4230		5,000	F	$9,020	2/04	NCKY	4-post ROPS, good rubber
4230			F	$12,400	1/04	SESD	MFWD
4230			G	$13,500	2/04	WCMI	2WD, factory cab, 18.4-38" tires, duals, 3 pt., PTO, 2 hyd., recent OH & transmission work, secnd owner, diesel
4230			G	$14,000	12/04	SCMN	PS
4230	1973	5,643	G	$9,500	4/04	WCMI	Cab, diesel
4230	1974	8,340	G	$9,250	4/04	WCMN	MFWD, 2 hyd., 3 pt., PTO, band duals
4230	1974	7,113	G	$10,100	1/04	ECIL	No cab, ROPS, 2 hyd.
4230	1976	11,500	G	$9,300	7/04	ECND	Cab, 3 pt., 540/1000 PTO, 3 hyd., 3,700 hrs. on OH
4230	1977	6,002	G	$15,900	2/04	NWIL	Cab, AC, 3 pt., 2 hyd., 18.4-34" tires, front weights
4230			G	$4,000	3/03	NCWI	Loaded
4230			G	$4,400	9/03	NEIN	
4230			F	$6,250	9/03	SCMN	No cab
4230		11,000	G	$7,500	11/03	WCMN	Cat engine, 3 pt., 2 hyd., syncro range
4230			F	$8,250	4/03	WCMN	Diesel, single cab
4230			F	$10,000	4/03	ECVT	No cab

Model	Year	Hours	Cond.	Price	Date	Area	Comments
4230			G	$10,100	6/03	SWMN	Diesel
4230			G	$10,600	10/03	NWMN	Cab, 3 pt., PTO
4230			G	$11,000	9/03	SCMN	
4230			G	$12,000	3/03	NCWI	PS, year-round cab
4230			G	$13,100	3/03	NWIL	Diesel
4230			G	$14,100	9/03	SCMN	Cab
4230			F	$17,150	3/03	NCCO	Deere 260 loader
4230	1972		E	$14,200	1/03	NENE	2 hyd., recent OH, new paint, excellent rubber
4230	1973		F	$2,400	7/03	NEWI	2 ranges have gone out
4230	1973		F	$7,900	11/03	ECND	Tach shows 2,007 hours, 3 pt., PTO, 2 hyd., 18.4-38" tires
4230	1973	8,675	F	$9,750	3/03	ECND	2 hyd., 3 pt., PTO, hub duals
4230	1973	6,767	G	$10,000	3/03	NCIL	Deere 148 loader, syncro, 2 hyd., 18.4-34" tires
4230	1973	7,200	G	$11,500	3/03	WCMN	3,000 hrs. on OH, 2 hyd., 3 pt., rock box, 18.4-34" tires
4230	1973	3,385	G	$12,250	2/03	NCIA	Cab, 2 hyd., 18.4-38" tires, axle duals
4230	1974		G	$8,700	12/03	NWIA	Cab, WF, 2 hyd.
4230	1974		G	$9,800	9/03	NWIL	No cab, 2 hyd., 16.9-38" tires
4230	1974	12,700	P	$9,900	4/03	NCIA	Duals
4230	1974		E	$11,500	9/03	SENE	Diesel
4230	1974		G	$12,100	3/03	NENE	
4230	1974	6,622	G	$13,250	3/03	NWIL	
4230	1974	3,992	G	$18,000	11/03	SEIA	Duals
4230	1975	8,000	G	$9,300	2/03	SCKS	3 pt., 2 hyd., duals
4230	1975	6,000	G	$12,250	5/03	NCWI	Cab, new rubber, 2 hyd., 3 pt.
4230	1977		G	$12,500	3/03	WCMN	Diesel, cab, 2 hyd., 38" tires
4230	1977	3,946	G	$13,300	2/03	NCOH	Cab, PS, 18.4-34" tires
4230	1977	3,494	E	$15,600	8/03	SENE	Diesel, PS, good rubber
4230	1977	3,100	G	$21,200	11/03	SCIA	PS
4230	1977	5,985	G	$24,500	6/03	WCSK	Canadian sale, 18.4-38" single rubber tires, 200 hrs. on rubber, powershift, 100 PTO hp.
430			G	$4,250	6/05	ECMN	Row crop, gas, WF, fenders, 3 pt., PTO, 1 hyd.
430			G	$13,750	7/05	SCIA	Hi crop, LP, good tag, restored, 1 of 183 built, PS, live PTO
430			F	$4,500	10/04	SEPA	Restored, NF, good rubber
430			E	$5,700	6/03	NEIL	WF, 3 pt.
430			E	$9,900	8/03	NWIL	LP, high crop, totally restored, no tag
430			G	$15,000	9/03	NEIN	Hi crop
4320	1971	6,080	G	$10,500	2/06	NCIL	
4320	1971	3,487	E	$18,750	2/06	SWNY	Restored, roll bar, 18.4-38 firestone tires, syncro, wghts
4320	1971	7,580	F	$7,400	2/06	NCIL	2 hyd.
4320	1972	8,630	F	$11,750	2/06	SCNY	2 WD, 1 hyd., syncro, no weights, 18.4-38"
4320	1972		G	$9,250	2/06	WCMN	2 WD, JD cab, clean
4320	1972		G	$9,300	2/06	WCMN	2 WD, 18.4-38" singles, sharp
4320			F	$5,400	5/05	SEPA	WF, poor paint, 20% rubber
4320			G	$7,750	11/05	WCIL	Std, diesel, unrestored, fenders, PTO
4320	1971	6,194	G	$12,100	9/05	WCIL	Diesel, 2 hyd, fenders, syncro range console shift, wghts
4320	1972	7,400	G	$12,500	7/05	WCMN	500 hours on factory rebuilt engine, diesel, cab, QR, 2 1/2 hyd., average rubber & duals
4320			F	$5,900	2/05	SCMN	
4320			G	$7,500	6/05	ECWI	4WD, diesel, cab
4320			G	$9,100	2/05	WCWI	Weights, 2 hyd., 3 pt., console
4320		8,102	G	$9,200	3/05	ECNE	Syncro range, 2 hyd., duals
4320			F	$9,600	7/05	SCMN	
4320			G	$10,000	2/05	WCIN	18.4-34" tires, duals, 3 pt., 2 hyd.
4320			G	$10,750	2/05	NEIA	711 hours on OH, cab

john deere

Model	Year	Hours	Cond.	Price	Date	Area	Comments
4320			G	$11,500	2/05	NEIA	1,000 hours on OH, fender, quick hitch
4320			G	$12,650	2/05	ECSD	Syncro, 3 hyd., 18.4-38" tires
4320	1971		G	$9,000	3/05	ECNE	2 hyd., 3 pt., 540/1000 PTO, WF, 18.4-38" tires, clamp-on duals, rear weights
4320	1971	8,942	G	$9,250	2/05	SWIN	6,518 hours on major OH, 3 pt., front & rear weights,
4320	1972	7,450	F	$8,500	2/05	WCOK	Hiniker cab, Farmhand F236 loader, 3 pt., PTO, 2 hyd., duals (fair), interior poor
4320	1972		F	$9,500	4/05	NWOK	Ansel cab, 2 hyd., 3 pt., PTO, 8 speed, r134a AC, loader (nice), diesel
4320	1972		G	$10,250	2/05	SCMN	Factory cab
4320	1972	6,000	G	$10,300	2/05	SCMN	Factory cab
4320			G	$2,675	6/04	ECWI	Cab, clamp-on duals
4320			G	$5,400	7/04	SEND	Cab, diesel, 3 hyd., 3 pt., PTO
4320			G	$5,400	7/04	NWMN	Cab, diesel, 3 hyd., 3 pt., PTO, syncro
4320		5,426	G	$9,600	4/04	NEIN	1 owner, original
4320	1972	11,000	G	$7,000	2/04	NWIL	Diesel, WF, console, front weights, 18.4-38"R tires, new clutch, flywheel & PTO
4320	1972	6,610	G	$8,700	12/04	ECND	Syncro, cab, AC, 3 pt., 540/1000 PTO, new style pioneer couplers, 20.8-34" tires
4320	1972	6,610	G	$8,700	12/04	ECND	2WD, synchro range, 3 pt., 540/1000 PTO, new style pioneer couplers, 20.8-34" tires
4320	1972	6,118	G	$9,000	2/04	NWIL	Cab, 3 pt., 2 hyd., 18.4-34" tires, front weights
4320			F	$5,000	2/03	ECAR	2 post canopy, fair sheet metal
4320		8,200	G	$6,000	2/03	WCIA	New tires, new batteries, new fuel injection pump
4320			G	$6,000	9/03	NEIN	
4320			F	$7,100	9/03	SENE	Diesel
4320			F	$8,000	4/03	WCMN	Diesel, Hiniker cab
4320			G	$8,000	3/03	SWPA	800 hrs. on engine, new rubber & duals
4320		9,200	G	$8,200	4/03	SEPA	No cab, diesel, good tires
4320			G	$8,600	11/03	SWWI	2,000 hrs. on major OH
4320		5,500	G	$10,000	4/03	WCWI	Diesel, WF, 3 pt.
4320			G	$10,000	8/03	WCIN	Clean, original paint
4320			G	$11,000	5/03	SWOK	Farmhand loader, 116 hp., cab, AC, 3 pt., 2 hyd.
4320	1971		P	$3,000	11/03	ECND	Did not run, cab, 3 pt., 1000 PTO, 2 hyd., 18.4-38" tires, duals
4320	1971		G	$4,700	4/03	WCSK	Canadian sale, 2WD
4320	1971		G	$4,750	1/03	NEMI	No cab, 2 hyd., power beyond, duals
4320	1971	4,250	G	$8,050	3/03	ECIL	Fender tractor, 2 hyd., front fuel tank, front/rear weights, 18.4-34" tires
4320	1971		G	$9,250	3/03	NCOH	Hinson cab, 3 pt., 20.8-34" tires
4320	1971	6,325	G	$9,500	8/03	NWIA	Diesel, 3 pt., 2 hyd., WF, year-round cab
4320	1972	6,960	G	$5,000	4/03	NCWI	Diesel, cab
4320	1972	8,035	G	$8,000	3/03	ECND	Cab, 3 hyd., 3 pt., PTO
4320	1972		E	$9,200	8/03	NEKS	Cab, AC
4320	1972	8,634	G	$11,000	1/03	NENE	Syncro, WF, 2 hyd., open station
4320	1973		G	$9,200	1/03	WCMO	Side console, good tires, complete OH, clean
4320	1973	6,768	G	$13,000	1/03	ECIL	Deere 148 loader, 2 hyd., weights
4320	1973	3,283	G	$15,500	4/03	SWMN	Diesel, new 18.4-34" tires, hub duals
435			G	$13,600	7/05	NEIA	Restored, 435d
435			G	$15,500	6/05	ECMN	Row crop, diesel, 3 pt., PTO, rebuilt, painted
435			G	$5,700	9/03	NEIN	
435			E	$6,900	8/03	NWIL	Restored, gas, GM diesel, WF

Model	Year	Hours	Cond.	Price	Date	Area	Comments
435	1960		E	$5,500	6/03	NEIL	WF, 3 pt.
440			G	$3,550	10/04	NEPA	
440			G	$3,700	9/04	NECO	Restored, loader, good tin, 2 pt., good rubber
440			G	$2,250	9/03	NEIN	
440			G	$2,500	9/03	NEIN	Loader
440C			P	$400	9/03	NEIN	Parts
4430		6,039	G	$12,300	2/06	ECMN	QR, 3 pt., 2 hyd., quick hitch, 1 owner
4430			F	$15,500	1/06	NEIA	
4430		3,357	G	$23,500	1/06	ECIA	
4430	1973	8,887	G	$11,750	2/06	NEIN	CAH, 2 hyd., new tires with inner cooler, 3,000 hrs on OH
4430	1973		F	$8,100	2/06	NCKS	QR, dual PTO, 3 pt., 2 hyd., uses lots of oil, 18.4-38" (40%)
4430	1974	4,478	G	$14,500	1/06	NEIN	New engine, cab, air, QR
4430	1974		P	$5,900	1/06	NECO	3 pt., PTO, PS
4430	1976		G	$13,250	1/06	SCMI	1,500 hours on OH, QR, cab, 3 pt., 2 hyd., axle duals
4430	1976	4,140	G	$17,250	2/06	SWOH	2 hyd., 18.4-38", duals, ext. lights, quick hitch, weights
4430	1976	6,659	G	$19,000	1/06	SCKS	QR, 18.4-38"R, 9 bolt duals, 3 pt., 2 hyd., 1,000-lb. rear weights
4430	1976		F	$9,750	2/06	WCMN	2WD, CAH, 1,562 hrs on OH, 18.4-38"
4430			G	$12,000	11/05	NCCA	Saddle tanks, cab
4430		8,700	G	$14,000	11/05	NEIA	OH, 2 hyd., QR, 18.4-38" tires
4430			F	$14,500	12/05	SWWI	QR
4430		6,708	G	$15,200	12/05	WCIN	Loaded, CAH, QR, hub mount duals, 700 hrs on lower end
4430	1875		G	$19,000	11/05	NWOH	Cab, QR, 3 pt., PTO, 18.4-38" duals
4430			F	$6,800	8/05	NECO	
4430			F	$9,600	9/05	SCMN	
4430	1973		G	$12,100	8/05	WCMN	1956 hours on OH, rock box, wheel wghts, 3 pt., 2 hyd., 540 & 1000 PTO, 18.4-38", duals
4430	1973	4304	G	$14,500	8/05	NCIA	Cab, air, QR, front tank, weights, 2 hyd., quick coupler, duals
4430	1974	4419	G	$14,000	10/05	NCND	CAH, 20.8-38"R, with 18.4-38" band duals
4430	1975		G	$13,100	7/05	SESD	CAH, PS
4430	1975	7583	G	$13,900	11/05	SCIA	QR, CAH, 2 hyd., 18.4-38"
4430	1976		G	$16,000	12/05	NEIA	PS, 2 hyd., air, straddle duals, 3 pt.
4430	1976	5081	E	$18,100	12/05	NCOH	Diesel, WF, CAH, 2 hyd., 3 pt., syncro, super clean
4430	1976		P	$4,100	12/05	NWIL	Project tractor, rough, 18.4-34"
4430	1976	9732	F	$6,100	8/05	SEMI	No cab, 2 hyd., 3 pt.
4430	1977		G	$15,500	9/05	WCIL	Diesel, cab, 2 hyd., QR, front weights
4430	1977		F	$7,900	9/05	ECND	QR, 3 hyd., front fuel tank, 540/1000 PTO, 14.9-38" tires
4430			F	$7,000	3/05	SEIA	
4430			F	$8,200	3/05	NWIL	Cab, diesel
4430		8,029	F	$9,000	4/05	NCOH	Cab, 2 hyd., 38" tires
4430			F	$9,000	4/05	WCMN	Sound guard cab, 2 hyd., diesel, high hours
4430			F	$9,500	1/05	ECMI	2WD
4430			F	$9,500	1/05	ECMI	2WD
4430			G	$10,900	2/05	SCMN	
4430			G	$12,000	3/05	SWCA	Front weights, PS, 3 pt., PTO, 2 hyd.
4430			F	$12,200	4/05	SCSD	
4430		7,753	G	$12,400	2/05	ECIL	2 hyd.
4430			G	$14,800	3/05	NECO	Farmhand F258 loader, good tires
4430	1973		F	$6,700	2/05	NEIN	Diesel, cab (aftermarket)
4430	1973	9,282	E	$7,250	4/05	NCOK	Snap-on duals, PTO, no 3 pt., front weights, rock shaft less arms, wide swing drawbar, 8-speed PS, 2 hyd.
4430	1973		P	$8,000	2/05	NWIL	Year-round cab, 2 hyd., less than 1,500 hrs. on major OH, 18.4-38" tires
4430	1973	9,100	G	$11,000	3/05	SEWY	Diesel, cab, 3 pt.

john deere

Model	Year	Hours	Cond.	Price	Date	Area	Comments
4430	1973	5,000	G	$13,600	3/05	NCCO	3 hyd.
4430	1973	6,745	G	$14,200	1/05	NEIA	Fully equip. cab, deluxe step, 38" near new tires, good rubber all around
4430	1973	7,000	G	$16,000	3/05	ECCO	Koyker 565 loader, 3 pt., PTO, 2 hyd., duals
4430	1973	5,550	E	$17,600	1/05	NENE	1 owner, axle duals
4430	1974	7,613	P	$4,500	1/05	SWOH	Canopy
4430	1974	10,000	F	$9,600	4/05	NWKS	2 hyd., 3 pt., PTO
4430	1974		F	$10,500	7/05	SCMN	20.8-38"R tires, very clean
4430	1974		G	$12,000	7/05	NCMN	Quad range, cab, 3 pt., 4 hyd., quick hitch
4430	1974	10,500	G	$12,000	7/05	NCMN	2WD, cab, 3 pt., 4 hyd., band duals
4430	1974	1,625	E	$19,250	8/05	SEIA	2 hyd., 6 front weights, 18.4-38" tires
4430	1975		G	$8,000	6/05	ECIL	Rice & cane, syncro range, front & rear weights
4430	1975		G	$13,500	3/05	ECNE	PS, 2,400 hours on OH, 2 hyd., 3 pt., 540/1000 PTO, 5,000-lb. rear weights, r134 AC, 18.4-42"R rears, 11-16" fronts, front fenders
4430	1975	5,113	G	$14,400	4/05	NCIA	Cab, AC, quick coupler, 2 hyd., front weights, extra steps
4430	1975		F	$14,750	6/05	NEND	3 hyd., 540/1000 PTO, no 3 pt., 18.4-38" tires singles, 90% rubber
4430	1975	3,695	G	$16,600	8/05	NWIL	
4430	1976		F	$5,300	2/05	NEIN	ROPS, diesel
4430	1976	9,800	F	$12,500	2/05	WCIA	18.4-38" tires
4430	1976	6,980	E	$13,750	4/05	NCKS	Cab, AC, 2 hyd., 540/1000 PTO, 8 front suitcase weights, extra rear weights, 20.8-38" rears w/ clamp-on duals, OH at 4,000 hrs., 40 Series rear end & radiator
4430	1976	8,900	E	$15,000	3/05	SCIL	Cab, 2 hyd., duals, chrome stacks
4430	1976	10,465	G	$16,000	4/05	NENE	OH at 9,200 hrs., 2 hyd., lift assist, power beyond, quick hitch, 18.4-38" tires, 10-16" front tires
4430	1976		G	$16,000	3/05	ECND	2WD, cab, 2 hyd., elec. splitter, 3 pt., 540/1000 PTO, front fuel tank, 18.4-38" tires, press steel duals (50% rubber)
4430	1976		G	$16,200	2/05	NWKS	2 hyd., Deere 158 loader, 8' bucket, grapple fork, 18.4-38" tires, rear weights, cab
4430	1976		G	$18,750	3/05	NECO	1,702 hours on OH, cab, 3 pt., PTO, 2 hyd., 18.4-38" tires, duals
4430	1977		G	$16,750	3/05	NWMN	2WD, cab, 3 pt., 540/1000 PTO, 3 hyd., band duals, push tank and 60 Series steps
4430	1977	6,591	G	$17,100	1/05	SEIL	Cab, AC, 2 hyd., quick hitch, heavy rear end, 18.4-38" tires
4430	1977	5,600	E	$17,500	2/05	WCIL	Diesel, aux. fuel tank, 18.4-38"R tires, cab
4430	1977	4,200	G	$24,300	2/05	SWIN	3,875 hours on major OH, cab, 3 pt., duals
4430	1977	2,252	E	$24,500	4/05	SEMN	1 owner, always shedded, 20.8-38" duals, full set front weights, new style step, 3 pt. quick, 2 hyd., 540/1000 PTO
4430	1979		F	$8,300	6/05	NENE	Syncro, 2 hyd., 6 front weights, 1 owner, AM/FM/cassette, 18.4-38" tires
4430			F	$7,000	1/04	NEOH	
4430		9,000	G	$7,920	2/04	NCKY	Duals, cab
4430			F	$9,000	3/04	NWMN	3 pt., 2 hyd.
4430			G	$9,400	3/04	SWPA	High hours, Hiniker cab
4430			G	$9,400	3/04	NWIL	Diesel, cab, weights
4430		9,360	G	$9,600	7/04	SEND	Quad range, 3 hyd., 3 pt.
4430		9,360	G	$9,600	7/04	NWMN	3 hyd., 3 pt., PTO, duals, Deere 158 loader
4430			F	$9,800	1/04	SESD	
4430		1,500	G	$10,250	1/04	WCKY	4-post canopy, duals, 2 hyd.
4430		6,988	G	$10,750	3/04	NWMN	Cab, PS, 3 pt., dual hyd. PTO, band duals
4430			G	$11,500	3/04	SCMN	

Model	Year	Hours	Cond.	Price	Date	Area	Comments
4430			G	$12,000	3/04	NCMI	2 hyd., diesel, good 18.4-38" tires
4430			G	$12,950	11/04	WCIL	Cab, duals
4430			G	$13,000	1/04	NEOH	
4430			G	$13,000	12/04	ECNE	
4430			G	$13,600	7/04	WCWI	Cab, front weights, hub duals
4430			G	$13,900	3/04	SEMN	Duals, wheel weights
4430			G	$14,400	12/04	NWIA	PS
4430			G	$14,500	12/04	SEMN	Duals, 65 hrs. on rebuilt engine
4430		5,175	G	$17,000	2/04	WCIL	Cab, diesel, 18.4-38" tires, duals
4430	1973		G	$8,600	6/04	NWMN	3 hyd., power beyond, 3 pt., PTO
4430	1973	9,070	G	$9,500	12/04	WCMN	18.4-38" tires
4430	1973	9,245	G	$11,000	4/04	WCMN	2 hyd., 3rd remote, 3 pt., PTO, 14.9-38" tires, band duals, front fuel tank
4430	1973	5,707	G	$14,950	3/04	NEND	3 pt., 540/1000 PTO, 3 hyd., 16.9-38" rear tires, band duals, front weights, front tank
4430	1974		G	$8,500	3/04	ECMI	Cab, 1 hyd., diesel, 18.4-38" tires
4430	1974		G	$9,100	2/04	WCMI	2WD, factory cab, 3 pt., PTO, 18.4-38" tires, diesel
4430	1974	7,910	G	$9,900	2/04	NCIN	2 hyd., T-rail tires
4430	1974	7,970	G	$10,500	7/04	ECMN	2 hyd., 3 pt.
4430	1974	9,500	F	$11,200	3/04	ECNE	Diesel, 2 hyd., 3 pt., am/fm, 18.4-38" tires, 9-bolt hub-mount duals, 6 front weights, 9,500 hrs. on second tach
4430	1974	9,545	G	$12,500	3/04	NESD	3 pt., 3 hyd., hub duals
4430	1974		G	$12,750	8/04	ECKS	Deere 158 loader
4430	1974		G	$13,500	3/04	NEMI	Trans. rebuilt, diesel
4430	1974	7,847	G	$14,500	12/04	NWOH	Cab, AC, 2 hyd., diesel, 18.4-38" tires
4430	1974		G	$16,900	2/04	NECO	3,200 hrs. on OH, cab, 3 pt., PTO, 18.4-38" tires, duals
4430	1974	4,107	G	$18,300	1/04	ECNE	Diesel, cab, 3 pt., 2 hyd., 18.4-38" tires
4430	1975		P	$9,000	6/04	NWMN	Aux. fuel tank, 3 hyd., 3 pt., PTO, cab, rough
4430	1975		G	$10,500	3/04	WCIL	
4430	1975		E	$11,100	2/04	NEKS	Cab, 18.4-38" tires, duals, front weights, 3,042 hrs. on OH
4430	1975	8,991	G	$12,000	12/04	NCIA	Cab, front tank, 2 hyd., quick coupler, 18.4-38" tires,
4430	1975	8,260	G	$12,500	8/04	NWIA	AC, extra light pkg.
4430	1975	8,973	G	$12,900	2/04	SENE	2 hyd., cab, AC, 3 pt., lift assist, radio, 18.4-38"R tires
4430	1975		G	$13,250	8/04	ECNE	PS, 18.4-38" tires, 2 hyd., rear weights
4430	1976		G	$11,000	5/04	ECND	3 hyd., 3 pt., PTO, hub duals
4430	1976		G	$12,250	12/04	NEND	3 pt., PTO, 3 hyd., 14.9-46" tires, duals
4430	1976	6,296	E	$12,700	6/04	NCND	Cab, 2 hyd.
4430	1976	7,500	G	$16,000	1/04	SENE	1,000 hours on OH, comfort cover, PS, diesel
4430	1976	5,600	G	$16,750	12/04	NWOH	Cab, AC, 2 hyd., front weights, quick hitch, 18.4-38" tires, clamp-on duals
4430	1977		G	$11,750	8/04	ECNE	18.4-38" tires, 2 hyd.
4430	1977		G	$12,750	12/04	WCMN	PS, 2 hyd., 3 pt., PTO, new clutch, 18.4-38" tires
4430	1977		G	$12,950	3/04	SCMN	1 owner
4430	1977	8,172	G	$13,100	1/04	ECIL	PS, AC, 3 hyd., weights, 18.4-38" tires, duals
4430	1977	5,300	G	$18,600	3/04	NWIA	
4430			F	$6,000	3/03	NCMI	Cab, 3 pt., 2 hyd., needs work
4430			F	$7,200	4/03	NCMD	Cab, diesel
4430			F	$8,100	5/03	SWOK	
4430			F	$8,200	8/03	NWIL	Cab, AC, weights, diesel
4430		10,595	G	$8,250	7/03	ECND	3 pt., PTO, duals, 3 hyd.
4430		10,595	G	$8,250	7/03	ECND	3 pt., PTO, 18.4-38" tires, 3 hyd.
4430			F	$8,600	8/03	NWIL	Cab, AC, PS, diesel
4430			G	$8,700	7/03	SCPA	Cab

john deere

Model	Year	Hours	Cond.	Price	Date	Area	Comments
4430			G	$9,250	12/03	SEMN	
4430		11,000	F	$9,400	2/03	ECCO	
4430		7,451	F	$9,700	8/03	SCNE	2 hyd.
4430		7,739	G	$10,000	3/03	SWIN	Cab
4430			G	$10,500	12/03	SWMI	Quad trans., cab, 18.4-38" tires, 3 pt., 2 hyd.
4430		6,424	G	$10,750	6/03	SWMN	Diesel, less than 1,200 hrs. on major OH
4430			G	$10,750	4/03	WCWI	Diesel, WF, 3 pt., dual hyd., 20.8x38" tires, no cab, 1,000 hrs. on major OH
4430		6,502	F	$10,750	8/03	SCNE	2 hyd.
4430			G	$11,250	8/03	WCIN	PS, cab, front fuel tank, duals, original
4430			F	$12,000	3/03	SWPA	Cab, full remotes, new rubber
4430		8,000	G	$12,000	2/03	SWIL	WF, cab, AC, PTO, 2 hyd., no weights or duals
4430			G	$12,200	3/03	NCWI	Cab, recent engine OH, diesel, 2 hyd.
4430		6,590	F	$12,500	2/03	SEMN	Cab, quad, dual hyd., 3 pt., PTO, diesel
4430		6,440	G	$12,600	2/03	WCMN	Cab, 2 hyd., rock box, air ride seat
4430		5,200	G	$13,800	3/03	NWIL	Duals, weights, diesel
4430			G	$14,000	11/03	NWSD	3 pt., cab, radio, Deere 158 loader and grapple
4430			G	$14,500	3/03	ECIN	
4430		5,387	G	$15,000	9/03	SCNE	2 hyd., duals, 10 front weights, Quick-Tach
4430		5,400	E	$24,500	5/03	WCSD	Cab, 3 pt., 3 hyd., new 650/65r38"xm128 Michelin tires, very clean
4430	1973		F	$8,250	3/03	NEND	2 hyd., 540/1000 PTO
4430	1973		G	$8,500	8/03	NCIA	ROPS, motor & rear end OH, syncro, 18.4-38" tires
4430	1973		G	$9,600	8/03	NCIA	991 hours on new motor in '93, 18.4-38" tires
4430	1973		G	$10,600	3/03	ECND	2 hyd., 3 pt., PTO, 14.9-38" tires, singles
4430	1973		G	$10,700	1/03	SEMI	Cab, AC, duals, 1,000 hrs. on major OH
4430	1973	7,063	G	$10,750	8/03	NCIA	Power quad, 3 hyd., quick coupler, front tank and weights, duals
4430	1973	8,383	G	$11,200	9/03	NCIA	Front tank and weights, 3 pt., duals
4430	1973	6,974	G	$11,700	3/03	ECIL	AC, 2 hyd., front fuel tank, front/rear weights, 18.4-38" tires, no duals
4430	1973		G	$13,600	5/03	NCWI	500 hrs. on OH, cab, front-mount fuel tank, 2 hyd.
4430	1973		G	$13,900	5/03	SWOK	Koyker front-end loader, 2 hyd., 1,300 hrs. on new OH & trans., 125 hp., factory duals, rubber 60%
4430	1973		G	$14,000	12/03	WCIL	3,000 hrs. on OH, 23.1-34" tires & duals
4430	1974	15,000	P	$9,000	3/03	NCCO	7,000 hrs. on OH
4430	1974		F	$10,600	12/03	NCIN	New clutch
4430	1974	7,985	G	$10,900	12/03	SCMN	18.4-38" tires
4430	1974		G	$11,000	7/03	SEND	Cab, 2 hyd., power beyond, 3 pt., PTO, band duals
4430	1974	7,850	G	$11,700	2/03	NCOH	Cab, 18.4-38" rears, 20.8-34" hub duals
4430	1974	7,247	G	$11,900	9/03	NCIA	Cab, AC, 2 hyd., 18.4-38" tires
4430	1974	11,000	G	$12,900	4/03	WCSK	Canadian sale, 2WD, 18.4x38" tires
4430	1974	5,176	G	$16,600	11/03	NCIA	Cab, AC, quad, 2 hyd., quick coupler, 18.4-38" tires
4430	1975		G	$10,400	9/03	SESD	
4430	1975		G	$11,000	4/03	NCKS	Cab, 3 pt., PTO, 9' dozer, forklift
4430	1975	7,355	G	$11,100	8/03	NWIL	18.4-38"R tires, 3 hyd., PTO, lift assist, 3 pt.
4430	1975	6,583	G	$12,000	4/03	WCIA	Sound-guard cab, good paint, clamp-on duals
4430	1975	6,500	G	$12,750	9/03	SCMN	
4430	1975		F	$14,000	3/03	SWMN	
4430	1975	5,077	G	$14,500	12/03	NCOH	Cab, 2 hyd., quick hitch, front and rear weights

Model	Year	Hours	Cond.	Price	Date	Area	Comments
4430	1975		F	$15,000	9/03	SCNE	2 hyd., duals, 10 front weights
4430	1975		G	$15,400	3/03	WCMN	600 hrs. on OH, 2 hyd., 18.4-38" tires
4430	1975	5,972	G	$18,000	4/03	WCSK	Canadian sale, 2WD, 130 hp., 540 PTO, 2 hyd.
4430	1976	7,684	P	$7,800	3/03	NCCO	
4430	1976	6,942	G	$11,000	7/03	NWOH	Cab, AC, T-rail duals, front weights, Cat II quick hitch, bottom end of engine redone, repainted
4430	1976	5,130	G	$11,000	2/03	NEIA	Engine knock
4430	1976		G	$11,300	12/03	SCMN	Duals
4430	1976		G	$12,000	9/03	ECND	3 pt., 540/1000 PTO, 2 hyd., 16.9-38" tires & duals, 13.6-24" front tires
4430	1976	9,100	G	$12,000	2/03	WCNE	Read duals, air suspension seat, front/rear weights, clean, 1 owner, fresh paint
4430	1976	5,635	G	$13,300	1/03	WCIL	Cab, duals, good paint
4430	1976	6,036	G	$13,400	9/03	NCIA	PS, front tank and weights, 3 pt., duals, OH and trans at 5,576 hrs.
4430	1976	5,930	G	$13,500	3/03	NWIL	2 hyd.
4430	1976	5,400	G	$14,100	2/03	ECIL	Complete OH 3 yrs. ago
4430	1976	3,784	G	$15,600	4/03	NCIL	Cab, 2 hyd., 1 owner, quick hitch, 18.4-38" tires
4430	1976	3,678	G	$16,900	8/03	NCIA	Cab, AC, PS, new batteries, quick coupler, 2 hyd., just inspected
4430	1976	7,500	G	$20,250	6/03	WCSK	Canadian sale, cab, 18.4-38" tires, 8-speed powershift, 126 PTO hp.
4430	1977	8,700	P	$8,850	12/03	SEND	2 hyd., 3 pt., PTO, 16.9-38" tires
4430	1977		F	$9,750	5/03	SWOK	Cab, 3 pt., 2 hyd., new paint, local tractor, 18.4-38"R tires, 75% rubber, full weights, 125 hp.
4430	1977		G	$11,000	3/03	SWIA	$7,000 spent on OH, PS
4430	1977	8,240	G	$11,000	1/03	SEIL	AC, 3 hyd., front fuel tank, weights, 18.4-38" tires, axle duals, OH
4430	1977		G	$11,500	3/03	ECND	3 hyd., 3 pt., 18.4-38" tires singles
4430	1977	8,471	G	$12,050	3/03	NWIL	2 hyd.
4430	1977	5,500	G	$12,500	2/03	WCIL	Cab, AC, 3 hyd., PTO, 18.4-38" tires, hub duals, front fuel tank, front & rear weights
4430	1977	7,300	F	$12,500	3/03	NCCO	PS
4430	1977	2,679	G	$12,600	5/03	NCWI	Cab, 3 hyd.
4430	1977	5,660	G	$13,700	3/03	NWIL	Cab, 2 hyd., front weights, hub duals
4430	1977	4,630	G	$14,400	3/03	NWIL	2 hyd.
4430	1977		G	$15,100	8/03	NWIA	3 hyd., 18.4-38" tires, axle duals
4430	1977	5,795	G	$15,400	9/03	ECNE	Cab, 3 pt., 2 hyd., 9-bolt hub mount duals
4430	1977	5,862	G	$15,700	9/03	WCIA	PS, front & rear weights
4430	1977	4,650	G	$17,500	2/03	WCOH	
4520			F	$7,500	4/05	SWPA	700 hours on engine OH, 2 hyd., needed new tires
4520	1969		G	$5,250	2/05	NCIN	4620 updates, 500 hours on complete OH, diesel
4520	1970		G	$13,500	2/05	SCKS	3 pt., PS, ROPS, 4620 motor
4520			F	$4,050	1/04	SENE	Syncro range, WF, 2 hyd., Koyker K5 loader
4520			F	$4,200	3/04	WCIL	Open station, diesel
4520		9,766	G	$5,000	11/04	SCCA	Diesel, hyd.
4520			G	$5,150	12/04	SEPA	Cab
4520			E	$5,850	4/04	NCWI	Diesel, new rubber
4520			G	$7,400	3/04	NWIL	Diesel, cab, good tin
4520			F	$2,100	8/03	WCMN	3 pt., PTO, 2 hyd., cab, Deere 158 loader, grapple, diesel
4520		8,404	F	$3,300	12/03	SEND	Cab, syncro, 2 hyd., Cornhusker 3 pt., 1000 PTO
4520			F	$3,600	9/03	SCMN	
4520			G	$5,500	4/03	WCSK	Canadian sale, diesel, duals, triple hyd., 8-speed synchro
Model	Year	Hours	Cond.	Price	Date	Area	Comments

john deere

Model	Year	Hours	Cond.	Price	Date	Area	Comments
4520	1969	6,737	G	$6,000	2/03	NWOH	Diesel, WF, ROPS cab, heat, AC, 3 pt., cast wheels & hubs, 18.4-34" tires rubber, weights
4520	1970	8,977	G	$8,100	2/03	NCIA	Open station, ROPS, PS, 18.4-38" tires, duals
4620			G	$8,500	12/05	WCWI	
4620			F	$4,400	4/05	SCSD	
4620	1971	9,079	F	$3,700	3/05	SEWY	Cab, diesel, no 3 pt.
4620	1971		G	$7,200	2/05	NEIN	Diesel, WF, no cab
4620	1971	6,320	G	$9,450	3/05	ECNE	PS, 3 hyd., 3 pt., 1000 PTO, diesel, PS, cab, console, 18.4-38" tires, 11-16" fronts
4620			G	$5,150	3/04	NWIL	Diesel, NF, new paint
4620			G	$6,300	3/04	NWIL	Diesel, new tires
4620			G	$7,100	8/04	WCMN	PS, 4,000 hrs. on major OH. Deere cab, band duals, 3 pt., PTO, 2 hyd.
4620			G	$8,600	1/04	NWIA	Factory cab
4620		7,700	G	$9,600	1/04	ECIA	Diesel, syncro
4620	1971		F	$5,000	3/04	NWIL	Diesel, WF, 18.4-38" tires, duals, 2 hyd., 3 pt., front weights, syncro, 1000 PTO
4620	1972	5,428	F	$5,000	3/04	SEIA	No cab, new water pump and PTO clutch
4620	1972		G	$8,500	10/04	SEMN	Deere 280 loader, PS, year-round cab
4620			G	$4,200	12/03	SEMN	
4620		5,800	G	$5,700	3/03	ECIN	
4620			G	$7,300	4/03	WCWI	Diesel, WF, PS, 1000 PTO recent OH, 20x38" tires
4620		8,000	G	$8,000	3/03	ECIN	
4620		6,078	G	$8,700	3/03	NESD	2 hyd.
4620	1972	4,560	E	$35,000	8/03	NWIL	PS, factory quick hitch, diesel
4620	1975		G	$6,200	3/03	NCCO	PS
4630	1973		P	$8,300	2/06	WCIL	ROPS, PS, IHC loader, no cab
4630	1976	5,886	F	$10,200	2/06	ECIL	QR, CAH, weights, 2 hyd., 3 pt.
4630	1976	5,900	G	$17,100	1/06	NEIN	Cab, air, QR
4630	1978		G	$15,700	2/06	SEIN	18.4-34"R duals, QR, 500 hours on remanufactured engine
4630	7209		G	$11,300	9/05	NWIL	PS, 2 hyd., 3 pt.
4630			P	$5,700	12/05	SEMN	Blown engine
4630	10387		F	$6,000	9/05	NWOR	Diesel, duals
4630	1975	6,708	G	$11,000	8/05	NCIL	QR, 2 hyd., 18.4-38" duals, 500 hrs. on major OH
4630	1976	8,316	G	$11,250	9/05	NWIA	2 hyd., 3 pt., diesel
4630	1977	4,700	G	$13,300	9/05	WCIL	Diesel, cab, weights, 2 hyd., QR, quick hitch
4630	1977	5,700	F	$8,000	12/05	SCIA	QR, no forward gears
4630			F	$4,600	2/05	SCMN	PS
4630			G	$8,100	3/05	NWIL	Cab, AC, diesel
4630			G	$9,750	3/05	NWIL	Weights, diesel
4630			G	$9,900	3/05	NWIL	Diesel
4630			F	$14,500	4/05	SCSD	
4630	1973	4,800	G	$9,250	2/05	WCIL	Cab
4630	1974		G	$13,100	1/05	ECIL	PS, front/rear weights, quick hitch, front fuel tank, new duals, OH, 18.4-38" tires
4630	1974		G	$15,250	3/05	SEWY	1,738 hours on newer tach, diesel, cab, 3 pt.
4630	1975	12,490	E	$12,500	4/05	NCOK	Front weights, 2,500 hours on reconditioned transmission, 2 hyd., quick coupler, PTO, 3 pt., axle duals
4630	1976		G	$9,300	7/05	SCMN	Rubber 85%
4630	1976	6,336	G	$10,000	6/05	NWMN	Cab, 8-speed, PS, 3 pt., PTO, 3 hyd.

Model	Year	Hours	Cond.	Price	Date	Area	Comments
4630	1976	10,000	G	$13,000	7/05	NCMN	3 pt., PTO, 4 hyd., band duals, 4,000 hrs. on new OH
4630	1976	3,500	G	$13,000	7/05	NCMN	3 pt., PTO, 4 hyd.
4630	1977	5,131	G	$11,800	8/05	NWIL	Cab, AC, quick hitch, 10 front weights, good 20.8-38"R tires, clamp-on duals, 2,000 hours on major OH
4630	1977		G	$15,500	3/05	SEWY	977 hours on new tach, diesel, cab, 3 pt.
4630			F	$8,500	12/04	SEMN	
4630			G	$10,100	3/04	SCMN	
4630			G	$10,250	2/04	WCWI	Cab, front fuel tank, 1,000 hrs. on OH
4630			G	$10,900	2/04	WCWI	Cab, front fuel tank
4630			G	$11,000	12/04	SEMN	
4630		4,000	G	$11,825	2/04	NCKY	Duals, cab, good rubber
4630		5,800	G	$13,300	3/04	NCWI	Cab, PS
4630	1973	5,772	G	$11,000	10/04	NCOH	
4630	1974		G	$11,000	2/04	WCMI	MFWD, factory cab, PS, 3 pt., PTO, 3 hyd., 20.8-38"R tires, diesel
4630	1974	9,180	G	$13,000	8/04	ECNE	Hyd., MFWD, PS, 3 hyd., 20.8-38" tires, sound-guard cab, 9-bolt hubs
4630	1975	7,168	G	$12,200	3/04	NWIL	Cab, AC, 3 hyd., 11 front weights, 18.4-38" tires,
4630	1975	5,462	G	$17,500	3/04	ECND	1 owner, reg. front, cab, 2 hyd., 3 pt., PTO, 20.8-38" tires, press steel duals, aux. fuel tank
4630	1976	7,100	G	$8,500	6/04	NCND	PS, duals
4630	1976	8,809	F	$8,500	3/04	SEWY	Diesel, duals, front weights, new clutch
4630	1976	6,810	G	$9,000	4/04	NCND	Cab
4630	1976	8,725	G	$9,100	8/04	WCMN	18.4-38" tires, duals, 3 hyd., 3 pt., PTO
4630	1976		G	$9,600	3/04	SEWY	Diesel, duals, recent transmission work
4630	1976	7,630	F	$9,700	3/04	SWMN	2 hyd., rock box, 18.4-42" tires, duals
4630	1976	9,024	G	$10,000	3/04	SEWY	Front weights, diesel
4630	1977		G	$10,500	11/04	WCOH	Duals
4630	1977	8,424	G	$12,000	7/04	NCIA	Cab, PS, 2 hyd., quick coupler, front rock box, transmission rebuilt
4630	1977	8,209	G	$12,800	12/04	SEMN	PS, 42" tires
4630	1977	3,836	G	$14,700	3/04	WCMI	Cab, 3 hyd., 3 pt., PTO, 20.8-38" tires, direct axle duals,
4630			P	$4,600	2/03	ECAR	Rough, fender tractor
4630		8,000	F	$5,750	3/03	NEND	PS, 2 hyd., PTO, duals
4630			G	$7,000	8/03	SEMN	2WD, 2 hyd.
4630		7,363	F	$7,500	8/03	ECKS	PS, 2 hyd., 3 pt.
4630			G	$7,600	8/03	WCIN	Cab, original paint, duals
4630			F	$7,750	4/03	WCMN	
4630			P	$7,850	9/03	SCMN	PS, rough
4630			G	$8,400	9/03	NEIN	
4630		6,400	G	$10,000	2/03	ECNE	827 hrs. on new tach, new 18.4-38" tires, 2 hyd., front fuel tank, PS
4630		5,813	G	$14,000	2/03	WCMN	New engine at 3,600 hrs., cab, quad, 2 hyd.
4630	1973		F	$5,500	11/03	ECND	Cab, syncro, 3 pt., 1000 PTO, 3 hyd., 18.4-38"R tires, front weights, front tank
4630	1973	6,750	G	$8,000	2/03	SETX	Syncro
4630	1973	7,045	F	$8,600	8/03	SCMN	Syncro, 20.8-38" tires, hub duals
4630	1973	7,230	G	$11,000	9/03	NCIA	Less than 1,000 hrs. on major OH, AC updates, 18.4-38" tires, duals, front weights & fuel tank, rock box, PS
4630	1973		G	$12,000	9/03	NWOH	Unknown hrs., 8-speed, cab, AC, 2 hyd., duals
4630	1974		P	$8,100	2/03	WCMI	MFWD, axle duals, 3 hyd., rough, tires rough
4630	1974	3,899	G	$18,000	3/03	NCIL	Clamp-on duals, front fuel tank, front weights, syncro range
4630	1975		F	$4,700	12/03	WCMN	18.4-38" tires, duals, 3 pt., PTO, 2 hyd.
4630	1975	11,000	F	$7,700	2/03	SCNE	

john deere

Model	Year	Hours	Cond.	Price	Date	Area	Comments
4630	1975	10,900	F	$8,000	3/03	NCCO	
4630	1975	7,147	F	$8,400	3/03	NCCO	
4630	1975	6,150	G	$11,000	8/03	NCIA	Cab, AC, 2 hyd., front tank
4630	1975	5,483	G	$12,100	1/03	NWIL	Cab, syncro, weights, duals
4630	1975		G	$15,500	8/03	SCMN	PS, recent OH & rear end overhaul, 18.4-42" tires, hub duals
4630	1976		F	$6,100	11/03	ECND	Hyd., cab, 3 pt., 1000 PTO, 3 hyd., 18.4-38"R tires, front tank, 14.9-26" tires
4630	1976	6,452	G	$11,800	8/03	NCIA	Front tank & weights, 20.8-38" tires duals, new motor
4630	1976		G	$12,000	12/03	NECO	5,700 hrs. on major OH, PS, cab, 3 pt., PTO, 3 hyd.
4630	1976	6,823	G	$12,100	9/03	WCIA	Front weights, front tank, 2 hyd., quick hitch, hub duals
4630	1976		G	$16,000	2/03	WCIA	20 hours on new short block, PS, 3 hyd., 18.4-42" tires
4630	1977		G	$11,000	1/03	NEMI	Cab, PS, 2 hyd., front weights, duals, quick hitch
4630	1977	7,810	F	$12,500	1/03	NENE	18.4-38" tires, 10-bolt duals, 3 pt., 3 hyd., AM/FM/cassette
4630	1977	5,533	G	$13,250	3/03	NWIL	
4630	1977	4,873	G	$13,600	2/03	NCIA	2WD, PS, 2 hyd., quick coupler, front weights, 18.4-38" tires, 10-bolt duals
4630	1977	1,589	G	$13,750	12/03	NECO	1,589 hrs. on a $17K OH, PS, cab, 3 pt., PTO, 3 hyd., 18.4-38" tires, duals
4630	1978		G	$11,000	8/03	SCKS	3 pt., 3 hyd., duals, PTO, '99 GB 870 loader
50			F	$1,050	9/05	NENE	PTO, drawbar, 12.4-38" tires, tire chains, JD 45 loader
50			F	$1,100	9/05	NENE	NF, Roll-o-Matic, PTO, drawbar, 12.4-38"
50			F	$1,500	9/05	NENE	NF, Roll-o-Matic, live PTO, drawbar, PS, 12.4-38"
50			G	$2,300	9/05	NEIN	All fuel, repainted, 3 pt.
50			G	$2,500	11/05	WCIL	NF, PS, manual & parts with tractor
50			F	$2,500	9/05	NENE	Factory WF, factory power steering, PTO, drawbar, new crank, needs assembly, 13.6-38" tires
50			G	$9,000	7/05	NEIA	LP, expo, restored, 1 of 731 built
50	1953			$4,000	12/05	NECO	Single front, 3 pt., PTO, new rubber, restored
50	1953		G	$4,200	9/05	SEMN	NF, front and rear weights, fenders, 3 pt.
50	1954		G	$2,550	8/05	ECMI	NF, new rubber
50			P	$400	6/05	ECWI	For parts
50			F	$1,450	1/05	ECNE	Hyd., $650 extra for 3 pt.
50			F	$1,650	7/05	SCIA	
50			F	$2,000	6/05	ECWI	Painted
50			G	$2,100	1/05	SWOH	
50			G	$3,250	6/05	ECMN	Row crop, gas, tricycle, new tires & paint
50			G	$5,500	6/05	ECMN	Row crop, gas, WF, 801 hitch, fenders, new paint, front weights, PS
50	1953		F	$2,050	1/05	NEIA	
50	1954		G	$2,800	7/05	NCIA	PS, Deere 45 loader, hyd. bucket
50	1955		G	$2,150	6/05	WCMN	Clean, original
50	1955		F	$2,650	1/05	NEIA	PS
50			P	$400	10/04	NEPA	For parts
50			P	$600	10/04	NEPA	For parts
50			F	$1,100	7/04	ECMN	Gas
50			F	$1,400	6/04	SEMN	
50			F	$1,400	11/04	NCOH	Rough but running, gas, no fenders
50			F	$2,000	1/04	SENE	3 pt., fenders
50			G	$2,000	6/04	SEMN	
50			G	$2,000	8/04	ECMN	Gas, loader, WF

Model	Year	Hours	Cond.	Price	Date	Area	Comments
50			G	$3,100	5/04	NEPA	1 owner, gas, bought new in 1956
50	1952		F	$1,350	3/04	ECNE	Gas, NF, electric start, PTO, 1 hyd., 13.6-38" tires
50	1953		F	$1,350	9/04	NECO	Runs, 3 pt., good tires & tin, Roll-O-Matic
50	1953		G	$2,200	9/04	ECNE	PS, Powertrol, 12.4-38" tires
50	1953		G	$4,100	1/04	NECO	Single front, 3 pt., PTO, new rubber, completely restored
50	1955		G	$2,000	3/04	WCMI	Gas, NF, PTO, electric start, 12.4-38" tires
50	1955		G	$3,300	3/04	NCMI	Gas, NF, PS, live power, 12.4-38" tires
50	1955		G	$3,500	6/04	NWIL	Gas, PS
50	1955		G	$4,600	5/04	SCPA	PS, restored
50			F	$1,200	8/03	SEMN	PS
50			F	$1,275	8/03	NEKS	
50			G	$1,400	9/03	NEIN	
50			E	$1,800	10/03	SENE	Gas, NF, good tires
50			G	$1,900	1/03	NENE	Gas, Behlen PS, Roll-O-Matic
50			G	$1,950	9/03	NEIN	
50			G	$2,100	4/03	WCMI	
50			G	$2,850	9/03	NEIN	Repainted
50	1953		G	$1,800	4/03	WCMN	Gas, hydraulic, Roll-O-Matic
50	1953		G	$1,800	8/03	WCMN	
50	1955		G	$2,200	8/03	WCMN	
5020			G	$3,400	12/05	NWIL	Diesel, with front blade
5020			G	$3,750	12/05	SWMS	Diesel, canopy, 3 pt.
5020			F	$3,750	9/05	NWOR	Diesel
5020			G	$5,250	9/05	SCON	Canadian sale, dsl
5020	1967		G	$4,800	11/05	ECNE	Syncro range, 2 hyd., 18.4-38"
5020			G	$9,250	6/05	ECWI	PTO
5020	1967		G	$5,700	6/05	ECIL	Q-Tach, 2 outlets, 162 hp., dyno, 24.5-32" rears, 12-volt conversion
5020			G	$4,000	9/04	NWMN	Diesel, standard 2 hyd., PTO, 24.5-32" rears, 18.4-38" tires, dual hubs, Fabrico fiberglass cab, syncro
5020			G	$4,200	11/04	NWNY	2 dual hyd. outlets, dual axles
5020	1967	7,100	F	$7,000	10/04	SEPA	Cab, diesel, rubber fair
5020			G	$2,500	12/03	SWMI	Syncro, canopy cover, 18.4-38" tires, 3 pt., 2 hyd., adj. wheels, bad motor
5020			G	$3,700	9/03	NEIN	
5020			E	$5,200	8/03	NWIL	Restored, diesel, WF
5020	1966		G	$1,400	3/03	ECNE	WF, cab & ROPS, syncro range
520			G	$2,600	1/06	SESD	NF
520			G	$2,100	8/05	SEMN	
520			F	$2,500	8/05	ECMI	NF, Roll-o-matic, PS, fenders, newer paint
520			F	$2,850	10/05	NEPA	
520			G	$4,900	11/05	WCIL	77th of 520 produced, new restoration, del seat, rollan eng
520	1957		G	$4,500	9/05	NWIA	Gas
520	1957		G	$8,850	9/05	SEMN	NF, 3 pt., front and rear weights, fenders, air stack
520			G	$3,300	6/05	ECMN	WF
520			G	$3,450	6/05	ECWI	Black dash, painted
520			G	$3,500	6/05	ECMN	Row crop, gas, tricycle, PTO, 1 hyd.
520			G	$3,900	6/05	ECMN	WF, 3 pt., fenders
520			G	$6,000	6/05	WCMN	Gas, PS, NF, original, new rear tires
520	1958		G	$2,900	4/05	NCCO	PTO, 3 pt., remote, complete OH and restored
520			P	$600	10/04	NEPA	For parts
520			P	$800	10/04	NEPA	For parts
520			F	$3,125	10/04	SEPA	Gas, NF, PS, burnt valve, rubber fair

john deere

Model	Year	Hours	Cond.	Price	Date	Area	Comments
520			G	$4,700	3/04	NWIL	Gas
520			G	$5,350	2/04	ECNE	3 pt., NF, PS, new paint & decals
520			E	$5,500	3/04	NEIA	PS, NF, clam shell fenders, rebuilt seat, 470 hrs. on OH, 45 over pistons, 3 front weights
520			F	$6,600	10/04	SEPA	LP, unrestored, WF, 3 pt., PS, rubber average
520	1957		F	$2,175	9/04	NECO	Runs, NF, 2 pt., electric start, good tires
520	1957		G	$4,400	3/04	WCMI	Gas, NF, 3 pt., PTO, PS, fenders, 13.6-36" tires
520	1957		G	$4,600	10/04	NEPA	3 pt.
520	1958		P	$1,200	10/04	NEPA	For parts
520	1958		G	$4,000	11/04	WCIA	No cab, runs good, fair rubber, needs paint, WF
520			P	$1,350	6/03	NWIL	Gas, row crop, with starter, lights, cast iron rear wheel, 3 pt.
520			G	$1,550	8/03	SENE	Gas, WF
520			E	$4,150	8/03	NWIL	Restored, Deere 45 loader, NF, PS, gas
520			E	$4,650	8/03	NWIL	Original, gas, NF, 3 pt., no fenders
520			E	$7,500	8/03	NCCO	Restored, gas, new tires, PS, WF, 3 pt.
520	1956		G	$3,100	8/03	WCMN	
520	1956		G	$3,750	8/03	NWIA	Tear drop fenders, gas
530			F	$4,500	4/05	SEPA	Gas, NF, nice tin, 30% rubber
530			G	$8,000	11/05	WCIL	NF, gas
530			G	$9,100	7/05	NEIA	LP, WF, 3 pt., 1 of 417 built
530	1958		G	$8,600	8/05	WCIA	
530	1959		G	$9,800	9/05	SEMN	Air stack, 3 pt., fenders, front and rear weights
530			G	$5,250	6/05	ECIL	PS, NF
530			G	$6,500	6/05	ECMN	Row crop, WF, PTO, hyd., new paint
530			G	$6,750	3/05	ECNE	
530			G	$7,750	6/05	ECMN	Row crop, gas, WF, fenders, 3 pt., PTO
530			G	$8,000	7/05	SCIA	
530			G	$8,500	6/05	ECMN	Row crop, new tires, 1 hyd., new paint, OH
530	1960		G	$6,700	7/05	NCIA	PS, 3 pt.
530			G	$4,950	12/04	ECNE	
530			G	$5,100	12/04	ECNE	Repainted
530			G	$7,100	12/04	ECNE	Original
530	1959		G	$1,400	3/04	SEMN	PS, like new
530			G	$2,250	8/03	SENE	Gas
530			G	$3,300	11/03	WCWI	Fenders, straight drawbar, cultivator
530			G	$5,600	9/03	NEIN	3 pt.
530			G	$5,750	4/03	ECMN	Gas, NF, 3 pt.
530			G	$6,300	9/03	NEIN	
530			G	$8,000	10/03	SEMN	PS, 3 pt.
530			G	$21,000	9/03	NEIN	All fuel
530	1959		G	$5,250	3/03	NEKS	3 pt.
530	1959		E	$5,450	6/03	NEIL	WF, 3 pt., ROPS
530	1959		G	$5,500	8/03	NWIA	Rear weights, NF
530	1959		G	$5,900	8/03	WCMN	
530	1959		G	$8,000	9/03	SCMI	Gas, 3 pt., NF
60			G	$2,100	1/06	SESD	Row crop, WF, fenders
60			F	$1,000	9/05	NENE	With Dual loader, gas, PS, PTO, drawbar, 13.6-38"
60			F	$1,225	7/05	SESD	NF
60			F	$1,400	9/05	NEIN	PS

Model	Year	Hours	Cond.	Price	Date	Area	Comments
60			G	$1,600	8/05	NWIL	Gas
60			F	$1,600	11/05	WCIL	NF, unrestored, PTO
60			G	$1,800	9/05	NENE	NF, good tin
60			F	$2,000	4/05	SEPA	Gas, NF, 30% rubber
60			G	$2,300	11/05	WCIL	NF, PS
60	1954		G	$4,850	9/05	SEMN	Low seat standard PTO, Powertrol, 2 hyd.
60	1955		G	$4,800	9/05	SEMN	Row crop, front and rear weights, 800 series, 3 pt.
60	1955		G	$4,800	9/05	SEMN	Standard, front and rear weights, 800 series, 3 pt.
60			P	$800	1/05	ECNE	Stuck, as is, NF
60			F	$1,100	7/05	SCMN	
60			G	$1,650	6/05	WCMN	WF, 1 owner
60			F	$1,800	6/05	ECWI	Painted
60			G	$3,750	6/05	ECWI	Std., low seat, new tires
60			G	$3,800	8/05	SWMN	PTO, NF, PS
60			G	$3,800	6/05	ECWI	New rubber, restored
60			G	$3,900	8/05	SWMN	PTO, WF, PS
60			G	$4,000	6/05	ECMN	Row crop, new tires & paint, 3 pt., hyd.
60			G	$4,100	7/05	SCIA	Row crop, restored
60			E	$57,000	7/05	SCIA	LP, Std., restored, 1 of 25 built
60	1952		G	$1,900	2/05	NEIN	Gas, NF
60	1952		F	$3,700	3/05	NECO	Dual loader, WF, 3 pt., PTO, hyd.
60	1953		P	$1,225	1/05	NEIA	Rough
60	1953		G	$3,600	4/05	NEIN	Gas, NF
60	1956		F	$2,450	1/05	NEIA	PS
60			P	$400	10/04	NEPA	For parts
60			P	$600	9/04	NWMN	WF, no engine
60			P	$800	9/04	NWMN	Parts missing, WF, PS
60			P	$800	10/04	NEPA	For parts
60			F	$900	8/04	NWIA	
60			P	$900	10/04	NEPA	For parts
60			F	$1,000	8/04	NWIA	
60			G	$1,400	3/04	NWIL	Gas
60			F	$1,550	11/04	NCOH	Rough but running, gas, fenders
60			F	$1,600	7/04	ECMN	Gas, loader, WF
60			F	$1,750	8/04	NWIL	NF, like new rear tires
60			G	$2,000	2/04	ECNE	13.6-38" tires
60			F	$2,500	9/04	NWMN	PS, WF
60			G	$2,700	2/04	ECMO	1 owner
60			G	$2,700	9/04	NWMN	PS
60	1952		G	$2,050	2/04	NCOH	
60	1952		F	$2,050	9/04	NECO	Runs, Roll-O-Matic, good tin & tires, 3 pt.
60	1952		G	$2,300	10/04	NEPA	LP, WF
60	1953		F	$1,600	5/04	NCKS	Good rubber, rock shaft, 540 PTO
60	1953		G	$2,400	10/04	NEPA	3 pt.
60	1953		G	$2,550	8/04	ECMI	Gas, restored, NF
60	1953		G	$2,900	8/04	ECIL	Repainted
60	1954		F	$1,550	11/04	NCIA	PS, repainted, poor tin
60	1954		G	$2,600	11/04	NWIL	Gas, painted like 620, runs good, good tin, new rubber
60	1954		E	$3,300	8/04	NESD	NF, restored
60	1955		G	$2,700	10/04	NEPA	WF
60	1955		G	$2,900	3/04	SEMN	PS
60	1955		G	$17,000	5/04	SCPA	Orchard, restored

john deere

Model	Year	Hours	Cond.	Price	Date	Area	Comments
60			F	$675	12/03	WCIA	Engine disassembled, gas, PS, WF
60			G	$800	10/03	ECWI	NF
60			F	$950	7/03	SCMN	
60			G	$1,100	9/03	NEIN	LP
60			G	$1,400	5/03	NEKS	NF, PS, no 3 pt.
60			F	$1,500	12/03	WCMI	Gas, single remote w/ fittings
60			G	$1,500	9/03	NEIN	
60			F	$1,600	2/03	NCMI	Gas, NF, PTO, PS
60			G	$1,700	9/03	NEIN	
60			G	$1,800	9/03	NEIN	
60			G	$1,850	9/03	NEIN	
60			G	$1,900	9/03	NEIN	45 loader
60		8,790	G	$2,100	8/03	SCNE	
60			E	$2,600	8/03	NWIL	Old restore, gas, NF, PS
60			G	$3,150	9/03	NEIN	
60			G	$3,950	9/03	NEIN	Loader
60			G	$7,400	9/03	NEIN	Hi crop, Std., all fuel
60			E	$8,000	8/03	NWIL	High seat, Std., restored
60			G	$10,000	9/03	NEIN	Hi crop
60			G	$38,500	9/03	NEIN	Hi crop
60	1952		G	$2,400	9/03	SEND	Square axle WF
60	1953		F	$1,700	9/03	SEND	
60	1953		G	$2,000	8/03	NWIA	PTO shield, NF, gas
60	1953		G	$2,300	1/03	SWOH	Gas, row crop, electric start
60	1953		G	$25,000	8/03	WCMN	Hi crop
60	1954		G	$1,350	9/03	NCIA	PS
60	1954		F	$1,700	8/03	WCMN	
60	1955		G	$1,050	7/03	NWMN	NF, Roll-O-Matic, live power hyd.
60	1955		G	$1,400	9/03	NCIA	PS, good tin
60	1955		G	$2,600	12/03	WCIA	Gas, fenders, PS
6030			G	$8,750	9/05	NEIN	Original, factory cab
6030			G	$8,000	2/05	NCIN	
6030			G	$14,000	3/05	SEIA	
6030			G	$4,600	9/03	NEIN	45 loader
6030			G	$5,900	10/03	NWMN	Factory cab, PTO, 18.4-38" tires, factory duals
6030		6,100	G	$6,500	10/03	WCSD	New batteries, cab, diesel, radio, duals
6030	1973	3,121	F	$6,000	4/03	ECND	Cab, 2 hyd., 3 pt., PTO, front fuel tank, 20.8-38" band duals
6030	1976	4,800	G	$6,500	9/03	ECND	Factory cab, AC, 1000 PTO, 3 hyd., 18.4-38" tires, axle duals
6030	1976		G	$7,500	6/03	ECND	Factory cab, heat, 1000 PTO, 3 hyd., 18.4-38" tires
620			G	$2,500	1/06	SESD	LP, NF, restored
620			G	$2,750	8/05	WCMN	Runs good, good tin
620			G	$3,250	11/05	WCIL	NF, gas, 3 pt., belt pulley, PS
620			F	$4,000	8/05	NECO	Sold with Farmhand F11 loader, 3 pt.
620	1956		G	$9,500	9/05	SEMN	Standard, front and rear weights, 3 pt., air stack
620	1958		G	$9,850	9/05	SEMN	NF, 3 pt., front and rear weights, air stack
620			F	$1,700	3/05	WCMN	NF, original
620			F	$2,000	8/05	SEIA	
620			G	$2,700	6/05	WCMN	PS, NF, new tires, gas
620		3,854	G	$3,100	6/05	WCMN	WF, 1 hyd., PS, duals, 325 hyd. loader

Model	Year	Hours	Cond.	Price	Date	Area	Comments
620			G	$3,100	2/05	NEIA	Newly repainted
620			G	$4,000	6/05	ECMN	Row crop, 3 pt., PTO, 1 hyd., fenders, new paint
620			G	$5,000	6/05	ECMN	Row crop, 3 pt., PTO, 1 hyd., fenders, new paint
620			G	$7,250	6/05	ECMN	Std., gas, PTO, 1 hyd., new paint
620	1956		G	$3,900	3/05	WCNJ	Nice tractor
620	1958		G	$2,300	4/05	NENE	NF, 13.6-38" tires
620			F	$1,050	10/04	SEPA	LP, NF, PS, rubber fair
620			F	$1,600	12/04	ECNE	NF, 3 pt.
620			F	$2,000	9/04	NECO	LP, runs, good tires, fair tin
620			G	$2,675	6/04	SEMN	
620			F	$3,100	1/04	SWOH	Motor stuck
620			E	$5,100	3/04	NEIA	PS, NF, new radiator, rebuilt seat, clam shell fenders, 3 front weights
620	1956		G	$2,800	9/04	ECNE	PS, Powertrol, 1 hyd., 13.6-38" tires
620	1956		G	$3,800	10/04	NEPA	3 pt.
620	1956		G	$4,700	5/04	SCPA	3 pt., PS, restored
620	1957		P	$1,500	10/04	NEPA	For parts, gas
620	1957		G	$3,000	8/04	NCIA	PS, NF, gas
620	1958		G	$2,150	2/04	ECNE	Gas, PS, 13.3-38" tires, 1 hyd.
620	1958		G	$3,600	5/04	SENE	Gas, NF, 3 pt.
620	1958		F	$3,600	9/04	ECMI	WF, 3 pt., PS, cracked manifold, gas
620	1958		G	$4,225	11/04	NWIL	Gas, NF, runs good, good tin, new rubber
620	1958		G	$4,400	2/04	SWIA	Restored, WF
620	1958		G	$4,800	6/04	NWIL	Gas, loader, 3 pt
620			F	$1,750	6/03	NCIA	Gas, NF, PS, PTO not working
620			P	$2,000	10/03	ECNE	Did not start, 3 pt., missing third link, PS, Powertrol
620			G	$2,000	9/03	NEIN	
620			F	$3,100	4/03	WCMN	Schwartz loader
620			G	$3,800	3/03	NESD	Square WF, PS
620			E	$3,800	8/03	NCCO	Gas, 3 pt., restored, new paint, good tires, PS, tricycle
620			G	$19,500	9/03	NEIN	Orchard
620			E	$80,000	6/03	SEMN	Exceptionally rare all-fuel hi-crop tractor, restored, new tires, shipped 7/21/58 to Pompano Beach, FL, SN 222522
620			G	$90,000	9/03	NEIN	LP, hi crop
620	1955		F	$4,000	7/03	NWIL	Gas, PS
620	1956	2,913	G	$7,200	2/03	SEMI	3 pt., duals, Std., original, 801 hitch
620	1957		P	$2,300	5/03	WCIN	Tricycle, 3 pt., PS, gas, rough
620	1957		G	$2,750	8/03	WCMN	
620	1958		G	$2,000	8/03	NWIA	NF, gas
620	1958		E	$7,500	3/03	NCOH	Very nice original, gas, NF, PS, factory 3 pt., live hyd. & PTO, fenders, new 13.6-38" tires
630			G	$6,250	1/06	SCKS	13.6-38" rear tires, Roll-o-Matic front end, 3 pt., 1 hyd., 3 sets rear weights, shedded, 50 hrs. on OH, runs great
630			E	$6,300	11/05	NEIA	NF, restored, flat top fenders
630	1958		G	$3,700	9/05	WCNE	Gas, 3 pt., 2,267 hours on tach
630	1958		G	$6,600	8/05	WCIA	
630	1959		G	$4,350	12/05	NCCO	WF, 3 pt.
630	1959		G	$9,250	9/05	SEMN	NF, air stack, 3 pt., front and rear weights
630	1960		G	$3,200	9/05	NENE	Gas, Roll-o-Matic, 13.6-38" unused tires
630		4,273	G	$3,400	6/05	WCMN	NF, PS, new rubber
630			G	$3,750	6/05	ECMN	Tricycle, float ride seat
630			G	$4,500	6/05	ECMN	Row crop, WF, del fenders, 3 pt., front weight set
630			G	$5,500	6/05	ECMN	Row crop, tricycle, 3 pt., PTO, 1 hyd.

john deere

Model	Year	Hours	Cond.	Price	Date	Area	Comments
630			G	$5,900	6/05	ECWI	3 pt., WF
630			G	$6,100	7/05	SCIA	Row crop
630			G	$10,500	6/05	ECMN	Std, gas, PTO, 1 hyd.
630			G	$14,000	6/05	ECMN	Std, gas, 3 pt., PTO, new paint, rebuilt
630	1958		E	$20,000	6/05	NEOK	LP, Std., 3 pt., adjustable front, rice special restored
630	1959	5,039	G	$9,450	1/05	NENE	NF, PS, live power, factory 3 pt., gas, 13.6-38" tires, rear wheel weights
630	1960		G	$4,200	6/05	ECIL	New rear tires, rock shaft, PS
630			F	$4,000	2/04	SWIN	NF, gas, needed paint & new starter
630			G	$7,400	12/04	ECNE	
630	1959		F	$2,500	3/04	SEMN	PS, 3 pt.
630	1959		G	$3,100	4/04	WCNE	3 pt., double front, gas
630	1960		G	$3,900	1/04	SENE	3 pt.
630	1960		G	$3,900	3/04	SEMN	PS
630			G	$2,500	9/03	NEIN	LP
630			G	$2,600	3/03	SENE	Gas
630			G	$2,600	9/03	NEIN	
630			F	$3,500	12/03	NWIL	NF, PS
630			G	$4,200	9/03	NEIN	
630			E	$5,100	8/03	NWIL	Old restore, gas, WF, fenders
630			G	$116,000	9/03	NEIN	Hi crop
630	1958		G	$2,700	8/03	NCIA	PS
630	1959		G	$3,000	8/03	NWIA	Gas
630	1959		G	$3,700	3/03	NENE	Tires fair
630	1959		G	$4,250	3/03	NWIA	Roll-O-Matic NF, 3 pt., fenders
630	1959		G	$36,000	7/03	ECCO	All fuel, 1 of 181, restored, mounted cotton picker
630	1959		G	$70,000	7/03	ECCO	LP, Std., 1 of 16
630	1960	4,600	G	$4,300	12/03	WCIL	Gas, NF, PS, 3 pt.
630	1960		G	$4,900	8/03	NWIL	NF, PTO, 1 hyd., 1 owner, gas
630	1960	4,021	G	$5,050	9/03	NCIA	3 pt., newer tires, gas
630	1960		G	$5,250	9/03	WCIA	PS
630	1960		E	$6,500	6/03	NEIL	OH, 3 pt.
70			G	$2,000	11/05	WCIL	JD adjustable WF, diesel, pony, PTO
70			F	$2,550	9/05	SEIA	
70			G	$2,600	11/05	WCIL	NF, diesel, pony
70			G	$3,000	11/05	WCIL	NF, diesel
70			G	$4,100	11/05	WCIL	Std, restored, PTO, PS, diesel
70			G	$4,500	12/05	WCWI	Standard
70			G	$7,700	7/05	NEIA	LP std, restored
70	1954		G	$5,200	9/05	SEMN	Row crop, front and rear weights, 800 series, 3 pt.
70	1954		G	$5,250	9/05	SEMN	Standard rear weights, PTO, Powertrol
70	1955		G	$5,600	9/05	SEMN	Pony start, front and rear weights, 3 pt., fenders
70	1955		G	$6,500	9/05	SEMN	Standard, pony start, PTO, Powertrol
70			P	$300	2/05	ECNE	Salvage tractor
70			G	$2,300	6/05	ECWI	PS, painted
70			G	$3,050	6/05	ECWI	PS, painted
70			G	$3,800	6/05	ECMN	Gas, rock shaft
70			G	$4,100	6/05	ECMN	Row crop, tricycle, fenders, PTO, hyd.
70			G	$4,500	6/05	ECMN	Row crop, tricycle, fenders, PTO, hyd.

Model	Year	Hours	Cond.	Price	Date	Area	Comments
70			G	$4,500	6/05	ECMN	Row crop, gas, WF, new paint
70			G	$5,600	7/05	SCIA	Gas, Std., restored, 1 of 1,035 built
70	1949		G	$5,100	6/05	ECIL	New paint, 45-degree tires, implement mounting brackets
70	1953		G	$4,000	3/05	SEIA	
70	1954		F	$1,400	7/05	NEIA	Gas, 13.6-38" tires, 1 hyd., not running
70	1954		G	$2,100	2/05	NENE	Gas, Behlen PS, 13.6-38" tires, 1 hyd.
70	1954		F	$2,200	7/05	NEIA	1 hyd., gas, 13.6-38" tires
70	1954		G	$5,000	7/05	NCIA	PS, 13.6-38" tires
70	1955		G	$2,300	4/05	SCMI	NF, gas, PS, fenders, original condition
70			F	$1,000	11/04	SEPA	Gas, did not run
70			G	$1,450	8/04	NWIA	Gas, Schwartz WF, excellent tin, ran good
70			F	$1,550	3/04	SCMN	
70			G	$2,500	9/04	ECNE	
70			F	$2,800	10/04	SEPA	NF, 3 pt., PS, fair rubber
70			F	$3,100	10/04	SEPA	Diesel, unrestored, pony start, PS, WF, rubber average
70			E	$8,000	3/04	NEIA	Completely restored, 12 on OH, new 12-38" tires
70	1951		G	$1,900	2/04	WCMN	NF, PS, PTO, hyd., gas
70	1954		G	$2,900	11/04	WCIA	No cab, NF
70	1955		G	$3,000	11/04	NWIL	Gas, painted like 720, runs good, good tin, new rubber
70	1955		G	$3,100	9/04	NECO	Older restoration, diesel, NF, 3 pt., new tires
70	1955		G	$4,600	1/04	NECO	WF, 3 pt., PTO, power string, completely restored
70	1956		F	$1,400	4/04	WCMI	Diesel
70	1956		G	$2,550	10/04	NEPA	Original cultivator, restored
70			F	$250	8/03	NWIL	WF, diesel
70			F	$1,250	8/03	NCIA	Good tin
70			P	$1,250	3/03	WCMN	NF, diesel
70			G	$1,450	9/03	NEIN	
70			F	$1,700	2/03	NENE	Gas, NF, fair tin
70			E	$3,300	2/03	SWOH	Restored, mint, diesel
70			G	$3,300	7/03	NWMN	Std., rare adjustable WF
70			G	$3,300	12/03	SEIL	Gas, reconditioned, good paint & tires, Roll-O-Matic, no 3 pt.
70			G	$3,300	9/03	NEIN	Electric start
70			G	$3,400	9/03	NEIN	
70			E	$3,500	8/03	NWIL	Restored, gas, NF
70			G	$7,750	9/03	NEIN	Fuel standard
70			G	$23,000	9/03	NEIN	All-fuel hi crop
70	1953		F	$1,350	12/03	WCIA	Gas, PS
70	1953		P	$1,700	3/03	NCCO	Loader
70	1954		G	$2,900	12/03	WCIL	Gas, Std. drawbar, low hours on OH
70	1955		F	$1,900	12/03	NWIL	NF, Deere 45 loader/bucket, gas
70	1956		G	$2,700	8/03	WCMN	WF
7020	1972		F	$5,700	1/06	SCMI	4WD, cab, 3 pt., 3 hyd., PTO, duals, front blade, diesel, tach shows 1857, 18.4-34"
7020	1987	1,770	G	$12,750	1/05	NEMO	4WD, cab
7020		6,078	G	$7,100	3/04	NCMI	4WD, 1000 PTO, 3 pt., outlets, 23.1-30" tires, diesel
7020	1975	1,445	G	$3,500	7/03	ECND	4WD, 16-speed, PTO, 3 hyd., 18.4x34" tires
720			F	$2,050	4/05	SEPA	Diesel, tricyle, good tin, poor paint, 50% rubber
720			G	$3,100	11/05	WCIL	Diesel
720			G	$3,800	9/05	NEIN	LP std, 3 pt.
720			G	$4,900	11/05	WCIL	WF, diesel, pony, PTO, PS
720			G	$5,500	7/05	NEIA	Pony, new tires, clamshell fenders, diesel
720			G	$5,600	11/05	WCIL	NF, OH, new front tires

john deere

Model	Year	Hours	Cond.	Price	Date	Area	Comments
720			G	$6,000	11/05	WCIL	Diesel, pony, PTO
720	1956		G	$10,250	9/05	SEMN	Standard, pony start, rock shaft, rear weights, air stack
720	1958	39,150	G	$2,500	9/05	WCNE	Gas, new paint, double front, 3 pt.
720	1958		F	$4,750	9/05	SCMI	Diesel, elec. start, NF
720	1958		G	$8,650	9/05	SEMN	3 pt., air stack, fenders, front weights
720			G	$3,800	6/05	WCMN	Original, NF, PTO, hyd.
720			G	$4,000	6/05	ECWI	LP, 2 hyd., 3 pt., new rubber
720			G	$4,100	7/05	SCIA	LP all-fuel row crop, 42" rubber, single front wheel, 3 pt., 2 hyd., fenders, 5 weights, 1 of 413 built
720			G	$5,400	8/05	SWMN	Diesel, WF, PS, 3 pt., PTO, restored
720			G	$6,000	6/05	ECMN	Gas, WF, 3 pt, 1 hyd.
720			G	$6,750	6/05	ECMN	Row crop, LP, WF, 1 hyd., 3 pt., new paint
720			G	$7,250	6/05	ECMN	Diesel, pony start, 3 pt., new paint & tires
720	1957		G	$3,600	2/05	NCIN	Diesel, NF, 3 pt., duals
720	1957		G	$7,500	6/05	ECIL	Restored 45 loader, Deere 3 pt.
720	1958		G	$3,900	2/05	WCIL	Diesel, pony motor, good rubber, 3 pt., PS
720	1958		G	$4,600	2/05	NCIN	Diesel, NF, rebuilt hyd.
720	1959		G	$4,950	3/05	NWMN	WF, PS, pony start, diesel, 1 owner
720			P	$550	10/04	NEPA	For parts, LP
720			P	$850	10/04	NEPA	For parts
720			F	$2,350	3/04	NWIL	Gas
720			F	$2,900	9/04	NWMN	WF, diesel
720			G	$3,900	8/04	WCMN	NF, 3 pt., PTO, wheel weights, gas
720			G	$4,000	3/04	NCMI	WF, factory 3 pt., PTO, 1 hyd., 15.5-38" tires, diesel
720			G	$4,350	10/04	SEPA	Restored, NF, good rubber
720			E	$4,400	3/04	NWIL	Gas
720			E	$6,100	3/04	NEIA	PS, NF, rebuilt seat, 2 hyd., clam shell fenders, 1,000 hrs. on OH, standard pistons
720			G	$8,800	2/04	NCIN	PS, electric start, fenders, 3 pt., original, diesel
720	1956		G	$3,000	9/04	ECMI	Pony start, NF, 3 pt., 2 hyd., duals, Roll-O-Matic, older restoration, diesel
720	1957		G	$310	7/04	SEND	PS, hyd., diesel, pony start, rock shaft
720	1957		G	$3,100	7/04	NWMN	WF, PS, hyd., diesel, pony start, rock shaft
720	1957		G	$5,000	1/04	SENE	Gas, pony motor, 3 pt.
720	1958		F	$1,800	4/04	WCNE	Needs work, 3 pt., NF, LP
720	1958		F	$2,200	9/04	NECO	LP, runs, NF, 2 pt., fair tires
720			P	$100	9/03	NEIN	For parts
720			G	$1,100	9/03	NEIN	Std., LP
720			P	$1,950	6/03	WCMN	Not running, diesel
720			E	$2,600	10/03	NWMN	Gas, WF, rock shaft, PTO, Farmhand F10 loader
720			F	$3,400	8/03	SEPA	NF, poor paint, fair rubber, diesel
720			G	$4,250	8/03	WCIN	
720			G	$4,400	9/03	NEIN	Pony
720			G	$4,700	9/03	NEIN	LP
720			E	$6,000	8/03	NWIL	LP, restored, WF, standard black dash
720			G	$6,000	9/03	NEIN	Std.
720			E	$6,900	8/03	NWIL	3 pt., 2 hyd., restored, diesel, electric start
720			G	$7,500	9/03	NEIN	Fuel standard
720			E	$8,700	8/03	NWIL	Restored, gas, WF, 3 pt.

Model	Year	Hours	Cond.	Price	Date	Area	Comments
720			G	$28,000	6/03	SEMN	Diesel, pony start, hi crop, unrestored, good runner, confirmed tag, SN 7200651
720			G	$31,000	9/03	NEIN	Pony, hi crop
720			E	$55,500	8/03	NWIL	Pony start, good tag, hi crop, restored, 1 of 77, diesel
720	1956	3,015	G	$5,600	8/03	WCIL	Diesel, NF, pony start, 1 owner
720	1957		F	$2,200	10/03	ECIN	Diesel, pony, not running
720	1957		E	$5,800	2/03	SEMI	PS, restored, NF
720	1957		G	$14,500	6/03	SEMN	Standard gas, restored, 3 pt., SN 722291
720	1958		G	$2,500	8/03	NWIA	PS, gas
720	1958		G	$2,800	12/03	WCIA	Gas, 3 pt., NF, good tires
720	1958		G	$3,700	8/03	WCMN	WF
720	1958		G	$4,600	7/03	NWMN	Live PTO, WF, 2 hyd., 3 pt.
730	1960		F	$5,500	1/06	NCCO	Gas, WF, 3 pt
730			G	$3,750	11/05	WCIL	Std., WF, magneto out of pony motor
730			G	$4,500	8/05	SEMN	Std., electric start, straight
730			G	$4,700	11/05	WCIL	Old restoration, repaint, PS
730			G	$4,900	11/05	WCIL	NF, diesel, pony, M&W pistons
730		3,800	F	$8,100	4/05	SEPA	Gas, 3 pt., PS, 90% rubber
730	1958		G	$4,400	11/05	WCIA	Diesel, good rear rubber, electric start, front weights sold separately for $800 and $400
730	1959		G	$7100	8/05	WCIA	
730		3,428	G	$3,700	6/05	WCMN	NF, PS
730			G	$5,500	6/05	ECMN	Row crop, electric start, WF, fenders, 3 pt., 1 hyd., 4 wheel weights
730			G	$6,000	6/05	ECMN	Row crop, gas, tricycle, 3 pt., PTO, 1 hyd., top link
730			G	$6,000	2/05	WCIN	Diesel, 15.5" tires, NF, belt pulley
730			G	$6,500	6/05	ECMN	Row crop, 3 pt.
730			G	$6,750	3/05	NWIL	LP, NF, PS, new paint
730			G	$7,750	6/05	ECMN	Row crop, WF, diesel, PTO, welded U-tie rods, new tires, fenders
730			G	$7,750	6/05	ECMN	Row crop, electric start, WF, fenders, 3 pt., 1 hyd., 4 wheel weights
730			G	$7,750	6/05	ECWI	3 pt., electric start
730			G	$9,700	7/05	SCIA	LP, hi crop, diesel, restored, no tag
730			G	$16,000	7/05	SCIA	Argentine, diesel
730			G	$17,000	7/05	SCIA	Restored, gas
730			G	$46,000	7/05	SCIA	Diesel, hi crop, electric start, good tag, restored, 1 of 78 built
730	1958	5,590	G	$4,700	4/05	SCMI	NF, diesel, electric start, clam fenders, 38" rubber
730	1958		E	$5,250	7/05	SENE	Gas
730	1959		G	$4,700	2/05	NENE	Diesel, 16.6-38" tires, direct start, factory 3 pt.
730	1959		G	$6,500	2/05	NWOH	Gas, original, WF, 3 pt., fenders
730	1959		E	$82,500	6/05	NEOK	LP, hi crop restored, rare, 1 of 28 built, SN 7312419
730			G	$0	12/04	ECMI	No sale at $4,500, diesel, NF, flat top fenders, 3 pt., electric start
730			F	$1,400	10/04	SEPA	Diesel, electric start, tricyle, poor rubber, won't start
730			G	$5,000	6/04	SEMN	Gas
730			G	$5,600	4/04	NWMN	NF, 3 pt.
730			G	$5,650	11/04	WCIL	Electric start, 3 pt., fenders, restored
730			G	$6,850	6/04	SEMN	
730			G	$11,300	3/04	SWKS	PTO, hyd., factory LP, in running order
730			E	$14,200	3/04	NEIA	PS, WF, flat top fenders, 3 pt., sway blocks and quick coupler, 3 front weights, 228 hrs. on OH, 45 over pistons and new head
730	1959		F	$3,000	9/04	NECO	Runs, LP, blade on front, new tires, 2 pt.

john deere

Model	Year	Hours	Cond.	Price	Date	Area	Comments
730	1959	6,894	G	$4,700	12/04	ECNE	LP, NF, 1 hyd., 3 pt., PS, 15.5-38" tires, PTO
730	1959		G	$5,100	10/04	NEPA	Gas, WF, 3 pt., new tires
730	1959		E	$8,000	8/04	NESD	NF, PS, restored
730	1960	2,000	E	$6,200	4/04	WCNE	Roll-O-Matic front, 3 pt., diesel
730			P	$1,050	9/03	NEIN	Parts
730			G	$3,850	12/03	SCMN	
730			G	$4,750	9/03	NEIN	Std.
730			G	$5,200	9/03	NEIN	3 pt.
730			G	$5,600	4/03	ECMN	Diesel, NF, 3 pt.
730			G	$5,800	9/03	NEIN	Gas
730			G	$5,900	9/03	NEIN	3 pt.
730			E	$6,500	8/03	NWIL	LP, restored, WF, 3 pt., fenders
730			E	$7,000	8/03	NWIL	NF, restored, electric start, 3 pt., diesel
730			E	$7,700	8/03	NWIL	WF, 3 pt., fenders, restored, diesel, electric start
730			E	$10,600	8/03	NWIL	LP, original, Std., WF
730			E	$10,750	8/03	NWIL	Electric start, WF, 3 pt., fenders, restored, diesel, weights
730			G	$11,900	8/03	NWIL	Electric start, WF, restored, gas, weights
730		1,340	E	$13,700	8/03	NWIL	Restored, WF, gas
730			G	$32,000	9/03	NEIN	Hi crop
730	1958		F	$2,500	12/03	NWIL	Electric start, 3 pt., diesel
730	1959		E	$0	6/03	NCIL	No sale at $5,500, NF, diesel, PS, PTO, 3 pt., pony motor, restored
730	1959		G	$3,300	5/03	SWOK	LP, WF, 3 pt., PTO, PS, 57 hp.
730	1959		G	$3,600	8/03	NWIA	WF, PTO, gas
730	1959	1,483	G	$4,100	9/03	NCIA	LP, new paint
730	1959		G	$5,700	8/03	WCMN	Std., electric start
730	1959		G	$5,700	8/03	WCMN	WF, fenders
730	1960		G	$3,975	12/03	WCIA	Diesel, 3 pt., NF
730	1960		G	$4,900	9/03	NCIA	PS, good tin, NF, OH
730	1961		F	$3,300	3/03	NWIL	NF, PS, gas
7520			F	$3,700	9/05	SESD	4WD
7520			F	$6,900	12/05	WCWI	4WD, bad PTO
7520			G	$8,000	8/05	NWIL	4WD, diesel, duals
7520	1972		G	$17,800	9/05	SEMN	4WD, singles, cab, air, 3 pt., 4 hyd., quick hitch, PTO
7520			F	$8,700	3/05	NWIL	4WD, diesel, 3 pt., PTO, duals
7520	1973	9,566	F	$4,500	3/04	SEWY	Duals, PTO, diesel, no 3 pt.
7520	1973	5,360	G	$12,250	8/04	ECIL	4WD, duals, complete OH at 5,000 hrs.
7520	1974	8,300	G	$10,250	5/04	NCKS	4WD, articulate steering, 16-speed, 3 pt., 3 hitch, PTO, 3 hyd., 18.4-34" tires (35%), no oil usage
7520	1975	9,437	G	$5,200	3/04	SEWY	Diesel, 3 pt., PTO, duals, cab
7520		9,125	G	$5,200	3/03	NESD	4WD, cab, 2 hyd., PTO, duals
7520	1972		F	$4,000	12/03	SEND	4WD, cab, AC, 3 hyd., PTO, 20.8-34" tires duals, front/rear weights
7520	1973	7,878	G	$4,800	6/03	SCOK	4WD, 3 hyd., 18.4-34" tires, new rubber duals, 175 hp.
7520	1973		G	$11,000	3/03	SWMN	4WD, 400 hours on new motor
80			G	$5,900	11/05	WCIL	Std, diesel, restored, fenders
80	1956		G	$8,000	11/05	SCKY	
80	1956		G	$8,900	9/05	SEMN	Standard, pony start, PS, front and rear weights, 2 hyd.
80			G	$9,000	6/05	ECMN	Std., diesel, pony start, no PTO, 2 hyd.
80	1956		G	$13,750	6/05	WCMN	Diesel, new tires, PS, WF

Model	Year	Hours	Cond.	Price	Date	Area	Comments
80			E	$11,400	3/04	NEIA	4 hrs. on new pony motor, PS, 2 hyd., new PTO and clutch
80	1955		G	$10,500	11/04	NWIL	Gas, WF, pony motor, runs good, repainted, good tin, new rubber
80			G	$6,000	9/03	NEIN	
80	1956		G	$6,800	8/03	WCMN	
80	1956	9,271	G	$9,750	10/03	WCSK	Canadian sale, 2WD, 18.4-34" tires, PS, cab, dual hyd.
820			G	$6,000	11/05	WCIL	Pony, fenders, PTO, PS
820			G	$8.100	8/05	WCIL	2 cyl., needed paint & tires
820	1956		G	$4.900	11/05	WCIL	Pony start, factory step, PTO, hyd, PS
820	1958		G	$11.500	9/05	SEMN	Standard, pony start, PTO, 2 hyd
820	1958	4,467	P	$1.350	9/05	NECO	Runs, pony motor, needs work, diesel
820			G	$6,250	6/05	ECMN	Diesel, new pony start, 1 hyd.
820			G	$4,100	9/04	NWMN	Diesel, WF
820			G	$4,100	9/04	NWMN	WF, diesel, PS, 18.4-34" tires
820			E	$6,600	3/04	NEIA	Pony start, PTO
820	1958		F	$3,200	9/04	NECO	Runs, poor tires, good tin
820	1958		G	$3,500	5/04	NWND	Running
820			G	$3,000	9/03	NEIN	
820		5,528	G	$3,600	6/03	WCSK	Canadian sale, diesel, PS, single hyd., pop start
820			G	$6,000	9/03	NEIN	
830			G	$8,000	11/05	WCIL	Diesel, pony, PTO, PS
830			G	$5,700	3/05	NWIL	Gas, NF, new paint
830			G	$8,900	6/05	ECIL	Pony start, new paint, 2 hyd.
830			G	$10,000	6/05	ECMN	Std., diesel, 2 hyd., new tires, 6 wheel weights
830			G	$12,250	6/05	ECMN	Standard diesel, 2 hyd., new paint
830			F	$3,700	11/04	NWMN	2-cyl. diesel, pony start, hyd., PTO, good rubber, sold "as is"
830			G	$6,000	9/04	NWMN	WF, diesel
830			E	$9,100	3/04	NEIA	Pony start, PS, foot throttle, rebuilt seat, new clutch
830	1960		G	$6,000	10/04	NEPA	Electric start, PTO
830			G	$8,000	3/03	NEND	Deere 146 loader, 2 hyd., 3 pt., PTO
830			G	$9,000	9/03	NEIN	Pony start
830		2,065	E	$11,100	8/03	NWIL	Restored, diesel, WF, electric start
830	1958		G	$5,900	8/03	WCMN	2 hyd., nearly new rear tires
830	1959		E	$7,200	6/03	NEIL	Duals
830	1975	2,200	G	$10,500	2/03	ECIL	Deere 145 loader, clean, shedded
840	1960		F	$1,150	10/04	NEPA	With pan, electric start
840	1960		G	$2,300	10/04	NEPA	Pony, restored
840	1959		G	$9,000	8/03	WCMN	Starter
8430	1978	6,477	G	$18,000	2/06	ECIL	4WD, CAH, quad range, PTO, 3 hyd., 4 inside new tires, duals
8430		7,710	G	$7,500	12/05	SCND	4WD, 3,700 hours on rebuilt engine, PTO, 20.8-38" duals (90%)
8430	1977		F	$6,250	9/05	ECND	4WD, 2,000 hours on engine & transmission OH, PTO, 3 hyd., 20.8-34"
8430	1978	6,595	G	$8,300	6/05	WCMN	4WD, 3 hyd, 16/4 speeds, average rubber
8430	1978	12,370	G	$6,000	4/05	ECND	PTO, duals
8430	1978	9,200	G	$10,000	6/05	NEND	4WD, cab, 3 pt., PTO, 3 hyd., duals, low hrs. on OH, very clean
8430	1978	6,498	G	$10,500	6/05	NENE	4WD, cast duals, radar, 3 hyd., 3 pt., PTO
8430			P	$4,800	9/04	ECSD	4WD
8430			F	$5,500	4/04	NEND	4WD, 3 hyd., PTO, Firestone 20.8-34" tires, hub
8430	1976	9,048	G	$10,700	11/04	NWMN	4WD, OH at 9,048 hours, 3 hyd., PTO, 3 pt., 18.4-38" tires (70%)
8430	1978	6,875	F	$7,000	2/04	NWKS	4WD, 3 pt., PTO, 18.4-38" tires, duals
8430			P	$5,000	9/03	SCMN	Rough, 4WD, 3 pt., PTO, duals
8430			F	$6,900	8/03	NWIL	4WD, duals, 3 pt., PTO, diesel

john deere

Model	Year	Hours	Cond.	Price	Date	Area	Comments
8430			G	$10,500	3/03	NWIL	4WD, diesel, no duals
8430			G	$11,600	8/03	NWIL	4WD, diesel, PTO, duals all around
8430			G	$14,750	3/03	NWIL	4WD, duals, diesel
8430	1976		F	$6,400	7/03	SEND	4WD, 3 hyd., PTO, low range of 2-speed, recent OH
8430	1976		F	$7,700	3/03	NCCO	4,000 hrs. on OH
8430	1977	8,520	G	$7,300	12/03	SCMN	4WD, 3 pt., PTO, 20.8-34" tires, duals
8430	1978	6,890	F	$4,000	3/03	NCOK	4WD, 3 pt., diesel, 20% rubber, PTO, 3 hyd.
8430	1978	5,211	G	$10,500	1/03	SCIL	4WD, 3 pt., PTO, 3 hyd., 18.4-38" tires, axle duals
8630			P	$200	1/06	WCCA	For parts
8630	1978	9,870	P	$8,800	2/06	NCKS	4WD, articulated diesel, QR, 3 hyd., 3 pt., with category 3, recent valve job
8630			P	$3,750	9/05	SESD	4WD
8630	1976	7,480	G	$8,100	9/05	NWIA	4WD, QR, 3 hyd., duals all around, diesel
8630		7,000	G	$0	3/05	NCOH	No sale at $15,750, 50 Series motor, 3 pt., quick hitch, PTO, duals
8630		5,200	G	$7,750	8/05	WCIA	4WD, 50 Series engine
8630			G	$11,600	3/05	WCIL	4WD, 1,000 hours on new 50 Series engine
8630	1975	6,492	G	$16,000	1/05	NWIL	4WD, 3 pt., 3 hyd., PTO, 18.4-38"R tires
8630	1976	10,011	G	$6,500	2/05	ECND	4WD, 20.8-34" tires
8630	1976		G	$7,300	4/05	NEKS	4WD, duals
8630	1977		G	$4,250	7/05	ECND	50 Series engine, PTO
8630	1977		G	$4,250	7/05	ECND	50 Series engine, PTO
8630	1977		G	$18,000	2/05	NENE	4WD, 1,670 hours on 50 Series engine, 18.4-42" tires, 10-bolt duals, 3 pt., 3 hyd., PTO
8630			G	$8,750	4/04	NWIA	4WD
8630			F	$11,000	8/04	NWPA	4WD, cab, dual wheels
8630			F	$11,900	8/04	SWPA	4WD, front & rear duals, silage blade, rubber 50%
8630			G	$16,200	1/04	ECIA	4WD, not a 50 Series engine
8630			G	$17,500	12/04	SEMN	4WD, 3 pt., PTO, duals
8630	1975	8,528	P	$2,500	3/04	SEWY	
8630	1976	7,800	G	$16,500	2/04	NECO	4WD, 3,600 hrs. on new 50 Series engine, 3 pt., PTO, 3 hyd., 18.4-38" tires, duals
8630	1977	7,310	G	$13,000	12/04	WCMN	4WD, 3 hyd., PTO, 3 pt., 20.8-38" tires
8630	1978		G	$12,800	2/04	ECIN	4WD, 50 Series engine
8630			G	$9,750	12/03	SCMN	4WD, PTO
8630		7,400	G	$10,500	3/03	NWSD	4WD, 50 Series engine, duals, 3 pt., PTO
8630			F	$13,500	8/03	NWIL	4WD, 3 pt., PTO, duals, diesel
8630	1976	7,865	G	$13,500	3/03	ECND	4WD, cab, 3 hyd., rock shaft, PTO, 20.8-38" tires, cast duals, 50 Series engine
8630	1976	7,230	G	$16,000	1/03	SEIL	4WD, 50 Series engine, 3 pt., PTO, 3 hyd., 20.8-34"R tires, axle cast duals
8630	1977		F	$7,200	3/03	NCCO	4WD, 1,200 hrs. on 50 Series engine
8630	1977	5,151	F	$7,900	3/03	NCCO	
8630	1977		F	$8,000	5/03	SWOK	4WD, 275 hp., cold air, 20.8-34" tires, duals, 50% rubber
8630	1977	7,750	G	$10,000	6/03	ECND	4WD, 50 Series engine, PTO, 3 hyd., 20.8-34" tires & duals, 5,000 hrs. on engine, rebuilt main hyd. pump 2002
8630	1977	6,700	G	$11,700	8/03	NCIA	4WD, 3 pt., newer motor, new 18.4-38" tires
8630	1978		F	$7,000	3/03	SWMI	4WD, duals, AC, new factory engine
8630	1978	4,809	G	$9,500	7/03	NEIA	4WD, 3 pt., 3 hyd., PTO, 20.8-38" tires, duals
8630	1978	7,800	G	$10,000	12/03	SCMN	4WD, 50 Series engine, transmission OH, 20.8-38" tires
A	1937		G	$3,350	1/06	SCKS	14.4-36" tires on round spoke rims, SN 459607

Model	Year	Hours	Cond.	Price	Date	Area	Comments
A	1947		F	$2,500	1/06	NCCO	WF, engine overhaul, only needs paint to finish restoration
A			G	$1,100	11/05	WCIL	NF, hand start crank, restored
A			G	$1,100	11/05	WCIL	NF, all fuel, PTO, belt pulley, styled sheet metal, hyd. lift
A			F	$1,500	8/05	ECMN	Sold with older loader
A			G	$1,600	9/05	NENE	PS, NF, clean
A			G	$1,700	11/05	WCIL	NF, M&W pistons
A			G	$2,800	11/05	WCIL	NF, PTO
A			F	$700	9/05	SEIA	
A			F	$750	8/05	ECMI	Good sheet metal, needs work, no spark
A			F	$900	12/05	WCWI	
A	1936		G	$7,250	9/05	SEMN	Unstyled factory rounds, rear weights
A	1941		G	$1,300	12/05	NWIL	Gas
A	1947		F	$1,300	10/05	WCIL	
A	1949		G	$1,400	12/05	ECIL	
A	1951		G	$6,700	11/05	SCKY	
A			P	$750	6/05	ECWI	For parts
A			G	$1,300	6/05	ECWI	9 bolt
A			G	$1,350	7/05	SCIA	
A			G	$1,650	6/05	ECWI	
A			G	$2,600	7/05	SCIA	Unstyled, open fan shaft, restored
A			G	$3,100	6/05	ECMN	Gas, tricycle, PTO, fenders, new tires, water pump
A			G	$3,250	6/05	ECMN	2-row corn picker mounted, 51-a, tricycle, new tires & paint
A			G	$5,000	6/05	ECWI	Painted, rear round spokes
A			G	$7,800	7/05	SCIA	Hi crop, good tag, restored, 1 of 246 built
A	1936		G	$1,250	1/05	NENE	NF, unstyled, Farmhand F10 loader
A	1936		G	$1,800	4/05	SCNE	Unstyled, 12.4-38" tires on spoke rims, rear wheel weights, spoke front wheels, runs
A	1936		F	$2,500	1/05	NWIL	Unstyled
A	1936		G	$3,500	2/05	NWOH	Unstyled, fenders, shutters
A	1937		G	$1,750	1/05	NEIA	Unstyled
A	1943		P	$600	7/05	NEIA	Hand start, gas, not running
A	1943		F	$800	6/05	WCMN	Original
A	1946		F	$1,000	2/05	NWOH	Buzz saw, original
A	1946		F	$1,100	2/05	WCOK	LP, ran, row crop, styled
A	1947		G	$1,300	2/05	NEIN	Gas, NF, good rubber
A	1947		G	$1,700	2/05	NENE	Slant dash, electric start
A	1948		P	$400	2/05	NWOH	Parts
A	1948		G	$1,000	1/05	SENE	Gas, NF, PS, Roll-O-Matic
A	1949		F	$500	3/05	NCIA	New rear tires
A	1949		G	$4,500	1/05	NENE	NF, 2-row front mount cultivator, 1 owner
A	1950		P	$550	7/05	NEIA	1 hyd., gas, not running
A	1950		G	$1,800	7/05	NEIA	1 hyd., 2 gas tanks, 11-38" tires
A	1951		G	$1,250	2/05	NEIN	Gas, repainted
A	1951		G	$2,250	7/05	SCIA	Row crop, restored
A	1951		G	$3,650	1/05	NENE	NF, 12.4-38" tires
A	1952		G	$1,350	2/05	SCMN	
A	1952		G	$1,550	4/05	NENE	12.4-38" tires, fuel burner
A			P	$50	9/04	NWMN	Just rear ½, parts
A			F	$450	9/04	NWMN	NF, loader
A			P	$850	12/04	SWIA	Needs work, gas, electric start, styled, 6-speed, 12.4-38" tires, Powertrol, PTO
A			G	$900	3/04	SEMN	
A			G	$1,150	2/04	NEIN	NF

john deere

Model	Year	Hours	Cond.	Price	Date	Area	Comments
A			G	$1,600	5/04	SCPA	
A			P	$1,650	4/04	NEND	WF, cyclone
A			G	$1,800	10/04	NEPA	Unstyled, fenders, cultivator, front round spokes
A			G	$2,000	9/04	NWMN	WF
A			G	$2,250	1/04	ECNE	Unstyled
A			G	$2,300	9/04	NWMN	General purpose "A," NF
A			G	$3,100	10/04	NEPA	
A			G	$9,250	9/04	NWMN	General purpose "A," WF, round spoke front & rear
A	1934		G	$4,500	6/04	WCWI	Open fan shaft, repainted, on full steel
A	1935		G	$0	12/04	ECMI	No sale at $2,100, unstyled, sharp
A	1936		G	$2,400	11/04	NWIL	Gas, runs good, good tin
A	1937		G	$2,300	8/04	ECMI	Unstyled, restored, NF
A	1937		G	$2,750	6/04	WCWI	Repainted, on full steel
A	1937		G	$3,750	6/04	NWIL	Gas, new rear tires, good tin
A	1938		F	$1,800	3/04	ECNE	Gas, unstyled, NF, Powertrol, 13.6-38" tires, cast rear wheels, PTO, 1 hyd.
A	1938		G	$2,300	7/04	NWMN	Unstyled, NF, new restoration & rear tires
A	1939		P	$200	5/04	NWND	Not running
A	1939		G	$1,400	10/04	NEPA	Original cultivator, new front tires
A	1940		P	$500	5/04	NWND	Not running
A	1940		F	$525	1/04	WCIL	Not running, gas
A	1940		G	$1,300	6/04	ECND	New tires, 2-row cultivator, 35.3 hp.
A	1941		P	$800	10/04	NWOH	Not running
A	1941		F	$1,725	11/04	SENE	Gas, NF, 3 pt.
A	1944		G	$950	9/04	NWMN	WF, PTO, not running
A	1944		G	$1,800	5/04	NCKS	Repainted, good tin and rubber
A	1945		F	$700	12/04	ECMN	Loader, new clutch/carb., rebuilt transmission
A	1946		F	$1,050	9/04	NECO	Restored, tin dented, poor tires, long hood
A	1946		G	$1,100	1/04	NEIN	Runs good, NF
A	1946		G	$2,500	2/04	ECMI	Modified pulling tractor, oversized componets
A	1947		G	$1,000	8/04	ECIL	Not running
A	1948		P	$750	10/04	NEPA	For parts
A	1948		G	$3,100	2/04	ECMI	Factory WF, good tires
A	1949		G	$1,100	9/04	NECO	Restored, good tires, Roll-O-Matic
A	1949		G	$1,300	6/04	ECND	
A	1949		G	$1,900	9/04	NCKS	3 pt., hyd., electric start, new rears
A	1950		G	$2,100	10/04	NWOH	
A	1950		G	$2,450	5/04	SCPA	Square axle, restored
A	1951		G	$1,390	10/04	SEMN	New tires, good tin
A	1951		G	$1,675	3/04	NWIA	Roll-O-Matic
A	1951		G	$2,050	10/04	NEPA	
A	1952		G	$1,200	2/04	ECNE	12-38" tires, Behlen PS, Deere 38 7' sickle mower bar
A	1952		F	$1,400	9/04	NECO	Runs, electric start, poor tires, NF, good tin
A	1952		G	$1,400	4/04	WCMI	
A			P	$450	9/03	NEIN	
A			G	$500	9/03	NEIN	WF
A			G	$500	9/03	NEIN	
A			P	$550	9/03	NEIN	Parts
A			P	$650	9/03	NEIN	Parts

Model	Year	Hours	Cond.	Price	Date	Area	Comments
A			G	$700	9/03	NEIN	
A			F	$725	8/03	NENE	
A			P	$800	8/03	NCCO	Gas, NF, drawbar, poor tires
A			P	$950	8/03	NCCO	Gas, 3 pt., drawbar, tricycle
A			G	$1,050	9/03	ECWI	
A			G	$1,100	9/03	NEIN	Rear round spokes
A			G	$1,375	9/03	NEIN	
A			G	$1,450	10/03	ECMN	
A			G	$1,500	8/03	NCCO	Gas, drawbar, Roll-O-Matic, NF, poor front tires, new rear tires
A			G	$1,500	9/03	NEIN	
A			G	$1,800	8/03	NWIL	Gas, NF
A			E	$1,800	8/03	NWIL	Gas, NF
A			E	$1,900	8/03	NWIL	Restored, rear steel, styled, fenders, hyd., NF, gas
A			G	$2,300	9/03	NEIN	
A			G	$2,600	9/03	NEIN	
A			G	$4,000	9/03	NEIN	Unstyled
A			G	$4,400	4/03	WCMI	OH
A			G	$4,700	9/03	NEIN	Restored, unstyled
A			G	$14,750	9/03	NEIN	Hi crop
A			G	$20,000	6/03	SEMN	The 59th Deere A produced! Original HC 125, early rock shaft, center fill tank, early seat bracket, all of the correct hard-to-find parts, restored, SN 410059
A			G	$20,000	6/03	SEMN	Hi crop, restored, new tires, confirmed tag, SN 67984
A			E	$40,500	8/03	NWIL	Hi crop, restored, 1 of 246, gas
A	1935		G	$5,300	8/03	NCIA	On distillate, old original turf tires, open shaft, original book, SN 413951
A	1936		G	$1,750	8/03	WCMN	Unstyled on steel
A	1936		G	$2,000	9/03	SEND	Unstyled
A	1936		F	$2,550	8/03	WCIL	Gas, unstyled, bad tires
A	1938		G	$1,100	7/03	NWMN	Powerlift PTO
A	1938		G	$1,500	8/03	WCMN	Unstyled
A	1941		P	$300	9/03	SEND	For parts
A	1941		E	$2,600	6/03	NEIL	
A	1942		G	$0	9/03	SEND	No sale at $1,700
A	1942		F	$750	9/03	SCMI	
A	1942		G	$1,800	7/03	NWMN	WF, powerlift, PTO
A	1945		F	$900	8/03	WCMN	
A	1946		F	$650	3/03	WCMN	NF
A	1947		F	$450	4/03	WCSD	Single front wheel, locked up, collectible
A	1947		F	$800	12/03	NWOH	Did not run
A	1947		F	$825	9/03	WCIA	2 shift levers, enclosed starter
A	1947		G	$1,500	12/03	SCIA	Good metal & rubber
A	1948		F	$1,100	3/03	NESD	Deere WF, good tin
A	1948		G	$1,900	7/03	NWMN	Power block, rock shaft, PTO, hyd.
A	1949		P	$350	6/03	NCIA	
A	1949		F	$1,000	9/03	SCMI	
A	1949		E	$2,950	7/03	NWMN	NF, restored
A	1949		E	$3,000	8/03	NCCO	Gas, 3 pt., restored, new paint, good tires, WF
A	1950		G	$800	6/03	SENE	Gas
A	1950		G	$1,600	9/03	SEND	Roll-O-Matic
A	1950		G	$1,600	9/03	SEND	Schwartz WF
A	1950		E	$1,600	2/03	SCKS	Roll-O-Matic, slick
A	1951		G	$1,900	11/03	ECND	

john deere

Model	Year	Hours	Cond.	Price	Date	Area	Comments
A	1952		F	$800	8/03	NWIA	PS, live pump, gas
A	1952		G	$1,600	8/03	WCMN	
AO			G	$8,000	8/05	NEIN	Unstyled, restored, shutters, electric start, lights
AO			G	$10,000	8/05	NEIN	Unstyled, restored, factory front round spokes
AO	1949		F	$1,300	10/04	NEPA	
AOS			G	$5,500	8/05	NEIN	Started restoring, sheet metal in primer
AOS			G	$7,750	7/05	SCIA	Restored
AOS			E	$15,500	8/03	NWIL	Restored, orchard, WF, gas
AR	1937		G	$3,200	9/05	SEMN	Unstyled, flat rear spokes, shutters
AR			G	$1,700	7/05	SCIA	
AR			G	$2,250	7/05	SCIA	Restored
AR			G	$4,600	6/05	ECMN	Gas, PTO, 1 hyd., new tires, new paint
AR			G	$5,100	6/05	ECWI	Painted
AR			G	$1,938	10/04	NEPA	
AR			G	$2,500	12/04	SEMN	Styled
AR			G	$3,200	9/04	NWMN	WF
AR			G	$1,850	5/03	WCSK	Canadian sale, styled, rebuilt motor & starter
AR			G	$1,850	9/03	NEIN	Unstyled
AR			G	$2,400	9/03	NEIN	
AR			G	$3,200	9/03	NEIN	
AR	1936		G	$1,900	7/03	ECND	PTO, on steel
AR	1937		G	$3,400	7/03	NWMN	Factory round spoke wheels, complete rebuild
AR	1949		F	$1,400	8/03	WCMN	Unstyled, OH but not reassembled
AR	1951		G	$1,600	7/03	NWMN	PTO
AR	1951		G	$3,300	8/03	WCMN	Styled
AW	1940		G	$2,900	10/04	NEPA	WF, new tires, restored
AW	1941		E	$1,200	8/03	NWIL	Original, factory WF, gas
B			G	$1,125	8/05	NWIL	Gas
B			G	$13,000	11/05	SCKY	
B			F	$1,400	12/05	NWIL	Gas, full steel
B			P	$150	8/05	SCMI	For parts
B			G	$2,000	11/05	WCIL	Unstyled, NF, all fuel, PTO
B			G	$4,700	11/05	SCKY	
B			F	$800	9/05	NENE	Later model, one of two on same sale
B			G	$900	11/05	WCIL	Styled, gas
B			F	$985	9/05	NENE	Later model
B	1935		G	$1,900	11/05	WCIL	Unstyled, NF, gas
B	1936		G	$3,400	11/05	WCIL	Hand start, spokes, belt pully
B	1937		G	$3,850	9/05	SEMN	Unstyled, factory round spokes front and back, rear weights
B	1938		G	$2,000	11/05	WCIL	NF, gas, cutoffs
B	1939		G	$2,000	11/05	WCIL	NF, hand start, spokes
B	1941		G	$1,700	7/05	SESD	
B	1946		G	$1,100	9/05	NECO	3 pt., new rear tires, gas
B	1948		G	$2,600	9/05	SEMN	Styled, rear weights, fenders
B	1948		G	$3,100	8/05	ECMI	Wide axle, 42" wheels, new tires
B	1950		G	$1,900	12/05	SEMN	Electric start, restored
B	1951		F	$1,200	11/05	NEIA	Gas, NF, 10-38" tires, starts & runs but seldom used
B	1951		F	$900	9/05	WCNE	Gas, 3 pt., single front
B	1952		G	$2,150	10/05	WCIL	New paint, needs trans. work

Model	Year	Hours	Cond.	Price	Date	Area	Comments
B			P	$650	7/05	SCIA	
B			G	$1,400	6/05	ECWI	Square axle, restored
B			G	$1,800	6/05	ECMN	Tricycle, repainted
B			G	$1,900	6/05	ECMN	Tricycle, fenders
B			G	$1,900	6/05	ECIL	New tires all around
B			G	$3,100	6/05	ECIL	Long frame, expo restoration, everything new or repaired, new tires all around
B			G	$3,600	6/05	ECWI	
B	1936		F	$1,450	6/05	WCMN	Stuck PTO
B	1937		G	$2,100	1/05	NEIA	Unstyled
B	1937		G	$2,150	2/05	NWOH	Restored on hard rubber
B	1937		G	$9,000	6/05	ECMN	Gas, tricycle, round spokes front & rear, new paint, OH
B	1938		G	$1,400	4/05	SCNE	Unstyled, 10-36" tires, spoke wheels, runs
B	1938		G	$2,100	7/05	NCIA	
B	1939		G	$1,650	1/05	NEIA	
B	1940		G	$1,400	3/05	WCIL	Engine OH, good tin, gas
B	1943		G	$2,400	1/05	NENE	NF, Deere #5 7' mower, 11-38" tires
B	1947		G	$5,900	7/05	SCIA	42" rears, single front, restored
B	1948		G	$1,200	7/05	NCIA	
B	1948		G	$1,400	1/05	NEIA	
B	1948		G	$2,700	8/05	NCIA	Single front wheel, repainted
B	1948		G	$2,900	6/05	ECIL	New paint, hyd., shutters, Roll-O-Matic
B	1949		F	$1,000	7/05	NEIA	1 hyd., gas, 12.4-38" tires
B	1949		G	$2,050	7/05	SCIA	Single front
B	1949		G	$2,600	2/05	NCKS	Restored, new rubber, electric start
B	1950		G	$1,525	1/05	NEIA	
B	1950		G	$1,650	8/05	SWOH	
B	1951		G	$1,600	7/05	NEIA	1 hyd., gas
B	1951		G	$3,300	2/05	NWOH	Fenders, good rubber
B	1952		G	$1,100	1/05	NEIA	
B	1952		G	$1,350	7/05	SCMN	Restored
B			P	$300	2/04	ECNE	For parts
B			P	$300	9/04	NWMN	NF, missing 1 front & rear rim & other parts
B			P	$500	2/04	ECNE	For parts
B			G	$725	10/04	NCOH	Not running, loader
B			F	$800	10/04	NEPA	
B			P	$950	3/04	SCMN	Not running
B			G	$1,100	10/04	NCOH	
B			F	$1,100	10/04	SEPA	Unrestored, good rubber
B			G	$1,300	10/04	NEPA	One-way plow
B			F	$1,300	9/04	NWMN	NF, fenders
B			F	$1,350	9/04	NWMN	NF, Deere 101 mounted picker
B			G	$1,500	7/04	NWMN	Hand start
B			F	$1,600	9/04	NWMN	WF, missing front & rear rims
B			G	$1,600	3/04	SEIA	
B			F	$1,800	9/04	NWMN	NF, 2-row cultivator
B			F	$2,100	9/04	NWMN	Rubber tire, rear spokes, missing 1 front wheel
B			G	$2,300	9/04	NWMN	WF
B			G	$2,500	9/04	NWMN	WF, round spoke, flat spoke rears
B			G	$2,700	6/04	SEMN	
B			G	$3,000	9/04	NWMN	General purpose "B," 11-38" tires, round spoke rears, fenders, Deere mounted sickle mower

john deere

Model	Year	Hours	Cond.	Price	Date	Area	Comments
B			G	$3,200	9/04	NWMN	WF, fenders, 1 hyd., Deere #5 mower
B			G	$3,300	2/04	NCIN	Restored, steel wheels
B			G	$3,300	9/04	NWMN	Rubber tires, rear spokes, complete
B			G	$4,250	6/04	WCWI	4-bolt
B			G	$5,000	10/04	SEPA	Restored, tricycle, good rubber
B			G	$5,800	11/04	WCIL	Late model, WF, fenders, restored
B	1935		G	$2,750	5/04	SCPA	On steel, restored
B	1935		G	$5,000	6/04	WCWI	Brass tag, factory rear spokes, single front
B	1937		G	$1,300	9/04	NWMN	Short frame, unstyled, new front tires
B	1938		G	$2,000	9/04	NWMN	Unstyled, spoke wheels, crank start, PTO
B	1939		P	$475	5/04	NWND	Not running
B	1939		F	$700	3/04	WCNE	Single front, mounted cultivator, needed 1 rear tire
B	1940		P	$350	5/04	NWND	Deere #5 mower
B	1940		F	$700	10/04	NEPA	
B	1940		F	$1,200	9/04	NECO	Runs, good tires & tin
B	1941		F	$650	9/04	NECO	Runs, poor tin, excellent tires, loader
B	1941		F	$750	2/04	ECNE	
B	1941		F	$1,200	9/04	NECO	Runs, fair tires, good tin
B	1941		F	$2,000	5/04	NWND	
B	1942		E	$1,300	6/04	ECND	New tires, 25 hp.
B	1943		P	$325	5/04	NWND	Not running
B	1946		G	$1,000	9/04	ECMI	NF, new rubber, electric start
B	1946		G	$1,600	9/04	NECO	Restored, long hood, good tires
B	1948		G	$1,650	11/04	NCIA	OH, good tin
B	1949		G	$1,600	9/04	NECO	Restored, Powertrol, good rubber
B	1950		P	$450	10/04	NEPA	For parts
B	1950		G	$1,250	6/04	ECND	25 hp.
B	1950		G	$1,800	8/04	ECIL	Woods 306 belly mower
B	1951		P	$200	10/04	NEPA	For parts
B	1951		E	$1,000	6/04	ECND	25 hp., new tires
B	1951		G	$1,700	2/04	ECMI	NF
B	1951		G	$1,950	6/04	ECND	25 hp.
B			F	$420	1/03	ECKS	Styled, not running
B			P	$550	10/03	ECNE	Electric start, as is, did not run
B			G	$600	9/03	NEIN	WF
B			P	$625	4/03	WCIA	NF, not running
B			F	$700	3/03	NWIL	Gas
B			G	$800	4/03	WCWI	Running condition
B			E	$800	10/03	SENE	Gas, NF
B			G	$825	9/03	NEIN	
B			G	$925	9/03	NEIN	
B			G	$950	9/03	NEIN	
B			G	$975	7/03	NEOH	
B			F	$1,000	8/03	NCCO	Gas, Deere 45W loader, 3 pt., tricycle front, fair tires
B			F	$1,050	6/03	NWIL	Gas, styled, enclosed flywheel, starter, cast iron wheels, Roll-O-Matic front end
B			G	$1,200	8/03	NCCO	Good tires, 3 pt., tricycle, gas
B			F	$1,275	6/03	NCWI	NF
B			F	$1,325	8/03	NCIA	Late model, good tin & rubber

Model	Year	Hours	Cond.	Price	Date	Area	Comments
B			G	$1,400	8/03	NCOH	Restored
B			G	$1,550	9/03	NEIN	
B			G	$1,600	9/03	NEIN	Unstyled
B			G	$1,750	9/03	NEIN	
B			F	$1,850	8/03	SEPA	NF, average rubber, rough paint
B			G	$1,900	5/03	WCSD	Dozer, buzz saw, mounted cultivator
B			G	$1,950	9/03	NEIN	
B			G	$2,100	9/03	NEIN	
B			G	$2,100	9/03	NEIN	Styled
B			E	$2,600	8/03	NWIL	Gas, WF
B			F	$2,800	9/03	SEMN	
B			G	$3,400	9/03	NEIN	
B			G	$4,250	9/03	NEIN	
B	1935		G	$1,600	9/03	WCIA	Hand start, 2 shifting levers
B	1935		F	$2,000	12/03	NCOH	General purpose, unstyled, round spoke fronts, flat spoke rears
B	1935		G	$3,300	6/03	NEIL	
B	1936		G	$3,200	9/03	SEND	Unstyled, rear round spoke wheels
B	1936		G	$3,800	8/03	WCMN	Unstyled, on steel, fenders
B	1937		G	$1,300	8/03	WCMN	Flat spoke
B	1937		F	$1,600	7/03	ECND	PTO, rear steel, rubber fronts
B	1937		G	$3,900	8/03	WCMN	Unstyled
B	1938		P	$650	8/03	NWIA	Motor stuck, unstyled, tires rotten & flat
B	1938		G	$1,600	8/03	WCMN	Unstyled, new tires
B	1938		G	$1,700	7/03	NWMN	PTO, rock shaft
B	1938		G	$3,200	6/03	NEIL	Skeleton wheels
B	1938		E	$3,600	8/03	NWIL	Old restore, gas, flat spoke
B	1939		F	$575	6/03	SEND	NF, flywheel start, 6 speed, hi/lo, magneto, hyd., 11.2-38" tires
B	1939		F	$900	8/03	WCMN	
B	1939		F	$900	8/03	WCMN	
B	1940		G	$1,250	8/03	WCMN	
B	1941		G	$1,700	8/03	NWIA	NF, gas
B	1943		G	$1,800	9/03	SEND	Flat spoke rears
B	1944		F	$650	12/03	WCIA	NF
B	1944		F	$950	8/03	WCMN	
B	1946		G	$650	4/03	SCND	NF, 6-speed hi/low, Deere B200 2-row front mount cultivator
B	1947		G	$1,400	3/03	NWIL	NF
B	1947		F	$1,550	12/03	WCMI	NF, 12.4-38" tires
B	1948		G	$1,800	7/03	NWMN	2 pt., PTO, hyd.
B	1949		G	$1,200	9/03	SEND	
B	1949		G	$1,400	8/03	WCMN	Single front tire
B	1949		G	$1,500	8/03	WCMN	
B	1949		F	$1,550	3/03	NCCO	
B	1949		G	$2,000	8/03	NWIA	Gas
B	1949		G	$2,900	8/03	WCMN	WF
B	1950		P	$500	4/03	NWPA	Not running, 27 hp., NF
B	1950		G	$1,100	8/03	WCMN	
B	1951		G	$1,600	9/03	SEND	Farmhand F10 loader, grapple, and yellow pump
B	1951		G	$2,000	6/03	NEIL	Roll-o-Matic
B	1952		E	$1,275	6/03	SENE	Gas
BNH	1941		E	$7,100	8/03	NWIL	Restored, single front styled round spoke wheel, gas
BO			G	$9,900	7/05	NEIA	Lindeman, repainted

john deere

Model	Year	Hours	Cond.	Price	Date	Area	Comments
BO			G	$9,250	8/05	NEIN	Restored, round spokes front and rear
BO			G	$9,900	8/05	NEIN	Restored, electric start, factory 7" lights
BO			G	$10,250	8/05	NEIN	Restored, round spokes front and rear
BO	1947		G	$15,500	7/05	SCIA	Lindeman, restored
BO	1936		F	$1,600	10/04	NEPA	Rear steel, stuck
BO			G	$7,750	8/03	WCMN	Lindeman crawler
BR			G	$7,000	9/05	NEIN	Brass tag
BR			G	$5,400	6/05	ECWI	Painted
BR			G	$5,500	7/05	SCIA	Full steel, restored
BR	1937		G	$4,700	6/04	NWMN	Complete, PTO
BR	1938		G	$4,250	6/04	WCWI	Repainted, on full steel, extensions
BR	1940		G	$4,600	9/04	NECO	Runs, fair tin, complete
BR	1936		G	$3,700	7/03	NWMN	Full rubber
BR	1937		G	$4,000	7/03	ECND	PTO, on rubber, spoked rims
BR	1937		G	$4,400	8/03	WCMN	Unstyled
BR	1937		G	$8,000	6/03	NEIL	Spoke fronts
BW			G	$1,800	6/05	ECMN	WF
BW			G	$2,900	10/04	NEPA	One-way plow
BW			F	$5,700	9/03	NEIN	Styled
BWH	1938		F	$61,000	7/03	ECCO	40" round rears, 1 of 14 sold
BWH	1938		F	$81,000	7/03	ECCO	40" round rears, stuck, 1 of 14 sold
D	1937		G	$2,250	2/06	WCIL	Restored and running
D	1937		G	$3,000	2/06	SCKS	Spoke front rims
D			G	$2,000	9/05	SCON	Canadian sale
D			G	$2,100	9/05	SCON	Canadian sale
D			G	$2,200	11/05	WCIL	Unstyled, WF, PTO
D			G	$3,200	9/05	NEIN	Styled ES with turning brakes
D			G	$3,400	12/05	NCCO	
D	1926		G	$6,000	6/05	SWOH	On steel, unstyled, accepted as the first Model D in county
D	1937		G	$8,600	9/05	SEMN	Styled, dual stacks, round front spokes
D	1941		G	$9,100	9/05	SEMN	Styled, rear weights, Powertrol installed by JD dealer
D	1950		G	$4,250	11/05	SCKY	
D			G	$3,150	6/05	ECWI	Hand start, painted, new rubber
D			G	$3,600	6/05	ECWI	Styled, crankshaft, full steel
D			G	$3,750	7/05	SCIA	Unstyled, full steel, restored
D			G	$4,500	6/05	ECMN	Electric start, new paint
D			G	$4,900	6/05	ECWI	Unstyled, painted, rear round spokes
D			G	$17,000	7/05	SCIA	Spoke wheel, 24", restored
D	1933		G	$5,600	2/05	NWOH	Restored
D	1947		G	$2,600	4/05	NCCO	Completely restored, steel wheels
D			P	$200	9/04	NWMN	No tin
D			P	$325	9/04	NWMN	Parts
D			F	$1,700	9/04	NWMN	On steel, round spoke fronts, flat spoke rears, with lugs
D			F	$1,900	9/04	NWMN	No rear wheels, has center cast
D			E	$10,500	3/04	WCOH	Sharp
D	1938		G	$1,900	10/04	NEPA	Unstyled, round front spokes
D	1947		F	$1,450	5/04	NWND	Running
D	1949		G	$2,000	10/04	NEPA	PTO, restored
D	1949		G	$2,250	2/04	WCMN	PTO, gas

Model	Year	Hours	Cond.	Price	Date	Area	Comments
D	1949		F	$2,500	1/04	WCKS	Styled, electric start, good rubber
D	1950		G	$2,200	9/04	NCKS	New paint
D			P	$100	9/03	NEIN	Full steel
D			P	$200	9/03	NEIN	Parts
D			P	$250	9/03	NEIN	Parts, unstyled
D			G	$425	9/03	NEIN	Round spokes
D			G	$900	9/03	NEIN	
D			G	$1,100	9/03	NEIN	
D			G	$1,350	9/03	NEIN	
D			G	$1,850	9/03	NEIN	
D			G	$2,050	9/03	NEIN	
D			G	$2,200	9/03	NEIN	Unstyled
D			G	$2,250	12/03	NWKS	Runs good, paint not so good
D			G	$2,500	10/03	ECMN	On rubber
D			G	$2,500	6/03	WCSK	Canadian sale, 14-20" tires, new paint
D			G	$2,900	9/03	NEIN	Styled
D			E	$3,000	8/03	NCCO	Diesel, restored, new tires & paint, drawbar hitch, WF
D			G	$3,100	9/03	NEIN	
D			G	$3,700	9/03	NEIN	
D			G	$4,000	9/03	NEIN	Unstyled
D			G	$4,000	9/03	NEIN	
D			G	$4,300	8/03	WCMN	No SN
D			E	$13,500	8/03	NWIL	Restored, gas, full steel
D	1925		G	$10,000	7/03	ECND	On steel, spoked, flywheel
D	1926		F	$1,200	8/03	ECNE	Gas, on steel
D	1927		G	$2,250	7/03	ECND	On steel
D	1929		G	$2,700	9/03	SEND	Unstyled, on steel
D	1929		E	$4,600	7/03	WCSK	Canadian sale, fully restored
D	1930		G	$1,800	7/03	NWMN	2-speed
D	1931		F	$1,650	8/03	WCMN	Unstyled, block weld
D	1932		P	$1,900	3/03	NCCO	
D	1936		F	$1,400	8/03	WCMN	Unstyled
D	1937		P	$800	5/03	WCIN	Not running
D	1937		G	$1,800	7/03	NWMN	Full rubber
D	1938		G	$2,200	9/03	SEND	
D	1939		G	$3,300	6/03	NEIL	Round, spoke front
D	1941		G	$2,550	9/03	SEND	
D	1945		G	$3,500	7/03	ECND	Full rubber
D	1947		F	$2,050	8/03	WCMN	Dual brakes
D	1948		G	$1,550	7/03	NWMN	PTO
G			G	$2,650	1/06	WCTX	WF, new paint, 70% rubber
G	1938		G	$5,200	1/06	SCKS	New 13.6-36" rear tires, new 6.00-16" front tires, SN 5678
G	1952		G	$2,100	1/06	WCTX	NF, new rubber
G			G	$2,700	11/05	WCIL	NF, styled, PTO
G			G	$3,000	11/05	WCIL	Gas, single front
G			G	$3,100	11/05	WCIL	NF, del seat, hyd.
G	1939		G	$8,850	9/05	SEMN	Round rear spokes, unstyled, front weights
G	1951		G	$4,000	11/05	WCIL	NF, electric, belt pulley
G	1953		G	$6,250	11/05	SCKY	
G			P	$425	6/05	ECWI	For parts
G			G	$4,000	6/05	ECIL	NF
G			G	$7,400	6/05	ECWI	New tin, painted

john deere

Model	Year	Hours	Cond.	Price	Date	Area	Comments
G			G	$9,200	7/05	SCIA	Unstyled, tall radiator, restored
G			G	$12,500	7/05	SCIA	Unstyled, low radiator, round spokes, restored
G	1938		G	$6,500	2/05	NWOH	Unstyled, restored, fenders
G	1952		G	$5,000	7/05	SCIA	Restored
G			P	$500	9/04	NWMN	Parts, has tires & rims on rear
G			P	$1,050	10/04	NEPA	For parts
G			F	$2,600	9/04	NWMN	NF, 14.9-38" tires, with mounted front blade, hyd. lift
G			G	$3,200	11/04	WCIL	Late model, original
G			G	$9,750	2/04	NCIN	
G	1938		F	$3,200	9/04	NECO	Does not run, complete
G	1938		G	$5,250	6/04	WCWI	On rubber
G	1938		G	$5,250	6/04	WCWI	Unstyled, on full steel
G	1938		G	$13,500	6/04	WCWI	Low radiator, repainted, on full steel
G	1939		F	$1,350	9/04	NECO	Runs, fair tin & tires
G	1947		F	$1,600	9/04	NECO	Runs, good tires, Powertrol
G	1947		G	$5,200	5/04	SCPA	PS, restored
G	1948		G	$2,500	3/04	WCNE	Dual front, live power, Deere 45 loader
G	1950		G	$4,700	8/04	WCMN	NF, gas
G			G	$3,700	9/03	NEIN	
G			G	$8,000	6/03	SEMN	Unstyled, restored, cast centers, SN 8851
G			G	$27,000	9/03	NEIN	Hi crop
G			E	$32,000	6/03	SEMN	Hi crop, restored, new tires, confirmed tag, SN 63304
G	1930		F	$1,700	9/03	NCIA	Engine rebuilt, on steel, runs, bad magneto
G	1938		G	$4,100	9/03	NCIA	Pulling tractor
G	1938		G	$4,250	8/03	WCMN	Unstyled
G	1938		G	$4,300	7/03	NWMN	Powerlift, PTO
G	1938		G	$5,600	7/03	NWMN	Full steel
G	1945		G	$2,650	8/03	NCIA	PS
G	1947		G	$3,500	6/03	NEIL	
G	1949		G	$3,200	8/03	WCMN	
G	1950		F	$2,200	7/03	NCND	Roll-O-Matic, NF
GM	1945		G	$3,100	11/05	WCIL	Cirrect #51 carb, new gauges
GM			F	$2,500	7/05	SCIA	
GM			G	$3,500	6/05	ECWI	New rubber, painted
GM			G	$4,900	7/05	SCIA	Handstart, restored
GM			G	$11,000	7/05	SCIA	Electric start
GM	1943		G	$4,200	9/04	NECO	Restored, good tires, nice
GM	1946		F	$1,200	9/04	NECO	Runs, fair tin, poor tires
GM	1947		G	$2,950	10/04	NEPA	Restored
GM	1947		E	$4,600	3/04	SEMI	Mint, fully restored, showroom condition
GM			G	$2,350	9/03	NEIN	
GM			G	$2,500	9/03	NEIN	
GM			E	$5,000	8/03	NWIL	Restored, gas, NF, hand start
GM	1946		G	$2,300	8/03	WCMN	
GP			G	$3,250	9/05	NENE	Steel wheels
GP			G	$3,300	11/05	WCIL	WF, not running, loose, cutoffs
GP	1930		G	$3,300	11/05	WCIL	Hand start, fenders, belt pulley
GP	1930		G	$7,900	9/05	SEMN	Factory round fronts and rears
GP	1951		G	$3,300	12/05	NCCO	

Model	Year	Hours	Cond.	Price	Date	Area	Comments
GP			G	$6,600	6/05	NEND	Unstyled, spoke wheels, PTO
GP			G	$26,000	7/05	SCIA	Top steer, restored, 1 of 417 built
GP	1930		G	$4,600	2/05	NWOH	On hard rubber, restored
GP	1931		G	$4,250	6/05	ECIL	Original tires
GP			P	$1,400	3/04	NWPA	Not running, bought to restore, engine not frozen
GP			G	$8,500	9/04	NWMN	WF, round spoke fronts, fenders
GP	1930		G	$6,500	6/04	WCWI	Repainted, on full steel
GP	1930		G	$11,500	6/04	WCWI	Wide tread, repainted, on full steel, correct 44" wheels
GP			F	$1,900	9/03	NEIN	Cracked block
GP			E	$3,500	8/03	NWIL	Old restore, gas
GP			E	$5,400	8/03	NWIL	Restored, gas, WF
GP			E	$6,100	8/03	NWIL	Restored, NF, gas, round spoke rears
GP			G	$10,250	4/03	ECMN	Gas
GP	1929		G	$5,000	7/03	NWMN	Full steel, complete restoration, brass carb, parade road bands, rear steel extensions
GP	1931		G	$3,200	7/03	ECND	WF, on steel, mid mount, PTO, very rare
GW			G	$5,000	6/05	ECMN	Row crop, WF, PTO
GW			F	$3,750	10/04	SEPA	Unrestored, WF, average rubber
H			F	$1,250	9/05	NENE	PTO, drawbar, 9.5-32" tires
H	1940		G	$4,750	11/05	SCKY	
H	1941		G	$3,300	9/05	NENE	Electric start, hyd. pump & lift cyl., 9.5-32" tires
H	1947		G	$6,100	9/05	SEMN	Cast fronts, fenders, hyd, elec. start, rear weights
H			G	$1,900	1/05	SWMN	
H			G	$2,500	6/05	ECWI	
H			G	$3,250	6/05	ECMN	Row crop, tricycle, fenders, hand start
H			G	$3,500	8/05	NEIN	Restored, hand start, factory fenders
H	1940		G	$4,300	2/05	NCKS	Restored, new rubber, hand crank
H	1941		G	$2,600	7/05	SCIA	Restored
H	1941		G	$3,500	2/05	NWOH	Restored, new rubber
H	1945		E	$5,400	1/05	NEIA	
H			P	$525	7/04	NEND	NF, PTO, rock shaft, hand start
H			G	$2,100	9/04	SEND	
H			G	$3,000	12/04	SEPA	1-row moldboard plow attached
H			G	$3,050	10/04	SEPA	Restored, NF, good rubber
H			G	$3,200	9/04	NWMN	NF
H	1939		G	$2,100	10/04	NEPA	New tires
H	1940		G	$2,400	5/04	SCPA	PTO, restored
H	1940		G	$2,600	9/04	NWMN	NF, rear weights
H	1941		F	$2,000	10/04	NWOH	
H	1942		G	$2,300	7/04	NWMN	NF, electric start, painted
H			G	$225	9/03	NEIN	
H			F	$1,300	5/03	SWOK	
H			G	$1,600	9/03	NEIN	
H			G	$1,850	9/03	NEIN	
H			G	$1,900	8/03	SWMN	NF, gas
H			E	$2,400	8/03	NCCO	Restored, new tires & paint, gas, NF
H			G	$2,400	9/03	NEIN	
H			G	$2,500	2/03	SWIN	
H			G	$2,600	9/03	NEIN	
H			F	$2,750	10/03	ECNE	PTO, new paint, ran
H			G	$2,800	8/03	NWIL	Gas, NF
H			G	$2,900	9/03	NEIN	Fenders

john deere

Model	Year	Hours	Cond.	Price	Date	Area	Comments
H			G	$3,000	9/03	NEIN	
H			G	$3,000	9/03	NEIN	No tag
H			E	$3,900	8/03	NWIL	Restored, electric start
H	1939		G	$2,050	7/03	ECND	PTO, on full rubber
H	1939		G	$2,300	8/03	WCMN	
H	1941		G	$1,700	3/03	SEIA	
H	1941		E	$2,600	8/03	NWIL	New tires, restored, gas
H	1941		G	$2,600	6/03	NEIL	
H	1941		G	$2,950	4/03	ECMN	Gas, NF
H	1942		G	$2,800	7/03	NWMN	PTO
HWH			G	$36,500	7/05	SCIA	Front weights, fenders, restored, 1 of 125 built
HWH			E	$3,600	8/03	NWIL	Old restore, gas, WF
HWH			E	$19,000	8/03	NWIL	1 of 125 built, restored, gas
L			G	$9,500	11/05	SCKY	
L	1937		G	$8,200	9/05	SEMN	Unstyled, belt pulley
L	1940		G	$7,750	9/05	SEMN	Styled, belt pulley, rear weights
L			P	$2,500	8/05	NEIN	Frame and rear end
L			P	$2,900	8/05	NEIN	Styled, parts
L			G	$3,100	6/05	ECWI	
L			G	$5,400	8/05	NEIN	Styled
L			G	$5,700	8/05	NEIN	Styled
L			G	$6,000	8/05	NEIN	Styled, restored, belt pulley
L			G	$6,250	8/05	NEIN	Unstyled, restored, belt pulley
L			G	$8,500	8/05	NEIN	Styled, restored, belt pulley, electric start, lights, dual rear wheels
L			G	$8,700	8/05	NEIN	Unstyled, restored
L			G	$8,800	8/05	NEIN	Unstyled, repainted
L			G	$9,100	8/05	NEIN	Unstyled, restored, belt pulley
L			G	$10,000	7/05	SCIA	Unstyled, belt pulley, restored
L			G	$10,200	8/05	NEIN	Unstyled, restored, mud lugs/1-bottom plow
L	1938		G	$1,950	3/05	WCIL	Ready to paint, gas
L	1939		G	$3,700	4/05	SCNE	Runs
L			G	$1,100	3/04	NCOH	Ran, looked good, cracked block
L	1938		G	$7,800	5/04	SCPA	Unstyled, restored
L	1938		G	$7,800	5/04	SCPA	Unstyled, restored
L	1939		G	$2,300	5/04	SCPA	Restored
L	1943		F	$2,350	9/04	NECO	Runs, good tires, new magneto, fair tin
L			P	$350	9/03	NEIN	Parts
L			G	$3,100	7/03	NWMN	5' sickle mower
L			E	$6,400	8/03	NWIL	Restored, gas, new tires
L	1937		G	$3,000	7/03	ECND	Side-mount mower
L	1940		G	$3,600	8/03	WCMN	
L	1944		G	$4,450	6/03	NEIL	With cultivator
LA			G	$3,500	11/05	WCIL	WF, fenders
LA	1945		G	$6,500	9/05	SEMN	Rear weights, belt pulley
LA			G	$2,400	2/05	NWOH	Restored, no serial plate
LA			G	$3,100	6/05	ECWI	New tires, painted
LA			G	$5,300	8/05	NEIN	Restored, electric start, lights, turf tires
LA			G	$1,800	11/04	WCIL	Mounted plow, original

Model	Year	Hours	Cond.	Price	Date	Area	Comments
LA			G	$5,300	10/04	SEPA	Restored, rubber fair
LA	1947		G	$7,500	5/04	SCPA	Restored, plow, sickle bar and cultivator
LA	1946		E	$7,600	7/03	WCSK	Canadian sale, fully restored & painted
LI			G	$7,000	8/05	NEIN	Restored, factory blade, hyd., lights, weights
LI			G	$9,500	8/05	NEIN	Styled, restored hyd. and lights
LI	1946		G	$1,000	6/05	ECIL	34th from last produced, modified add-on hyd. & homemade hood
LI			G	$2,750	9/04	NWMN	Industrial, electric start, new front tires, OH
LI			G	$3,200	9/04	NWMN	WF, mower
LI			G	$6,300	5/04	SCPA	Restored
LI	1940		G	$3,300	7/04	NWMN	WF, electric start, new front tires
M			G	$1,850	1/06	SESD	Restored
M			F	$1,600	11/05	WCIL	WF, rear wheel weights
M			G	$2,600	7/05	NEIA	Repainted
M			G	$3,200	11/05	NEIA	WF
M	1948		G	$6,500	9/05	SEMN	Fenders, belt pulley, PTO shield
M			G	$3,400	6/05	ECMN	Plow, WF, new paint
M			G	$3,500	6/05	ECIL	New paint, new tires all around, restored
M			F	$1,400	10/04	SEPA	Diesel, NF, rubber average
M	1947		G	$2,300	8/04	SEIA	WF, fenders, restored, 11-24" & 5-15" tires
M	1948		G	$5,400	5/04	SCPA	Restored, sickle bar
M			G	$1,200	9/03	NEIN	
M			G	$2,450	3/03	NWIL	Gas
M	1948		G	$3,200	8/03	WCMN	
M	1949		F	$1,100	7/03	NEOH	
M	1949		G	$3,000	7/03	SEND	Good tires, new paint, runs good
MC			G	$3,250	6/05	ECWI	
MC	1950		F	$1,550	9/04	NECO	Does not run
MC			G	$350	9/03	NEIN	Parts, crawler
MC	1950		G	$5,100	8/03	WCMN	Crawler
MI			G	$7,500	7/05	NEIA	1 of 1032
MI			E	$8,500	8/03	NWIL	Restored, 1 of 1,032, WF, gas
MI	1947		G	$4,000	8/03	WCMN	Mower
MI	1949		G	$4,900	4/03	SCND	WF, 4-speed, midmounted sickle mower, DOT tractor
MT			G	$2,750	1/06	SESD	Restored
MT			G	$1,500	11/05	WCIL	NF, restored, 3 pt.
MT			G	$2,000	7/05	NEIA	Repainted
MT			G	$2,300	11/05	WCIL	NF, gas, 2 pt.
MT			F	$1,200	7/05	SCIA	Runs good
MT			F	$1,900	7/05	SCIA	Plow
MT			G	$1,900	6/05	ECWI	Good rubber, lights
MT			G	$3,000	6/05	ECMN	Row crop, WF, gas, belt pully, new paint
MT	1951		F	$2,000	4/05	SCNE	WF, 11.2-34" tires, fenders, PTO, runs
MT	1951		G	$3,400	4/05	SCNE	WF, 10-34" tires, fenders, runs
MT	1952		E	$3,000	3/05	SEIA	
MT			G	$2,350	12/04	ECMI	NF, hyd. lift, runs good
MT	1949		F	$1,025	8/04	WCMN	
MT	1949		G	$1,600	10/04	NEPA	WF
MT	1950		G	$1,600	8/04	SEIA	NF, tear drop fenders
MT	1950		G	$3,650	9/04	NECO	Restored, 2 pt., cracked block, new tires, nice
MT	1951		G	$2,700	5/04	SCPA	Restored

john deere

Model	Year	Hours	Cond.	Price	Date	Area	Comments
MT	1952		G	$2,600	5/04	SCPA	Restored
MT			F	$850	8/03	SWMN	NF, gas
MT			E	$1,225	10/03	SENE	Gas
MT			F	$1,450	12/03	WCMI	Snowplow
MT			G	$1,500	9/03	NEIN	
MT			F	$1,800	3/03	NWIL	Gas
MT			F	$2,000	7/03	SWOH	
MT			E	$2,350	8/03	NWIL	Restored, gas, NF
MT	1949		F	$775	9/03	NEIN	Gas, NF
MT	1949		G	$1,900	8/03	WCMN	
MT	1950		G	$2,800	7/03	ECND	Rock shaft, PTO
R			G	$2,500	1/06	SESD	Original, diesel
R			G	$3,700	1/06	SESD	
R			G	$5,250	11/05	WCIL	Diesel, restored, PTO
R	1951		G	$4,000	12/05	NCCO	
R			G	$2,250	6/05	ECIL	Rear weights
R			G	$3,600	6/05	ECMN	Standard diesel, pony start
R			G	$4,200	6/05	ECWI	
R			G	$5,250	6/05	ECMN	Diesel, new paint, pony start
R	1951		G	$4,400	3/05	SEIA	
R	1952		G	$2,950	4/05	NCCO	New pony engine, new front tires, PTO, remote, completely restored
R			P	$500	9/04	NWMN	Parts off engine (head & piston), WF
R			G	$3,500	10/04	NWMN	Diesel, good running unit
R	1951		G	$1,500	5/04	NWND	Running
R	1952		F	$3,900	9/04	NECO	Restored, OH, tin dented, new oils & tires
R	1952		G	$4,600	10/04	NEPA	Restored, new front tires
R			G	$300	9/03	NEIN	
R			G	$3,300	9/03	NEIN	
R			G	$4,300	9/03	NEIN	
R			F	$4,500	8/03	NCCO	Cab, diesel, WF, good tires, drawbar hitch, 1 hyd.
R	1950		G	$2,500	7/03	NWMN	Bareback
R	1952		G	$3,550	6/03	NEIL	
R	1952		G	$4,000	8/03	WCMN	
350	1969		G	$5,000	9/03	NEIN	Diesel, crawler/loader, new clutches
350	1974		G	$6,200	10/03	SWWI	Dozer, gas, blade
350B	1973		G	$4,500	7/04	ECND	Track loader, new undercarriage
40	1954		F	$0	12/04	ECMI	No sale at $1,900, dozer, needs 1 steering brake fixed, runs
420	1956		G	$3,100	6/05	ECIL	6' blade, recent repairs
420	1956		F	$1,800	12/04	ECMI	Crawler/loader, drive clutch out, runs good, hyd. good
440	1958		F	$1,900	3/03	NCWI	Bucket dozer, 253 Detroit diesel motor, needs work
544A	1972	7,400	G	$17,100	3/04	WCNE	Articulating payloader, Deere grapple
544A	1973		G	$10,000	8/03	ECKS	Wheel loader
644A	1972	7,704	G	$10,000	6/03	ECND	Payloader, 6-cyl. diesel, 2 -speed, hi/lo, snow bucket, 3 yd. bucket, ext. to 5 yd., new batteries & fuel injection, 20.5-25" tires
690B	1975		G	$7,000	6/05	ECNE	Excavator, 24" bucket, 3,175 hours on meter

Old iron estate planning?

By Roger Welsch

A few years ago I was in the hospital with some fairly serious health problems. Lovely Linda was sitting by my bedside working on something with a pen and paper. I was not the least bit encouraged when she asked me, "What do you think, Rog? Would it be bad protocol to include a sale bill for your tractors in with your funeral announcement?"

The conversation went downhill from there. "Are you going to date if I wind up dying of this problem?" I asked.

"Well," she said after a moment, "Not to the funeral. Probably."

I was really shocked. I hadn't even thought about what would happen with Linda when I was gone, not to mention my tools and tractors. "Are you going to let your new husband use my tools?" I asked her.

"Rog, I'm telling you, this is not the time to talk about this."

"OK, but we do need to talk about my tractors. How about my tractors? Are you going to let him have my Allises?"

"Rog," she said, taking my hand, "I want you to put your mind at ease. You definitely don't have to worry about that. He's a John Deere man."

I recovered from that episode because of something Linda said. She's much younger than I am, bright, pretty, lively, and healthy. So I told her that should anything happen to me, I want her to go and get on with her life and get married again. "I couldn't possibly do that, Rog," she said.

"No, really, Honey, if I die, just forget me, and get married again."

"No, Rog, there's no way I'll get married again. Sure, I'll fool around . . . but I'm sure as heck not getting married again!"

That did it for me. I decided right then and there to recover. I also resolved to take care of a lot of details before the time comes when I shake off this mortal coil. I thought about forgiving all the loans (money and tools mostly) I've made to friends but which have never been returned. It was my buddy Woodrow, however, who pointed out that probably they're like him and have no intentions of returning the stuff anyway, so it wouldn't be much of a gesture if you really think about it.

I thought about being buried with my tools, but that would put the value of my grave at roughly that of King Tut's and only encourage tomb looters. So instead I request that I be buried with my favorite pages from the naughty lady calendars that decorate my shop. That way, even if I don't go to heaven, I'll be in heaven.

I thought about offering my body to science, but Linda says they haven't invented that science yet. My pal Eric advised against cremation because it would take the volunteer fire department a week to put out the grease fire. It was also Eric who recommended I not have an honor guard at my funeral fire a salute since it would be hard to find four men in the county who wouldn't be tempted to shoot into the coffin.

So I really don't have a lot of advice for you guys. I would suggest you get your stone early so your wife can't write the epitaph. I got mine right after I heard Linda wanted mine to read, "Here lies Rog. Same as always."

Probably the very best advice I got was from correspondent Allen Pruehs, who said that "For your estate auction, I recommend that you or your ashes be buried on your homestead. That will allow the tractor and tool auction to take place over your dead body."

Mine a treasure trove of Roger Welsch's musings and talk to the master of tractor mayhem in person at agelessiron.com.

massey-harris-ferguson

By the late 1940s the Ontario-based Massey-Harris Company had grown to become a major player in the tractor industry offering 62 models in six power sizes, in addition to a full complement of implements including the industry's first self-propelled combine. The next great advance in the company's history came in 1953 when Massey-Harris merged with Harry Ferguson Incorporated to form Massey-Ferguson. That merger brought with it one of the greatest engineering advances known to tractors, Ferguson's three-point hitch and internal hydraulic system. This innovation spawned a new generation of tractors that helped Massey-Ferguson to become one of the largest tractor builders in the world.

Model	Year	Hours	Cond.	Price	Date	Area	Comments
101			G	$1,100	11/05	WCIL	Old restoration, big 6 cyl., NF
101			G	$1,850	11/05	NCOH	101 Junior
101			G	$975	8/05	WCIL	101 Junior, cleaned, painted, drawbar, gas, NF
101	1942		F	$550	9/04	NECO	101 Junior, runs, good tires & tin
101			F	$1,000	1/03	ECIA	Engine not stuck
101	1940		F	$2,600	6/03	NEIL	Chevy engine
20			G	$1,475	8/05	WCIL	New tires, cleaned, painted, drawbar, gas, NF
20	1946		G	$900	6/05	ECIL	Restored
22			G	$1,050	8/05	WCIL	Cleaned, painted, drawbar, gas, NF
22			G	$2,400	11/05	ECNE	3 pt., 11.2/10-34" tires
22	1951		G	$1,150	8/05	NEIN	Gas, straight, no paint
22			G	$1,300	10/04	ECPA	Older repaint, good tires, hyd., PTO
22			G	$1,800	12/04	ECNE	Runs
22			G	$1,900	3/03	WCMI	WF
30			G	$1,550	1/06	SESD	Standard
30			G	$1,050	8/05	WCIL	Clean, painted, drawbar, gas, NF
30			G	$1,100	8/05	WCIL	Cleaned, painted, drawbar, gas, NF
30			G	$1,650	11/05	NCOH	
30			F	$360	9/04	SEIA	
30			F	$1,100	10/04	SEPA	NF, lights, good paint
30	1950		G	$1,000	10/04	ECPA	Original, PTO, hyd., new tires, straight tin
30			F	$700	10/03	NWIL	Fenders
33			G	$1,700	8/05	WCIL	WF, 3 pt., not painted, gas, drawbar
33			G	$2,000	8/05	WCIL	Cleaned, new tires, painted, drawbar, gas, NF
33			F	$800	10/04	ECPA	Live PTO, belt pulley, hyd. lift, 1 owner, new manifold & carburetor, straight tin
33			P	$625	7/03	NEOH	Did not run
333		3,771	G	$2,450	11/05	NCOH	3 pt.
333			F	$625	10/04	ECPA	Needs restoration, diesel, parts motor
333	1956		G	$2,300	10/04	ECPA	Gas, older repaint, 3 pt., PTO, power adjust wheels, add on PS
333	1956		G	$7,000	10/04	ECPA	LP, professional restoration w/ Imron paint, power adjust wheels, new tires, 3 pt., rebuilt electrical & hyd. systems, factory toolbox, new gauges & factory WF
333			G	$3,900	8/03	SEMN	Std.
44	1944		F	$700	2/06	WCSD	Runs
44	1946		F	$800	1/06	SESD	With Dual loader
44	1954		G	$2,000	2/06	WCKS	3 pt, PTO
44			G	$1,000	8/05	WCIL	Clean, painted, drawbar, gas, NF
44			G	$1,050	8/05	WCIL	Motor overhauled, not painted, gas, NF
44			G	$1,050	8/05	WCIL	OH, gas, NF, cleaned, painted, drawbar
44			G	$1,050	8/05	WCIL	6 cyl., gas, cleaned, painted, NF, drawbar
44			G	$2,400	11/05	NCOH	44 special
44			G	$900	11/05	WCIL	WF
44			F	$600	3/04	SCMI	Gas, NF
44			F	$675	10/04	ECPA	Recent OH, power lift
44			F	$850	1/04	SENE	3 pt., PS
44			G	$2,200	3/04	NCIA	Loader, hyd. bucket
44	1949		F	$2,300	10/04	ECPA	Gas, std., original, clamshell fenders, loose
44	1950		F	$1,150	9/04	NECO	Runs, loader, WF, poor tires
44	1950		G	$1,600	1/04	WCIL	PS, hub-mount duals, gas

massey-harris-ferguson

Model	Year	Hours	Cond.	Price	Date	Area	Comments
44	1952		G	$1,300	10/04	ECPA	Original, 3 pt., PTO, belt pulley, 12-volt system, good runner
44			P	$300	1/03	ECKS	Not running, old loader
44			F	$450	2/03	SEMN	WF, not running
44			G	$550	9/03	NEIN	
44			G	$900	9/03	NEIN	WF
44			P	$1,400	3/03	SWPA	44 special, NF
44			G	$1,700	9/03	NEIN	LP
44	1954		E	$2,650	6/03	NEIL	WF, live power
444			G	$2,400	1/06	SESD	3 pt., PS
444			F	$2,250	9/04	NECO	Runs, loader, 2 pt., rough tin, fair tires, WF
444			G	$3,700	10/04	ECPA	Diesel, original, nice & straight, WF, live PTO, 3 pt., lights, factory toolbox, rebuilt electrical system, power adj., aux. hyd., original lights
444	1957		G	$6,500	10/04	ECPA	LP, professional restoration, Imron paint, live power, hand clutch, motor & electrical rebuilt, new gauges & tires, PTO, 3 pt., aux. hyd. plow clutch
444			G	$1,100	3/03	WCMN	Gas, live hyd. & PS
444			G	$1,800	4/03	WCSK	Canadian sale, 2WD, loader
44-6	1947		G	$2,400	10/04	ECPA	Row crop, bought from original owner, sold locally, PTO, power lift, motor OH 100 hours ago, never sat outside, all original paint, original toolbox
50			G	$2,150	8/05	NCOH	
50			F	$1,200	4/04	NEPA	
55	1949		G	$4,000	10/04	ECPA	Gas, weights, clamshell fenders, PTO, hyd. PS, belt pulley, sharp
55	1950		G	$5,500	10/04	ECPA	Diesel, professional restoration, Imron paint, rebuilt motor, injectors, was original western Kansas tractor, very straight, PTO, Wheatland fenders
55	1955		G	$4,750	10/04	ECPA	LP, professional restoration, Imron paint, rebuilt motor, ground crankshaft, propane system OH, Wheatland fenders
555	1957		G	$3,500	3/05	WCNE	Diesel, 4 speed, PS, 15-34" rear tires, 7.50-18" front tires, PTO
555			F	$4,000	3/04	SCMI	WF, duals, diesel
555	1956		G	$1,750	10/04	ECPA	LP, original, Wheatland fenders, air cleaner, aux. hyd.
555	1958		G	$2,100	10/04	ECPA	Original, aux. hyd., lights, PTO, belt pulley, Wheatland fenders
555	1958		G	$6,000	10/04	ECPA	Diesel, orginal, PS, aux. hyd., PTO, Wheatland fenders, air cleaner, factory lights
81			F	$1,025	8/05	WCIL	Not painted, cleaned, gas, NF, drawbar
81	1946		G	$1,000	9/05	NENE	PTO, drawbar, 12.4-28" tires
81			F	$900	6/05	ECWI	
Colt			G	$3,000	10/04	ECPA	Original, WF, 3 pt., local tractor with original bill of sale & cancelled check
Colt			G	$3,250	10/04	ECPA	Std., original, straight, hard to find, PTO
Mustang	1953		G	$3,750	8/05	WCIL	WF, 3 pt, original rear tire
Mustang			G	$1,500	10/04	ECPA	WF, 3 pt., belt pulley, steps
Pacer			G	$4,100	10/04	ECPA	Runs good, cultivator, good tires, straight, belt pulley, PTO, factory lights
Pacer	1954		G	$4,000	6/03	NEIL	2-12 mounted plow
Pony			G	$1,600	11/05	WCIL	WF, repaint, 3 pt.

Model	Year	Hours	Cond.	Price	Date	Area	Comments
Pony			F	$2,000	8/05	WCIL	WF, OH
Pony			G	$2,400	9/05	NENE	N62 continental engine, WF, live hyd., 9.5-24" tires
Pony			G	$3,900	7/05	SCIA	Restored
1080			F	$4,600	3/04	SWPA	Poor rubber
1100			G	$2,750	2/06	NWSD	Cab, 3 pt., Westendorf loader, scoop and grapple, 1 owner, diesel
1100			F	$2,300	12/05	NCCO	No cab
1100			G	$2,900	8/05	SEMN	
1100			G	$3,500	8/05	SEIA	Cab, 18.4-34"
1100			G	$4,800	11/05	NCOH	New cab
1100		7,466	G	$1,750	2/05	NEIN	Diesel, WF, no cab
1100	1968	5,720	G	$3,400	3/05	WCNE	Diesel, dual 325 Quick-Tach loader, grapple, 2 hyd., 18.4-38" rear tires, PTO
1100	1976		P	$1,175	5/05	NCKS	3 pt., PTO, really rough
1100			F	$1,550	4/04	NEPA	
1100			G	$8,000	4/04	NWIA	WF, 3 pt., fenders, OH, diesel
1100	1969	5,740	F	$5,000	1/04	SEMI	8 front weights, diesel, multipower, new 18.4-38" tires, 2 hyd.
1100		7,000	F	$3,750	7/03	WCSK	Canadian sale, PTO, PS, cab, Leon loader
1100			G	$5,600	3/03	SWWI	Westendorf loader
1100	1965	4,661	G	$3,400	6/03	WCSK	Canadian sale, diesel, 20.8x34" tires, dual hyd., 94 PTO hp.
1100	1969	4,300	F	$3,400	3/03	NCCO	
1105	1980	5,687	P	$1,000	9/05	NECO	Cab, 3 pt.
1105	1973	7,366	G	$4,300	8/05	NCIA	Open station, 2 hyd., 3 pt.
1105			G	$1,850	2/04	NCWI	Diesel, cab
1105	1973	6,029	G	$3,050	11/04	NCKS	Excellent rubber & paint, 354 motor, 12-speed multipower
1105	1973	4,189	G	$4,000	11/04	NCKS	Excellent rubber & paint, 354 motor, 12-speed multipower, 2 hyd., cab, weights
1105	1973	3,907	F	$5,600	1/04	SEMI	Diesel, 2 hyd., 18.4-38" tires
1105	1975	3,943	G	$6,000	11/04	NCKS	Excellent rubber & paint, cab, 2 hyd., 12-speed multipower, 354 motor
1130	1966	4,584	G	$4,600	8/05	NCOH	Diesel, hi/lo multi power, 2 hyd, 18.4-34" tires, 4 seasons cab
1130			P	$700	2/05	SCCA	Front weights, canopy, 3 pt., PTO, 2 hyd., 15.5x38" tires
1130	1973		G	$4,750	3/05	SWIN	Diesel, 2 hyd., full weights, 2-speed PTO, power spread wheels, hub duals
1130			G	$2,000	1/04	NEOH	
1130		1,520	G	$4,200	11/04	NCKS	Diesel, dual loader
1130			G	$3,900	9/03	ECMI	6 cyl., Perkins diesel, newer radial tires, duals
1130	1967		G	$3,700	8/03	NCIA	Cab, 3 pt., 2 hyd., WF, diesel
1130	1971	5,638	F	$4,800	3/03	NCCO	
1150			F	$2,400	4/03	NWPA	Cab
1150	1971	4,375	F	$2,400	4/03	NWPA	135 hp., Perkins V8, full vision cab
135			G	$2,950	10/05	WCTN	
135			G	$3,000	9/05	SCON	2WD, gas, loader, 3 pt.
135		3,145	G	$3,400	12/05	ECIN	Utility
135			G	$3,950	9/05	SCON	Canadian sale, loader, 3 pt.
135			G	$4,100	9/05	SCON	Canadian sale, gas, 3 pt.
135	1965		G	$4,000	10/05	WCIL	3 pt.
135	1967	5,450	G	$3,000	12/05	ECMN	Open station, 8 speed hi/lo, 3 pt., PTO, 13.6-28" rears
135		2,327	G	$3,250	1/05	SWOH	Loader
135			G	$4,500	1/05	NWGA	3 pt., PTO
135			G	$4,650	3/05	NEKS	WF, 3 pt., PTO, low hours, new tires, gas
135		2,332	G	$5,050	1/05	SWOH	

massey-harris-ferguson

Model	Year	Hours	Cond.	Price	Date	Area	Comments
135			F	$1,350	12/04	SEPA	
135			F	$2,900	10/04	SEPA	Diesel, WF, PS, rubber good
135		2,080	E	$3,050	11/04	NCKS	PS, good rubber & paint, gas, 4 cyl.
135	1968	1,858	G	$6,800	1/04	SEMI	Loader, gas
135			P	$2,700	3/03	NCCO	Diesel
135			G	$3,800	9/03	NEIN	
135			G	$7,200	6/03	NCOH	Gas
135	1969		G	$4,200	8/03	NCOH	3 pt., PS, 1 hyd., gas
150			G	$2,750	11/05	WCIL	Utility, gas, WF
150			G	$3,000	1/04	NEOH	Gas, 3 pt.
150			G	$3,200	4/03	WCWI	WF, loader
1505		2,559	G	$5,800	3/03	SCMN	4WD, 3 hyd.
165		6,180	G	$2,500	8/05	NEIN	Gas, WF
165			G	$3,100	11/05	WCIL	Perkins diesel, fenders
165			G	$3,250	12/05	SWMS	Diesel, 3 pt.
165			F	$3,700	5/05	SEPA	Very clean, WF, 75% rubber, diesel
165			G	$3,750	9/05	SCON	Canadian sale, 2WD, 3 pt.
165	1973	3,205	G	$4,750	9/05	SWOH	WF, utility
165			P	$2,700	2/05	NCIL	3 pt., 2 hyd., WF, rough
165		2,694	G	$3,350	1/05	SWOH	
165		5,955	G	$4,000	3/04	WCMI	Multipower, 1 hyd., 3 pt., PS, diesel, 16.9-28" tires
165			G	$4,600	6/04	SEMN	500 hrs. on OH
165	1966	2,000	G	$5,100	3/04	NCKS	Loader, dirt bucket, hay buck, push off and front blade, gas, 3 pt., 540 PTO, PS
165	1968		F	$4,200	4/04	NEIA	3 pt., 2 hyd., PTO, flat top fenders, 15.5-38" tires, new brakes & hyd. pump
165			F	$1,675	9/03	SEIA	Multipower out
165			G	$2,500	3/03	NEKS	Gas, 3 pt., PS
165			F	$2,600	3/03	NCIL	3 pt., PTO, diesel, 15.5-38" tires, bad clutch
165			F	$4,400	10/03	NWIL	
175		3,314	F	$4,750	9/05	SEIA	With loader
175	1967	5,200	G	$3,900	3/04	WCMI	Superior 2-60 hyd. loader, tine and snow buckets, multipower, 1 hyd., 3 pt., diesel
175			G	$4,400	10/03	WCWI	Diesel, loader
175		2,260	G	$8,500	2/03	SWIL	WF, Freeman-Bush Hog hyd. bucket loader, 3 pt., single remote hyd. outlet, like new rear tires, 6' material bucket
180			G	$2,600	9/05	SCON	Canadian sale, 2WD, diesel, 3 pt., hyd.
180		2,624	F	$2,500	3/05	SCMI	Diesel, WF
180			G	$5,300	1/05	SWOH	1 hr. since OH
180	1966	3,599	F	$2,000	3/05	SEWY	Diesel, no 3 pt.
180			F	$3,400	4/04	NEIA	
180			F	$3,750	7/04	NWMN	Diesel, hyd., 3 pt., PTO
180			G	$3,750	7/04	SEND	Diesel, 3 pt., PTO
180			G	$4,700	2/03	SWIL	WF, 3 pt., 2 hyd., approx. 1.000 hrs. since complete OH
180			G	$6,000	2/03	ECKS	GB Workmaster loader, 7' bucket, diesel, WF, multipower, 3 pt., 2 hyd., good rubber
1805	1975	2,776	G	$4,500	2/05	WCIL	4WD, Cat 3208 motor, factory turbo, cab, AC, 4 hyd., 3 pt.
1805			F	$2,200	7/04	NWMN	4WD, 3208 Cat

128

Model	Year	Hours	Cond.	Price	Date	Area	Comments
1805	1980	3,420	F	$2,800	2/04	NWIL	4WD, 3208 Cat engine, 3 pt.
1805		2,867	F	$2,200	3/03	NCIL	4WD, 3 pt., 18.4-38" tires, duals, bad transmission
1805		5,062	G	$4,700	3/03	NWSD	3 pt., 3 hyd., duals, 3208 Cat engine
1805	1975	3,625	F	$3,500	3/03	SEIA	4WD, 3 hyd., bobtail
20			G	$5,000	10/04	NWMN	Industrial utility tractor, 3 pt., PTO, PS complete loader
20			G	$3,500	10/03	WCIL	Industrial gas tractor, loader, 6' bucket, shuttle transmission
202			F	$1,500	12/03	WCMI	Loader, gas, WF, PTO
235			G	$3,800	6/05	ECPA	
235			F	$5,000	3/03	NWIL	Utility, diesel
245			G	$4,500	9/05	SCON	Canadian sale, diesel, ROPS, 3 pt.
245			G	$5,500	6/04	WCWA	Farm tractor, 4-cyl. diesel, 3 pt., rear PTO, ROPS, Ransome 7-gauge reel mower attachment
245		1,235	G	$5,700	7/03	SWIN	Power spread wheels, diesel, 2 hyd., hi/low range
245	1976	2,765	G	$4,800	12/03	NCIA	
30			G	$5,000	1/06	ECIL	Industrial gas tractor, WF, 3 pt., weights, new 16.9-24" tires, ROPS, PS, attached hyd. quick attach 80" bucket
30			F	$4,750	4/04	NEIA	Industrial tractor, 3 pt., PTO, loader & boom
30	1953		E	$1,750	11/04	NCKS	1 owner, gas, 4 speed, good rubber
30			F	$900	6/03	WCMN	NF
30			G	$2,000	7/03	NWOH	Utility, 3 pt., WF
300	1973		G	$4,400	11/03	WCKS	Diesel, 3 pt., PTO, MF 34 scoop
35			G	$1,500	9/05	SCON	Canadian sale, gas, 2WD, 3 pt.
35			G	$2,200	12/05	SWMS	Diesel, 3 pt
35			G	$3,500	6/05	ECWI	Loader, restored
35			F	$1,750	3/04	NWIL	Gas
35			F	$2,650	12/04	ECTN	35 special, gas, good tin
35			E	$3,000	11/04	NCKS	Diesel, grill guard, good rubber & paint
35			G	$3,600	2/04	ECNE	Gas, 12-28" tires, 3 pt., loader, bucket, shedded
35			G	$3,900	5/04	ECMN	Gas
35			E	$4,200	11/04	NCKS	Davis loader, front PTO pump, gas
35	1963		G	$2,975	3/03	NWIL	Deluxe, WF, PS, 3 pt., has been OH
40			G	$2,850	9/05	SCON	Canadian sale, gas, loader, weight box
40			G	$5,000	10/03	ECMN	Loader, WF
50			G	$1,600	11/05	NECO	Loader, box scraper
50	1958		G	$2,800	6/05	ECIL	3 pt., PS
50	1959		G	$3,100	4/05	SCNE	Gas, WF, 3,361 hrs. on tach, 12.4-38" tires, fenders, 3 pt., 2 hyd., runs
50		2,783	G	$1,800	11/04	NCKS	NF, good rubber
50			G	$2,050	3/04	SWKS	Rebuilt motor, 3 pt.
50			F	$2,850	12/04	ECTN	Gas, good tires
50	1958	1,891	F	$3,550	4/04	WCNE	Mounted loader, backhoe
50			F	$1,500	12/03	WCMI	Gas, 14.9x24" tires
65		18,118	F	$1,250	11/05	NWIL	Gas, WF, 3 pt., loader, hand trip
65			P	$450	2/05	SCCA	For parts
65			G	$1,600	6/05	ECNE	3 pt.
65			F	$1,700	1/05	ECNE	WF
65			G	$4,200	2/05	ECNE	Loader, gas
65	1958		G	$4,350	2/05	NEIN	Gas, WF
65			F	$1,700	7/04	NWMN	Gas, loader
65		1,517	G	$4,500	11/04	NCKS	MF individual loader, diesel

massey-harris-ferguson

Model	Year	Hours	Cond.	Price	Date	Area	Comments
65			G	$5,000	5/04	ECND	Multipower hyd., 3 pt, PTO, hyd. loader, grapple, snow and dirt buckets
65			F	$1,050	12/03	WCMI	3 pt., PTO, loader, gas, 14.9x28" tires
65			G	$2,750	3/03	NWIL	Loader, gas
65			G	$3,500	4/03	WCMI	
85	1960	5,514	P	$925	9/05	NECO	WF, 3 pt., engine stuck, gas
85			P	$750	2/05	NCIN	Gas, rough, salvage
85			F	$1,400	2/05	SCMN	LP, WF, 3 pt.
85	1961		F	$1,400	10/03	WCIL	Gas, needs paint & sheet metal
85	1961		G	$2,000	10/03	WCIL	Diesel, new paint, NF
Super 90			G	$1,500	12/04	ECNE	
Super 90			G	$1,200	3/03	SWWI	
Super 90			F	$2,000	2/03	ECNE	
Super 90			F	$2,000	8/03	NWIL	Diesel
Super 90	1963	7,533	G	$2,500	7/03	WCMN	3 pt., PTO, diesel
TO 20	1950		G	$1,350	2/05	NEIN	Gas
TO 30			G	$2,000	4/05	SCNE	3 pt., runs, 11-38" tires
TO 30			G	$1,800	5/03	ECMN	Gas, fresh OH
TO 30	1953		P	$600	12/03	NECO	Needs work, 3 pt., PTO

The French Masseys

The international appeal of Massey-Ferguson tractors is readily apparent from the sheer number of the firm's French tractor models, among them the Model 25 seen at right. The 25 was one of at least six models Massey built in France starting in the 1950s.

"Built" is a subjective term since these tractors were often fabricated in Coventry, England, before being shipped to France as "knock-down" kits for assembly. The tractors would then be fitted with a French-built Simca or Peugeot engine and dressed out with French styling and components.

The Massey-Ferguson 25 was one of over a half dozen models built for the French market.

The Model 25's engine was a British Perkins four-cylinder, 107-cubic-inch diesel that generated 25 hp. Power was transferred through an eight-speed transmission that offered a top speed of 14 mph.

Assembled in Beauvais, France, from 1963 to 1965, the 25 offered an impressive array of standard features including a 540-rpm PTO, dual clutch, and a hydraulic system with a 2,231-pound maximum lift at the three-point hitch. Other French Massey models included the 65 Mk I, 21, 20-25 Special, 30, 835, and 42.

Four-wheel drive faltered but still left its mark

In the late 1920s Massey-Harris wanted to make a big splash. They had entered the tractor business 10 years before, much later than most of their competitors. Fortunately, Massey was able to buy Case Plow Works and with it the great Wallis tractor line.

But the head of Massey, J.N. Shenstone, wanted the firm to make its own mark in the world of horsepower. So he encouraged Massey engineers to think big and be different. They didn't let him down. Although it isn't known how long it took to come up with the design, the engineers rewarded Shenstone with the GP (for General Purpose) 15-22 in 1930. That made it one of the few four-wheel-drive tractors of this time period.

The GP was not the first four-wheel-drive tractor to be built. But its design was thoroughly modern. Plus, the GP was long on added features such as an electrical system, starter, and lights.

The GP had four equal-size wheels powered through the use of a transfer case and front and rear differentials. The front axle employed a universal joint steering design that allowed the tractor to turn in an amazingly tight 6-foot diameter.

Another nice touch was a rear axle that pivoted side-to-side. This allowed the drive wheels to stay in contact with the soil regardless of field contours.

The thoughtful engineering in the GP was also reflected in the fact that the tractor was offered in four widths to accommodate different row spacings. Orchard, industrial, and turf variations of the GP were built during the tractor's six-year production run.

Power for the GP came from the reliable Hercules Model OOC four-cylinder engine. This 226-cubic-inch power plant provided 22 drawbar horsepower through a three-speed transmission.

All-wheel-drive tractors prior to the GP had not enjoyed enormous success. Case in point was John Deere's 1917 All-Wheel Drive. But the GP had the massive will of Massey-Harris behind it and was destined to be a huge success. What Massey did not bargain on, however, was the advent of the Great Depression.

The GP cost $1,000 when first introduced. While that was a reasonable sum in 1930, that price tag caused buyers to flee once times turned bad. Then, too, the GP had to compete against IHC's row-crop revolution, the Farmall. Massey was still determined to make a go of the GP, but by 1936, only a paltry 3,000 or so of the machines had sold. This was the kiss of death for the tractor, and production ceased that same year.

You can learn more about the GP, All-Wheel Drive, and other four-wheel-drive tractors at www.agelessiron.com.

The first Massey-Harris "Four-Wheel-Drive Tractors" were sold on steel. But the firm soon started equipping the GP with pneumatic tires, which greatly improved its traction. Other GP features included a belt pulley, rear PTO, and optional implement lift system. The tractor underwent several improvements during its six-year production run including the addition of a sloping hood in 1936. That same year saw the GP designation dropped in favor of the new "4-WD" identification.

minneapolis-
moline

It's not surprising that Minneapolis-Moline would grow to become one of
the leading tractor manufacturers in the mid-twentieth century. The firm
got its start from the 1929 merger of Moline Implement, Minneapolis
Threshing, and Minneapolis Steel & Machinery – all three of which had
their own tractor lines. In fact, Moline Implement's Universal Model D,
introduced in 1915, was considered one of the most advanced tractors
of the early 1900s. The best machines from all three companies were
evaluated and kept to create the new firm, Minneapolis-Moline, which
went on to build an impressive fleet of tractors greatly appreciated by
farmers who affectionately referred to them as "Minnie Mos."

Model	Year	Hours	Cond.	Price	Date	Area	Comments
335	1957		F	$1,000	9/04	NECO	Runs, 2 pt.
4 Star			F	$3,000	10/04	SEPA	Loader, NF, gas, poor rubber
445	1956		F	$975	9/03	NEIN	WF, loader, gas
445	1956		F	$2,600	6/03	SEND	WF, 2 hyd., 3 pt., PTO, 13.6-38"
5 Star	1957		G	$2,750	1/06	SESD	LP gas, standard
5 Star			G	$3,000	11/05	WCIL	Western air cleaner, Wheatland LP
5 Star			G	$1,300	7/03	SCMN	WF, 1 hyd., live power
500			G	$2,850	8/04	ECMN	Industrial, loader, all hydraulic, diesel
602	1968		F	$2,400	1/06	SCNE	LP, WF, 1 hyd, 18.4-34", front weights
602	1963		F	$1,875	9/03	NEIN	Diesel, WF
620			G	$1,350	9/03	NEIN	
670			P	$1,400	4/05	NCOH	Salvage, gas, 3 pt., fenders, weights
670			F	$1,650	7/05	SCMN	WF, 3 pt., needs restoring
670			F	$2,150	3/04	SWPA	Poor rubber
705			G	$825	9/03	NEIN	LP
706			F	$2,600	11/05	WCIL	FWA, LP, PTO, PS
950			G	$0	9/04	NCIA	No sale at $3,000, loader
AT1400			F	$3,000	6/03	SEND	4WD, does not run, 18.4-34" tires, duals
BF			G	$3,100	11/05	WCIL	WF, gas, rear weights, fenders, PTO, belt pulley, all original
BF			G	$4,000	8/05	NEIN	Repainted, 3 pt., belly mower
BF			G	$1,000	8/04	NCOH	Gas, NF
G			G	$1,050	9/05	SCON	Canadian sale
G			G	$5,200	11/05	WCIL	Std, LP, rear wheel weights, PS, cab
G			P	$175	11/04	SCKS	For parts
G	1950		F	$875	3/04	SCKS	LP
G			G	$3,700	9/03	NEIN	
G1000	1967		G	$2,600	1/06	SESD	Vista standard, LP gas
G1000			G	$1,900	4/05	NCOK	LP, Wheatland model, cab & water cooler
G1000			G	$5,100	3/05	WCKS	LP, 3 pt., excellent tires, PTO, 2 hyd., bad seat
G1000			G	$4,200	2/03	NCOH	Propane, 3 pt., duals
G706			F	$3,500	6/03	SEND	MFWD, cab, propane, hyd., 540 PTO
G707			G	$6,750	6/05	ECMN	New paint, WF, diesel
G900			F	$3,500	9/04	ECSD	
G900			F	$2,600	3/03	NWIL	Gas
GB	1956		G	$2,000	1/06	SESD	LP gas, standard
GB	1956		F	$2,300	5/05	WCNE	Been in storage for 25 years, diesel
GB			F	$550	9/04	NECO	Does not run, complete, cab
GB			G	$1,650	9/03	NEIN	LP
GTA			G	$3,300	11/05	WCIL	Wheatland, gas, 4 cyl.
Jet Star			G	$2,500	12/04	SEIA	WF, 3 pt., gas
Jet Star			G	$3,350	8/04	NCIA	Super Jet Star, gas, WF, 3 pt., fenders, good tin
Jet Star			F	$800	6/03	WCSD	Dual loader & scoop
Jet Star	1960		F	$3,100	6/03	SEND	WF, hyd, 3 pt., PTO, new tires
Jet Star	1962		G	$1,600	1/03	WCKS	3 pt., PTO
Jet Star3			G	$1,200	11/05	WCIL	WF, gas
Jet Star3			G	$3,100	11/05	WCIL	WF, gas, elect
JT	1937		F	$775	6/03	SEND	Twin City model, NF
M			G	$700	6/05	ECIL	Rear & front weights, power adj.
M5			F	$800	11/05	ECNE	Gas, WF, 15.5-38", hydraulics, PTO, 3 pt., fenders
M5	1961		G	$1,200	11/05	WCIL	PTO, 3 pt.
M5			G	$1,700	6/03	WCSK	Canadian sale, diesel, dual hyd.

minneapolis-moline

Model	Year	Hours	Cond.	Price	Date	Area	Comments
M5			G	$2,500	8/03	NEKS	3 pt., LP
M670	1967	6,613	F	$2,650	2/06	WCNE	LP, 3 pt., PTO, MM cab
M670	1970	3,500	G	$3,700	2/06	WCNE	LP, 3 pt., PTO, MM cab
M670			G	$1,800	11/05	WCIL	New seat, LP
M670			F	$2,500	12/04	WCIL	Super M670, LP
N/A			F	$500	6/03	SEND	Industrial, Lull loader
N/A			G	$5,700	9/03	NEIN	Universal
R			F	$900	1/05	SWOH	
R			G	$2,300	8/03	WCIL	WF, Ottowa loader & backhoe
U	1950		F	$950	8/05	NWIL	Gas, NF
U			F	$500	9/04	SEND	WF
U			G	$1,400	2/04	SCKS	Fully restored, new paint, loader
U	1944		F	$500	9/04	NECO	Runs, fair tires, good tin, belt pulley
U	1950		G	$3,900	3/04	WCIL	
U			F	$1,575	6/03	NCIA	WF, 16.9-30" tires, chains to fit
UB	1955		F	$3,000	2/06	NWIA	NF, 2 pt., clamshell fenders
UB	1955		G	$2,550	6/05	SEND	WF, 1 hyd., PTO, gas, 13-38" tires
UB			G	$975	9/03	NEIN	
UB			F	$1,300	7/03	NEOH	
UB	1953		G	$1,700	6/03	NEIL	Clean
UT	1950		G	$1,225	1/06	SESD	LP gas
UTE			G	$1,200	11/05	WCIL	WF, live PTO
UTS	1952		G	$1,100	11/05	WCIL	LP, hyd
UTU			F	$500	12/04	NWIA	
UTU	1946		F	$450	6/03	SEND	WF, nonrunning
Z			G	$2,100	11/05	WCIL	Hand start, mag rebuilt
Z			P	$150	10/04	NCOH	For parts
Z			P	$375	10/04	NCOH	For parts
Z			G	$1,025	9/04	NCIA	Fenders, running
Z	1941		F	$350	8/04	WCMN	
Z			P	$350	8/03	NCIA	Torn down to fenders
Z			F	$500	6/03	SEND	NF, nonrunning
Z			P	$650	3/03	SWWI	Nonrunning, excellent tin
Z			F	$725	10/03	NWIL	
Z			G	$1,050	3/03	NCCO	
Z	1949		F	$750	4/03	SCND	NF
ZA			G	$475	9/03	NEIN	
ZA			G	$1,600	10/03	ECNE	Fresh paint, new rubber
ZA	1951		F	$1,300	11/03	WCIN	Aux. hyd. pump, PTO, belt pulley attachment
ZAU			G	$1,625	10/04	ECMN	Gas
ZB			G	$1,800	8/05	ECMN	
ZB			G	$800	11/05	WCIL	NF
ZB	1955		G	$3,400	5/04	SCPA	Restored
ZB			F	$700	7/03	NEOH	
ZB	1955		F	$1,400	10/03	NWIL	
ZTN			G	$1,000	9/03	NEIN	
ZTS	1945		F	$900	4/03	SCND	WF, fenders
ZTU	1940		G	$850	11/05	WCIL	NF, missing side shield
ZTU			F	$975	6/05	WCMN	NF, wide fenders

134

Tractors from down under

AUSTRALIAN TRACTORS

GRAEME R. QUICK

INDIGENOUS TRACTORS AND SELF PROPELLED MACHINES IN RURAL AUSTRALIA

Caterpillar has long been given credit for being the first manufacturer in the world to produce a tractor with a diesel engine. Well, it may bruise our national pride, but the truth is that honor goes instead to an Australian venture, A.H. McDonald & Company.

Indeed, in 1922, nine years before Caterpillar introduced its efficient Diesel Sixty, the Australian firm built and sold its first diesel-powered tractors.

First Aussy tractor

McDonald actually holds the distinction of being Australia's first tractor manufacturer, one of many such historical tidbits you'll find in the book *Australian Tractors – Indigenous Tractors and Self Propelled Machines in Rural Australia*. This gem was written by noted agricultural engineer Graeme Quick, who also penned the definitive guide to harvesting equipment, *The Grain Harvesters*.

Agricultural engineer

Quick's knowledge of Australian engineering is thorough. *Australian Tractors* covers the whole gamut of tractor development in the land down under with in-depth discussions of that nation's leading tractor makers as

well as the influence U.S. agricultural firms had on Australian farming. Also included are histories of little-known outfits like Jelbart, Caldwell Vale, Howard, Deutscher, Sunshine, and Ronaldson-Tippett.

Want another surprise? The largest tractor in the world was not the U.S.-built Big Bud, as is often claimed, but rather the Australian-built Baldwin!

Make other such discoveries in Australian Tractors, *which sells for $24.95 and can be ordered by calling* 800/678-5752 *or by going to* www.farmhomecollection.com.

Australian agricultural engineer and tractor buff Graeme Quick (above) delves into the world of Australian horsepower in a fascinating 167-page book (seen above). Quick thorough research allows you to uncover the impact U.S. concerns had on Australian agricultural development as well as the growth of such homebred Aussy ventures as Ronaldson-Tippett and its Super-Drive tractors (at the right).

oliver

Oliver tractors trace their roots back to the reputation of Hart-Parr horsepower. Oliver Corporation actually began with the merger of Nichols & Shepard, American Seeding Machine, Oliver Chilled Plow, and Hart-Parr. Oliver sold tractors under the name Hart-Parr for years afterward. The merger instantly created one of the top 10 farm machinery firms in the U.S. In 1935 Oliver brought out the streamlined Model 70, which set the tone for a new generation of row-crop tractors. Then, in the late 1940s, Oliver's new Fleetline generation of horsepower garnered high sales, which established the firm as one of the leading tractor manufacturers of the mid-twentieth century. Oliver itself merged with Minneapolis-Moline and Cockshutt in 1960 to form the White machinery line.

Model	Year	Hours	Cond.	Price	Date	Area	Comments
Hart Parr 10-20			G	$6,300	6/05	ECWI	
Hart Parr 12-24			G	$8,600	10/03	SEMN	Older restoration, steel and rubber both, runs great
Hart Parr 18-36			F	$3,000	4/05	NCCO	Steel wheels, not stuck and complete with extra radiator, restorable
Hart Parr 70			G	$1,400	7/04	WCIL	Gas, good tin
Hart Parr 70			G	$2,800	8/04	ECMI	Restored
Hart Parr N/A			P	$160	9/03	NEIN	For parts
1250			F	$2,800	4/04	NEPA	
1250			F	$3,300	10/04	NWOH	Utility
1250	1972		G	$2,250	2/03	WCMN	Utility, tin good
1365		1,800	E	$4,700	8/03	WCIN	Diesel, like new
1365			G	$6,600	3/03	SEIA	Loader
1450			G	$1,100	11/05	WCIL	Diesel
1500			F	$2,600	9/03	NCSD	Gas, Farmhand F10 loader
1550			G	$3,750	1/03	NENE	PS, WF, good rubber, hydra drive, hi/lo, gas
1550	1965	4,700	G	$3,000	12/03	NWIL	NF, gas
1555			G	$6,000	11/05	WCIL	High crop, diesel
1555	1974		G	$3,950	3/05	SEND	Livestock special, WF, gas, hydra power drive, PTO, Farmhand F11 loader, fenders, new tires
1555		3,505	F	$1,800	3/03	SWMN	Std., Farmhand 25 loader & grapple
1600		4,500	F	$4,400	1/06	SCMI	Gas, WF, 3 pt., Oliver 1610 front end loader
1600			G	$2,250	2/05	NCOH	
1600	1963	2,500	G	$4,100	4/05	NCOH	Diesel, NF, hydra power, 3 pt., 1 hyd.
1600			F	$1,800	12/04	ECMI	WF, duals
1600			F	$2,550	2/04	SEMN	WF, gas, 3 pt., PTO
1600			G	$4,600	7/04	NCIA	Gas, WF, 3 pt., fenders, 2 hyd.
1600	1963		G	$3,000	2/04	SENE	Gas, over/under, 15.5-38" tires, NF, fenders, 3 pt.
1600			G	$3,400	10/03	NWMN	Rock shaft, PTO, 18.4-34" tires
1650			F	$2,500	1/06	SCMI	WF, gas, 3pt., OH in 2004
1650	1965	4,671	G	$4,000	2/06	WCIL	WF, 3 pt., fenders, 2 hyd., gas, 16.9-34"
1650			P	$1,800	10/05	ECIL	Row crop tractor, gas, rough shape, 3 pt., 15.5-38", with hyd. front brush blade
1650			G	$2,550	10/05	ECMN	Diesel, cab, 3 pt.
1650			G	$3,500	11/05	WCIL	NF, diesel, PS, deluxe seat
1650			G	$6,250	11/05	WCIL	High crop, front spokes, fenders
1650	1967	7,750	F	$3,450	10/05	NCOH	Gas, needed rear tires
1650			G	$2,500	1/05	SWMN	Schwartz loader
1650			G	$2,900	1/05	ECIA	Older, gas, NF, 3 pt., fenders
1650			G	$4,800	2/05	NCOH	
1650			F	$1,300	6/04	NWIA	Gas
1650			G	$1,900	5/04	ECWI	WF
1650			G	$2,500	7/04	WCIL	Gas, WF, 3 pt.
1650			G	$2,750	7/04	WCIL	Diesel, NF, 3 pt., steps
1650			F	$4,000	4/04	NEPA	
1650		3,665	E	$4,000	8/04	ECMI	Gas, good rubber, WF, PS, sharp
1650			G	$4,300	11/04	SWOH	WF, cab, diesel
1650			E	$4,600	11/04	NCKS	Farmhand F11 loader, NF, good paint & rubber, gas, 2 hyd., hyd. pump
1650		3,800	G	$4,800	3/04	WCIL	Diesel
1650	1964		G	$2,000	5/04	SENE	Diesel, NF, 3 pt.
1650			P	$350	8/03	SEMN	WF, 3 pt.
1650			F	$2,400	11/03	NWIL	Diesel, WF, 3 pt.

oliver

Model	Year	Hours	Cond.	Price	Date	Area	Comments
1650			F	$3,550	3/03	SEIA	Gas, WF
1650			G	$3,750	11/03	SENE	Diesel, WF, recent OH
1650			G	$4,400	8/03	WCIL	
1650			F	$5,400	3/03	NCCO	
1650	1965		G	$6,000	9/03	WCIA	WF, White 1710 loader, gas
1655			F	$5,500	2/06	WCIL	
1655	1971		G	$7,000	2/06	NCOH	Diesel, WF, 16.9-34" rubber, 2 hyd, over/under trans.
1655			G	$3,900	11/05	WCIL	Deluxe seat, wheel weights, fenders
1655			G	$5,600	12/05	SCMN	
1655	1972		G	$4,200	12/05	ECNE	Diesel, 2 hyd., over/under hyd. shift trans., 16.9-34", 540 PTO
1655	1972		G	$7,900	9/05	NCND	Gas, row crop, 540 PTO, 320 dual loader, very clean
1655			F	$4,000	7/05	SCMN	Cab, 500 hrs. on OH, diesel
1655			G	$6,100	6/05	NCIL	5,400 hrs., WF, 3 pt., good tin
1655		7,700	G	$3,800	2/04	ECIA	WF, 2 hyd., 2,200 hrs. on OH, 16.9-38" tires
1655			G	$5,100	3/04	SEMN	Cab, 3 pt.
1655			G	$6,250	6/04	SEMN	NF
1655	1972	2,180	G	$12,200	11/04	NCOH	WF, over/under trans., 2 hyd., front and rear weights
1655			E	$4,850	8/03	NEKS	Dual loader
1655		5,100	G	$6,000	3/03	SWWI	
1655			G	$7,600	10/03	SEMN	Gas, cab
1750			F	$3,500	8/05	NWIA	WF, cab, 3 pt., Koyker K5 loader
1750		3,216	G	$4,500	7/05	SCMI	Gas, WF, Himaster 900 loader
1750			F	$2,100	3/05	WCIL	WF, gas
1750	1967		G	$2,675	2/05	NEIN	Diesel, WF, tach shows 1,461 hours
1750			G	$2,250	8/04	ECMN	Diesel, WF
1750			G	$5,000	3/04	NWMN	
1750			G	$5,800	5/04	ECMN	Gas, IHC 2000 loader
1750			P	$2,700	2/03	NEIA	Junk, bad engine, diesel
1755		9,244	F	$3,300	11/05	SCMI	Diesel, WF
1755	1972		G	$3,800	12/05	NWIL	Clamp duals, WF, 2 hyd., short axles, diesel
1755		4,275	G	$5,700	8/04	ECIL	Fender tractor, gas, 2 hyd., new 18.4-34" tires
1755		4,479	G	$6,900	1/04	SENE	3 pt., 2 hyd., PTO, WF
1755			G	$3,300	9/03	NWIA	Perkins diesel motor, WF, 3 pt., 2 hyd., 18.4-34" tires
1755			F	$3,800	3/03	NWIL	WF, poor rubber
1755			F	$4,700	2/03	NENE	Diesel, WF, fuel fenders
1800			F	$1,300	11/05	WCIL	WF, gas, fenders, PTO
1800			F	$2,100	8/05	NWIA	3 pt.
1800			G	$3,250	11/05	SEND	Gas, 2 hyd., 3 pt., 540 PTO, fenders, band duals
1800			G	$5,200	11/05	WCIL	Std, diesel, wheel weights, PTO shift, front weights, western tractor
1800			F	$2,900	4/05	SEND	3 pt., diesel, cab
1800	1964		G	$3,900	3/05	ECNE	3 pt., 2 hyd., 540 PTO, diesel, WF, rear fenders, 18.4-34" tires, clamp-on duals, rear weights
1800			F	$2,700	3/04	NWIL	Diesel, NF
1800			G	$5,250	6/04	WCWI	OH, 3 pt.
1800	1962	7,435	F	$2,400	1/04	NEIN	Gas, WF, 3 pt., hydra power
1800			G	$1,100	9/03	NEIN	Diesel
1800			F	$2,100	3/03	WCWI	Gas

138

Model	Year	Hours	Cond.	Price	Date	Area	Comments
1800			G	$4,700	4/03	SCMN	Diesel, WF, 3 pt., nice paint, new head
18-27			G	$1,900	7/04	WCIL	Gas, single
1850			F	$2,750	7/05	ECND	Wheatland, XL cab, 2 hyd., PTO, Farmhand F11 loader and grapple
1850	1967		G	$4,400	9/05	SEIN	
1850	1967	6,900	G	$3,950	2/05	NEIN	Diesel, OH
1850			F	$1,650	10/04	SEMN	Gas
1850			G	$3,100	3/04	SCMN	
1850			G	$4,100	11/04	NCOH	Diesel, NF
1850			G	$5,100	3/04	WCMI	Freeman hyd. loader, new clutch, 2 hyd., 3 pt., PTO, diesel, 16.9-34" tires
1850			G	$5,500	6/04	WCWI	Weights, 3 pt.
1850			F	$5,600	4/04	NEPA	4WD
1850	1966	4,600	F	$1,450	1/04	NEIN	Engine needs work, gas, cab, new rear rubber
1850			F	$1,200	10/03	SEMN	
1850			G	$3,350	2/03	WCMN	Over/under, hyd. loader, 2 hyd., 3 pt.
1850			G	$3,750	12/03	NEIA	Diesel, WF, 3 pt., 2 hyd., like new 18.4-34" tires
1855			G	$3,800	3/04	WCMN	New engine, 3 pt., PTO, 2 hyd., WF, new batteries
1855		5,372	F	$5,000	4/04	NEPA	Loader, bucket, new hyd. pump & hoses, PTO
1855	1971		G	$4,300	1 04	NCOH	Gas
1855			P	$2,000	4/03	WCMN	Over/under, 2 hyd., 3 pt.
1855		4,085	F	$5,100	4/03	NEPA	2WD, cab, 2 hyd., 2 PTOs, 18.4-38" tires
1855			G	$5,100	10/03	SEMN	129.7 hrs on complete OH and clutch, 500 hrs. on new over/under, gas
1855			F	$5,800	3/03	SWMI	Westendorf loader
1900	1961		G	$5,100	9/04	NECO	OH, new tires, Std., 3 pt.
1900			G	$8,500	10/03	SEMN	Wheatland
1950			G	$5,000	2/06	NWSD	Industrial tractor, 4WD, yellow, underground cable plow
1950			G	$4,500	8/04	ECIA	3-speed over/under, 18.4-34" tires, turbo
1950	1974	3,400	G	$6,300	12/03	SEIL	Bush Hog loader
1955		4,587	G	$8,250	3/05	ECMI	Diesel, cab, heat, axle duals, dual PTO, stone box and front weights, power beyond hyd.
1955			G	$6,500	6/04	WCWI	Cab, fender tanks, 3 pt., weights
1955		3,421	G	$6,700	8/04	ECIL	Fender tractor, 2 hyd., 18.4-38" tires, axle duals
1955		4,880	F	$1,700	2/03	SETX	
1955			G	$4,000	3/03	SEIA	
1955		4,279	G	$5,000	3/03	ECMI	Cab, axle duals, dual outlets, 3 pt., diesel, 16.9-38" tires
1955			F	$7,000	3/03	SEIA	MFWD, diesel, cab
1955	1975	3,543	G	$7,500	2/03	NWIL	WF, cab, 3 pt., 2 hyd., recent OH, diesel, 18.4-38" tires, sharp
2150			G	$8,600	11/03	NCOH	
2150			G	$9,350	10/03	SEMN	Planetary differential weights, 3 pt., 2 hyd.
2255			G	$6,600	3/05	WCIL	Cab, weights, 3150 engine, diesel
2255			F	$5,600	3/03	SEIA	
2255			G	$11,250	10/03	SEMN	3160 Cat diesel, 2 hyd., 3 pt.
2655			G	$6,750	2/05	NCIN	LP, 3 pt., PTO, 800cc engine
440			G	$9,250	6/04	WCWI	3 pt., new tires
55			G	$1,600	11/05	WCIL	Ind. WF, gas, fenders, restored
55			G	$2,800	11/05	WCIL	
550			G	$4,000	2/04	WCWI	3 pt., WF, Westendorf loader
550			G	$4,600	1/04	SENE	WF, 3 pt.
550	1964		G	$5,000	7/04	WCIL	PS, adj. wheels

oliver

Model	Year	Hours	Cond.	Price	Date	Area	Comments
550			G	$3,900	12/03	NWIA	Utility, gas, trip-type bucket loader
550			F	$4,000	3/03	SEIA	Gas, PS
550	1973	1,450	E	$6,600	8/03	WCIL	PS, runs great, 1 owner
555			G	$3,900	3/05	NWIL	Loader, blade, gas
555			F	$1,000	3/03	WCMI	Gas, loader, canopy, PTO
60			G	$1,100	11/05	WCIL	NF
60			G	$1,300	11/05	WCIL	Restored
60			G	$1,300	11/05	SCKY	
60			G	$1,600	11/05	ECMN	Gas, with saw rig
60			G	$4,300	11/05	WCIL	NF, gas, side dress fert.
60			G	$1,400	7/04	WCIL	Gas, Std.
60			G	$1,400	7/04	WCIL	Gas, row crop, missing tin
60			G	$4,900	6/04	WCWI	Industrial, new tires
60			G	$5,500	6/04	WCWI	Std., new tires
60	1945		G	$2,200	8/04	WCMN	Row crop
60			F	$1,300	6/03	WCMN	Row crop
60			P	$1,500	8/03	NCCO	Drawbar hitch, gas, NF
60			G	$1,500	9/03	NEIN	
60			G	$2,875	4/03	WCMN	NF, fenders
60			G	$3,250	9/03	NEIN	WF
60			G	$4,500	10/03	SEMN	Std.
66			G	$1,800	11/05	WCIL	NF, gas
66			G	$21,000	11/05	WCIL	Orchard, gas
66			G	$3,000	11/05	WCIL	Row crop, NF, gas, restored
66			G	$3,250	11/05	WCIL	Std, gas
66			G	$825	3/05	ECMI	Row crop, new paint
66			G	$825	3/05	SCMI	New paint, row crop
66			F	$2,000	6/05	SEND	Belly mower
66			G	$1,400	7/04	WCIL	Row crop, gas
66			G	$2,000	7/04	NCIA	Side panels, fenders
66			G	$3,000	8/04	ECIL	Row crop, new 12.4-38" tires, fenders, partially restored, runs good, attached Stanhoist loader
66			G	$3,250	6/04	WCWI	Std., diesel, repainted, hyd., new rubber
66			G	$4,000	7/04	WCIL	Gas, new tires
66			G	$4,250	6/04	WCWI	Std., gas, new tires
66			G	$4,900	6/04	WCWI	WF, restored
66	1953		G	$2,550	5/04	SCPA	Restored
66			G	$525	9/03	NEIN	
66			G	$2,000	9/03	NEIN	
66			G	$2,500	10/03	SEMN	Row crop, new front tires
66	1950		E	$2,700	1/03	NENE	Row crop, restored, sharp
660			G	$3,450	11/05	ECMN	Gas, with older loader
660			G	$4,200	7/04	WCIL	Gas, steps, WF
660			G	$4,500	6/04	WCWI	Rare diesel engine, WF, repainted
660			G	$5,000	6/04	WCWI	Gas, WF, repainted
70			G	$2,600	11/05	WCIL	Stlyed row crop, original side panels, converted to 12 volt, NF, 6-speed trans, new spark plugs & wires
70			G	$650	11/05	WCIL	Original

Model	Year	Hours	Cond.	Price	Date	Area	Comments
70			F	$800	4/05	SCMI	NF, gas
70	1946		G	$1,100	3/05	SEND	NF, older restoration
70			F	$425	9/04	NECO	Runs, fair tires
70			G	$1,400	7/04	WCIL	Gas, orchard, new fenders
70			P	$375	3/03	SEIA	Not running, gas, NF, steel tiptoe wheels
70			G	$650	9/03	NEIN	
70			G	$700	9/03	NEIN	Row crop
70			P	$850	3/03	SEIA	Not running, NF, gas
70			G	$1,000	8/03	NCIA	Gas
70			G	$1,950	10/03	SEMN	Row crop, steel wheels, tiptoes
70			G	$2,100	9/03	NCIA	Row crop, side panels, fenders, 2-row cultivator and original book, good tin
70	1936		G	$3,850	10/03	SEMN	Round spoked wheels all around, side curtains, OH engine
70	1946		G	$1,500	6/03	NEIL	
77			G	$1,000	11/05	WCIL	WF
77			G	$1,300	11/05	WCIL	Gas
77			G	$1,400	11/05	WCIL	Row crop, gas, coil battery & plugs
77			G	$2,000	11/05	WCIL	Std, diesel
77			G	$900	11/05	WCIL	Std, gas, 12 volt, tool box radiator, center brake link, original gauges
77	1950		F	$425	11/05	ECNE	Gas
77			F	$1,400	3/05	WCIL	Gas, new rear tires, good tin
77			G	$1,750	3/05	SEND	NF, hyd. PTO, older restoration, new 14.9-38" tires
77	1949		F	$1,300	4/05	SCNE	Row crop, PTO, gas, fenders, 13-38" rear tires, lights, PS, runs
77	1953		F	$1,100	4/05	SCNE	Row crop, single front wheel, runs
77			E	$1,500	2/04	ECNE	Sharp
77			G	$1,650	3/04	NCWI	WF
77			G	$2,400	8/04	ECMI	Gas, NF, restored
77			G	$3,750	6/04	WCWI	Standard
77	1953		G	$1,500	2/04	SENE	Row crop, gas, 14.6-38" tires, disc brakes, fenders, engine side panels, 2 hyd.
77			G	$750	9/03	NEIN	Row crop
77			G	$1,050	5/03	ECMN	Gas, NF
77			F	$1,125	10/03	SEMN	
77			G	$1,350	9/03	NEIN	
77			F	$1,400	3/03	SEIA	Gas, NF
77			G	$1,600	9/03	NEIN	
77			G	$1,700	3/03	NWIL	NF
77			G	$1,850	9/03	NEIN	Std.
77			G	$1,900	2/03	WCIA	Row crop, gas, side curtains, rear fenders
77			G	$1,900	4/03	WCWI	Row crop, NF, new paint, excellent rubber
77			G	$1,900	10/03	SEMN	Row crop, NF, near new tires
77			G	$2,300	2/03	WCIL	Row crop, NF, new tires
770	1962		G	$2,350	1/06	NWIL	Row crop, new paint, gas
770			G	$1,400	11/05	WCIL	Orchard, diesel, fenders
770			G	$1,700	11/05	WCIL	Single front, 3 pt.
770			G	$2,500	11/05	WCIL	Motor needs work, orchard
770			G	$5,000	11/05	WCIL	High boy sprayer, WF, high crop, LP
770			F	$2,100	4/05	SCMI	WF, gas
770	1962		E	$3,400	3/05	SCIL	Factory 3 pt., original paint good, NF
770		3,370	G	$3,900	1/05	SWMN	WF

oliver

Model	Year	Hours	Cond.	Price	Date	Area	Comments
770	1958		E	$2,300	3/05	SCIL	PS, 2 hyd., NF, original paint, straight
770			F	$2,400	4/04	NEPA	
770			G	$2,500	8/04	NCIA	NF, diesel
770			F	$2,750	10/04	SEPA	Gas, NF, PS, 3 pt., average rubber
770			G	$3,600	9/04	WCMN	Loader, gas, WF
770	1959		G	$1,600	7/04	WCIL	Diesel, WF, PS, steps, metal grill
770			F	$625	9/03	NEIN	NF, patched block, diesel
770			F	$1,300	9/03	SEMN	WF, cultivator, gas, not running
770			F	$1,525	8/03	NWIL	Gas, NF
770			G	$2,400	8/03	SEMN	High crop, totally restored
770			E	$3,050	11/03	NEKS	Gas, WF, 1 hyd., good 13.6-38" tires, good paint
770	1964		F	$1,100	11/03	NWIL	NF
770	1964		G	$2,450	9/03	NEIN	Gas, NF
80			G	$1,500	11/05	WCIL	Gas, NF, front steel
80			F	$1,300	7/04	WCIL	Gas
80			G	$700	9/03	NEIN	Std.
80			G	$2,150	10/03	SEMN	Row crop
80			G	$3,500	10/03	SEMN	Std., OH
88			G	$1,500	11/05	WCIL	Brass throttle, WF, gas, PTO, hyd
88			F	$1,600	9/05	WCMN	NF, row crop 88, side tins, PTO fenders, lights
88			G	$1,800	11/05	WCIL	Diesel
88			G	$2,000	11/05	WCIL	Std, gas
88			G	$2,900	11/05	WCIL	Row crop, NF, new wrist pins & bushings
88			G	$7,800	11/05	WCIL	Old style, gas, OH, fenders, PTO
88			G	$900	11/05	WCIL	NF, gas, unrestored
88	1953		F	$1,100	12/05	NWIL	Standard WF, side shields, good rubber, runs
88			P	$550	3/05	SEND	WF, for parts
88			F	$1,700	4/05	SCNE	Row crop, Farmhand F11 loader, gas, 13.6-38" tires, 8' bucket, Quick-Tach, runs
88			G	$1,800	6/05	NCIL	Row crop, repainted, good tin
88	1949		F	$1,700	4/05	SCNE	Row crop, 6-cyl. gas engine, WF, 13.6-38" tires, fenders, runs
88			F	$850	7/04	NCIA	Side panels, 12 volt, PS
88			G	$1,500	3/04	NCIL	Row crop
88			G	$1,500	7/04	WCIL	Diesel, PS
88			F	$1,900	7/04	WCIL	Gas, old style row crop
88			G	$1,950	3/04	NWIL	Gas
88			G	$2,000	7/04	WCIL	Diesel, WF, PS
88			F	$2,100	3/04	SCMI	NF, gas, row crop
88			F	$2,400	7/04	WCIL	Gas, NF, missing tin, 1800 engine
88			G	$4,500	6/04	WCWI	Old style, adj. WF
88			P	$325	3/03	SEIA	Not running, NF, gas
88			G	$425	9/03	NEIN	
88			G	$1,675	1/03	ECIL	Row crop, live PTO, belt pulley, engine skirts, new 13.6-38" tires
88			F	$1,900	8/03	NCSD	Live power, WF, Farmhand F11 loader
88			G	$1,975	10/03	SEMN	Std., new tires
88			G	$2,200	9/03	NEIN	Std., gas

Model	Year	Hours	Cond.	Price	Date	Area	Comments
88			G	$2,450	10/03	SEMN	NF, side panels
88			G	$2,500	9/03	NEIN	Std.
88			G	$2,850	10/03	SEMN	Row crop, WF, side panels, live hyd.
88			G	$3,000	8/03	WCIL	Row crop, complete OH, hydra-lectric controls
88	1950		G	$1,800	11/03	ECND	Row crop, 14.9-38" tires, clean & restored
88	1957		P	$1,100	12/03	WCIL	NF, loader, front mount cultivator, rough shape
88 RC	1953	3,200	G	$3,400	6/05	ECIL	
880			F	$1,700	9/05	NWIA	
880	1959		G	$2,450	9/05	SEIN	
880			F	$3,300	6/05	NCIL	9,913 hours, WF, gas, good tin
880			G	$2,575	6/04	NWIA	3 pt., gas
880			G	$2,800	1/04	NEOH	
880			G	$4,300	6/04	WCWI	Diesel, Wheatland, hyd., PTO
880			F	$1,450	3/03	SEIA	Gas, NF, power booster
880			F	$1,750	4/03	WCMN	
880			G	$2,750	8/03	SEMN	Std.
99				$4,800	11/05	WCIL	Diesel, rear wheel wghts, western
99			G	$7,000	7/04	WCIL	6 cyl., 4 speed
99	1951		G	$1,500	7/04	WCIL	Gas, 4 cyl.
99			G	$2,800	9/03	NEIN	88 engine
99			G	$3,500	10/03	SEMN	Std., new fenders, front tires
990			G	$15,250	10/03	SEMN	
HG3			G	$4,250	7/04	WCIL	Gas, 31" gauge
N/A	1945		G	$5,800	11/05	WCIL	HG68, crawler, Hercules, restored, PTO, belt pully
N/A			G	$250	9/03	NEIN	WF
Super 55	1954		G	$2,150	9/05	SEIN	With loader
Super 55			F	$3,400	3/05	NCIL	Loader, backhoe
Super 55			P	$1,100	3/03	SEIA	Not running, gas
Super 55	1955		G	$2,600	9/03	SCMI	Restored, diesel, WF
Super 55	1956		G	$3,500	4/03	WCMN	Gas, 3 pt., 12 volt, live power
Super 66			G	$3,250	6/04	WCWI	Gas, cultivator
Super 66			G	$4,750	6/04	WCWI	WF, original, diesel
Super 77	1955		F	$1,050	3/03	SWMI	NF
Super 88			F	$1,250	8/05	WCMN	WF, good tin, motor & clutch weak
Super 88			F	$1,750	12/05	NWIL	Diesel, NF, good rubber, runs
Super 88	1957		E	$3,100	3/05	SCIL	PS, 2 hyd., new paint, NF, diesel
Super 88			F	$1,300	7/04	WCIL	Gas
Super 88			F	$1,450	12/04	WCMN	WF, 540 PTO, 14.9-38" tires
Super 88			G	$3,500	6/04	WCWI	Industrial, new head, fresh motor
Super 88	1953		G	$1,750	2/04	WCIL	Gas, NF, fenders, runs good
Super 88	1956		F	$2,225	3/04	SCMI	WF, gas
Super 88			F	$1,050	1/03	SCMI	25% rubber
Super 88			G	$1,450	9/03	NEIN	
Super 88			G	$1,850	10/03	SEMN	WF
Super 88			G	$2,200	9/03	NEIN	LP
Super 88	1953		G	$1,700	6/03	NEIL	Diesel
Super 99			G	$8,200	11/05	WCIL	Unrestored
Super 99			F	$3,100	9/03	ECND	GM engine, 23.1-26" tires

balers

Make	Model	Cond.	Price	Date	Area	Comments
AC	302	F	$350	2/05	NCIN	
AC	N/A	P	$75	11/04	NCKS	Round baler, rough
AC	N/A	G	$160	11/04	NCKS	Round baler, white top
AC	N/A	F	$5	8/03	NEKS	Round baler
AC	N/A	P	$50	7/03	NWIL	Small round baler, old
AC	N/A	F	$150	3/03	NWIL	Roto baler
J.I. Case	220	F	$450	2/04	SWIN	Square baler
J.I. Case	330	G	$200	7/03	NWIL	
J.I. Case	3650	F	$750	9/05	NECO	
J.I. Case	NL	G	$1,100	11/05	NCOH	Old baler, wire type
Ford	530	G	$635	10/05	WCIL	
Ford	530	F	$150	3/05	SCMI	Square baler
Ford	530	G	$350	12/03	NCIA	PTO baler
Ford	532	G	$300	5/04	ECWI	PTO baler
Ford	532	G	$1,000	3/03	NWIL	
Ford	552	F	$500	8/05	ECMI	Round baler, missing knotter
IHC	2400	F	$625	8/05	SEMN	Round baler

Make	Model	Cond.	Price	Date	Area	Comments
IHC	2400	F	$50	4/04	ECMT	Round baler
IHC	2400	P	$375	1/04	ECNE	Round baler
IHC	2400	F	$550	9/04	SEIA	Big round baler
IHC	2400	F	$750	2/04	NEIN	Round baler
IHC	241	P	$150	9/05	SEIA	Round baler
IHC	241	F	$375	8/05	NEIN	Round baler
IHC	241	G	$500	12/05	SEMN	Round baler
IHC	241	G	$525	12/05	SEMN	
IHC	241	G	$400	3/04	SEIA	Round baler
IHC	241	F	$900	3/03	NWIL	Round baler
IHC	241	F	$1,900	3/03	NWIL	Round baler
IHC	241	F	$1,900	3/03	SWPA	Round baler
IHC	27	F	$95	7/03	NEOH	
IHC	37	G	$225	4/04	ECWI	Baler, thrower
IHC	37	G	$250	3/03	WCMI	Square baler
IHC	37	G	$600	12/03	WCIL	Twine square baler
IHC	420	G	$1,000	3/04	WCMI	Square baler, kicker
IHC	420	G	$750	1/03	NWIL	Small square baler
IHC	425	E	$1,600	10/05	NCOH	Square baler
IHC	430	F	$350	4/04	NCWI	
IHC	430	G	$600	8/04	WCIL	Twine square baler, new feeder and shaft
IHC	430	F	$650	3/04	WCIL	Small square twine baler
IHC	430	P	$250	3/03	SWPA	Thrower
IHC	430	F	$400	8/03	SEPA	Thrower
IHC	430	G	$1,350	10/03	WCSK	Canadian sale, square baler
IHC	435	G	$875	1/05	WCIL	Square baler
IHC	435	F	$500	12/04	SEPA	Belt thrower
IHC	435	E	$1,000	10/04	NEIA	
IHC	435	G	$1,500	9/04	SEIA	Square baler
IHC	435	F	$1,200	3/03	WCMI	Thrower super sweep, wide pick up
IHC	440	F	$300	9/05	NECO	Wire tie, PTO
IHC	440	F	$650	4/05	SEPA	With kicker
IHC	440	G	$200	3/04	NEKS	
IHC	440	G	$550	11/04	NCKS	Wire tie square baler, hyd. bale tension bank greaser
IHC	440	G	$1,600	9/03	WCSD	Small square baler, Farmhand bale accumulator, 8-pack accumulator
IHC	440T	G	$675	2/04	NEIN	
IHC	440T	G	$1,000	5/04	NWND	Square baler
IHC	445	G	$1,400	3/05	NEOH	Thrower
IHC	45	P	$16	11/04	NEKS	Rough
IHC	45	P	$40	7/03	NWIL	Baler
IHC	45	F	$550	3/03	WCMI	Square baler
IHC	46	G	$370	8/05	NCIA	PTO baler
IHC	46	G	$200	8/04	NCIA	PTO baler
IHC	46	F	$300	2/04	NEIN	
IHC	46	F	$200	9/03	NWOH	Wire baler
IHC	47	G	$1,000	2/06	WCIL	String tie baler
IHC	47	G	$500	3/05	NESD	Small square baler
IHC	47	G	$400	2/04	ECNE	Wire tie small square baler
IHC	47	G	$900	8/04	SEIA	
IHC	N/A	G	$650	8/05	NEIN	Small square baler

balers

Make	Model	Cond.	Price	Date	Area	Comments
Deere	14T	F	$360	2/06	NEIA	
Deere	14T	F	$375	11/05	SCMI	Square baler
Deere	14T	G	$525	1/05	SENE	
Deere	14T	G	$850	1/05	SENE	
Deere	14T	P	$90	4/04	NCWI	Parts
Deere	14T	G	$400	4/04	ECWI	Baler
Deere	14T	F	$450	2/04	NEIN	
Deere	14T	F	$625	8/04	NWIL	
Deere	14T	G	$675	11/04	WCIL	Kicker
Deere	14T	G	$1,100	6/04	NWIL	Small square baler, kicker
Deere	14T	F	$60	4/03	WCIA	Square baler
Deere	14T	F	$100	9/03	ECWI	
Deere	14T	G	$200	12/03	WCIA	
Deere	14T	G	$225	3/03	WCMI	Square baler
Deere	14T	F	$300	8/03	SEPA	
Deere	14T	F	$325	2/03	NCIL	540 PTO
Deere	14T	G	$400	9/03	ECMI	
Deere	14T	G	$700	12/03	SEIA	
Deere	240	F	$900	3/04	NWIL	
Deere	24T	F	$250	9/05	NWIA	
Deere	24T	F	$400	8/05	SEMN	
Deere	24T	F	$550	7/05	SESD	Square
Deere	24T	G	$750	11/05	SWMN	
Deere	24T	F	$800	8/05	NWIL	
Deere	24T	G	$500	2/05	WCOH	Square baler
Deere	24T	G	$525	7/05	ECND	Square baler
Deere	24T	G	$625	8/05	SWOH	Square baler
Deere	24T	G	$825	4/05	NCOH	
Deere	24T	F	$850	2/05	NWIL	
Deere	24T	G	$900	2/05	NEIN	
Deere	24T	G	$1,350	2/05	WCIL	Square baler
Deere	24T	G	$1,450	8/05	NWIL	
Deere	24T	G	$1,500	1/05	NENE	Twine tie square baler
Deere	24T	P	$65	10/04	NCWI	For parts
Deere	24T	F	$275	3/04	NEMN	Thrower
Deere	24T	F	$275	10/04	NCWI	
Deere	24T	G	$450	3/04	NWMN	Square baler
Deere	24T	G	$750	2/04	NCIA	
Deere	24T	G	$750	2/04	NEIN	
Deere	24T	G	$1,450	9/04	ECNE	Twine tie
Deere	24T	G	$1,500	3/04	NCMI	Square hay baler
Deere	24T	F	$200	9/03	ECWI	Kicker
Deere	24T	G	$275	9/03	NEIN	Kicker
Deere	24T	G	$375	7/03	ECND	
Deere	24T	P	$400	6/03	NWIL	
Deere	24T	G	$410	6/03	WCWI	Thrower
Deere	24T	G	$425	9/03	NCIA	
Deere	24T	F	$640	2/03	NWIL	Square baler
Deere	24T	G	$800	8/03	NCIA	

Make	Model	Cond.	Price	Date	Area	Comments
Deere	24T	G	$925	9/03	NEIN	
Deere	24T	G	$950	1/03	NCOH	
Deere	24T	G	$1,000	3/03	NWIL	
Deere	24T	G	$1,050	9/03	NEIN	Square baler
Deere	24T	G	$1,800	3/03	NWIL	
Deere	336	G	$1,800	2/06	WCOH	Wire tie baler
Deere	336	G	$1,800	2/06	WCOH	Wire tie baler
Deere	336	G	$2,600	1/06	NEIN	
Deere	336	G	$3,000	1/06	SCMI	Thrower & extra thrower
Deere	336	G	$1,500	9/05	SCON	
Deere	336	G	$1,900	7/05	WCMN	Thrower
Deere	336	G	$2,000	9/05	SCON	Canadian sale
Deere	336	F	$2,200	11/05	NEIA	With thrower
Deere	336	G	$2,000	7/05	NEIA	Baler, thrower
Deere	336	G	$2,200	3/05	SCMI	Square baler, thrower
Deere	336	G	$2,500	3/05	WCMN	
Deere	336	G	$2,700	4/05	NEIN	Kicker
Deere	336	G	$3,500	1/05	SWIL	Wire baler
Deere	336	E	$3,500	3/05	WCWI	Square baler, 30 kicker
Deere	336	F	$3,800	4/05	SEPA	#30 ejector
Deere	336	G	$4,000	2/05	NCIN	Hay baler, thrower, 1976 model
Deere	336	G	$4,500	4/05	WCWI	Baler, thrower, automatic 30-gal. liquid applicator
Deere	336	P	$500	1/04	WCMI	Square baler, kicker doesn't work
Deere	336	G	$825	3/04	SWPA	Kicker
Deere	336	G	$1,075	6/04	ECWI	Baler, thrower
Deere	336	F	$1,200	1/04	SESD	
Deere	336	G	$1,250	3/04	SWWI	Thrower
Deere	336	G	$1,300	10/04	SEMN	
Deere	336	G	$1,400	3/04	SEMN	
Deere	336	G	$1,750	3/04	SEMN	
Deere	336	G	$2,150	3/04	SEMN	Ejector
Deere	336	G	$2,300	6/04	NWIA	Square baler
Deere	336	G	$2,350	4/04	ECWI	Thrower
Deere	336	G	$2,600	7/04	WCWI	Thrower
Deere	336	G	$2,650	3/04	SEPA	#40 thrower
Deere	336	F	$2,700	12/04	ECMI	Thrower needs repair
Deere	336	G	$3,000	3/04	ECMI	Square baler, bale ejector
Deere	336	G	$3,000	3/04	SEMN	Injector
Deere	336	E	$3,025	2/04	NEKS	Twine, always shedded
Deere	336	G	$3,550	3/04	NWIL	
Deere	336	G	$300	10/03	ECWI	Hay baler, ejector
Deere	336	G	$1,000	3/03	WCMI	Square baler, kicker
Deere	336	G	$1,000	3/03	WCMI	Square baler, kicker
Deere	336	G	$1,300	11/03	WCWI	Thrower
Deere	336	G	$1,425	8/03	WCMN	Square baler, thrower
Deere	336	G	$1,800	9/03	SEMN	Thrower
Deere	336	G	$1,850	3/03	NESD	Small square baler
Deere	336	G	$1,875	2/03	WCMN	Small square baler, ejector
Deere	336	G	$2,000	8/03	ECMN	#40 ejector
Deere	336	G	$2,000	4/03	NCWI	Kicker
Deere	336	E	$2,100	2/03	NEIA	Thrower
Deere	336	G	$2,150	2/03	NCMI	Square baler

balers

Make	Model	Cond.	Price	Date	Area	Comments
Deere	336	G	$2,300	4/03	WCMN	#30 ejector
Deere	336	G	$2,300	1/03	SWOH	PTO baler
Deere	336	G	$3,200	12/03	WCIL	Twin square baler
Deere	336	F	$3,400	8/03	SEPA	Thrower
Deere	336	G	$3,450	3/03	NEKS	Twine
Deere	336	G	$4,400	3/03	ECTN	
Massey	7	G	$650	3/03	SEIA	Square hay baler
Massey	10	F	$70	4/03	WCIA	Works
Massey	10	G	$170	8/03	NCIA	PTO baler
Massey	10	G	$200	9/03	SEMN	
Massey	10	G	$290	8/03	NCIA	
Massey	12	F	$160	1/06	SESD	Square
Massey	12	G	$600	8/05	SCMI	
Massey	12	G	$1,850	9/04	NWIA	Square baler
Massey	12	F	$265	9/03	ECWI	Thrower
Massey	12	F	$325	3/03	WCMI	
Massey	124	P	$260	4/05	SCSD	Salvage
Massey	124	F	$400	12/04	SEMN	Baler, thrower
Massey	124	F	$950	10/04	SEPA	Square baler, kicker
Massey	124	E	$1,100	11/04	NCKS	Square baler, twine tie
Massey	124	G	$2,200	2/04	WCWI	Thrower
Massey	124	G	$550	9/03	ECNE	Twine tie
Massey	124	G	$575	6/03	ECNE	PTO, twine tie
Massey	124	G	$3,800	7/03	SWIN	
Massey	128	G	$3,800	2/06	SEIL	Baler, string
Massey	130	E	$1,950	11/04	NCKS	Square baler, wire tie
Massey	1560	F	$750	1/06	SESD	Round baler
Massey	1560	F	$800	2/05	NCOK	Round baler
Massey	224	G	$3,300	5/05	NEKY	Square baler
Massey	3	F	$350	2/05	NEIN	
Massey	3	F	$750	3/03	WCMI	Square baler
Massey	3	F	$750	3/03	WCMI	Square baler
Massey	560	F	$225	8/04	NEKS	
Massey	560	P	$375	3/04	SEIA	Big round baler
Massey	9	G	$375	3/04	SEIA	Square baler
Massey	N/A	G	$375	3/04	SEIA	Square baler
Massey	N/A	G	$200	4/03	WCSK	Canadian sale, square baler
Massey	N/A	F	$225	7/03	WCSK	Square baler
New Holland	268	F	$200	11/05	SCMI	Square baler
New Holland	268	F	$500	6/05	SEND	Square baler, PTO
New Holland	268	G	$800	3/05	NECO	Small square baler
New Holland	268	G	$275	4/04	ECWI	Hay baler
New Holland	268	G	$400	2/04	NCIN	Thrower
New Holland	268	E	$450	12/04	SENE	
New Holland	268	F	$485	2/04	NEIN	
New Holland	268	F	$500	2/04	NEIN	
New Holland	268	G	$550	3/04	NEKS	Square baler, twine tie
New Holland	268	E	$600	5/04	SENE	
New Holland	268	E	$1,050	2/04	NEIN	

148

Make	Model	Cond.	Price	Date	Area	Comments
New Holland	268	G	$1,300	2/04	NEIN	
New Holland	268	F	$175	7/03	NWIL	
New Holland	268	F	$325	2/03	SEMN	Pickup, thrower
New Holland	268	G	$475	10/03	WCSK	Canadian sale, square baler
New Holland	268	G	$600	2/03	SWOH	
New Holland	268	E	$1,100	11/03	SENE	
New Holland	269	E	$1,100	9/05	NENE	Small square twine tie baler, sharp, shedded
New Holland	269	G	$1,000	1/05	ECNE	Square baler
New Holland	269	G	$2,600	4/05	SCMI	
New Holland	269	F	$300	2/04	NEIN	
New Holland	269	F	$550	4/04	SWPA	Square baler, thrower
New Holland	269	G	$650	9/04	ECNE	Square baler
New Holland	269	G	$725	7/04	WCIA	Wire baler
New Holland	269	F	$725	11/04	NCOH	Thrower, average
New Holland	269	G	$775	2/04	NEIN	Small square baler
New Holland	269	F	$550	9/03	NEIN	Square baler
New Holland	269	G	$560	4/03	SCMN	
New Holland	271	F	$450	4/04	NEPA	
New Holland	271	F	$475	1/04	ECNE	Square
New Holland	271	F	$4,900	3/04	SEPA	Square baler, 2-cyl. Wisconsin engine
New Holland	271	F	$600	2/03	SEMN	Thrower
New Holland	271	G	$1,000	2/03	SCKS	Wire tie
New Holland	66	G	$350	2/05	NEIN	Small square baler
New Holland	66	F	$55	1/04	ECIA	Wisconsin engine
New Holland	66	F	$100	4/04	NEPA	PTO
New Holland	66	G	$400	7/04	NCIA	PTO baler
New Holland	67	G	$1,050	1/06	WCIL	String tire square baler
New Holland	67	F	$290	3/05	SCMI	
New Holland	67	F	$500	2/04	NWIL	
New Holland	67	G	$575	4/04	ECWI	PTO baler
New Holland	67	F	$85	6/03	NCWI	PTO
New Holland	67	F	$250	10/03	WCMN	Small square baler
New Holland	68	P	$225	2/06	NWIL	Hayliner baler
New Holland	68	P	$100	8/05	SEMN	
New Holland	68	F	$500	3/05	SCMI	Square baler
New Holland	68	F	$500	3/04	WCIL	
New Holland	68	G	$600	7/04	NCIA	PTO baler
New Holland	68	G	$675	11/04	NCKS	Square twine baler
New Holland	68	F	$70	2/03	SWOH	
New Holland	68	F	$100	12/03	WCMI	
New Holland	68	F	$150	1/03	WCKS	
New Holland	68	F	$300	9/03	NEIN	Square baler
New Holland	68	F	$350	3/03	NWIL	
New Holland	69	G	$1,150	9/03	NEIN	
New Holland	78	F	$10	4/04	NEPA	Bale chute & hitch
New Holland	78	F	$475	5/04	NENE	Small square baler, twine tie
New Holland	Super 66	G	$400	2/03	NWOH	
New Holland	Super 67	F	$400	4/05	NCOH	
New Holland	Super 69	G	$900	11/03	ECNE	Wire baler
Oliver	62T	F	$95	3/05	SCMI	Square hay baler
Oliver	720	G	$450	11/03	NEKS	Twine tie

combines

Make	Model	Year	Cond.	Price	Date	Area	Comments
J.I. Case	660		G	$500	3/04	WCMI	Bean combine, 10' grain platform & 2-row corn head
Gleaner	A	1959	P	$150	2/06	WCNE	Gas, 14' wheat header, engine turns
Gleaner	A		G	$200	4/05	NCOK	LP, ran good, 14' header, pickup reel & attachment
Gleaner	A		P	$160	8/03	NEKS	Rough, did not run, cab
Gleaner	C2		G	$875	3/04	ECMI	Sold with 4-row corn and 14' rigid head
Gleaner	C2	1965	E	$525	11/04	SCKS	Set up for alfalfa, 18' header, good tires, cab & cooler, great shape
Gleaner	E		P	$450	4/05	NCOH	For parts
Gleaner	E		P	$600	3/04	WCMN	
Gleaner	F	1969	G	$900	2/06	WCNE	Gas, 18' wheat header, 3r-30 corn head, cab
Gleaner	F		P	$150	4/05	NCOH	With 13' grain head, salvage
Gleaner	F		F	$500	4/05	NCOH	13' flex head, variable speed reel, straw chopper
Gleaner	F		G	$800	4/05	NCOH	Variable speed reel, straw chopper
Gleaner	F		G	$500	8/04	NCOH	Gas, sold with 13' head
Gleaner	F		G	$900	4/04	NCKS	16' header
Gleaner	F		G	$1,000	3/04	WCMI	Special corn/soybean, gas
Gleaner	F	1968	P	$100	5/04	NCKS	18', gear drive with variable speed, salvage

Make	Model	Year	Cond.	Price	Date	Area	Comments
Gleaner	F	1969	F	$700	3/04	NEKS	Gas, 13' Hume reel, AC
Gleaner	F	1974	F	$450	9/04	NCIA	Chopper, gas
Gleaner	F		F	$200	2/03	ECNE	AC, chopper, side blower
Gleaner	F		G	$2,600	2/03	WCMI	13' flex head, 23.1-26" tires
Gleaner	G	1972	G	$1,300	5/04	NCKS	20', near new 350 Chevrolet engine, gear drive with variable speed
Gleaner	G		G	$1,200	10/03	SEMN	300 hrs. on complete engine OH
Gleaner	G	1971	G	$2,200	6/03	WCSK	Canadian sale, cab, gas, 18' straight cut header with steel bat reel, 150 hp.
Gleaner	G	1972	G	$2,500	3/03	NCOK	20' header, straw chopper, variable speed, AC, diesel
Gleaner	K		F	$300	2/03	SWOH	13' grain table & 2-row corn head
Gleaner	K2		F	$700	11/04	NWNY	2 heads
Gleaner	K2		F	$2,250	3/03	SWPA	12' grain head, hour meter didn't work
Gleaner	L	1976	G	$1,300	7/05	ECND	Diesel, corn/soybean special, variable speed
Gleaner	L	1975	G	$1,000	11/03	ECND	Diesel, 4 speed, chopper, pickup head, 18.4-34" tires
Gleaner	L	1976	G	$3,000	5/03	SWOK	24' header, duals, new turbo, straw chopper, shedded, field ready, 1 owner
Gleaner	M		F	$1,100	1/06	SCMI	2,545 hours, gas, V-8, 13' grain table
Gleaner	M		G	$1,450	12/05	SEMN	
Gleaner	M		G	$2,700	8/05	SEMN	With 438 corn head
Gleaner	M	1974	G	$3,000	9/05	WCNE	Sold with 20' #980 header & Renn pickup
Gleaner	M	1978	P	$1,600	3/05	WCIL	Diesel, with 6-row 30" corn head
Gleaner	M		G	$2,000	5/04	NWND	20' header
IHC	303		P	$110	8/03	NEKS	Rough, did not run, cab
IHC	315		F	$125	6/04	NCWI	13' grain head, gear drive
IHC	315		F	$450	6/04	NCWI	13' grain head
IHC	503		G	$500	8/03	SENE	
IHC	503		G	$900	4/03	NCKS	AC, hyd., pickup reel
IHC	503		E	$2,000	9/03	SEIN	13' head & 4-row corn head
IHC	615		G	$625	8/03	ECNE	Gas, 3-gear manual trans., cab, PS, 16.9-26" tires
IHC	715		G	$1,700	10/05	NCND	Windrow special, cab and McRenn pickup, diesel
IHC	715		P	$800	8/05	NWIL	Diesel
IHC	715		G	$1,750	4/05	NCOH	Corn/soybean special, hyd., 13' grain head
IHC	715		P	$150	9/04	ECIA	For parts, sold with grain head, doesn't run
IHC	715		F	$200	3/04	WCMN	Grain head
IHC	715		F	$250	9/04	SEIA	
IHC	715		F	$500	3/04	WCMN	Corn head
IHC	715		G	$3,000	3/04	SEIL	Grain table, diesel
IHC	715	1976	G	$1,100	8/04	WCIL	Hyd., corn/soybean special, cab, monitor, diesel
IHC	715		P	$125	3 03	NEKS	Gas, motor not working, not used in over year
IHC	715		F	$450	3/03	SWPA	844 corn head, 810 13' grain head, diesel, cab
IHC	715		G	$600	11/03	SEIL	Gas, no heads
IHC	715		P	$600	3/03	NWIL	Corn/soybean special, gas
IHC	715		F	$675	9/03	NEIN	
IHC	715		F	$800	8/03	SEMN	15' bean head
IHC	715		F	$850	4/03	NCWI	16' grain platform & Hume reel, cab,
IHC	715		F	$1,000	3/03	NEKS	Diesel, cab, 18' header
IHC	715		G	$2,250	4/03	WCMI	
IHC	715	1974	G	$1,250	6/03	NCIA	Gas, hyd., chopper
IHC	715	1975	F	$600	3/03	NWIL	Gas, 13' platform
IHC	715	1979	G	$1,650	8/03	ECNE	Diesel, corn/soybean special, hyd., cab, 278.8
IHC	815	1973	G	$1,550	2/05	WCIL	Hyd., cab, like-new steering tires, 500 hours on major engine OH

combines

Make	Model	Year	Cond.	Price	Date	Area	Comments
IHC	815		G	$3,500	8/04	NWIL	Sold with 2 heads
IHC	815		G	$1,250	1/03	SWOH	Hyd.
IHC	82		G	$975	2/06	NEIA	Pull type
IHC	82		E	$450	8/03	ECWI	
IHC	914		E	$2,400	7/05	SCMN	Pull type, like new
IHC	914		F	$175	4/04	SEND	Belt pickup & chopper
IHC	914		F	$200	3/04	NWMN	
IHC	914		F	$500	7/04	NWMN	
IHC	914		G	$600	3/04	SEND	Air foil sieves
IHC	914		G	$750	3/04	SEND	Air foil sieves
IHC	914	1980	F	$900	7/04	NEND	Pull-type combine, red top, chopper
IHC	914		F	$300	9/03	WCSD	Pull-type combine
IHC	914		G	$400	10/03	WCSK	Canadian sale, PTO, white top
IHC	914		G	$550	7/03	ECND	IH, new concave, cab control
IHC	914		G	$800	10/03	WCSK	Canadian sale, red top
IHC	914		G	$875	10/03	NWMN	PTO combine, white top
IHC	914		G	$1,100	6/03	WCSK	Canadan sale, straw chopper
IHC	914	1977	F	$1,300	7/03	WCSK	Canadian sale
IHC	914	1978	G	$475	7/03	ECND	
IHC	914	1979	F	$1,300	7/03	WCSK	Canadian sale, red top, ext. hitch
IHC	915		G	$1,800	4/05	NEKS	No heads, hyd., cab
IHC	915	1976	G	$1,300	7/05	ECND	Diesel, hyd.
IHC	915		G	$1,600	3/04	NCMI	Hyd. turbo, flotation tires, diesel,
IHC	915		F	$1,600	3/03	ECNE	IHC 844 4-row corn head, diesel, corn/soybean special, hyd.
IHC	915		G	$1,875	7/03	SCMN	Hydrostatic low profile, corn/soybean special
IHC	915		G	$3,500	7/03	ECND	Hyd., diesel, chopper,
IHC	915	1976	G	$2,200	7/03	SEND	
IHC	915	1977	G	$2,200	7/03	SEND	
John Deere	105		G	$1,800	12/05	NCOH	Gas, sold with JD 216 grain head
John Deere	105		F	$125	3/04	WCMN	With corn head
John Deere	105		G	$2,250	3/04	ECMI	Gas, spike cyl.
John Deere	105		G	$300	9/03	ECWI	4-row corn, 14' grain head
John Deere	105		G	$350	9/03	ECWI	4-row corn, 14' grain head
John Deere	105	1961	G	$1,300	3/03	NCWI	SP, gas, 15' grain platform, John Deere 435 4-row corn head
John Deere	105	1968	G	$1,550	12/03	SEND	SP, cab, finger reel, stored inside
John Deere	25		G	$100	9/03	NEIN	
John Deere	30		P	$50	6/05	ECWI	
John Deere	30		P	$100	6/03	NWIL	
John Deere	30		G	$400	9/03	NEIN	
John Deere	3300		F	$1,300	12/05	WCWI	
John Deere	3300	1976	G	$2,400	11/05	NEIA	2050 hours, second owner, diesel, sharp
John Deere	3300		G	$800	2/05	NCOH	
John Deere	3300	1970	G	$900	3/04	WCMI	Gas, cab, clean
John Deere	3300		F	$150	8/03	SEMN	Gear drive, bean head and 3-row 30" corn head
John Deere	3300		F	$250	8/03	SEMN	Gear drive, bean head and 3-row 30" corn head
John Deere	3300		F	$650	3/03	SWWI	2-row corn head and 13.5' grain head
John Deere	40		P	$375	8/04	SWPA	

Make	Model	Year	Cond.	Price	Date	Area	Comments
John Deere	40		G	$1,525	1/04	ECIA	2-row corn head & 10' grain table
John Deere	42		F	$200	4/03	WCMN	Belt pickup, new belts, bean head
John Deere	42		G	$350	3/03	NWPA	8.5' grain head
John Deere	4400	1979	F	$1,400	2/06	SCMI	Diesel, chopper, 23.1-26" tires, approx. 100 acres on new concave & cyl. bars & feeder house chain, 1 owner, one of last 4400s made, 5,700 hours
John Deere	4400	1979	G	$6,250	2/06	WCIL	1,733 hours, no heads
John Deere	4400		G	$1,900	7/05	WCMN	2,200 hours, diesel, cab, no heads
John Deere	4400		G	$2,400	8/05	SEMN	
John Deere	4400	1971	G	$600	9/05	NECO	1,570 hours, cab
John Deere	4400	1974	G	$1,900	11/05	ECNE	3,660 hours, diesel
John Deere	4400	1974	G	$2,400	11/05	ECNE	2,687 hours, diesel
John Deere	4400	1977	G	$2,950	12/05	SEMN	Straw chopper, monitor, AC, auto header control 3,600 hours
John Deere	4400	1977	G	$4,200	8/05	NCOH	Sold with JD 215 flex grain head, cab, AC, heat, 23.1-26" front rubber, 12.4-24" rear, rebuilt sieves/shaker, 2,911 hours
John Deere	4400		G	$1,400	1/05	NENE	Never used after $6,000 in repairs, gas
John Deere	4400	1971	G	$350	3/05	SWIN	Gas, chopper
John Deere	4400	1971	F	$550	3/05	SEWY	Cab, gas
John Deere	4400	1974	F	$2,000	4/05	SCMI	John Deere 16' grain head
John Deere	4400		F	$750	9/04	ECSD	
John Deere	4400		F	$875	9/04	NCIA	No heads
John Deere	4400		G	$1,000	12/04	ECNE	Gas
John Deere	4400		F	$1,500	1/04	ECNE	With John Deere 213 flex head
John Deere	4400		G	$1,900	9/04	NCIA	No heads
John Deere	4400		G	$2,300	10/04	NCOH	Gas, sold with 13' head
John Deere	4400		E	$4,700	12/04	WCIL	1 owner, late model, diesel, perfect paint, good rubber, all lights work
John Deere	4400	1974	P	$50	5/04	NCKS	Salvage, sold with 20' platform, cab and water cooler
John Deere	4400	1974	G	$1,500	3/04	WCMI	Cab, gas, 18.4-26" tires
John Deere	4400	1974	G	$3,500	3/04	NCMI	Straw chopper, diesel, new bearings and cyl., new parts, clean unit, rigid grain platform
John Deere	4400	1975	G	$2,100	9/04	NCIA	Diesel, chopper
John Deere	4400	1977	F	$3,900	9/04	SCMI	John Deere 215 grain head, diesel
John Deere	4400	1979	P	$275	11/04	WCIA	For parts
John Deere	4400	1979	G	$2,000	11/04	NCIA	Chopper, engine OH at 2,500 hours, new bars and concaves
John Deere	4400		F	$500	2/03	NEKS	13' rigid grain table, gas
John Deere	4400		F	$600	2/03	WCMI	Diesel, 18.4-26"
John Deere	4400		G	$1,100	9/03	NEIN	
John Deere	4400		F	$1,300	9/03	SCNE	15' platform, Hume reel, Milo guards
John Deere	4400		G	$1,600	4/03	WCWI	Diesel, new clutch
John Deere	4400		G	$2,150	9/03	SEMN	Gear drive, straw chopper
John Deere	4400		G	$3,000	9/03	SCNE	14½' platform
John Deere	4400		G	$3,700	10/03	SEMN	
John Deere	4400	1972	F	$600	10/03	NWIL	
John Deere	4400	1976	G	$1,400	12/03	SCMN	Diesel
John Deere	4400	1977	G	$2,200	3/03	NWIL	Diesel
John Deere	4400	1978	G	$1,350	8/03	SEMN	Gear drive, AC
John Deere	4400	1978	G	$3,000	4/03	SCMN	Straw chopper
John Deere	45		G	$230	8/04	NCOH	Round back, sold with 10' head
John Deere	45		F	$500	9/03	NEIN	Platform & 2-row head, gas

combines

Make	Model	Year	Cond.	Price	Date	Area	Comments
John Deere	55		E	$650	2/03	NEIA	2-row corn head
John Deere	55		G	$1,100	9/03	WCSD	
John Deere	6600	1974	F	$2,000	1/06	SCMI	300 hours on OH, 13' grain table
John Deere	6600	1978	G	$3,350	1/06	SCMN	Hydro, cab, air, diesel
John Deere	6600		F	$1,300	12/05	WCWI	
John Deere	6600		F	$1,600	9/05	NWOR	
John Deere	6600		G	$1,700	8/05	NWIA	JD 444, 4-row corn head, JD 454, 4-row crop head
John Deere	6600		P	$2,100	11/05	NEIA	Rough, no heads
John Deere	6600		F	$3,650	9/05	SEIA	3,175 hours
John Deere	6600	1976	G	$4,800	9/05	WCMN	All new rubber, 23.1-26" fronts, add-on auto header (robot), 3 yrs on new cylinder, concaves, 3,823 hours
John Deere	6600	1977	F	$3,750	10/05	NCOH	JD 215 grain head, hydrostatic
John Deere	6600		F	$700	3/05	SEIA	
John Deere	6600		F	$700	1/05	ECNE	
John Deere	6600		F	$900	4/05	SEND	
John Deere	6600		G	$3,700	7/05	SCMN	
John Deere	6600		F	$3,900	4/05	SCMI	Sold with John Deere 216 head & John Deere 443 corn head, diesel, flat screen
John Deere	6600	1971	F	$900	4/05	SCMI	Diesel, flat screen, no heads
John Deere	6600	1975	G	$4,400	2/05	SWIN	Gear drive, chopper, diesel
John Deere	6600	1976	G	$2,200	3/05	SWIN	Diesel, chopper, rice tires
John Deere	6600	1977	F	$3,600	8/05	NWIL	Gear drive, diesel, chopper
John Deere	6600		P	$375	2/04	NEKS	Rough, gas
John Deere	6600		P	$1,250	12/04	ECNE	Rough
John Deere	6600		F	$1,250	12/04	SEMN	
John Deere	6600		G	$1,600	6/04	ECWI	13' grain head
John Deere	6600		G	$1,700	9/04	NCIA	Diesel
John Deere	6600		P	$1,800	10/04	SWWI	Rough, sold with John Deere 444 4-row corn head
John Deere	6600		G	$1,900	12/04	NWIA	Hyd.
John Deere	6600	1973	P	$1,300	2/04	NWIL	Diesel
John Deere	6600	1974	F	$900	12/04	WCMN	Gear drive, chopper
John Deere	6600	1974	G	$2,275	9/04	SEIA	
John Deere	6600	1975	F	$1,100	12/04	WCMN	Gear drive, chopper
John Deere	6600	1975	F	$2,025	3/04	ECNE	Diesel, hyd., cab, 18.4x26" front tires, rear chopper, rear wheel weights
John Deere	6600	1975	G	$3,200	2/04	WCMI	2WD, diesel
John Deere	6600	1977	F	$1,025	5/04	NWPA	14' grain head, hyd., cab, 6-cyl. turbo diesel engine
John Deere	6600	1977	G	$3,100	2/04	NWIL	Cab, AC, hyd., chopper, diesel, clean
John Deere	6600	1977	G	$3,700	9/04	NWIA	Chopper, diesel
John Deere	6600	1978	G	$1,200	4/04	SEND	Cab, Posi-torque, air foil sieve
John Deere	6600	1978	G	$3,300	11/04	SENE	Gear drive, always shedded
John Deere	6600	1979	G	$5,200	3/04	SCKS	Sold with John Deere 222 header on trailer, hyd., diesel, chopper, spreader, always shedded
John Deere	6600		G	$450	7/03	NWOH	New engine 8 years ago, 15' grain head, chopper
John Deere	6600		F	$500	3/03	SWMN	Diesel
John Deere	6600		F	$900	3/03	NESD	Hyd.
John Deere	6600		P	$1,250	2/03	NCOH	Gear drive, 404 diesel engine
John Deere	6600		F	$1,500	2/03	WCMI	Diesel
John Deere	6600		G	$1,850	9/03	SEMN	Gear drive

Make	Model	Year	Cond.	Price	Date	Area	Comments
John Deere	6600		F	$2,000	7/03	SEND	SP, chopper
John Deere	6600	1972	G	$1,400	6/03	SWMN	Gas, gear shift, straw chopper, 500 hours on eng.
John Deere	6600	1973	G	$1,300	7/03	ECND	Diesel, variable speed, feeder house, chopper
John Deere	6600	1974	F	$1,100	2/03	ECNE	Belt drive, diesel, pump out
John Deere	6600	1974	G	$2,600	1/03	NWIL	Diesel
John Deere	6600	1977	F	$1,400	7/03	WCMN	Hyd., 2,733 sep. hrs
John Deere	6600	1977	G	$1,675	9/03	ECNE	Hydrostatic trans, cab, AC, heat, rear chopper
John Deere	6600	1977	G	$2,500	12/03	WCIL	Cab, gear drive
John Deere	6600	1977	E	$6,300	2/03	ECNE	Corn/soybean special, always shedded
John Deere	6600	1978	G	$3,600	2/03	ECIA	
John Deere	6600	1978	G	$4,600	2/03	NWOH	John Deere 218 grain head, diesel
John Deere	6600	1978	G	$5,600	1/03	WCIL	Hydrostat, chopper, bin ext., diesel
John Deere	6600	1978	G	$8,200	8/03	WCIL	Clean, diesel, chopper, auto header control, slow down kit, hyd.
John Deere	7700	1973	F	$2,300	2/06	WCNE	Turbo, cab, monitor
John Deere	7700		F	$1,100	9/05	NWOR	
John Deere	7700		F	$1,100	9/05	NWOR	
John Deere	7700		F	$2,800	12/05	NWIL	Diesel, no heads
John Deere	7700		P	$300	12/05	WCCA	With head
John Deere	7700		F	$950	12/05	SCND	
John Deere	7700	1972	G	$2,300	9/05	WCNE	Diesel, new sieves, straw chopper 3,126 hours
John Deere	7700		G	$2,200	2/05	SCMN	Hyd., diesel
John Deere	7700		G	$9,500	8/05	SWOH	Sold with John Deere 915 grain table
John Deere	7700	1974	G	$3,150	2/05	ECMI	Turbo, diesel, John Deere 220 20' flex head
John Deere	7700	1976	P	$1,300	4/05	NCOH	Rough, hyd., turbo, diesel, 28-36" tires, straw chopper
John Deere	7700	1978	G	$5,500	1/05	NEIA	Turbo, rear wheel door, diesel, fully equipped cab, large grain bin ext.
John Deere	7700		F	$1,000	5/04	ECND	Gear drive, engine out
John Deere	7700		F	$2,000	4/04	WCMI	2WD, hyd., diesel
John Deere	7700		G	$2,500	6/04	SEMN	
John Deere	7700	1972	G	$1,100	8/04	WCMN	23.1-26", with 7720 engine
John Deere	7700	1974	G	$2,400	4/04	WCMI	2WD, diesel
John Deere	7700	1975	P	$1,400	7/04	NWMN	Posi-torque
John Deere	7700	1975	F	$1,400	7/04	SEND	Posi-torque
John Deere	7700	1975	F	$1,500	6/04	NCND	
John Deere	7700	1976	G	$1,600	11/04	NWMN	Gear drive, chaff spreader, diesel
John Deere	7700	1976	G	$2,400	7/04	SEND	Turbo hyd., John Deere 100 Series
John Deere	7700	1976	F	$2,400	7/04	NWMN	Turbo hyd., John Deere 100 Series
John Deere	7700	1977	E	$3,000	6/04	NCND	
John Deere	7700	1977	G	$3,500	1/04	WCKS	Hyd., 1,000 hours on rebuilt motor, 24' platform
John Deere	7700	1978	F	$1,200	4/04	SEND	Corn/bean, cab, turbo, hyd.
John Deere	7700	1978	G	$3,000	11/04	NCIA	Hyd., tank ext, chopper
John Deere	7700	1978	G	$3,800	7/04	ECND	
John Deere	7700	1978	F	$4,250	7/04	NWMN	Turbo hyd., air foil sieve,
John Deere	7700	1978	G	$4,250	7/04	SEND	Turbo hyd., air foil sieve
John Deere	7700	1978	G	$10,500	8/04	ECIL	Turbo, hyd.
John Deere	7700		F	$1,000	10/03	WCSD	
John Deere	7700		F	$1,000	10/03	WCSD	Diesel
John Deere	7700		G	$1,300	7/03	ECND	
John Deere	7700		P	$1,600	2/03	NCMI	4WD, engine compartment fire, for parts
John Deere	7700		G	$2,200	7/03	NWIA	Turbo, hyd., nice

combines

Make	Model	Year	Cond.	Price	Date	Area	Comments
John Deere	7700		F	$2,500	2/03	SEMN	Diesel, turbo, like-new rubber
John Deere	7700		G	$5,000	4/03	WCSD	Turbo hyd., 24' header, cab, shedded
John Deere	7700	1973	G	$1,250	2/03	WCMN	
John Deere	7700	1974	G	$3,250	4/03	NCND	John Deere 212 header, diesel
John Deere	7700	1975	G	$700	7/03	ECND	Diesel/hyd., chopper, 23.1-26" tires
John Deere	7700	1975	G	$1,300	9/03	ECND	Diesel, hyd., 23.1×26" tires
John Deere	7700	1975	G	$1,400	3/03	ECNE	Turbo diesel engine, hydro trans., cab, 23.1-26", rear spreader, grain tank ext.
John Deere	7700	1975	P	$1,600	12/03	SEND	
John Deere	7700	1975	G	$6,200	4/03	NCIL	Diesel, hyd., chopper, turbo
John Deere	7700	1977	F	$2,000	7/03	SEND	Turbo hyd., variable speed feeder house, airflow sieve, new concave and bars
John Deere	7700	1977	G	$4,500	1/03	NEMI	Rasp bar
John Deere	7700	1978	G	$3,100	7/03	SEND	100 hours on concave and bars, turbo hyd.
John Deere	7700	1978	G	$3,400	7/03	SEND	Turbo hyd., air foil chaffer, header height control
John Deere	7700	1978	G	$4,500	1/03	NWIL	Diesel, hydrostatic, chopper, always shedded, $3,500 in parts last year
John Deere	7700	1978	F	$4,700	4/03	ECND	Turbo, gear drive
John Deere	7700	1978	G	$6,500	4/03	NCIL	Hyd. spreader, turbo, diesel
Massey	300		F	$600	8/05	SEMI	Gas, 13' grain head
Massey	300		F	$300	12/04	ECNE	
Massey	300		F	$600	9/03	SCNE	1-row corn head
Massey	300		G	$1,300	3/03	SCMN	13' bean head, auto head control, gas
Massey	410		F	$400	3/04	NEMN	Gas, 4-row corn head
Massey	510		G	2000	11/05	NCOH	Diesel, no heads
Massey	510	1977	G	1350	8/05	NWIA	Hydro, factory air, 15' bean platform
Massey	510		P	$350	4/05	SEND	Perkins engine
Massey	510	1976	F	$650	5/05	WCNE	Diesel, no reverse gear
Massey	510		F	$360	6/03	NCIA	Cab, chopper, rear weights
Massey	510		G	$800	9/03	NCKS	
Massey	510		G	$1,200	8/03	SEMO	Grain head
Massey	510		G	$1,600	4/03	NWPA	6 cyl., diesel, cab, no heads
Massey	510		G	$5,000	3/03	SCMN	6-row corn head
Massey	550		G	$1,600	11/05	ECNE	Hydro, diesel, 23.1-26" rubber
Massey	550		G	$2,100	8/05	SEMN	
Massey	550	1979	G	$1,450	12/05	NCCO	Hydrostat, Perkins 6 cyl., 16' grain head, 43 4-row ch
Massey	550		G	$1,350	1/05	ECNE	
Massey	550		G	$6,000	3/05	NCOH	Massey 4-row corn head & 13' grain head, 4WD, 356 engine, hyd. drive
Massey	550		E	$4,400	1/04	NEIA	Sold with 4-row corn head
Massey	550	1979	G	$5,300	8/04	NEIA	Gear drive, sold with Massey corn head & 13' grain head
Massey	550		G	$5,200	9/03	SWWI	4-row corn head
Massey	750		G	$1,100	9/05	NWIL	Hydro, gray cab, 1 owner, nice 2,381 hours
Massey	750		G	$3,800	11/05	SCMI	MF 44 corn head sold with combine 3,000 hours
Massey	750	1980	G	$1,100	12/05	WCMN	
Massey	750		P	$300	2/05	WCIL	For salvage, diesel
Massey	750		F	$500	6/05	WCMN	20' head
Massey	750		F	$1,700	6/05	SWMN	20' flex head
Massey	750		G	$3,400	2/05	WCWI	Gray cab, no heads

Make	Model	Year	Cond.	Price	Date	Area	Comments
Massey	750	1975	F	$1,100	1/05	NCIA	Cab, newer motor, diesel, hyd.
Massey	750	1977	G	$1,800	8/05	NCIA	AC, hyd., chopper, tank extensions, motor rebuilt
Massey	750		F	$1,100	3/04	SCMI	
Massey	750		F	$1,700	12/04	NWIA	Hyd.
Massey	750		F	$4,000	3/04	SCMI	
Massey	750		G	$4,300	3/04	SCKS	Sold with 24' header & 8-row Hesston header, diesel, hyd.
Massey	750	1979	E	$8,100	8/04	ECIL	Massey 1859 15' platform, diesel, hyd., good 28I-26" tires, chopper, straw spreader, well maintained
Massey	750		F	$675	1/03	ECIL	Massey 20' platform, Perkins, 24.5-32" tires, chopper
Massey	750		F	$1,800	8/03	SEPA	16.5' flex head
Massey	750		G	$1,900	9/03	SEIA	
Massey	750		G	$2,100	12/03	SEIL	Massey 18' platform, AC, Firestone 28I-26" tires, chopper, long out auger
Massey	750		G	$2,200	10/03	WCSK	Canadian sale, diesel, chopper
Massey	750		F	$2,200	8/03	SEPA	Corn/soybean special, no heads
Massey	750	1978	G	$3,200	5/03	WCSK	Canadian sale, cab, chopper
Massey	750	1979	F	$800	7/03	SEND	Cab, 6 cyl.
Massey	750	1979	F	$1,700	7/03	SEND	Silver cab, 6-cyl. gear drive platform
Massey	750	1979	G	$4,900	4/03	WCSK	Canadian sale, diesel
Massey	750	1979	G	$7,500	10/03	WCSK	Canadian sale, diesel, 23.1x26" front tires, sieve, new variable speed
Massey Super 92		1961	F	$175	9/04	NECO	Would run but has stuck valve
Massey Super 92			F	$200	10/03	WCSK	Canadian sale
New Holland 1400			F	$1,650	9/03	SEMN	NH 4-row corn head 13' bean head, gas
New Holland 1400		1974	G	$7,000	4/03	WCSK	Canadian sale, 6-cyl. Ford diesel, header, chopper
New Holland 1500			G	$2,800	4/03	WCSK	Canadian sale, 3208 Cat eng., chopper
New Holland 975			G	$425	4/03	WCIL	Grain head, 300 V6 engine, 23.1-26" tires
New Holland TR 70		1980	G	$2,200	2/06	WCNE	22' wheat head, cab, Cat V8 engine 1,817 hours
New Holland TR 70			F	$2,500	9/05	NENE	Sold with 4R corn head
New Holland TR 70			F	$2,000	2/05	WCOH	15.5 grain table, floating cutter bar, Cat 3208 diesel
New Holland TR 70			F	$1,000	12/04	NWIA	
New Holland TR 70		1978	F	$5,000	8/04	NWIL	3,410 hours, sold with 4-row corn head & 15' flex platform
New Holland TR 70		1978	G	$1,000	12/03	NWIL	Cab, air chopper, hyd., 3208 Cat eng., 28I-26" tires
New Holland TR 70		1978	F	$2,700	7/03	WCSK	Canadian sale, diesel, Calmar spout
New Holland TR 70		1978	G	$8,000	4/03	WCSK	Canadian sale, Ford 6-cyl. diesel

corn pickers

Make	Model	Cond.	Price	Date	Area	Comments
Deere	227	G	$200	1/05	NENE	
Deere	227	F	$10	1/04	SWOH	2-row mounted
Deere	227	F	$325	6/04	NWIL	Sheller
Deere	227	P	$10	2/03	ECNE	Old, stuck in the trees
Deere	227	G	$200	8/03	WCIL	2-row mounted, cart
Deere	227	G	$800	8/03	WCIL	2-row mounted
Deere	237	G	$450	2/05	NCIN	Mounted
Deere	237	F	$100	7/03	NWIL	
Deere	300	G	$1,100	1/06	WCNE	3R-30", pt, JD 344 head
Deere	300	G	$1,900	8/05	SEMN	
Deere	300	F	$300	2/05	NEIN	
Deere	300	G	$1,600	4/05	NCIA	Husker, Deere 343 3-row corn head
Deere	300	G	$650	11/04	WCIA	Elec. controls, pt.
Deere	300	G	$1,300	8/04	NCOH	2 row
Deere	300	G	$1,350	11/04	NCIA	Deere 244 corn head
Deere	300	G	$1,650	9/04	WCWI	2 row
Deere	300	G	$2,300	2/04	SWMN	Husker, Deere 343 corn head

158

Make	Model	Cond.	Price	Date	Area	Comments
Deere	300	G	$950	3/03	NWIA	Husker, Deere 244 2-row, 36" corn head
Deere	300	G	$1,100	3/03	NESD	3-row 22
Deere	43	F	$350	4/05	NCOH	Corn sheller
Deere	43	G	$400	3/03	WCMI	Corn sheller
Deere	4420	F	$11,500	4/05	SEPA	Deere 443 corn head & 213 grain head
Deere	6	G	$320	10/04	SEMN	Corn sheller on cart
Deere	6	P	$150	3/03	NWIL	Corn sheller
Deere	71	G	$325	2/05	WCIN	Corn sheller with 40' of drags
Deere	n/a	F	$950	3/04	SCMI	3-row pt, Deere 343 corn head
Deere	n/a	G	$225	7/03	SEND	2-hole corn sheller
Deere	n/a	G	$420	8/03	WCIL	Sheller attachment for Deere 227 picker
MH	N/A	G	$2,600	8/05	WCIL	2 row
MM	D	G	$500	3/05	NCIL	Corn sheller
McCormick	N/A	G	$700	11/05	NCOH	Old, pt
N/A	N/A	G	$180	2/06	SEMI	Wood corn sheller
N/A	N/A	G	$975	6/05	SWOH	Cast corn sheller
N/A	n/a	G	$1,300	11/04	NCIA	Rare large wood Western corn sheller with wood drags on steel wheels
New Idea	10	E	$750	11/04	NEKS	1 row, always shedded, good paint
New Idea	234	G	$650	11/03	SWWI	2-row pt
New Idea	311	G	$75	4/04	ECWI	2 row
New Idea	311	F	$150	3/04	WCMI	2 row
New Idea	311	F	$360	9/03	NEIN	2 row
New Idea	311	G	$400	9/03	NEIN	
New Idea	321	G	$330	10/04	SEMN	2 row
New Idea	323	G	$1,300	8/05	NEIN	1 row
New Idea	323	E	$1,800	8/05	NEIN	1 row
New Idea	323	G	$600	12/05	NCOH	1 rowr
New Idea	323	G	$900	8/05	NEIN	1 row
New Idea	323	G	$300	4/05	NCOH	1 row
New Idea	323	G	$675	3/05	SWIN	1 row
New Idea	323	F	$150	3/04	SWPA	1 row
New Idea	323	G	$350	3/04	NEPA	
New Idea	323	G	$950	2/04	NEIN	1 row
New Idea	323	G	$1,000	2/04	NEIN	
New Idea	323	G	$1,250	5/04	ECWI	1 row
New Idea	323	F	$10	4/03	NWPA	1 row
New Idea	323	F	$300	1/03	NCOH	
New Idea	323	F	$375	2/03	SWOH	1 row
New Idea	323	G	$700	2/03	SWOH	1 row
New Idea	323	G	$1,050	3/03	NWPA	1 row
New Idea	324	G	$1,000	8/05	NEIN	
New Idea	324	G	$300	8/05	SEMN	
New Idea	324	F	$400	7/05	SESD	
New Idea	324	F	$400	7/05	SESD	Sheller
New Idea	324	G	$725	7/05	SESD	2 row
New Idea	324	E	$2,400	3/05	WCWI	12-roll husking bed
New Idea	324	F	$125	3/04	SWWI	2 row, grinder attachment
New Idea	324	G	$170	1/04	NWIL	2-row pt
New Idea	324	F	$200	1/04	ECIA	Pt husking unit with super sheller
New Idea	324	G	$400	9/04	WCWI	2 row, sheller attachment
New Idea	324	G	$650	2/04	SWWI	2 row, 8-roll husking bed

corn pickers

Make	Model	Cond.	Price	Date	Area	Comments
New Idea	324	G	$700	3/04	NEIA	2 row, 12-roll husking bed
New Idea	324	F	$100	4/03	NWPA	2 row
New Idea	324	F	$200	11/03	NWIL	Pt
New Idea	324	F	$500	9/03	NEIN	2 row
New Idea	324	G	$700	12/03	ECWI	
New Idea	324	G	$725	12/03	ECWI	
New Idea	324	G	$750	9/03	NEIN	2 row
New Idea	324	F	$925	8/03	SEPA	2-row pt
New Idea	324	G	$950	9/03	SWWI	2 row, 12-roll bed
New Idea	324	G	$1,100	9/03	SEMN	2 row, 12-roll husking bed
NI	324/327	F	$250	4/05	SCMI	2 row, 12-roll husking bed
New Idea	325	E	$2,700	8/05	NEIN	2 row
New Idea	325	F	$200	4/05	SCMI	2 row, 12-roll husking bed
New Idea	325	G	$1,850	2/05	NEIN	2 row
New Idea	325	G	$2,200	4/05	SCMI	2 row, 12-roll husking bed
New Idea	325	G	$500	4/04	WCMI	2 row, 12-roll husking bed
New Idea	325	F	$610	3/04	SCMI	2-row pt, 327 husking bed
New Idea	325	G	$700	4/04	NCWI	2 row, 12-roll husking bed
New Idea	325	G	$1,700	4/04	ECWI	2 row, 12-roll husking bed
New Idea	325	F	$2,600	3/04	SEPA	2 row, steel wheel, hydraulics
New Idea	325	E	$2,800	3/04	NEWI	2 row, 327 12-roll husking bed, hyd.
New Idea	325	G	$950	9/03	NWOH	12-roll husking bed
New Idea	325	F	$1,900	3/03	SWPA	2 row, 12-roll husking bed
New Idea	326	G	$1,900	8/05	NCIA	2-row pt
New Idea	326	F	$200	3/04	ECMI	2 row
New Idea	327	E	$2,100	10/04	SWWI	2-row pt
New Idea	328	G	$850	9/03	SEMN	2 row
New Idea	7	G	$170	3/03	ECMI	1 row
New Idea	n/a	G	$125	1/06	WCNE	2R-30, pt
New Idea	n/a	G	$1,250	10/05	NEPA	2R picker
New Idea	n/a	F	$150	9/05	NECO	2R-30, conveyor twisted
New Idea	n/a	F	$200	9/05	NECO	2R-30, pt
New Idea	n/a	G	$200	9/05	NECO	2R-30, pt
New Idea	n/a	G	$650	3/04	NEWI	Sheller
New Idea	n/a	F	$15	7/03	NWIL	2-row pt
New Idea	n/a	F	$150	9/03	SCMN	2-row pt
New Idea	n/a	F	$250	3/03	NWIL	2 row
New Idea	n/a	G	$450	9/03	SEMN	2 row, mounted
New Idea	n/a	G	$510	9/03	NEIN	1 row
New Idea	n/a	G	$525	8/03	NWIL	2-row pt
New Idea	n/a	G	$800	9/03	WCSD	2 row
Oliver	73	G	$650	6/03	NCIA	2 row, sheller
Oliver	73H	F	$300	6/03	NCIA	2 row
Oliver	n/a	F	$450	3/03	NWIL	2 row

Looking for the world's oldest tractor

By Dave Mowitz

Please allow me to set the record straight. In the February-March 2004 issue of the Ageless Iron Almanac (www.agelessiron.com), I declared that the oldest existing tractor in the world had been found. It was, I said at the time, a 1903 Ivel residing in England.

Boy, was I wrong!

A good friend, Graeme Quick, stumbled across an even older tractor in Germany. His find, a Hungarian-built Mechwart'sche Pertroleumpflug, was built in 1896. That makes it seven years older than the Ivel – and four years the senior of the McCormick Auto-Mower that historian Guy Fay found in Wisconsin.

But I'm convinced there are even older tractors out there waiting to be found. So I need your help.

Historians tell us many tractors were built prior to the Mechwart's. Here's a little background to help with our search. (Notice I said "our" – as in "everybody join in.")

Tractor historian R.B. Gray pegged the earliest production tractor as the Charter Model 10-20 built in 1889 by the Charter Gas Engine Company. The thing didn't look much like a tractor. But those were the days when an innovator would mount an engine on to a

The world's oldest existing tractor, the Hungarian-built 1896 Mechwart's was discovered by Graeme Quick (left) shown with curator Klaus Kerrmann, in the museum where the tractor now resides.

steam traction engine frame, throw in some gears, and call it a tractor.

Other early tractor makers and the dates of their first tractors:

- Deering – 1891
- John Froelich (Waterloo Boy), Case, and Dissinger – 1892
- Hockett – 1893
- Lambert, Otto, and Van Duzen – 1894
- Davis and Webster –1895

That brings us to the year the Mechwart's came to be. Surely an example of one of the U.S.-built tractors mentioned above still exists!

To inspire fellow collectors to join in the hunt, I'm offering a bushel of encouragement and some prizes!

For starters, if you find one of these babies, how about I come to your place and wash and wax one of your tractors (please, one only).

Shoot, I'll get Roger Welsch to autograph the tractor for you when I'm done. Heck, Roger and I will take you out to lunch – no, wait, DINNER!

The one-of-a-kind 1899 McCormick Auto-Mower served as the model for a patent, establishing it as the first tractor with a cast-iron frame and independent PTO.

If you get lucky in your quest or just want to talk about the project, please contact me at 515/284-3287 or via e-mail at dave.mowitz@meredith.com.

corn planters

Make	Model	Cond.	Price	Date	Area	Comments
Allis-Chalmers	330	G	$900	3/04	NEWI	4-row air planter, monitor
Allis-Chalmers	333	P	$240	4/05	NCOH	6 row, 30"
Allis-Chalmers	333	F	$350	4/03	SWIN	4-row no-till planter, older unit
Allis-Chalmers	390	P	$95	12/03	NCOH	30' folding tool
Allis-Chalmers	600	F	$115	3/04	SCMI	13-row, bean planter
Allis-Chalmers	600	F	$800	4/04	SWPA	
Allis-Chalmers	600	G	$625	3/03	NCOH	Bean planter, 71 unit hoppers
Allis-Chalmers	N/A	G	$500	7/05	SWOH	4 row
Allis-Chalmers	N/A	F	$350	2/04	NEIN	4 row, dry
Allis-Chalmers	N/A	G	$250	3/03	WCMI	4 row, handbook in planter box
Ford	509	F	$650	10/04	SEPA	2 row, insect hopper, 3 pt.
Ford	N/A	G	$400	4/04	NWPA	2 row, 3 pt.
IHC	400	F	$200	11/05	SCMI	4R-38" dry corn planter, bean drum
IHC	400	G	$400	11/05	NCIN	4R-36" planter, harrow
IHC	400	F	$60	4/05	SEND	Cyclo planter, 4 row, corn, bean, and Sunflower drums
IHC	400	F	$140	6/05	SWMN	8 row
IHC	400	F	$150	8/05	ECNE	8-row air planter
IHC	400	F	$150	2/05	NWKS	6-row Cyclo planter
IHC	400	F	$185	4/05	NCOH	6-row Cyclo dry planter
IHC	400	F	$200	8/05	ECNE	8-row air planter
IHC	400	G	$300	3/05	WCMN	8 row
IHC	400	G	$350	4/05	SEND	Cyclo planter, 6 row
IHC	400	G	$450	3/05	WCIL	6 row

162

Make	Model	Cond.	Price	Date	Area	Comments
400	G	$800	2/05	SCMN	4 row	
IHC	400	G	$850	4/05	ECND	6-row 30" Cyclo planter, dry fertilizer
IHC	400	F	$50	4/04	NEPA	6 row
IHC	400	F	$70	10/04	SEMN	4-row planter
IHC	400	G	$175	2/04	NEIN	6 row
IHC	400	P	$185	2/04	NWIL	8 row
IHC	400	G	$200	4/04	ECWI	4-row air corn planter
IHC	400	P	$210	2/04	NWIL	8 row
IHC	400	G	$250	12/04	SENE	Corn & bean drums
IHC	400	F	$270	2/04	NCIN	6-row Cyclo planter
IHC	400	F	$325	2/04	NEIN	8 row
IHC	400	G	$500	3/04	WCMN	6 row, dry fertilizer
IHC	400	G	$950	4/04	NCWI	6-row air corn planter, insect boxes
IHC	400	F	$50	6/03	NCIA	8-row pull planter, insect and monitor
IHC	400	F	$50	6/03	WCSD	Cyclo corn planter, 4 row
IHC	400	F	$150	7/03	WCMN	8 row
IHC	400	P	$300	2/03	SEND	Cyclo planter, 8 row, end pull, Gandy box
IHC	400	G	$450	9/03	WCSD	Cyclo corn planter, several extra drums
IHC	400	F	$600	6/03	SEND	Cyclo, 6 row, 30", seed flow monitor
IHC	400	F	$700	3/03	NCND	Cyclo planter, 8 row, extra drum
IHC	500	F	$200	2/06	WCKS	Cyclo planter, 8 row, 3 pt.
IHC	500	G	$3,400	1/06	NWIA	Cyclo, 15R-18" bean planter with Kinze row units, monitor, and lift assist
IHC	500	F	$550	4/05	SEND	12-row Cyclo planter, 3 pt.
IHC	500	G	$600	4/05	ECND	Cyclo 12-row 30" planter, Allis-Chalmers cup plant shoes, monitor, soybean, sunflower and corn drums and transport
IHC	500	F	$525	11/04	ECND	Cyclo planter, 12 row, bean, corn, sunflower drums, monitor, hyd. fold
IHC	500	G	$950	8/04	ECIL	12-row skip-row planter, monitor
IHC	500	P	$500	4/03	ECND	Cyclo planter, 12 row, folding
IHC	500	F	$950	7/03	WCMN	12 row
IHC	500	G	$1,050	3/03	NCOH	12-row bean planter
IHC	500	G	$1,300	7/03	NWIL	16-row bean planter, end transport
IHC	56	G	$175	8/05	SEMN	4 row
IHC	56	G	$850	3/05	WCWI	4 row
IHC	56	G	$20	5/04	ECWI	Corn planter
IHC	56	G	$45	4/04	ECWI	4 row
IHC	56	G	$85	4/04	ECWI	4 row, insect boxes
IHC	56	G	$100	2/04	NEIN	4 row, dry fertilizer
IHC	56	F	$250	3/04	NEMN	4 row, fertilizer
IHC	56	G	$350	12/04	SEPA	4 row
IHC	56	F	$450	2/04	NEIN	6 row
IHC	56	F	$500	4/04	NEPA	
IHC	56	E	$800	2/04	NEIN	4 row
IHC	56	G	$1,025	3/04	NEPA	4 row
IHC	56	P	$100	3/03	NCWI	4 row
IHC	56	F	$125	12/03	WCMI	4 row
IHC	56	F	$250	12/03	WCMI	4 row
IHC	56	P	$250	3/03	SWPA	4 row
IHC	56	G	$300	11/03	WCWI	Corn planter
IHC	N/A	G	$70	4/05	NCOH	2 row, front-mounted

corn planter

Make	Model	Cond.	Price	Date	Area	Comments
IHC	N/A	G	$125	4/05	NCOH	4 row
IHC	N/A	G	$600	2/05	ECND	12 row
IHC	N/A	E	$1,100	2/05	NEIN	4 row, disc openers
IHC	N/A	F	$325	2/04	NEIN	4 row
IHC	N/A	F	$800	4/04	NEND	Cyclo, 8 row
IHC	N/A	F	$60	6/03	WCSD	Cyclo 6-row planter,
IHC	N/A	G	$170	7/03	NWIL	4 row, steel wheel
HC	N/A	G	$180	7/03	NWIL	4 row, steel wheel, fertilizer, check wire
Deere	1240	F	$100	8/05	ECMI	4-row plateless planters, insect, dry fert
Deere	1240	F	$100	4/05	NCOH	
Deere	1240	F	$125	1/05	ECNE	4 row
Deere	1240	F	$200	4/05	SCMI	4 row
Deere	1240	G	$300	2/05	NEIN	Plates, 4 row
Deere	1240	F	$450	8/05	NWIL	4 row, fertilizer
Deere	1240	G	$1,250	1/05	ECMI	4-row plate corn planter
Deere	1240	F	$25	4/04	NEPA	
Deere	1240	G	$25	4/04	ECWI	4 row
Deere	1240	G	$50	5/04	ECWI	4 row
Deere	1240	G	$375	3/04	ECMI	4 row
Deere	1240	P	$35	4/03	NWPA	4 row, for parts
Deere	1240	F	$90	11/03	NEKS	4 row
Deere	1240	F	$125	4/03	NWPA	4-row
Deere	1240	G	$900	3/03	NWPA	4-row
Deere	1240	F	$1,650	4/03	NEPA	4 row
Deere	1250	P	$170	4/05	NCOH	8 row
Deere	1250	F	$200	2/05	WCIL	6 row, monitor
Deere	1250	G	$150	2/04	NCWI	6-row plateless corn planter
Deere	1250	E	$500	3/04	ECMN	4 row
Deere	1250	F	$50	12/03	NWIL	Converted to bean planter
Deere	1250	G	$160	8/03	NCIA	6-row plateless planter
Deere	1250	G	$700	3/03	ECMI	6 row
Deere	1280	F	$90	8/05	NCIA	8-row 30" plateless planter with transports and monitor
Deere	246	G	$600	1/05	NCPA	2 row
Deere	246	G	$1,000	7/05	SCIA	
Deere	290	G	$1,100	9/05	SEMN	
Deere	290	G	$50	7/05	NEIA	Planter with check wire
Deere	290	F	$40	10/04	NCWI	2 row
Deere	290	G	$650	11/04	NWIL	Complete, wire & duck bill
Deere	290	F	$200	3/03	NWIL	2 row
Deere	290	G	$725	4/03	ECMN	2 row
Deere	490	G	$300	2/05	NEIN	4 row
Deere	490	G	$350	2/04	NEIN	4 row
Deere	490	G	$90	7/03	NWIL	4 row
Deere	490	G	$225	8/03	WCIL	Clutch trip
Deere	494	E	$190	9/05	NENE	4 row, dry fertilizer, insect and herb boxes
Deere	494	F	$90	7/05	SEND	4 row, corn planter
Deere	494	G	$250	7/05	SWOH	Planter unit
Deere	494	G	$250	1/05	NENE	4 row

Make	Model	Cond.	Price	Date	Area	Comments
Deere	494	G	$100	3/04	NWMN	4 row
Deere	494	P	$150	1/04	NEIN	Liquid fertilizer planter, planter plates, for parts
Deere	494	G	$475	3/04	WCMI	4 row, liquid and dry fertilizer
Deere	494	G	$65	7/03	SEND	4 row
Deere	494	F	$75	7/03	NWIL	4 row
Deere	494	F	$125	9/03	WCMI	4 row
Deere	494A	G	$225	2/06	WCIL	4 row
Deere	494A	G	$275	2/06	WCIL	6 row
Deere	494A	G	$250	4/05	SCKS	4 row
Deere	494A	F	$300	4/05	SCMI	6 row
Deere	494A	G	$35	11/04	NEKS	4 row
Deere	494A	P	$7	4/03	WCIA	4 row
Deere	494A	G	$110	2/03	ECNE	Insect, shedded
Deere	495	F	$75	12/05	NWIL	4 row
Deere	495A	G	$75	5/03	ECSD	4 row, extra plates, shedded
Oliver	N/A	G	$250	1/05	WCIL	2 row
Oliver	N/A	G	$200	7/04	WCIL	Corn planter, 2 row

Oldest existing combine?

There are certainly older "combine harvesters" around. But the Hines harvester is possibly the oldest self-propelled harvester in the world. And even if older machines are found in the future, the Hines harvester, built in 1917, qualifies as one of the most advanced combines of its time. Relatively compact in size compared to other harvesters of this era, the Hines had the capacity to harvest 40 to 50 acres of wheat a day. Simpler machines, such as binders, were lucky to knock down 20 acres in the same time.

What makes the story behind this combine even more compelling is that the only model known to exist is owned by Tony Trenkamp Sr., a relative of its inventor, M.J. Hines. "M.J. was my great-uncle," Trenkamp says. "All of his early prototype combines, some built as early as 1911, were tested on my grandfather's farm near Spearville, Kansas."

Trenkamp goes on to explain that those early Hines machines qualify as the first self-propelled combines built in the world. "The combine I own is one of the first Hines units built for sale," he adds.

That makes this combine rare indeed, for only 63 Hines harvesters were ever built over a two-decade period. Besides the advantages of the combine's size, the Hines harvester packed a number of unique features that made it stand out. For example, its cutting sickle bar was driven from the center of the platform. But the most significant innovation was its rear steering mechanism. This feature would become an industry standard still in use today.

For more information on the Hines combine, go to www.agelessiron.com.

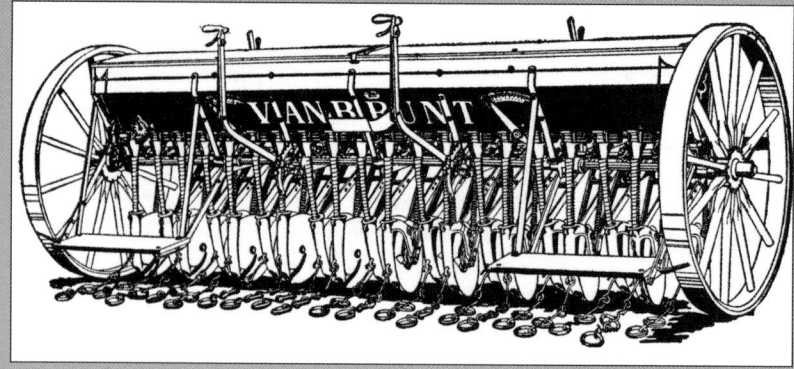

grain drills

Make	Model	Cond.	Price	Date	Area	Comments
J.I. Case	10'	G	$500	11/05	NEIA	Grain drill, grass seed and low rubber
J.I. Case	10'	F	$525	2/03	SEMN	
IHC	10'	F	$275	2/06	SCMI	16 run, seeder
IHC	10'	F	$300	2/06	WCNE	14'×8", pt
IHC	10'	F	$425	8/05	NWIL	
IHC	10'	F	$250	2/06	ECMN	Double disc, grass seeder, hyd. lift
IHC	10'	G	$700	1/06	SCMN	
IHC	10'	P	$90	4/05	NEKS	Rough
IHC	10'	F	$350	3/05	SCMI	16 run
IHC	10'	F	$400	3/05	SCMI	16 run
IHC	10'	G	$825	4/05	WCWI	8' drill, grass seed attachment
IHC	10'	G	$600	3/04	WCMI	18-hole drill, seeder
IHC	10'	G	$1,050	2/04	WCIL	
IHC	10'	G	$1,100	3/04	SWWI	10'
IHC	10'	G	$2,400	4/04	NCWI	10' single-disc drill, grass seed and fertilizer attachments
IHC	10'	F	$95	4/03	NCWI	Grass seed attachment
IHC	10'	G	$350	9/03	NEIN	
IHC	10'	G	$400	4/05	WCWI	Grass seed attachment
IHC	10'	F	$250	12/04	NCWI	Double disc, grass seed attachment
IHC	10'	F	$100	4/03	SEMN	
IHC	10'	F	$250	6/03	NCWI	
IHC	10'	F	$900	4/03	NWPA	
IHC	100	G	$925	2/06	WCNE	12' double disc drill with 6" spacing
IHC	100	F	$70	7/03	WCSK	Canadian sale
IHC	100	G	$240	7/03	SEND	12' press drill
IHC	100	G	$600	9/03	WCSD	14' drills, grass seed attachment
IHC	100	G	$600	9/03	WCSD	14' drill, 7" spacings, transport
IHC	11'	F	$60	4/05	SWMN	Double-disc grain drill, low rubber, grass seed attachment, hyd. lift
IHC	11'	F	$500	2/05	NWIL	Grain drill, grass seed attachment

Make	Model	Cond.	Price	Date	Area	Comments
IHC	12'	F	$110	12/05	NWIL	Grass seed
IHC	12'	F	$100	8/05	SWMN	Grain drill on low rubber
IHC	12'	F	$80	8/03	WCMN	Grain drill, grass seed attachment
IHC	12'	F	$150	9/03	WCSD	12" spacing
IHC	12'	E	$1,100	6/03	WCSK	Canadian sale, solid packer wheels
IHC	14'	G	$2,800	5/04	WCSD	Disc drill, grass seed and fertilizer attachment, wheel, 7" spacing
IHC	14'	G	$350	3/03	WCMN	Press drill, fertilizer, rubber press wheels
IHC	14'	G	$1,000	4/03	SCMN	
IHC	150	F	$100	2/06	WCNE	(2) 12'x14" drills, hitches
IHC	150	F	$500	2/06	WCNE	(2) 12' grain drills, 14" spacing, pt, hitch
IHC	150	G	$500	2/06	WCNE	(2) 10' shoe drills, 2" spacings, pt
IHC	150	F	$550	1/06	NCCO	15x10 shoe drill, seeder
IHC	150	F	$350	9/05	NECO	14'
IHC	150	F	$200	2/05	NWKS	Hyd. hitch, spoke press wheels, case openers
IHC	150	F	$250	6/05	NENE	16-hole hoe drill, press wheels
IHC	150	P	$100	11/04	SCKS	Hoe drill, old
IHC	150	F	$250	5/04	WCSD	Three drills, hitch, 10" spacing
IHC	150	G	$300	1/04	SCNE	Press drill
IHC	150	F	$400	11/04	WCKS	Hoe drills 16'x10", transports
IHC	150	G	$1,000	11/04	NCKS	Hoe drills, transport
IHC	150	F	$275	3/03	NCOK	Hoe drill
IHC	150	G	$600	10/03	NCOK	14-10 hoe drill
IHC	150	G	$1,600	10/03	WCSD	Three sections, 42' total, 12" spacing, on transport
IHC	16'	G	$2,700	4/03	WCSK	Canadian sale, press drill
IHC	510	G	$1,600	2/06	WCIL	18-7, grass seeder, used very little
IHC	510	G	$950	1/06	SCMI	18 run, seeder
IHC	510	G	$1,500	11/05	NCIN	7" 21-hole, grass seeder
IHC	510	G	$1,500	12/05	WCMN	
IHC	510	G	$3,750	8/05	SEMN	12', 24-6" openings, press wheel
IHC	510	P	$450	10/05	NCOH	10", rubber press wheels, rough
IHC	510	F	$550	4/05	SCMI	21-run grain drill
IHC	510	F	$600	2/05	WCIL	
IHC	510	E	$725	3/05	SCIL	21 flute
IHC	510	G	$800	8/05	NWIL	15' disc drill
IHC	510	G	$1,050	2/05	NCIN	
IHC	510	P	$1,100	3/05	WCNY	Single disc, 13 hole
IHC	510	G	$2,700	3/05	WCWI	12', double disc, grass and brome seed attachment
IHC	510	G	$150	3/04	NEKS	Single disc, drag chains
IHC	510	F	$175	11/04	SCKS	16x10, single disc
IHC	510	G	$800	1/04	SEMI	18 run, seeder
IHC	510	G	$1,000	2/04	NEIN	
IHC	510	G	$1,500	12/04	NEIL	
IHC	510	F	$1,600	3/04	NEKS	
IHC	510	G	$2,050	5/04	ECWI	Grass seed attachment
IHC	510	F	$2,300	4/04	NEPA	
IHC	510	G	$2,325	3/04	SCMN	12', press wheels, grass seed attachment
IHC	510	G	$2,600	4/04	NCWI	Grass seed attachment
IHC	510	G	$325	8/03	NEKS	18', rubber press wheels, seeder
IHC	510	F	$350	10/03	NCOK	
IHC	510	G	$375	2/03	ECKS	Double disc, press wheels
IHC	510	P	$375	3/03	SWPA	15 hoe

grain drills

Make	Model	Cond.	Price	Date	Area	Comments
IHC	510	G	$900	4/03	NCOH	
IHC	510	F	$900	8/03	SEPA	Double disc, grass seed attachment
IHC	510	G	950	9/03	NWOH	21x7
IHC	510	G	$1,250	5/03	NCWI	12', grass seed attachment
IHC	510	G	$1,650	2/03	NWIL	12' end-wheel drill on 7" spacing, grass seed attachment
IHC	510	G	$1,700	12/03	SEIA	Grass seed attachment, 21 disc openers, 7.5" spacing
IHC	510	G	$2,750	1/03	WCMN	12' grain press drill
IHC	610C	G	$1,050	9/03	SEIL	Wheat drill, double disc, 18 hole
IHC	620	F	$200	11/05	SCMI	Grain drill & seeder, 24 run
IHC	620	G	$500	9/05	NECO	14', pt
IHC	620	G	$650	9/05	NECO	14', pt, seeder
IHC	620	P	$250	4/05	NCOH	15', 24"x7" drill, press wheels
IHC	620	G	$900	3/05	SENE	20x7
IHC	620	F	$300	8/04	NESD	Press drill, 14', grass seed attachment
IHC	620	G	$600	4/04	ECND	(2) 14' press drills, 6" space, rubber press wheels, big box
IHC	620	F	$650	3/04	SEND	Markers
IHC	620	G	$700	3/04	WCMN	14', 6" space
IHC	620	G	$750	4/04	SEND	24', 2-12
IHC	620	G	$800	10/04	NWMN	28' (2-14) press drill, dry fertilize
IHC	620	F	$900	11/04	ECND	Press drills, two 12s, rubber press wheels, dry fertilizer, 6" space, rock guards, front fold
IHC	620	E	$925	4/04	WCMN	12' fertilizer, grass seed attachment
IHC	620	G	$200	4/03	WCSK	Canadian sale, press
IHC	620	G	$375	4/03	WCSK	Canadian sale
IHC	620	P	$450	3/03	ECND	Drill, 20', folding markers, solid press wheels, discs measure 13$\frac{7}{8}$"
IHC	620	G	$500	7/03	SEND	Press drill, 12', 6" space, no fertilizer, rubber press wheels, 1 pt.
IHC	620	G	$500	6/03	WCSK	Canadian sale, press drill, 24'
IHC	620	G	$600	4/03	WCSK	Canadian sale, 28' press drill, transports
IHC	620	G	$625	10/03	WCMN	14' press drill
IHC	620	F	$800	7/03	WCSK	Canadian sale, 28' press drill
IHC	620	G	$900	9/03	SCMN	14' press drill
IHC	620	G	$900	4/03	WCSK	Canadian sale, 36', press drills, transport & grass seed attachment
IHC	620	1F	$950	3/03	ECND	Press drills, 6" space, dry fertilizer, rubber press wheels, markers
IHC	620	G	$2,000	4/03	WCSK	Canadian sale, grass attachment, markers, rubber press wheels
IHC	620	G	$2,000	10/03	NWSD	16'
IHC	620	1G	$3,000	4/03	WCSK	Canadian sale
IHC	7200	F	$1,100	3/03	NCCO	Hoe drill
IHC	7200	G	$5,500	4/03	WCSK	Canadian sale, 28' hoe drill
IHC	8'	G	$200	9/03	WCSD	Press drill
IHC	N/A	F	$155	3/05	WCNE	Pt, transport
IHC	N/A	G	$525	3/05	NCCO	Grass seed attachment
IHC	N/A	F	$50	2/04	NWIL	Endgate seeder
IHC	N/A	G	$250	9/04	NEIA	Broadcast seeder, grass seed attachment
IHC	N/A	F	$900	4/04	NEPA	Grain drill
IHC	N/A	G	$210	11/03	NEKS	Alfalfa seeder, on low rubber
IHC	N/A	F	$250	3/03	SWPA	10-hoe grain drill
Deere	10'	F	$200	2/06	WCNE	7", pt, seeder, high wheels
Deere	10'	G	$525	4/04	ECWI	Grain drill, grass seed attachment

Make	Model	Cond.	Price	Date	Area	Comments
Deere	10'	F	$500	3/04	WCNE	Grain drill, older pt, alfalfa seeder
Deere	10'	G	$650	2/04	SWWI	Grain drill, grass seed attachment
Deere	10'	G	$150	9/03	WCMN	Low rubber, grain drill, grass seeder
Deere	10'	F	$275	3/03	NCWI	Single-disc grain drill
Deere	10'	G	$400	4/03	WCMN	Low rubber, grass seed attachment
Deere	10'	F	$425	9/03	SWWI	
Deere	11'	G	$950	11/03	NEIA	Galvanized boxes
Deere	12'	G	$475	2/06	NWSD	
Deere	12'	G	$160	8/05	NCIL	Drill, double disk
Deere	12'	F	$48	4/05	SEND	Drill
Deere	12'	G	$250	4/04	WCNE	Single disc
Deere	12'	F	$290	12/04	NWIA	Grain drill
Deere	12'	G	$300	2/04	ECIA	Broadcast seeder, grass seed attachment
Deere	12'	G	$425	3/04	WCMN	Grain drill, grass, hyd. lift
Deere	12'	G	$525	1 04	NWIL	Seed
Deere	12'	F	$200	4/03	NCIL	Double disc
Deere	14'	P	$10	4/05	SEND	
Deere	14'	F	$50	3/03	WCMN	Low rubber
Deere	14'	G	$425	6/03	WCSD	Double-disc drill
Deere	1690SCS	E	$61,000	3/05	WCOH	40' soybean special planter, 15" rows
Deere	1690SCS	G	$55,000	2/04	NWMN	42' soybean special air disc, 15" spacing, 450 monitor, only 1,900 acres
Deere	246	F	$1,900	4/03	WCMN	12' press drill, grass seed attachment
Deere	270	E	$70,000	6/05	NEND	Air drill, 60', split 120/150 tow-between tank
Deere	41'	G	$3,000	4/04	SEND	Air seeder
Deere	452	G	$5,500	8/05	WCMN	13' end wheel press drill
Deere	452	G	$4,800	2/05	WCOK	21x8, double disc
Deere	5'	G	$200	6/03	WCSK	Canadian sale, pony drill
Deere	616	F	$2,250	11/05	ECWA	(4) HZ 616 grain drills, 6" spacing x 16 drop, like new packer rings, with Telecky hitch
Deere	780	F	$1,750	9/04	ECSD	Seed cart, 40' air drill
Deere	8'	G	$150	9/05	NECO	Seeder, pt
Deere	8'	G	$110	4/04	ECWI	Grain drill
Deere	8'	G	$325	6/04	ECWI	Grain drill
Deere	8000	F	$700	2/05	WCOK	Single disc
Deere	8000	F	$850	2/05	WCOK	Single disc
Deere	8000	G	$900	9/04	SEIA	
Deere	8100	G	$850	12/03	SWMI	18 hole
Deere	8220	G	$1,100	9/03	NWIA	12'
Deere	8250	F	$975	4/05	SEPA	With seeder
Deere	8250	G	$2,000	4/05	SEPA	Single disc, grass seed
Deere	8250	F	$1,000	4/04	NEPA	
Deere	8250	G	$1,975	4/04	ECWI	8' grain drill
Deere	8250	G	$2,050	4/04	NCWI	13', fertilizer, grass seed
Deere	8550	G	$8,100	1/05	SCKS	Double-disc drill
Deere	9'	G	$1,200	4/04	NCWI	Grass seed attachment
Deere	9'	G	$5	10/03	NCWI	On steel
Deere	B	G	$825	2/06	ECIL	20/7 grain drill, grass seed
Deere	B	G	$1450	12/05	NCIL	Grain drill, 12', grass seed, double disk
Deere	B	G	$400	12/05	NEIA	10' grain drill, grass seed
Deere	B	G	$400	9/05	WCNE	12', pull type, seeder, rubber tires
Deere	B	G	$800	9/05	NECO	12', seeder

grain drills

Make	Model	Cond.	Price	Date	Area	Comments
Deere	B	F	$75	2/05	SCCA	Grain drill
Deere	B	G	$275	1/05	SENE	16x7
Deere	B	G	$400	7/05	SENE	20 hole
Deere	B	E	$625	1/05	SENE	16x7
Deere	B	G	$400	1/04	ECIA	11' grain drill
Deere	B	G	$600	3/04	SCMN	14' grain drill, grass
Deere	B	G	$625	2/04	ECIL	21x7 grain drill, grass
Deere	B	G	$325	3/03	SENE	
Deere	DF	G	$30	4/05	NEKS	
Deere	FBB	F	$25	11/05	SCMI	13 run grain drill
Deere	FBB	F	$400	4/05	SCMI	15 run, grain drill
Deere	FBB	G	$110	3/04	SENE	
Deere	FBB	G	$350	4/04	ECWI	9' double-disc grain drill, fertilizer and seed attachment
Deere	FBB	G	$450	4/04	WCMI	15 hoe grain drill
Deere	L166	F	$500	7/05	WCMN	24' press drill (3) 8' drills & hitch
Deere	LL	G	$250	6/03	SENE	20x7
Deere	LL166	G	$550	12/04	WCMN	24'
Deere	LL-246A	F	$350	7/05	WCMN	Press drill, 12', transport
Deere	LL247A	G	$850	12/04	ECNE	Double-disc grain drill, grass seed attachment
Deere	LLA	F	$150	9/05	NECO	14' seeder, hyd lift
Deere	LLA	G	$2,500	2/05	ECSD	12' press drill
Deere	LLA	G	$275	3/04	WCMN	12' press drill, 6" spacing, grass seeder
Deere	LLA	G	$500	3/04	NEND	28', markers, grass seeder, 7" space, fertilizer
Deere	LLA	G	$1,050	3/04	SEND	Two 14' drills, hyd. transports, end pull and markers
Deere	LLA	G	$500	3/03	WCMN	8' press drills
Deere	LLA	G	$610	9/03	ECNE	Grain drill, dual front dolly wheels, grass seed attachment, rear spoke-type packer wheels
Deere	LZ	G	$200	6/03	WCSK	Canadian sale, 14' hoe press drill, fertilizer box
Deere	LZ	G	$250	4/03	WCSK	Canadian sale, steel press drill, rams & hoses & homebuilt transports
Deere	LZ	G	$5,100	11/03	WCKS	8x16 hoe drills, hillsides, split press wheels, transports
Deere	LZ1010	F	$660	1/06	NECO	3 drill units
Deere	LZ1010	G	$50	4/05	NCOK	Older hoe drills, sowed wheat last fall, 20-hole opening
Deere	N/A	F	$175	9/05	NECO	8' hyd lift
Deere	N/A	G	$475	10/05	NCOH	Older 18x7 grain drill, seeder, galvanized boxes
Deere	N/A	G	$425	6/05	ECWI	Pony drill & packer
Deere	N/A	G	$400	2/04	NEIN	Mechanical lift
Deere	N/A	G	$425	2/04	NEIN	Metal box
Deere	N/A	G	$1,300	3/04	SEWY	3-14, hitch
Deere	N/A	F	$150	4/03	SWIN	13 hole, single disc
Deere	N/A	G	$240	9/03	NEIN	Seeder
Deere	N/A	F	$250	2/03	NCMI	18-hole grain drill, seeder, galvanized boxes
Deere	N/A	G	$400	2/03	ECNE	8.5'x14' hole grain drill, 7.5" spacing, on rubber, seeder
Deere	N/A	G	$700	12/03	NEIA	Grain drill, galvanized boxes
Deere	VB	F	$250	1/06	WCNE	Grain drill, 7" spacing, seeder
Deere	VB	F	$300	2/06	WCNE	14', 10" spacings
Deere	VB	G	$325	11/05	ECNE	Model B
Deere	VB	G	$625	9/05	NCIA	12', grass seed, hyd. lift

Make	Model	Cond.	Price	Date	Area	Comments
Deere	VB	G	$950	8/05	WCIA	
Deere	VB	F	$100	2/05	NENE	18-hole grain drill on rubber, grass seeder
Deere	VB	G	$175	3/05	NCIL	12', double disc, grass seed
Deere	VB	F	$225	1/05	NWIL	12' grass seed
Deere	VB	F	$250	2/05	WCIL	10' grain drill, grass seeder
Deere	VB	G	$500	4/05	NCIA	12' drill, grass seed, hyd.
Deere	VB	G	$560	2/05	WCIA	12' grain drill, rubber
Deere	VB	F	$10	7/04	NEKS	
Deere	VB	G	$160	4/04	ECWI	12'
Deere	VB	F	$170	9/04	SEIA	
Deere	VB	F	$175	5/04	NCKS	16x10 disc drill
Deere	VB	F	$250	1/04	ECNE	18 shoe, 7" spacing
Deere	VB	G	$310	8/04	NCIA	10' grain drill, grass seeder
Deere	VB	G	$400	6/04	NWIL	10', grass seed
Deere	VB	G	$410	8/04	SWIA	20x7, hydraulic drill, grass seed
Deere	VB	F	$500	4/04	SWPA	13 hoe
Deere	VB	G	$750	3/04	NEIA	12', grass, oat and fertilizer attachments
Deere	VB	G	$800	6/04	NWIL	10', grass seed
Deere	VB	G	$1,300	4/04	WCNE	8', seeder
Deere	VB	F	$50	3/03	SEIA	10'
Deere	VB	P	$50	2/03	NCIL	10', single openers, rough
Deere	VB	G	$75	9/03	ECKS	Used to plant alfalfa, shedded
Deere	VB	F	$80	4/03	WCIA	10' grain drill
Deere	VB	F	$150	2/03	NEMI	17-hole, seeder
Deere	VB	G	$170	9/03	WCIA	16' grain drill, oats and grass, trip lift, on rubber
Deere	VB	G	$200	4/03	WCMN	Grain drill, low rubber, grass
Deere	VB	F	$225	3/03	ECNE	18-hole grain drill, seeder, on rubber, steel press wheels
Deere	VB	E	$600	3/03	ECNE	10' grain drill, 18 hole, 7" spacing
Deere	VB	F	$1,700	3/03	NCCO	Drill
Deere	VB	F	$35	2/03	ECNE	18-hole drill on steel
Massey	10'	F	$375	2/06	NWIL	Grain drill, grass seed, 15" tires
Massey	13'	G	$2,600	3/03	SCMN	Hi-rubber grain drill
Massey	33	F	$90	3/05	SCMI	15 row
Massey	33	G	$750	3/04	WCMI	17-hole grain drill, double disc openers, seeder
Massey	33	G	$950	1/04	WCMI	
Massey	424	G	$1,200	1/06	NEIN	Markers, seeder
Massey	427	G	$5,400	11/05	NCOH	No-till drill, 18x7
Massey	43	F	$465	3/04	SCMI	22-run grain drill
Massey	63	F	$500	3/04	NEMN	16' press drill, grass
Massey	63	G	$300	5/03	WCSK	Canadian sale, press drill, 16', soild steel packers, markers, fertilizer attachment, hyd. lift
MM	10'	G	$450	4/03	WCMN	Grain drill, double disc, low rubber, grass
MM	N/A	P	$90	11/04	NEKS	Rough, 8x16, on rubber
MM	N/A	F	$300	3/03	SWPA	18-hoe grain drill
Oliver	10'	F	$55	10/04	NCWI	Single-disc grain drill
Oliver	12'	G	$175	9/05	WCIL	On steel
Oliver		G	$250	3/03	NWPA	13-hole grain drill, on steel
Oliver	Superior	G	$260	7/03	WCIL	10', grass seeder

horse equipment

Cond.	Price	Date	Area	Comments
G	$100	10/03	NWSD	Horse-drawn mower
G	$100	10/03	NWSD	IHC horse-drawn mower
F	$30	5/05	WCNE	IHC 1-row horse-drawn cultivator
G	$550	2/05	NEIN	IHC horse-drawn manure spreader
G	$90	11/04	NEKS	IHC 1-row lister planter
P	$50	2/06	WCNE	John Deere N/A 1-bottom, horse-drawn walk behind plow, no handles
E	$475	11/04	SENE	John Deere horse-drawn mower, restored
G	$500	2/05	NEIN	John Deere horse-drawn manure spreader
E	$1,000	2/05	NWIL	John Deere antique wagon, "Triumph," rubber gear
E	$100	11/04	SENE	John Deere horse-drawn walking plow
E	$350	11/04	SENE	John Deere horse-drawn 2-way plow
G	$50	10/03	NWSD	John Deere 2-bottom plow, horse-drawn
G	$180	12/03	NCIA	John Deere 2-row horse-drawn planter with cast iron lids on boxes, seat, wire & markers, complete
F	$10	5/05	WCNE	Horse-drawn tumble bug
F	$110	8/05	NCIA	Pony sulky cart, pony harness
F	$150	5/05	WCNE	Walk behind horse-drawn potato digger, 1-bottom
F	$275	3/05	NEKS	Horse-drawn buckboard wagon, no seat, box off of running gears, rough
G	$350	1/05	ECIN	Horse buggy
G	$525	6/05	ECWI	Black sleigh
G	$525	1/05	ECIL	Sleigh
F	$550	3/05	ECND	Parade buggy, 2 seat

172

Cond.	Price	Date	Area	Comments
G	$750	6/05	ECWI	Doctor's buggy
G	$925	2/05	WCIL	Antique high wheel wagon
G	$65	4/04	NCWI	Sleigh
G	$130	3/04	SEPA	Walking plow
E	$1,825	11/04	SENE	4-wheel buggy, rubber tires
G	$40	11/03	NEKS	Horse cultivator, good shape for age
G	$65	6/03	WCSK	Canadian sale, refinished horse-drawn cultivator
G	$100	10/03	NWSD	(3) horse-drawn cultivators
F	$200	12/03	WCMI	Horse-drawn covered buggy
G	$325	6/03	WCSK	Canadian sale, team cart
G	$350	10/03	NWSD	Single-horse cart, 2 wheels
F	$350	12/03	WCMI	Bobsleigh
G	$425	6/03	WCSK	Canadian sale, set of nylon harnesses
G	$500	3/03	ECMI	Antique 1-horse cutter
G	$500	3/03	ECMI	2-wheel buggy
G	$500	6/03	WCSK	Canadian sale, set of bobsleighs
F	$500	12/03	WCMI	1-horse sleigh, harnesses
F	$500	12/03	WCMI	Bobsleigh
G	$550	3/03	WCMI	Horse-drawn covered wagon
F	$575	12/03	WCMI	Horse-drawn wagon
G	$600	10/03	NWSD	Antique fire engine
G	$800	6/03	WCSK	Canadian sale, set of nylon harnesses
G	$900	5/03	SWOK	2-seat buggy, surry top, 1- or 2-horse, very nice
G	$1,200	6/03	WCSK	Canadian sale, set of nylon harnesses
G	$1,300	4/03	SCOK	2-seat buggy
G	$1,500	10/03	NWSD	Wagon with clam belly dump, used for road construction & hauling grain
E	$1,800	8/03	NWIL	Doctor's buggy
G	$1,350	6/03	NCIA	Oliver "Red River Special" threshing machine, on steel wheels, it works
G	$1,000	3/04	SEIA	Doctor's horse buggy, new wheels, shafts included

You're an ageless iron nut when . . .

- Instead of family pictures in your wallet, you have pictures of all your tractors and implements.
- All of your tractors have names . . . and they are all female in nature.
- You wore bib overalls at your wedding.
- You use an IHC carriage bolt for a paperweight.
- The family car is parked outside so you have more room for your tractors in the garage.
- You own a tractor even though you live in a town house.
- You drive your tractor instead of the pickup when the wife sends you for groceries.
- You know more about your tractor and machinery's ancestries than you do about your wife's family.
- You think that gas, diesel, and grease smell good.
- You are working on your tractor and your wife says, "Honey, come to bed," and you reply, "Not now, I'm busy!". . . and you're a newlywed.

trucks

Make	Model	Year	Cond.	Price	Date	Area	Comments
Autocar	N/A	1970	F	$500	8/05	SEMI	18' potato bed, Cummins 8 speed
Autocar	N/A	1975	G	$700	12/05	ECIN	Diesel, 13 speed
Autocar		1968	G	$2,750	11/03	ECND	3½ ton, 250 Cummins, 13 spd., 10.00-20" rear tires, 13-80R20" front tires, 20' Hart box, hoist, 3-in-1 combo endgate
Autocar		1975	G	$4,200	7/03	ECND	Tandem axle, 230 hp., 13 spd., Pitman HL-170 8-ton crane, 47' boom, mounted on 22' steel flatbed, 4.25/65-22" front tires, 10.00/20" rear tires, 297,750 miles
Chevrolet	10	1972	P	$300	2/06	NWSD	Custom 10 pickup, standard
Chevrolet	10	1975	G	$1,550	2/06	WCIL	Scottsdale
Chevrolet	10	1967	G	$200	10/03	WCSK	Canadian sale, 3 spd.
Chevrolet	20	1966	F	$500	8/05	NCIA	Pickup, V8, 4 spd.
Chevrolet	20	1964	F	$200	2/03	ECIL	Pickup
Chevrolet	2500	1975	F	$550	11/05	SEND	292, 6 cyl., 4 speed
Chevrolet	30	1974	G	$1,800	10/03	WCSK	Canadian sale, custom del., steel box & hoist, 350, V8, 4 spd.
Chevrolet	3100	1953	G	$19,000	1/05	NENE	Pickup, 28K miles, 1 owner, 3 speed on column, 6 cyl.
Chevrolet	3100	1956	G	$8,750	3/05	ECCO	4WD, auto
Chevrolet	3800	1957	G	$1,100	8/05	NCIA	9' step side box, 6 cyl., 4 speed, originally from California
Chevrolet	4100	1953	G	$4,300	2/05	ECNE	Obeco 10' wood box w/ hoist, 46,346 actual miles, 6-cyl. gas engine, 4 speed, shedded
Chevrolet	4400	1950	G	$400	11/04	ECND	Single axle, 6 cyl., 4 spd., 12' box, hoist
Chevrolet	50	1968	G	$840	8/03	NWIA	96K miles, 14' wood box, hoist

174

Make	Model	Year	Cond.	Price	Date	Area	Comments
Chevrolet	50 Viking	1958	G	$1,600	9/04	NEKS	16' steel bed, hoist, grain sides, V8 283, 4x2 spd., 9:00-20" tires, hay extensions
Chevrolet	50 Viking	1960	F	$800	6/04	ECMT	Hoist
Chevrolet	5700	1950	G	$1,600	4/05	NCKS	6 cyl., 4x2 spd., with 250-bu. gravity box, rollover tarp, hyd. auger
Chevrolet	60	1967	G	$2,500	2/06	NECO	With 20' bed, 427 engine, 5x3sp
Chevrolet	60	1964	F	$750	11/05	NEND	Single axle fuel truck, 6 cyl., 4/2 sp, 4 comp, hose and pump
Chevrolet	60	1966	G	$1,600	12/05	WCIN	Single axle grain truck, 13' wooden bed with steel floor, scissor hoist, 6 cyl., 4 speed, 45,815 miles
Chevrolet	60	1964	P	$500	2/05	WCIL	Does not run, 14' steel box, tag axle, 5x2 spd., needs engine work
Chevrolet	60	1966	G	$1,850	1/05	SCNE	Grain truck, 87,500 miles, 4x2 spd., 15.5' box/hoist, 350, V8
Chevrolet	60	1961	G	$1,500	11/04	NEKS	80K+ miles, 2-ton farm truck, 261 engine, 6 cyl., 4x2 spd., 13' Haulmor, all-wood bed, fold-down racks, 20-ton cap, good 8.25-20" rubber, good brakes, green cab, red box
Chevrolet	60	1961	G	$1,600	3/04	ECND	Single axle, 6 cyl., 4 speed, 13.5' Midwest box, hoist
Chevrolet	60	1962	F	$750	2/04	SENE	16' wood box, hoist, 5x2 spd., 327 V8, 9:00-20" tires, 1500-gal. poly tank, inductor cone, transfer pump, hoses
Chevrolet	60	1963	G	$1,000	9/04	NCIA	V8, 4x2 spd., 14' wood box and hoist
Chevrolet	60	1964	F	$800	3/04	ECMI	Dead tandem grain truck w/ 17' wood box, twin-post hoist, V8
Chevrolet	60	1964	G	$1,200	3/04	SEND	16' steel box, 366 engine
Chevrolet	60	1965	F	$1,000	11/04	NWOH	Grain truck, 16' box, hoist, 6 cyl., 4x2 spd.
Chevrolet	60	1965	G	$1,175	4/04	NCND	Wood box, hoist, roll tarp
Chevrolet	60	1973	F	$500	9/04	WCWA	14' van truck
Chevrolet	60	1959	F	$500	3/03	NESD	V8, 4x2 spd., 15.5' wood box, hoist
Chevrolet	60	1964	F	$1,700	4/03	SCND	Heavy-duty gravel truck, 38,476 miles
Chevrolet	60	1966	G	$2,600	12/03	SEND	Single axle, 454 big block, 4x2 spd., 16' steel box, hoist
Chevrolet	60	1966	E	$3,250	9/03	SEIN	38,400 miles, 3,000 miles on new engine, 15' bed, hoist
Chevrolet	60	1968	G	$1,000	8/03	NEKS	427 engine, 20' bed, hoist, 50K miles
Chevrolet	60	1973	G	$5,600	12/03	SCNE	350 engine, 2,000 to 3,000 miles on OH, 51K miles, 4x2 spd., 16' combination box, hoist
Chevrolet	6100	1955	F	$500	12/05	ECNE	Single axle, 4x2sp, Bradford 240-316 gravity box, 8.25-20 tires
Chevrolet	6100	1957	G	$1,200	3/05	WCMN	Single axle, Parker 2000 gravity box and hyd. brush auger
Chevrolet	6100	1949	P	$125	3/04	ECMI	Single-axle dump truck, 6 cyl., gas eng., 50-gal. fuel tank
Chevrolet	6400	1957	G	$525	11/05	NWMN	Single axle, 4/2 sp, 13' Omaha std. box, hoist
Chevrolet	6400	1950		$300	6/04	NCWI	Single-axle dump truck, flatbed hoist, 6 cyl., 3 speed
Chevrolet	6400	1955	F	$1,000	4/03	SCND	2 ton, wood box, hoist, 41,147 miles, 1 owner
Chevrolet	6400	1957	F	$600	6/03	ECND	Tag tandem, 4+2, 18' Knapheide box & hoist
Chevrolet	6500	1951	G	$450	8/03	SENE	13' box, hoist
Chevrolet	6500	1953	F	$450	9/03	WCIA	4x2 spd., single axle, 16' comb box and hoist
Chevrolet	70	1961	G	$1,150	11/05	SEND	Tilt cab tag axle, 409 engine, 5/2 sp, PS, 19' wood box, hoist
Chevrolet	70	1970	G	$2,250	3/04	WCIL	V8, tag axle
Chevrolet	80	1967	G	$8,200	3/04	ECMI	Cabover Spartan tag tandem truck, 18' steel box with 30-ton hoist, V6, 5x2 spd.
Chevrolet	80	1975	P	$2,100	11/03	ECND	Digger truck
Chevrolet	Apache	1960	F	$700	3/04	NWMN	½ ton, 235, 4 spd.
Chevrolet	C10	1974	G	$850	4/04	WCNE	2WD, V8, auto, 75,000 miles, gas
Chevrolet	C20	1975	F	$900	3/04	SEND	350, V8, 4 speed, 4WD, flatbed, 5th wheel, lockout hubs, 15K miles on rebuilt engine
Chevrolet	C20	1967	P	$20	8/03	NWIA	4 speed
Chevrolet	C20	1968	F	$275	10/03	WCSD	Runs well
Chevrolet	C20	1975	P	$375	8/03	NWMN	Pickup, automatic, 4WD
Chevrolet	C30	1969	G	$2,000	2/06	NCOH	1 ton, 4 speed, 10' bed & scissors hoist, only 32,430 miles

trucks

Make	Model	Year	Cond.	Price	Date	Area	Comments
Chevrolet	C30	1963	G	$600	4/05	SENE	Gas, 8' box, hoist
Chevrolet	C30	1970	G	$1,150	6/05	NEND	1 ton, 350 V8, 4 speed., flatbed, 400-gal. fuel tank, 12-volt pump
Chevrolet	C30	1973	G	$1,400	1/05	NWGA	
Chevrolet	C30	1967	G	$1,875	3/03	SEPA	283 V8, 4 spd., farm permit
Chevrolet	C30	1968	G	$2,500	4/03	NEKS	350, 4WD, tag axle, 18' bed, hoist
Chevrolet	C30	1975	g	$1,400	3/03	ECNE	1-ton dually, 350 V8, gas, 4 spd. manual, 8'x9' flatbed
Chevrolet	C40	1971	F	$800	9/04	NWMN	Single axle, 2' flatbed, 292, 6 cyl., 30,606 miles
Chevrolet	C50	1967	F	$450	2/06	NCIL	4-sp. trans. and 6-cyl. engine
Chevrolet	C50	1967	G	$4,500	2/06	NWKS	Single-axle grain truck, V8 gas engine, 4x2sp, 16' steel box, 19,500-lb. GVW, 9.00-20 tires, 50,700 miles
Chevrolet	C50	1968	G	$2,600	2/06	ECIL	4x2sp, Knapheide grain bed hoist, 52,510 miles
Chevrolet	C50	1968	G	$1,200	12/05	SWMS	Single axle, trash body
Chevrolet	C50	1969	G	$3,200	7/05	ECND	Single axle, 350, 4/2 sp, 14.5' steel box, hoist, 63,079 miles
Chevrolet	C50	1969	F	$800	9/05	SEIA	90,646 miles, grain truck
Chevrolet	C50	1971	G	$1,150	11/05	SEND	Single axle, small block 400 engine, 5/2 sp, wood box
Chevrolet	C50	1964	P	$500	2/05	WCIL	13' farm box, twin hoist, 6-cyl. engine, 4x2 spd.
Chevrolet	C50	1968	G	$4,900	3/05	ECMI	Tandem axle grain truck, 16' wood box, twin-post hoist, 4x2 spd., V8 gas engine, 45,310 miles
Chevrolet	C50	1969	F	$950	3/05	WCMN	Single axle, 14' wood box scissor hoist, 4/2 sp, 350, V8
Chevrolet	C50	1969	E	$4,000	1/05	SENE	Gas, 18' box, hoist
Chevrolet	C50	1970	G	$1,400	3/05	SEND	Single axle, 350, 4x2, 14' steel box
Chevrolet	C50	1970	G	$2,000	1/05	NENE	16' wood box and hoist, 6 cyl., 5x2 spd., 77,529 miles, shedded, not used in 4 yrs
Chevrolet	C50	1971	F	$2,000	4/05	NWOK	Feed truck, 6 cyl., mixer bed feed truck
Chevrolet	C50	1971	G	$2,200	6/05	NWMN	Tag tandem, plumbed, 350, V8, steel box, hoist and roll tarp
Chevrolet	C50	1972	P	$300	3/05	SEIA	13' silage box
Chevrolet	C50	1972	F	$1,050	1/05	NCPA	350 engine, 4 spd., 18' bed with 4' high removable side racks, wooden bottom, new tires on rear
Chevrolet	C50	1972	G	$3,200	1/05	NWIL	350 V8, 4x2 spd., 14½' steel grain box, 62,728 miles
Chevrolet	C50	1972	G	$3,400	1/05	NWIL	350 V8, 4x2 spd., 14½' steel grain box, 42,828 miles
Chevrolet	C50	1972	G	$3,650	1/05	NWIL	350 V8, 4x2 spd., 14½' steel grain box, 42,332 miles
Chevrolet	C50	1975	G	$3,750	7/05	NWMN	Single axle, 350, V8, 4x2 spd., Kiefer 16' box, hoist, roll tarp, 62,177 miles
Chevrolet	C50	1965	E	$2,300	11/04	SCKS	6 cyl., 292 engine, 13' grain bed and lift, good rubber, good floor & body, ran good
Chevrolet	C50	1967	F	$800	4/04	NWIA	4x2 spd., 350 Chevrolet eng., 16' steel box with hoist, single axle
Chevrolet	C50	1967	F	$950	3/04	SEND	Single axle, 327, 4/2 spd., 16' wood box
Chevrolet	C50	1967	G	$2,550	3/04	ECND	2 ton, 292, 4/2, 15' Knapheide steel box with wood floor and hoist
Chevrolet	C50	1968	F	$1,500	3/04	NWMN	Single axle, 327, 4/2, 250-bu. tender box, PTO drive
Chevrolet	C50	1968	G	$5,600	2/04	SCKS	366 V8, 5x2 spd., 16' bed & lift, sells with Westfield hyd. drill fill auger with steel & brush augers
Chevrolet	C50	1969	F	$550	1/04	NEIN	V8, 4 spd., grain bed, hoist
Chevrolet	C50	1969	G	$600	5/04	ECWI	Single axle truck
Chevrolet	C50	1969	F	$1,150	8/04	NEKS	
Chevrolet	C50	1969	G	$3,050	3/04	SEND	Single axle, 350 V8, 4x2 spd., 16' box, hoist, roll tarp, 82K miles
Chevrolet	C50	1969	G	$3,600	3/04	NEND	Single axle, 366, 5/2, 15.5' Knapheide box, headlift hoist & roll tarp,
Chevrolet	C50	1970	G	$900	4/04	SEND	18' van body
Chevrolet	C50	1971	F	$1,000	2/04	NECO	16' bed, hoist, 350 engine, 5x2 spd., tag axle
Chevrolet	C50	1971	G	$2,600	2/04	NECO	15' grain bed, 366 engine, 5x2 spd., single axle
Chevrolet	C50	1971	G	$5,000	5/04	NCKS	6 cyl., 4x2 spd., 13' steel bed, rollover tarp, good rubber,

Make	Model	Year	Cond.	Price	Date	Area	Comments
Chevrolet	C50	1972	G	$3,750	1/04	WCIL	76K miles, 2 ton, 350 V8, 4x2 spd., 75,755 miles, 15' Knapheide box
Chevrolet	C50	1960	G	$3,400	9/03	SCNE	67K miles
Chevrolet	C50	1967	G	$850	6/03	ECNE	350 V8 gas, 4x2 trans., hyd. brakes, Browne 1500-gal. fuel tank
Chevrolet	C50	1967	F	$1,100	8/03	SWMN	Single axle truck, large 6-cyl. eng, 4x2 spd. axle,
Chevrolet	C50	1967	G	$2,750	2/03	ECKS	327 V8, 4x2 spd., 15.5' Midwest grain bed, hoist
Chevrolet	C50	1968	F	$4,500	4/03	NCND	57,700 miles, box, hoist, roll tarp
Chevrolet	C50	1969	F	$800	6/03	WCWI	Dump
Chevrolet	C50	1969	F	$1,300	3/03	ECTN	85K miles, 12' grain box, hoist didn't work
Chevrolet	C50	1969	G	$1,325	2/03	SEMN	Single axle truck, 350, V8, 4x2 spd. trans., 13' box and
Chevrolet	C50	1969	F	$2,900	3/03	NCND	Single axle, 350, 4 spd., 16' Frontier box, hoist, roll tarp
Chevrolet	C50	1969	G	$3,000	6/03	SCOK	Grain truck, hoist, 4 spd., showing 49K miles
Chevrolet	C50	1970	F	$325	1/03	ECNE	Fuel transport
Chevrolet	C50	1970	F	$1,050	2/03	SCMN	366, 5 spd., tag axle, 20' steel box and hoist
Chevrolet	C50	1971	P	$350	11/03	ECND	
Chevrolet	C50	1972	P	$285	8/03	WCMN	Single axle, 350, V8, 5x2 spd., 18' Delta van body
Chevrolet	C50	1972	G	$3,600	2/03	ECNE	Omaha standard 17' box and hoist, 46,700 miles, 350, V8, 4/2 spd., PS, shedded
Chevrolet	C50	1972	E	$5,700	1/03	NCCO	60,700 miles, 16' bed
Chevrolet	C50	1972	G	$6,100	3/03	NESD	1.5 ton, 4x2 spd., 350 eng., Schweigers 16' steel box w/ twin-cyl. hoist, 28,000 miles, shedded
Chevrolet	C60	1962	G	$150	1/06	NEMO	Grain truck
Chevrolet	C60	1964	F	$150	1/06	NEMO	Grain truck
Chevrolet	C60	1974	G	$3,650	1/06	NECO	16' steel box
Chevrolet	C60	1964	G	$1,700	11/05	ECNE	16.5' box and hoist, V8, 4x2sp
Chevrolet	C60	1966	G	$3,400	11/05	ECKS	2 ton truck, 5x2sp, 9.00 tires, 16' steel bed & hoist, 54" sides
Chevrolet	C60	1969	G	$3,100	11/05	ECWA	366 gas engine, 5x2sp, 10:00-20 rubber, 86k total miles, 16æ flatbed, hoist & new wood deck, 300 bu grain box
Chevrolet	C60	1969	G	$4,000	12/05	WCMN	Tandem axle truck, V8, 5/2 sp, 20' wood box and hoist, 136,690 miles
Chevrolet	C60	1970	G	$4,400	9/05	WCMN	427, V8, 5x2sp, 20' Schwartz wood floor box, air tag/air brakes,
Chevrolet	C60	1972	G	$12,750	12/05	SCMN	Twin screw, 20' Crysteel box, hoist, 427 engine, 5x4sp, air brakes,
Chevrolet	C60	1972	G	$12,750	12/05	SCMN	Twin screw, 20' Crysteel box, hoist, 427 engine, 5x4sp, air brakes,
Chevrolet	C60	1972	P	$450	12/05	NWIL	V8, 4x2sp, 14' grain box and hoist
Chevrolet	C60	1972	G	$7,750	12/05	ECMN	Twin screw, 427, 5/4 sp, 18' Knapheide box, hoist, 91,485 miles
Chevrolet	C60	1974	G	$2,450	9/05	WCIL	13' Knapheide box, dual hoists, 350 V8, 2 ton, 4x2sp
Chevrolet	C60	1974	G	$6,650	11/05	ECNE	4x2sp, V8, 17.5' OS box, 74,450 miles
Chevrolet	C60	1975	F	$1,700	8/05	NWIA	Single axle with 16' wood box
Chevrolet	C60	1975	G	$2,800	11/05	SCIA	366 motor, 5x2sp, steel grain box, 86k miles
Chevrolet	C60	1975	G	$3,500	11/05	NEIL	
Chevrolet	C60	1960	F	$525	7/05	ECND	Single axle, 6 cyl., 4/5, 8,000 miles on new eng., 51,046 miles
Chevrolet	C60	1966	G	$3,400	1/05	NWIL	327 V8, 4x2 spd., 14½' steel grain box and hoist, 47,346 miles
Chevrolet	C60	1967	G	$2,600	1/05	NCMN	V8 5/4, 18' Knapheide box & hoist
Chevrolet	C60	1970	F	$700	2/05	WCOH	1200-gal. tank and spray booms
Chevrolet	C60	1971	G	$1,000	7/05	ECND	Eng. rebuilt 2002, new hyd. pump, roll tarp
Chevrolet	C60	1972	G	$5,600	6/05	NEND	Single axle, 366 V8, Allison auto, 2-spd. rear end, 16' Knapheide steel box w/ hoist, 39,000 miles
Chevrolet	C60	1973	P	$3,600	1/05	NCKS	16' steel bed w/ hoist, 5 spd. trans. with 2-spd. axle, 350, V8, rough
Chevrolet	C60	1973	G	$4,250	3/05	NWMN	Lift tag tandem w/ steel box and hoist, new roll tarp
Chevrolet	C60	1974	P	$300	6/05	ECNE	Dump truck
Chevrolet	C60	1974	F	$2,300	6/05	SEND	Single axle, V8, 4x2 spd., 15' box, hoist, flip-down stock rack
Chevrolet	C60	1974	F	$2,500	2/05	WCIL	13.5' farm box with new floor, hoist, 350V8, 4x2 spd., 147K miles
Chevrolet	C60	1974	G	$2,800	4/05	SEMI	Grain box, cattle rack, 16' hoist, 68K miles
Chevrolet	C60	1974	G	$3,600	2/05	WCIL	45,200 miles, 13' bed
Chevrolet	C60	1974	F	$3,600	5/05	NCKS	16' bed and hoist, V8, 4/2

trucks

Make	Model	Year	Cond.	Price	Date	Area	Comments
Chevrolet	C60	1974	F	$3,950	2/05	NECO	Jacobs 16' steel box, power up & down rear hoist, new 350 V8
Chevrolet	C60	1974	G	$4,950	1/05	NWIL	350 V8, 5x2 spd., 14½' steel grain box and hoist, tarp, 75,683 miles
Chevrolet	C60	1975	F	$2,700	3/05	WCKS	16' steel bed, hoist, 82,215 miles, stock rack, 5x2 spd.
Chevrolet	C60	1975	F	$7,200	1/05	SWOH	4x2 spd., 53K miles, 10' dump bed
Chevrolet	C60	1958	G	$1,500	4/04	NCKS	Wheat truck, 13½' steel bed, hoist, Goodwrench 350 eng., 4/2
Chevrolet	C60	1959	G	$1,000	4/04	NCND	2 ton, 13' box & hoist
Chevrolet	C60	1962	G	$4,100	3/04	NWMN	6 cyl., 4/2
Chevrolet	C60	1963	F	$400	3/04	NEKS	13' grain bed
Chevrolet	C60	1964	P	$300	3/04	ECMI	Tandem truck, 18' wood box with Perfection hoist, 4x2 spd., 292, 6 cyl.
Chevrolet	C60	1964	G	$2,800	5/04	NCKS	Cabover truck, 350, 4x2 spd., 15.5' bed & hoist
Chevrolet	C60	1964	G	$3,800	3/04	WCKS	6 cyl., 4x2 spd., 14' bed & lift
Chevrolet	C60	1965	G	$2,100	3/04	SCKS	15' all-steel bed & stock racks, 283 V8 engine, 4x2 spd.
Chevrolet	C60	1966	G	$875	7/04	ECND	Tag axle, 327, 5/2, 18' Lockwood box with grain pan and hyd. unload
Chevrolet	C60	1966	F	$2,200	12/04	NCOK	Tandem truck, 20' box, hoist, tag axle
Chevrolet	C60	1966	G	$2,600	10/04	NWMN	Single axle, 6 cyl., 4/2, 55K
Chevrolet	C60	1968	P	$1,500	7/04	NWMN	Tandem, 427, 5+2 spd., air brakes, 18' combo box, 86,000 miles
Chevrolet	C60	1969	F	$1,250	4/04	NEPA	Dump truck
Chevrolet	C60	1970	F	$900	2/04	ECMI	Gas
Chevrolet	C60	1970	G	$3,500	2/04	SENE	Grain truck, 427 V8, 5x4 spd., tandem axle, Schwartz 20' steel box, hoist
Chevrolet	C60	1970	G	$3,700	2/04	NEIN	Grain truck, 366 gas engine, 18' grain bed, 38,305 miles
Chevrolet	C60	1971	G	$1,500	4/04	SEND	Tag trailer
Chevrolet	C60	1971	G	$2,500	2/04	NEKS	4x2 spd., 366 V8, 9.00-20" tires, Haul-Mor 18' bed, hoist
Chevrolet	C60	1971	G	$3,000	12/04	WCIL	366 engine, 5x2 spd., 66,600 miles
Chevrolet	C60	1971	G	$4,100	2/04	WCIL	16' box, hoist, 427 V8, 4x2 spd.
Chevrolet	C60	1972	P	$400	1/04	ECNE	Dump truck, 10' box, bad motor
Chevrolet	C60	1972	P	$550	3/04	NEKS	Rough, fertilizer truck
Chevrolet	C60	1972	G	$1,900	6/04	WCWA	16' flatbed, 5/4, PS
Chevrolet	C60	1972	G	$2,150	3/04	SEMN	V8, 4x2 spd., box, 16' and hoist
Chevrolet	C60	1972	G	$8,000	2/04	ECNE	Grain truck, 20' steel box, new Shurlock tarp, equalizer tag
Chevrolet	C60	1974	F	$550	4/04	NEPA	Dump
Chevrolet	C60	1974	F	$1,500	12/04	SCMN	10' dump box
Chevrolet	C60	1974	F	$1,750	2/04	ECIL	Tag tandem, 16' bed
Chevrolet	C60	1974	F	$1,750	3/04	SEND	14' Omaha standard box with silage box and endgate
Chevrolet	C60	1974	G	$4,100	1/04	ECIL	366 engine, 15' bed, 65K miles
Chevrolet	C60	1974	G	$4,650	1/04	ECNE	Grain truck, 4x2 spd., 350 V8, 16' box & hoist
Chevrolet	C60	1974	G	$5,900	3/04	SCKS	16' all-steel bed & lift, 366 V8 engine, 4x2 spd.
Chevrolet	C60	1974	G	$6,900	1/04	WCIL	2 ton, 33,646 miles, 350 V8, 4x2 spd., PS, 16'
Chevrolet	C60	1974	G	$10,000	9/04	NWSD	366 V8, 4x2 spd., 14' Harsh mixer box, 44K miles
Chevrolet	C60	1974	G	$12,100	3/04	SCKS	16' bed & lift, 350, V8, 4x2 spd., 9:00x20" tires, tip tops
Chevrolet	C60	1974	G	$12,600	3/04	SCKS	16' bed & lift, 350 V8, 4x2 spd., 9.00x20" tires, tip tops
Chevrolet	C60	1960	F	$700	9/03	SCNE	14' Schwartz box and hoist
Chevrolet	C60	1963	F	$400	12/03	NWIL	292-cu.-in. engine, 4x2 spd., 14' grain box and hoist
Chevrolet	C60	1964	G	$1,200	4/03	ECNE	6-cyl. engine, 4x2 spd., 51,716 miles, 13' box, 2-cyl. hoist
Chevrolet	C60	1964	F	$1,675	12/03	SCNE	100K miles plus, 16' box, hoist
Chevrolet	C60	1964	F	$2,200	9/03	ECND	Single axle, cherry picker boom lift
Chevrolet	C60	1964	G	$4,000	7/03	ECND	Single axle, cherry picker boom lift
Chevrolet	C60	1965	F	$1,400	1/03	NWIL	Gas, new 18' box, V8, tandem, 5 spd.
Chevrolet	C60	1965	G	$1,550	1/03	ECIL	4x2 spd., 350 bu., 13.5' Knapheide grain bed twin post hoist
Chevrolet	C60	1965	G	$2 000	1 03	SWOK	Grain bed

Make	Model	Year	Cond.	Price	Date	Area	Comments
Chevrolet	C60	1965	G	$5,950	2/03	SWOH	Grain truck, 14' bed
Chevrolet	C60	1966	F	$600	3/03	NENE	16' box, hoist
Chevrolet	C60	1966	F	$1,600	4/03	SWIN	16' grain/livestock bed, hoist, 6 cyl., 4x2 spd.
Chevrolet	C60	1968	P	$275	3/03	SEIA	1200-gal. stainless steel tank
Chevrolet	C60	1968	F	$2,000	7/03	SEND	327 V8, 4 spd., 14' box, hoist
Chevrolet	C60	1968	G	$3,200	4/03	NCND	Hoist, box, w/ new steel floor, tip top, roll tarp
Chevrolet	C60	1968	G	$3,750	9/03	ECMN	Dump truck
Chevrolet	C60	1970	G	$4,100	8/03	NCIA	Tandem truck, 5/2, 18' Obeco steel box
Chevrolet	C60	1971	G	$3,500	8/03	NCIA	Tandem big block, V8, 5/2, 16' wood box and hoist
Chevrolet	C60	1971	G	$8,000	10/03	NWSD	Tandem dual truck, 20' grain box, 45K miles, super clean
Chevrolet	C60	1972	G	$500	6/03	ECND	Twin screw, V8, 5 spd., 9.00x20 tires, 18' Lockwood box
Chevrolet	C60	1972	G	$6,000	8/03	WCMN	Twin screw, 427, V8, 5/4 spd., 18' steel box and hoist
Chevrolet	C60	1972	G	$6,000	2/03	SCIL	V8, 4x2 spd., 14' Parkhurst grain bed, hoist, 23,745 miles
Chevrolet	C60	1973	G	$5,600	8/03	NWIA	33K actual miles, 14' wood box
Chevrolet	C60	1973	G	$5,600	11/03	ECND	Twin screw, 366, 5/4, PS, aux. tanks, 9.00-20" tires, hoist
Chevrolet	C60	1973	F	$6,750	7/03	WCSK	Canadian sale, single-axle grain truck, 350 V8, 5+2, 15' steel
Chevrolet	C60	1973	G	$8,000	4/03	WCSK	Canadian sale, single-axle grain truck, 350 V8, 4+2 trans.
Chevrolet	C60	1973	G	$8,000	4/03	WCSK	Canadian sale, single-axle grain truck, 4+2 trans.
Chevrolet	C60	1974	P	$3,500	7/03	NWKS	350, V8, 4x2 spd., 16' steel bed with hoist
Chevrolet	C60	1974	G	$4,600	1/03	NWIL	1 owner, 2 ton, 15' Knapheide grain box, dual hoists, 350 V8
Chevrolet	C60	1974	G	$5,100	2/03	WCIL	Grain truck, 39,000 miles
Chevrolet	C60	1974	G	$6,000	5/03	SWOK	2 ton, 336 V8, 4x2 spd., steel sides, hyd. grain auger, good
Chevrolet	C60	1975	G	$4,450	2/03	ECIL	Grain truck, 15' bed, 44,902 miles, always shedded
Chevrolet	C60	1975	G	$5,050	11/03	SENE	V8, 4x2 spd., 16' wooden combination box, 34,941 miles
Chevrolet	C60	1975	G	$5,200	9/03	SCNE	4x2 spd., V8, 16' combination box
Chevrolet	C60	1975	E	$7,700	3/03	NEKS	Very clean, 350 engine, 4x2 spd., 43K miles, 16' deep side
Chevrolet	C60	1975	G	$8,000	4/03	WCSK	Canadian sale, grain truck, 350 V8, 4+2 trans., 14' steel box
Chevrolet	C60	1975	G	$9,200	8/03	WCMN	Single axle, 32,806 miles, 366, 5/2 spd., 16' box, two-way
Chevrolet	C65	1974	G	$12,000	1/06	ECIL	Grain truck, 10 wheeler, air tag axle, cargo doors, 18' bed
Chevrolet	C65	1974	G	$7,250	1/06	NEMO	Grain truck, 69K miles
Chevrolet	C65	1975	G	$10,000	2/06	NWKS	Grain truck, 69,158 miles, 5/2 sp, V8, 22' steel box with hoist
Chevrolet	C65	1961	F	$750	6/05	ECNE	6-cyl. gas engine, 4-speed trans, PTO, Progress 1200 gal
Chevrolet	C65	1973	G	$10,100	12/05	SCMN	18' steel box, hoist, twin screw, 427 gas, PS, 5x4sp
Chevrolet	C65	1974	G	$4,100	12/05	NCKS	Grain truck, steel box, bought new
Chevrolet	C65	1974	F	$4,900	11/05	NWMN	Twin screw, 427, 5/4 sp, 19' steel box, tip tops, 3 pc. endgate, 52,800
Chevrolet	C65	1973	P	$350	2/05	SWNE	Single-axle dump truck
Chevrolet	C65	1973	G	$2,250	1/05	NWGA	350, 5 spd., 10' box dump
Chevrolet	C65	1973	G	$4,500	3/05	SWIN	5x4 spd., 427 gas engine, Hendrickson suspension, air brakes,
Chevrolet	C65	1973	G	$4,900	1/05	ECIL	Tandem axle, 466 eng., 15' aluminum bed, hoist, gravel gate, 5/2
Chevrolet	C65	1974	G	$4,500	6/05	NWMN	Tag tandem, 366, V8, 5/2 spd., 16' steel box, hoist and roll tarp
Chevrolet	C65	1974	G	$5,400	7/05	ECND	Auto, 20' box, center-mount hoist, 40,000 miles
Chevrolet	C65	1974	G	$7,000	6/05	ECNE	
Chevrolet	C65	1975	F	$500	2/05	NCIN	Grain truck, 16' grain box
Chevrolet	C65	1975	G	$6,000	3/05	ECND	Single axle, 366, 5/2 spd., 16' box, hoist, roll tarp, 67,100 miles
Chevrolet	C65	1975	G	$7,000	7/05	NCMN	Twin screw, 427 V8, 19' Knapheide box & hoist
Chevrolet	C65	1973	G	$1,700	4/04	SEND	Air tag tandem axle
Chevrolet	C65	1973	G	$2,300	3/04	NWMN	Twin screw, 18' Knapheide box & hoist, V8, 5x4 spd. trans.
Chevrolet	C65	1973	F	$3,000	7/04	NWMN	Tag tandem, 366, 5+2 spd., 20' Knapheide box, roll tarp
Chevrolet	C65	1974	G	$2,250	3/04	NWMN	Tandem tag axle, 427, 5/2, air brakes, dual tanks
Chevrolet	C65	1974	F	$2,400	3/04	NEKS	Tandem axle, 20' steel bed & Schwartz hoist with power down
Chevrolet	C65	1974	G	$5,200	3/04	NENE	Knapheide 18' steel box, Harsh hoist, single axle with hyd. rear tag
Chevrolet	C65	1974	G	$10,000	4/04	ECND	Twin screw, 427, 5/4 spd., box, roll tarp, combination endgate, new

trucks

Make	Model	Year	Cond.	Price	Date	Area	Comments
Chevrolet	C65	1974	G	$11,900	1/04	ECNE	427 engine, 5x4 spd., twin screw, 20' box, tarp, 81,119 miles
Chevrolet	C65	1974	G	$12,250	7/04	NWMN	Twin screw, 427, 5+2 spd., air brakes, 68,000 miles, roll tarp
Chevrolet	C65	1975	G	$3,200	3/04	SEND	Twin screw, 427, 5/2 spd., cab, and chassis, air brakes
Chevrolet	C65	1975	G	$5,900	1/04	ECIL	15' bed, 366 engine, 5/2, 59,990 miles
Chevrolet	C65	1975	G	$6,000	8/04	NEIA	Cheater axle, air brakes, 5x2 spd., 427 engine, Knapheide 16' box
Chevrolet	C65	1975	G	$8,700	3/04	NWMN	Single axle, 366, 5/2
Chevrolet	C65	1975	G	$9,000	7/04	NWMN	Lift tag, 427, 5+2 spd., Westgo diamond box, hoist, roll tarp, 60,000 miles
Chevrolet	C65	1975	G	$9,100	4/04	SEND	
Chevrolet	C65	1973	P	$700	5/03	NCKS	Rough, 1,500-gal. water tank, 366, V8, 5x2 spd.
Chevrolet	C65	1973	G	$2,000	1/03	WCIL	115K miles, 13.5' bed
Chevrolet	C65	1973	G	$7,200	2/03	SCMN	19' wood box, hoist, tag axle
Chevrolet	C65	1973	G	$19,000	4/03	WCSK	Canadian sale, hyd. tag axle grain truck, 5+2, custom cab
Chevrolet	C65	1974	F	$3,600	2/03	WCIL	Rusty, 93K miles, 18' bed, air tag
Chevrolet	C65	1974	F	$4,750	7/03	SEND	Twin screw, 427, 5/4 spd., 19' box, roll tarp
Chevrolet	C65	1974	G	$4,750	2/03	SWIN	Single axle, 14' Midwest steel bed, hoist
Chevrolet	C65	1974	G	$9,500	7/03	SEND	Lift tag tandem, 427, V8, Eaton 5/2 spd., 19.5' box, roll tarp
Chevrolet	C65	1975	F	$900	9/03	ECND	Single-axle dump truck
Chevrolet	C65	1975	P	$2,000	11/03	ECND	Boom truck, gas
Chevrolet	C65	1975	G	$3,100	9/03	NCWI	Tandem dump truck, 427, 5x3 spd., 14' gravel box, hoist
Chevrolet	C65	1975	G	$4,550	1/03	SESD	Grain truck, 18' box, recent motor repair
Chevrolet	C65	1975	F	$5,250	8/03	NWMN	Twin screw, 427, V8, 5/4 spd., 18' Midland box, 3-pc. endgate
Chevrolet	C65	1975	E	$6,300	4/03	WCIL	Grain truck, 16' bed, new tires
Chevrolet	C65	1975	G	$6,600	1/03	ECIL	PS, 4/2 spd., 450 bu., 15' Knapheide grain bed and hoist,
Chevrolet	C65	1975	G	$7,900	2/03	SWIL	Tandem axle grain truck, 454, V8 eng., extra saddle fuel tank
Chevrolet	C65	1975	G	$9,250	3/03	ECMI	Dead tandem grain truck, 17,322 miles, 16' Parkhurst grain box
Chevrolet	C6500	1961	F	$1,100	12/04	ECNE	Midwest flatbed, 5th-wheel hitch
Chevrolet	C75	1975	G	$10,000	1/03	SWIA	Tandem axle grain truck, 427 V8 eng., 5/4 trans., hyd. brakes
Chevrolet	K60	1966	F	$1,400	3/05	SWIN	Dump truck, 5x2 spd., heavy bed
Chevrolet		1964	G	$1,700	2/06	NWKS	Fleetside pickup, red
Chevrolet		1964	F	$800	2/06	WCKS	292 motor, 4 speed, 15.5' bed & hoist, 12-volt drill fill auger
Chevrolet		1973	G	$7,200	2/06	WCKS	Tandem truck, 366 motor, 5x2 spd., 20' bed, hoist, tarp
Chevrolet		1974	G	$9,250	2/06	SCKS	4 speed, 13.5' steel box, roll tarp, V8, 58,779 miles
Chevrolet		1969	G	$1,900	9/05	NENE	Pickup, 46K miles, 6-cyl. engine, 3 speed on the column, long box
Chevrolet	N/A	1923	G	$5,000	4/05	NCIA	Repainted, new box and bed
Chevrolet	N/A	1941	G	$1,500	2/05	NWKS	Pickup, shedded, restorable
Chevrolet	N/A	1946	G	$1,050	8/05	NCIA	Pickup, extra early 6-cyl. Chevrolet engine
Chevrolet	N/A	1959	G	$900	3/05	SEND	2 ton, single axle, 6 cyl., hi/lo, box, hoist, low miles
Chevrolet	N/A	1968	F	$1,800	2/05	NWOH	Cabover, 16' grain bed and hoist, 366, hi/lo
Chevrolet	N/A	1971	G	$4,000	1/05	NEMO	Tandem, Scott 18' bed, cargo doors, roll tarp
Chevrolet	N/A	1972	G	$3,300	7/05	NCIA	V8, hi/lo, single axle, 14' box with cargo doors
Chevrolet	N/A	1972	G	$3,800	1/05	SCMN	15' steel box
Chevrolet	N/A	1974	G	$5,000	1/05	SCMN	15' steel box
Chevrolet	N/A	1975	G	$1,900	7/05	NCMN	4WD, 400 gas, auto, flatbed
Chevrolet	N/A	1935	F	$2,600	5/04	NWND	Suicide doors
Chevrolet	N/A	1946	P	$90	5/04	NCKS	As is
Chevrolet	N/A	1948	G	$1,900	12/04	SEMN	½-ton Loadmaster truck, 19,000 miles
Chevrolet	N/A	1949	G	$1,000	7/04	NEND	1½-ton snub nose truck, 6 cyl., 4 spd., 14' wood box and hoist
Chevrolet	N/A	1954	G	$1,100	12/04	SEIA	5-window pickup, not been on road in 20 years, shedded
Chevrolet	N/A	1956	G	$700	9/04	NWMN	2 ton, 350 V8, 4x2 spd., box, hoist

Make	Model	Year	Cond.	Price	Date	Area	Comments
Chevrolet	N/A	1959	P	$200	2/04	NEKS	½-ton pickup, rough, 3 spd., 6 cyl., 235
Chevrolet	N/A	1962	F	$1,750	2/04	NWIL	4x4, new flatbed, diesel
Chevrolet	N/A	1965	F	$25	4/04	ECWI	¾ ton, needs work
Chevrolet	N/A	1966	G	$2,600	1/04	WCKS	292 motor, 4x2 spd., 40,659 miles
Chevrolet	N/A	1971	G	$2,300	7/04	NCIA	¾-ton pickup, 115K miles
Chevrolet	N/A	1974	P	$525	11/04	NWMN	¾-ton, V8, 4 spd., steel flatbed with concealed 5th wheel hitch
Chevrolet	N/A	1974	G	$2,050	3/04	SCMN	
Chevrolet	N/A	1975	P	$450	9/04	SEIA	Grain truck
Chevrolet	N/A	1975	G	$550	9/04	ECNE	¾-ton pickup, 2WD, 350, automatic, 65K original miles
Chevrolet	N/A	1975	G	$1,600	3/04	SCKS	½ ton, 350 V8, automatic, 200-gal. fuel tank, toolbox
Chevrolet	N/A	1942	G	$2,700	4/03	SCND	1½ ton, wood box, hoist, 42,906 miles
Chevrolet	N/A	1946	F	$150	7/03	WCMN	1½ ton, wood box
Chevrolet	N/A	1956	F	$375	11/03	ECND	2 ton, 400, V8, box and hoist
Chevrolet	N/A	1956	F	$850	7/03	WCSK	Canadian sale, 3 ton, wooden box, hoist, 4+2
Chevrolet	N/A	1958	G	$600	5/03	SWOK	2 ton, lift, grain boards
Chevrolet	N/A	1961	G	$2,300	9/03	WCSD	4x2 spd., single axle
Chevrolet	N/A	1963	F	$600	3/03	NCOH	Tender truck, tandem V8 gas, 5x2 spd., 18' grain bed, twin
Chevrolet	N/A	1964	G	$450	6/03	WCSK	Canadian sale, ½ ton, 6 cyl., std. trans.
Chevrolet	N/A	1966	F	$500	5/03	WCSD	Will run, no bed
Chevrolet	N/A	1967	F	$400	3/03	WCMN	¾-ton pickup, 6 cyl., 4 spd.
Chevrolet	N/A	1967	G	$1,500	4/03	WCSK	Canadian sale, 3-ton truck, 14' steel box, 327 V8, 5 spd.
Chevrolet	N/A	1969	G	$1,300	5/03	SWOK	2 ton, hoist
Chevrolet	N/A	1970	G	$2,600	11/03	WCKS	4x2 spd., 350 engine, 16' bed
Chevrolet	N/A	1971	G	$275	6/03	WCSK	Canadian sale, ½ ton, 350 auto
Chevrolet	N/A	1972	G	$5,750	3/03	NCCO	
Chevrolet	N/A	1973	F	$500	6/03	WCMN	¾ ton, 350, automatic, 4WD
Chevrolet	N/A	1973	F	$1,250	3/03	WCMN	427, 5x2 spd., V-plow
Chevrolet	N/A	1974	P	$400	7/03	SEND	Single axle, tilt cab, 366, 4/2 spd., PS, 12' box, hoist
Chevrolet	N/A	1974	F	$475	9/03	ECND	¾-ton 292 6 cyl., 4 spd., 10' utility box, new rear rubber
Chevrolet	N/A	1974	P	$625	5/03	NCKS	Rough, ½-ton pickup, full-time 4x4, V8, auto trans.
Chevrolet	N/A	1974	G	$5,900	12/03	NCOK	2-ton truck, 18' Mabar box and hoist, 4x2 spd., 37K miles
Chevrolet	N/A	1974	G	$6,200	6/03	WCMN	Single axle, 350, 4/2 spd., 16' Knapheide box, hoist, 39,000 miles
Chevrolet	N/A	1975	P	$95	3/03	NESD	½-ton pickup, 4WD, 350, automatic, for parts
Chevrolet	N/A	1975	G	$900	7/03	ECND	Cube van, 15' cube, 350 V8, automatic
Chevrolet	N/A	1975	G	$2,500	6/03	SCOK	¾-ton 4WD feed truck, 350 V8, automatic, new rubber, cake
Chevrolet	N/A	1975	F	$4,000	12/03	SEIL	10 wheeler, 427, 13 spd., twin screw, cab not reconditioned
Chevrolet	Viking	1958	P	$600	3/03	NCOK	Wheat truck, 16' bed, hoist, 4x2 spd., engine needs work
Chevrolet	Viking	1958	G	$3,300	11/03	WCKS	6 cyl., 4x2 spd., 13.5' bed, hoist, Westfield hyd. drill fill auger
Chevrolet	Viking 60	1959	F	$525	7/04	NEND	Single axle, 6 cyl., 4x2 spd., 14' steel box, hoist
Chevrolet	Viking 60	1961	F	$1,200	9/04	ECND	Single axle, 238 V8, 4x2 spd., box, hoist
Diamond Reo	N/A	1973	G	$500	5/04	ECWI	20' steel grain box and hoist
Dodge	200	1964	F	$1,000	3/04	WCMN	Power wagon, V8, 4 spd., 4WD
Dodge	200	1974	F	$1,300	3/03	ECMI	4WD pickup, 318 auto
Dodge	250	1971	F	$1,700	1/03	NENE	4x4, <5,000 miles on new 318 motor, PTO, hyd. pump
Dodge	2500	1970	g	$1,050	3/04	NEKS	5+2 spd., 10' steel bed, gas, hyd. pump, dual hyd.
Dodge	400	1957	F	$1,050	4/03	SCND	Single-axle gravel truck, 20,517 miles, won't stay in 2nd gear
Dodge	400	1966	G	$7,400	6/03	WCSK	Single-axle grain truck, 8.25x20" tires, 313 V8, 4 spd.
Dodge	500	1969	F	$400	11/05	SCMI	54K miles, 15' grain box, no hoist
Dodge	500	1963	F	$600	4/05	SEND	15.5' steel box, 4x2 trans., V8 eng.
Dodge	500	1968	F	$800	10/04	NWMN	Single-axle truck, V8, 4/2, 14' box and hoist
Dodge	500	1969	G	$3,000	2/04	NECO	Knapheide 18' grain box, 318 engine, 5x2 spd., flotation tag
Dodge	500	1961	G	$2,000	1/03	WCKS	318 motor, 4x2 spd. trans., 43,186 miles, 15.5' bed, hoist

trucks

Make	Model	Year	Cond.	Price	Date	Area	Comments
Dodge	500	1971	F	$2,200	7/03	WCSK	Canadian sale, grain truck, roll tarp, steel box, 318, 4+2
Dodge	600	1974	F	$2,100	11/04	NWSC	Flatbed dump truck
Dodge	600	1974	G	$4,300	8/04	ECMI	Grain truck, single axle, 24K miles, new rubber
Dodge	600	1975	F	$950	1/04	NEIN	Grain truck, 318 engine, 4x2 spd., 300-bu. box, hoist, 74,850 miles
Dodge	600	1964	F	$300	2/03	NCMI	Grain truck, V8, 5x2 spd., no brakes
Dodge	600	1974	G	$2,600	9/03	SENE	Gas, 16' box, hoist
Dodge	600	1975	G	$2,100	9/03	WCIA	4x2 spd., single axle, Knapheide, all steel box and hoist, 52,079 miles
Dodge	800	1964	F	$900	3/05	NWMN	Twin screw w/ 15.5' steel box and hoist
Dodge	D250	1975	F	$750	6/05	NWMN	¾ ton, 4x4 pickup, 360 V8, auto, A/C, cruise
Dodge	D50	1974	G	$550	10/03	WCSK	Canadian sale, ¼-ton
Dodge	D500	1966	G	$2,000	2/03	ECIL	318, V8, 2-spd. trans., 13' bed, 60,418 miles
Dodge	D600	1971	G	$1,000	3/04	NWMN	Single-axle truck, 413, V8, 5x2 spd., service body
Dodge	D600	1973	G	$1,000	12/04	ECNE	2-ton truck, 4x2 spd., AM, 24,000-lb. GVWR, 17' box, cattle racks
Dodge	D600	1974	G	$4,750	7/04	NEND	Lifting tag tandem, V8, 5/2, 19' Frontier box, hoist and roll tarp,
Dodge	D600	1975	G	$2,250	7/04	NEND	Single axle, V8, 4/2, 15' Omaha box and hoist, 39,890 miles
Dodge	D600	1967	G	$1,650	3/03	NCOH	Grain truck, single axle, 318 engine, 4x2 spd., Omaha 13.5' bed, twin-cyl. hoist
Dodge	F700	1965	G	$500	7/04	ECND	391, V8, 5/3, air brakes, 16' steel grain box
Dodge	N/A	1959	P	$350	4/05	NCOK	13' bed & hoist, 5x2 spd.
Dodge	N/A	1962	G	$1,750	4/05	NCOK	4x2 spd., 15' steel bed, hoist
Dodge	N/A	1963	P	$1,150	4/05	NCOH	1 ton, 9' hoist bed, 66,589 miles
Dodge	N/A	1968	G	$400	3/05	NECO	Single axle, 5th wheel, 318 engine, 4x2 spd.
Dodge	N/A	1955	P	$70	3/04	SEND	2 ton, Chevrolet 6-cyl. engine
Dodge	N/A	1974	P	$500	7/04	SEND	¾ ton, 2WD
Dodge	N/A	1974	P	$500	7/04	NWMN	¾ ton, 2WD
Dodge	N/A	1964	F	$750	7/03	ECND	V8, 4 spd., sewer pumper, new vac. & fresh water pump
Dodge	N/A	1964	F	$800	6/03	WCSK	Canadian sale, 3 ton, 9:00x20", 16' steel box, 4+2 trans.
Dodge	N/A	1972	G	$1,250	5/03	WCSK	Canadian sale, 3 ton, single axle, V8, 4+2 trans., 14' steel
Ford	100	1965	G	$1,250	3/04	SEND	Twin I-beam pickup, 302 engine, 4 spd.
Ford	350	1960	G	$1,100	11/04	NCIA	25,443 miles, 6 cyl., 8x10' box
Ford	500	1968	F	$775	2/05	NEMI	Grain truck, 14' wood rack and hoist, 390 gas engine
Ford	500	1969	G	$1,700	2/03	NCIA	330, V8, 4/2, PS, 12' box, hoist
Ford	600	1968	G	$3,200	2/06	WCKS	4x2sp, V8 motor, 13.5' b&h, ro tarp, 12-volt drill fill auger
Ford	600	1969	G	$2,500	9/05	WCMN	Single axle gravel truck, 4-yard box, 10' single-cyl. hoist, 127K miles
Ford	600	1967	G	$2,900	5/04	SCMN	Bucket truck
Ford	600	1969	F	$1,100	4/04	NEND	Single axle, 331, V8, 4x2 spd., box and hoist
Ford	600	1970	G	$2,050	3/04	NCMI	Single axle, 16' metal grain box w/ twin-post hoist, 330, V8
Ford	600	1970	F	$2,200	1/04	WCIL	Lime truck, gas, V8 engine, 5x2 spd., lime box
Ford	600	1966	P	$350	3/03	WCMN	Grain truck, V8, 14' steel box w/ wooden floor, 4x2 spd.
Ford	600	1967	G	$1,700	12/03	NCOH	Grain truck, 14' Omaha bed, twin cyl., 4x2 spd., 65,065 miles
Ford	600	1968	P	$250	12/03	SCIA	14' box
Ford	600	1970	F	$1,300	4/03	ECND	Single axle, 330, 4/2 spd. w/ OD, 15½' Westeel box
Ford	600	1970	G	$2,600	8/03	NCIA	391, 5x2 spd., 20' wood box, tag axle, 111,358 miles
Ford	600	1972	G	$5,000	5/03	WCSK	Canadian sale, grain truck, 330, V8, rebuilt motor, 4+2 trans.
Ford	6000	1969	F	$750	3/03	NCIL	Custom cab, 3208 Cat, 5 spd.
Ford	650	1969	F	$400	3/03	SWWI	Knapheide grain box, scissor hoist
Ford	700	1965	G	$2,200	11/05	NWPA	V8, 5 speed, 14' steel dump
Ford	700	1970	F	$950	4/05	NEIN	47,027 miles, 14' grain dump box
Ford	700	1967	G	$3,800	2/03	SWIN	10 wheeler, 20' wooded sided bed, 49,558 miles

182

Make	Model	Year	Cond.	Price	Date	Area	Comments
Ford	700	1974	G	$8,000	10/03	WCSK	Canadian sale, Louisville single-axle grain truck, 361 V8, 5+2, steel box, roll tarp, 21,500 miles
Ford	750	1972	G	$3,200	11/05	NCCA	2-axle dump
Ford	7000	1973	G	$1,350	3/05	NCIL	3208 Cat, 10 spd., 16' box
Ford	800	1972	F	$1,700	12/05	ECMI	59,227 miles, 20' box & hoist, tandem axle, 391 engine, 5 speed, gas
Ford	800	1968	F	$850	6/05	SEND	Cabover tag tandem, air lift, V8, 5x2 spd., Frontier box, hoist
Ford	800	1972	F	$3,600	12/03	WCMN	Twin screw, 20' flatbed, 361, V8 5/4 trans.
Ford	800	1974	F	$520	9/03	ECND	Twin screw, tandem gravel truck, gas, 10-yard dump body
Ford	800	1975	F	$2,700	4/03	WCMN	Line truck
Ford	8000	1970	G	$12,000	3/05	ECND	Louisville twin screw, 3208 Cat, 10 spd., 20' box, hoist
Ford	8000	1973	G	$3,600	9/03	ECMN	Boom truck, log clam
Ford	8000	1973	G	$4,500	12/03	SEMN	Dump truck, Cat. 3208 eng., single axle
Ford	8000	1974	G	$5,000	1/03	ECIA	V8 Cat, 20' box, hoist, air tag, tarp, cargo doors
Ford	8000	1975	G	$1,600	7/03	ECND	Tandem, cab & chassis, 3208 Cat, 10 spd., 11R22.5" tires
Ford	850	1968	P	$1,150	2/05	WCWI	18' box, hoist, for parts, did not run
Ford	880	1974	G	$5,100	6/05	SEND	Twin screw, 534, 5x4 spd., 18½' Frontier steel box, tip tops
Ford	880	1974	G	$5,600	2/05	WCIN	10 wheeler with 477, 5/3 trans., air brakes, 18' Scott bed
Ford	880	1973	F	$3,700	7/04	NWMN	Twin screw, auto, 20' Westgo box, roll tarp, 59,000 miles
Ford	880	1973	F	$4,250	6/04	NWMN	Twin screw, 3208 Cat, 5/4 spd., 20' box
Ford	880	1973	G	$8,300	12/04	SEND	Louisville twin screw, 475 OH'd engine, Allison auto
Ford	880	1974	P	$900	6/04	NWMN	Twin screw, 478 gas, 5x4 spd., 18' box, hoist, plumbed for drill
Ford	880	1974	G	$3,300	12/04	ECND	Twin screw, V8, gas
Ford	880	1974	F	$5,500	5/04	ECND	Louisville twin screw, 475 gas, auto, 19' Frontier box, roll tarp
Ford	880	1974	G	$9,750	4/04	ECND	Twin screw, 534 V8, 5/4 spd., box, roll tarp, 91K miles
Ford	880	1975	P	$1,950	6/04	NWMN	Twin screw, 534, 13 spd., air brakes, 19' stake box
Ford	880	1975	G	$7,750	3/04	SEND	Twin screw, 475, Allison auto, Westgo 19' box, hoist, roll tarp
Ford	880	1973	G	$9,000	9/03	WCMN	475 engine, 5x4 spd., 20' steel box, roll top tarp, twin screw
Ford	880	1973	G	$12,100	2/03	WCNE	534 V8, 10 spd., twin screw, Aulick 20' box with beet gate
Ford	880	1974	G	$11,500	4/03	NWMN	Louisville twin screw, 477, 5x4 spd., 19' Midland unibody box, 72K miles
Ford	900	1970	G	$3,700	3/05	NWMN	Louisville twin screw tandem, 20' steel box and hoist, roll tarp, 534
Ford	900	1972	F	$6,200	12/03	NWOH	Tri-axle, 477 gas eng., 22' bed with hoist
Ford	900	1975	P	$525	5/03	SWOK	Gas, tandem drag, lift, hyd. auger, grain/feed bed
Ford	900	1975	G	$12,750	4/03	NWMN	Louisville twin screw, 535 gas, automatic, 19' Midland box, 60" sides
Ford	9000	1974	G	$11,000	3/05	SEND	Louisville twin screw, 9 spd., Henderson suspension, Scott 20' all-steel
Ford	9000	1974	G	$16,500	2/05	NECO	398K miles, 350 Cummins, 20' slip box w/ full hyd. endgate
Ford	9000	1974	F	$2,500	3/04	SCMI	Tandem axle, wet kit
Ford	9000	1971	P	$1,200	11/03	ECND	Single axle
Ford	9000	1972	F	$3,100	9/03	ECND	Semi
Ford	9000	1973	G	$13,500	12/03	NCOH	Tandem axle truck, air brakes, cheater, Detroit dsl V8-318 w/ 871 blower, 13 spd., 20' Scott bed, roll tarp
Ford	9N	1940	G	$950	6/04	ECND	3-pt. blade
Ford	A	1929	G	$2,000	8/05	SEND	Truck with stake box
Ford	C600	1960	F	$600	2/04	SENE	Grain truck, 18' wood box, hoist, auto. tranny, 292 V8 gas, 9:00-20" tires
Ford	C600	1965	G	$1,300	3/04	NENE	Cabover truck, 18' box, hoist
Ford	C600	1966	G	$8,500	9/04	WCWA	14' flatbed, 5 spd., PS, Pitman Unidyne 11, 40.5' 4,600-lb. boom bkt., bkt. attachment
Ford	C600	1966	G	$1,200	9/03	ECNE	Cabover, V8 engine, 4/2 spd., hyd. brakes, PS
Ford	C700	1967	F	$550	2/04	ECNE	Tilt cab grain truck, 18' box, 4x2 spd., 330 gas motor, cheater axle
Ford	C700	1969	G	$1,900	4/04	SEND	Tag tandem
Ford	C750	1971	G	$2,800	1/03	SEMN	16' steel Obeco box, 54" sides, hoist, single axle, 5/2 spd.
Ford	C800	1975	G	$4,400	2/05	NCIL	5x2 spd., air tag, 20' grain body, hoist and roll tarp
Ford	C800	1970	F	$2,100	3/03	NENE	18' box, hoist

trucks

Make	Model	Year	Cond.	Price	Date	Area	Comments
Ford	C800	1972	G	$3,800	1/03	SEMN	20' box, tag axle, dual hoist, tarp, 5/2 spd.
Ford	F100	1974	P	$850	3/05	WCKS	½ ton, 4x4, Dudrey wire roller, V8, automatic
Ford	F100	1959	F	$450	1/04	ECNE	Short box, 6 cyl., 4 spd.
Ford	F100	1966	P	$450	7/04	ECMN	Custom cab, 352 engine, 4 spd., 95,000 miles
Ford	F100	1967	F	$350	11/04	NWMN	Pickup, 240 engine, 3 spd.
Ford	F100	1954	G	$1,500	7/03	ECND	6 cyl., 4 spd.
Ford	F100	1965	F	$500	7/03	WCSK	Canadian sale, ½ ton, 6 cyl., gray, 83,632 miles
Ford	F100	1974	F	$325	7/03	WCSK	Canadian sale, Ranger, 3 spd.
Ford	F100	1975	G	$925	4/03	WCSK	Canadian sale, 360 V8, auto, green & white
Ford	F100	1975	G	$4,700	6/03	WCSK	Canadian sale, Ranger XLT, 25,000 miles on rebuilt eng., 151,873 miles
Ford	F150	1969	G	$300	6/03	WCSD	2WD, runs/looks good
Ford	F150	1974	G	$700	7/03	ECND	V8, auto
Ford	F250	1954	P	$120	4/05	NCOK	2WD, flatbed, rebuild project
Ford	F250	1969	G	$800	3/05	WCKS	89K miles, ¾ ton, 4x4, V8, 4 spd.
Ford	F250	1975	F	$1,000	3/05	ECND	High boy, 390, 4 spd., 4WD
Ford	F250	1974	G	$600	9/04	ECNE	Crew cab, 2WD, 390 cubic inch, automatic, 129K miles
Ford	F250	1975	G	$3,200	3/04	SEND	High boy, factory 390, 4 spd., 4WD, lockouts, split window
Ford	F250	1970	F	$200	12/03	WCMN	Pickup, flatbed, 4 spd., V8
Ford	F250	1975	G	$375	7/03	ECND	¾-ton crew cab, 390, auto, 6' box
Ford	F250	1975	G	$1,250	2/03	SWOH	4WD
Ford	F350	1974	F	$850	12/05	SCND	Flatbed, 1-ton service truck
Ford	F350	1967	F	$1,300	3/05	ECND	1-ton dually, 352, V8, 4 spd., 58,000 original miles
Ford	F350	1972	G	$2,050	2/05	SWIN	1 ton, steel floor, hoist, V8, 4 spd., 98K
Ford	F350	1971	G	$2,250	7/04	WCWA	9' flatbed, 4 spd., PS
Ford	F350	1957	G	$1,500	6/03	WCSK	Canadian sale, 1 ton, custom cab, 272, V8, box & hoist
Ford	F350	1962	G	$2,100	6/03	SEND	1 ton, 292 V8, 2WD, cross box toolbox, 78,900 miles
Ford	F350	1973	F	$750	11/03	WCKS	Pickup, 4 spd., V8 motor, 74,000 miles
Ford	F500	1963	G	$600	3/05	NECO	13' box, hoist, 292 engine, 4x2 spd.
Ford	F500	1959	F	$300	4/04	SEND	V8, box, hoist
Ford	F500	1967	G	$600	9/04	WCWA	Bus conversion, 6 cyl.
Ford	F500	1971	P	$700	7/03	SEND	Single axle, 330, 4 spd., 14' flatbed
Ford	F500	1974	F	$400	3/03	NCND	1½-ton single axle dually, 331, V8, 4 spd., 12' flatbed, 300-gal.
Ford	F500	1975	G	$4,250	4/03	WCSK	Canadian sale, single axle grain truck, 4+2 trans.
Ford	F6	1950	G	$2,500	6/05	ECNE	Flatbed
Ford	F6	1950	F	$200	2/04	ECMI	Single axle, stake rack, runs
Ford	F6	1948	G	$1,200	3/03	SEMN	Single axle farm truck, 4 spd. trans., 13.5' wooden box
Ford	F600	1968	G	$2,000	2/06	NWIL	13.5' farm box, 330v8, 75K miles
Ford	F600	1969	G	$1,100	1/06	WCIL	Grain truck, V8, 4/2 trans, 15' Knapheide bed, 95,000 miles
Ford	F600	1972	G	$3,700	1/06	SCNE	Grain truck, 34,500 miles, single axle, 4x2sp, Schwartz box
Ford	F600	1973	G	$1,500	1/06	ECNE	Grain truck, 15½' Obeco box, 5x2sp, V8 gas engine, PTO, cylinder hoist
Ford	F600	1961	F	$800	9/05	WCMN	Single axle, 4x2sp, 292, V8, 13½' box, 100,000 miles
Ford	F600	1963	F	$600	11/05	ECNE	13' wood box, 8.25-20" tires, 6-cyl. gas engine
Ford	F600	1969	G	$1,700	12/05	SCND	Single axle, box, hoist, roll tarp
Ford	F600	1971	F	$1,600	7/05	ECND	Single axle, 302, 4/2 sp, frontier 14' box, hoist, roll tarp
Ford	F600	1971	E	$2,900	11/05	NCIN	15.5' Delphi bed and hoist, 28k miles, 4x2sp, sharp
Ford	F600	1972	F	$525	11/05	NCIN	13' bed & hoist
Ford	F600	1973	G	$3,500	9/05	ECMN	Roadside sprayer
Ford	F600	1974	G	$2,050	12/05	NCIL	Grain truck, 390 engine, 4 speed, 62,395 miles, Knapheide 15' box
Ford	F600	1975	G	$1,400	11/05	NECO	Dump truck, 1 axle, gas, 4+2

184

Make	Model	Year	Cond.	Price	Date	Area	Comments
Ford	F600	1975	G	$6,750	8/05	WCIA	42K miles, 14' Obeco box
Ford	F600	1956	G	$900	1/05	NEMO	Grain truck
Ford	F600	1959	F	$325	6/05	NWMN	Single axle, 292, V8, 13' steel box and hoist
Ford	F600	1960	G	$700	3/05	NECO	13' box, hoist, 291 engine, 4x2 spd., single axle
Ford	F600	1964	G	$925	1/05	NENE	16' steel flatbed
Ford	F600	1966	G	$2,000	3/05	NWMN	Tag tandem w/ 17½' steel box and hoist
Ford	F600	1967	F	$900	3/05	WCNE	Grain truck, 16' steel box, roll tarp, scissor hoist, 4x2 spd., 9:00-20" tires
Ford	F600	1971	G	$3,500	2/05	SCKS	79,656 miles, 4x2 spd., V8, Knapheide 16' grain bed
Ford	F600	1973	G	$4,100	3/05	NECO	20' box, hoist, 361 engine, 5x2 spd., tag, low miles on OH
Ford	F600	1974	G	$2,600	2/05	ECIL	Grain truck, 51,600 miles, 14' bed, 4/2 trans.
Ford	F600	1974	G	$2,800	3/05	WCNE	Grain truck, 16' Omaha standard steel box, 360 gas engine
Ford	F600	1974	G	$3,200	2/05	WCIL	2 ton, 361 heavy-duty V8 engine, 5x2 spd., dual hoists, stock
Ford	F600	1975	F	$1,700	3/05	NECO	16' steel box, single axle, split shift, 361 motor
Ford	F600	1975	E	$5,600	1/05	SENE	24,695 miles, 13' box, hoist
Ford	F600	1954	F	$700	3/04	NWMN	Single axle, 292, 5/2, 14' wood box & hoist
Ford	F600	1954	G	$2,275	3/04	WCKS	13' bed & lift, V8
Ford	F600	1955	F	$300	3/04	WCMN	Single axle, 5x2 spd., 6 cyl., 13' box, St. Paul hoist
Ford	F600	1959	P	$220	5/04	NCKS	As is, bed & hoist
Ford	F600	1960	F	$200	2/04	ECNE	4x2 spd., V8 gas, 14' wood box, Harsh hoist, 8.25-20" tires
Ford	F600	1960	P	$350	9/04	NCKS	Rough, not running, V8, 4x2 spd., bed & hoist
Ford	F600	1960	G	$775	4/04	NWMN	Single axle truck, box and hoist
Ford	F600	1961	F	$800	11/04	NCKS	149,479 miles, 17' bed, hoist, 292 V8, 5x2 spd., tag, 8.25-20 tires
Ford	F600	1963	F	$2,000	7/04	NWMN	Tag tandem, Ford V8, 5+2 spd., 6,000 miles on rebuilt eng.
Ford	F600	1964	F	$700	10/04	NWMN	Single axle truck, V8, 4/2, 14' box, hoist, and roll tarp
Ford	F600	1964	G	$2,900	1/04	ECNE	262 big 6 cyl., 4x2 spd., 12' box, 54" sides, twin-cyl. hoist
Ford	F600	1967	G	$1,050	4/04	NWMN	Single axle truck, box and hoist
Ford	F600	1967	G	$6,700	3/04	SCKS	16' bed & lift, V8, 4x2 spd.
Ford	F600	1968	F	$1,800	2/04	NEKS	2 ton, 4x2 spd., 16' steel box, hoist, 93K miles
Ford	F600	1969	F	$400	7/04	NWMN	Fuel truck, 1000-gal., pump & hose
Ford	F600	1969	P	$400	7/04	SEND	Fuel truck, 1000-gal., pump & hose
Ford	F600	1969	P	$800	7/04	SEND	Single axle, gas, 4+2 spd.
Ford	F600	1969	P	$800	7/04	NWMN	Single axle, 4+2 spd., box, hoist, new 2 spd.
Ford	F600	1969	G	$1,475	3/04	WCMN	Single axle truck w/ 15' wood box and hoist
Ford	F600	1969	G	$2,100	6/04	WCWA	14' flatbed dump, V8, 4/5, pb
Ford	F600	1970	F	$650	11/04	NWOH	Grain truck, V8, 4 spd., Kilbros 450 center dump bed
Ford	F600	1970	G	$1,650	3/04	NESD	Bulk fuel truck, V8, 4x2 spd.
Ford	F600	1971	F	$400	9/04	WCWA	3-yard dump, V8, 4 spd.
Ford	F600	1974	P	$650	7/04	NWMN	Single axle, 4+2 spd., 18' flatbed, 2400-gal. fiberglass tank
Ford	F600	1974	P	$650	7/04	SEND	Single axle, 361, gas, 4+2 spd, 18' flatbed
Ford	F600	1974	G	$5,900	3/04	WCMN	Single axle, 39,300 miles, V8, 4/2, 15' steel box with hoist
Ford	F600	1975	G	$2,900	2/04	WCIL	V8, 14' box, 330-cubic-inch gas engine, 4x2 spd., twin-cyl. hoist, stock
Ford	F600	1954	G	$0	4/03	NCKS	No sale at $1,000, hoist
Ford	F600	1957	F	$275	7/03	WCMN	Single axle, 1,500-gal. poly tank, transfer pump, chem cone
Ford	F600	1958	F	$950	6/03	SEND	Single axle, 292 V8, 4/2 spd., 13' Westgo box, tip tops, roll tarp, 10,000 miles on OH motor
Ford	F600	1960	G	$1,275	8/03	SCKS	4x2 spd., 13' bed and lift, V8
Ford	F600	1961	F	$1,350	11/03	ECND	Single axle, 331, V8, 4/2 spd., 15' box, hoist, roll tarp
Ford	F600	1962	G	$600	7/03	SEND	2 spd., box, hoist
Ford	F600	1964	F	$1,200	9/03	ECKS	136,025 miles, 15' bed, hoist, shedded
Ford	F600	1966	G	$3,700	9/03	ECKS	36,558 miles, snubnose, 16' bed, hoist, shedded
Ford	F600	1967	F	$1,000	2/03	ECNE	Rough, grain truck, 92,166 miles, 292 motor, 16' steel box,
Ford	F600	1971	G	$2,300	1/03	NWIL	5x2 spd., 13' metal grain box, hoist, like new, 57,079 miles

trucks

Make	Model	Year	Cond.	Price	Date	Area	Comments
Ford	F600	1971	G	$9,000	10/03	WCSK	Canadian sale, single axle grain truck, 330 V8, 4+2
Ford	F600	1972	F	$600	3/03	SWMI	70K miles, 16' dump grain box
Ford	F600	1973	G	$3,700	9/03	ECKS	Shedded, 15' bed, hoist, wood floor/racks, 53K miles, metal
Ford	F600	1973	G	$3,750	1/03	ECIL	13.5' Midwest bed and hoist, 41,594 miles
Ford	F600	1975	G	$3,200	2/03	WCIL	13.5' bed, hoist, 4x2 trans., 330-cubic-inch motor, 36,200 miles
Ford	F600	1975	G	$4,500	7/03	SEND	Single axle, 300 6 cyl., 13½' Omaha standard box, Heil hoist, new rears, 62,000 act. miles
Ford	F600	1975	G	$5,600	2/03	ECIL	Grain truck, V8, 2 spd. trans., 13' bed, 27,684 miles
Ford	F600	1975	G	$11,750	10/03	WCSK	Canadian sale, single-axle grain truck, 361 V8, 5+2, Grainmaster 15' steel box, wood floor, box ext., Renn hoist, drill fill plumbing, 35,184 miles
Ford	F700	1975	G	$4,250	2/06	NWIL	15' farm box, new floor, 361, V8, 5x2sp, 64,650 miles
Ford	F700	1967	G	$2,700	2/05	WCIL	2 ton, 361 heavy-duty V8 engine, 5x2 spd., dual hoists, good rubber, 16' bed
Ford	F700	1973	G	$9,700	4/05	SCKS	Custom 16.5' bed with Harsh twin-cyl. scissor hoist, 5x2 spd., 361 motor, 57,916 miles, 1 owner, good tires
Ford	F700	1974	F	$350	3/04	NEMN	Grain truck, 13' box & hoist
Ford	F700	1974	F	$3,200	11/04	SEND	Lift tag, 390, 5x2 spd., 20' Midwest box, plumbed for drill fill
Ford	F700	1974	E	$7,100	11/04	SENE	1 owner, 46K miles, 361, 5x2 spd., 15' steel box, hoist, 9:00-20" rubber
Ford	F700	1975	G	$2,650	4/04	NWMN	Tag tandem with box and hoist
Ford	F700	1975	G	$4,300	4/04	NCND	Custom cab, 4x2 spd., 9-20 front, 15' steel box w/ Shurlock roll tarp
Ford	F700	1968	G	$5,750	3/03	SENE	Grain truck, 57,508 miles, Badger 20' combination box, twin cyl. hoist, hyd. tag axle, 390 motor, 5x2 spd., tilt cab, clean
Ford	F700	1969	P	$1,000	7/03	SEND	Single axle, 360, 5/2 spd., 15' steel box, hoist, roll tarp
Ford	F700	1974	F	$600	3/03	NWIL	Cabover grain truck, 15' box, 9.00-20" tires, gas
Ford	F700	1974	G	$2,300	3/03	SEMN	Single axle farm truck, 5x2 spd., 16' steel box and hoist, 400-bu. cap
Ford	F700	1975	P	$150	8/03	WCMN	Single axle, V8, 5/2 spd., 18' van box and lift gate
Ford	F700	1975	F	$700	9/03	ECWI	24' grain rack and hoist
Ford	F7000	1974	G	$4,250	6/04	WCWA	4-yard dump, Cat V8 diesel, 5/2, PS
Ford	F750	1975	G	$1,000	12/05	SWMS	Single axle, spread body
Ford	F750	1959	F	$2,000	3/05	NCAL	Fire truck
Ford	F750	1974	G	$5,700	2/05	SCKS	94,998 miles, cracked windshield, fender dent, 5x2 spd., V8, Mabar 18' grain bed
Ford	F750	1969	G	$1,750	4/04	NWMN	Tag tandem with box and hoist
Ford	F750	1973	F	$525	4/04	NEPA	
Ford	F750	1974	P	$1,350	4/04	ECMT	Flatbed dump truck
Ford	F750	1974	F	$1,900	7/04	NWMN	Tag axle, tandem, V8, 5+2 spd., 19' Knapheide box, hoist
Ford	F750	1974	G	$3,300	11/04	NCKS	30,866 miles, 27.5' bed, rear tandem axles, 391 V8, 5x2 spd., PS
Ford	F750	1975	F	$2,200	3/04	SEND	Single axle, 361, V8, 5 spd., 10' gravel box, new rubber
Ford	F750	1974	P	$700	11/03	ECND	Single axle, flatbed
Ford	F750	1974	G	$3,250	6/03	WCSK	Canadian sale, cabover grain truck, 10:00x20" tires,
Ford	F750	1975	P	$1,800	11/03	ECND	Bkt. truck, hot stick 6' elbow style, remotes, hyd. outriggers
Ford	F800	1972	G	$8,100	12/05	NCCO	18' end dump, 392, rollover tarp and beet gate, twin screw
Ford	F800	1968	G	$1,700	4/03	NCKS	15.5' steel bed, hoist
Ford	F800	1973	F	$3,200	6/03	ECMN	Prentice loader
Ford	F900	1975	G	$5,450	3/03	SEPA	10 wheel, 18' Omaha bed, 5x2 spd., 52,000-lb. GVWR
Ford	L750	1974	G	$6,500	3/05	SEND	Tag tandem, V8, 5/2 spd., Westgo 19' diamond box, hoist, roll tarp
Ford	L8000	1970	F	$600	12/05	WCNJ	Dump truck, diesel, 10' steel body, single axle
Ford	L8000	1974	G	$3,500	9/04	ECMN	Tandem axle
Ford	L900	1974	G	$2,100	12/04	WCMN	Single axle, 20' implement bed

Make	Model	Year	Cond.	Price	Date	Area	Comments
Ford	LN600	1970	F	$1,600	3/03	NWIL	V8, 5x2 spd., 13.5' metal grain box, hoist
Ford	LN600	1971	F	$1,800	3/03	ECNE	351 V8 gas engine, 4x2 spd., hyd. brakes, PS, 20,000-lb. GVWR
Ford	LN600	1971	G	$3,900	9/03	ECNE	Grain truck, V8 gas eng., 4/2 trans., hyd. brakes, PS
Ford	LN600	1972	G	$5,500	1/03	ECCO	Oswalt mixer box and scales
Ford	LN600	1974	G	$5,600	1/03	ECNE	Cheater, 57,700 actual miles, 33,500 miles on new engine & clutch
Ford	LN6000	1972	F	$1,100	7/05	ECND	Cat, 5x2sp, 14' flatbed
Ford	LN700	1971	G	$4,850	1/05	SCNE	110K miles, 5x2 spd., Tradewinds 16' steel box/hoist, 50" sides
Ford	LN7000	1974	G	$9,000	3/05	WCKS	Feed truck, 350 Harsh mixer bed & scales, $16K spent on
Ford	LN750	1974	F	$2,750	3/03	NENE	Gas, 16' box, hoist, tarp
Ford	LN800	1975	F	$5,000	3/03	ECMN	National crane
Ford	LN8000	1975	F	$6,000	7/03	SEND	Twin screw, Cat 3208, 13 spd., 20' Frontier box, 3-piece endgate
Ford	LN880	1973	G	$6,000	6/05	ECNE	Dump truck, Caterpillar 1160 diesel engine, 7-speed transmission
Ford	LN880	1974	F	$5,000	7/04	ECMN	Twin screw, 477, 5/4 spd., Dakota box, 80,000 miles
Ford	LN880	1974	F	$6,000	7/04	ECMN	Twin screw, 534, 13 spd., Frontier box, 73,000 miles
Ford	LN880	1975	G	$12,750	4/04	SEND	
Ford	LN880	1974	G	$10,000	6/03	SEND	Twin screw, 477, V8, 5/4 speed, 19' Frontier box, hoist, roll tarp
Ford	LN9000	1971	G	$3,500	7/03	NEWI	Tandem axle truck, Cummins dsl, 10 spd., Lockwood 22'
Ford	LN9000	1972	G	$4,500	7/03	NEWI	Tandem axle truck, Detroit 671, 10 spd. trans. with aux trans.
Ford	LN9000	1972	G	$4,500	7/03	NEWI	Tandem axle truck, Detroit 671, 10 spd. trans. with double I 801 belt
Ford	LN9000	1972	G	$5,000	7/03	NEWI	Tandem axle truck, Detroit 671, 10 spd. trans., tandem axle
Ford	LN9000	1973	G	$6,750	7/03	NEWI	Tandem axle truck, Detroit 671, 13 spd. trans. with double I
Ford	Louisville	1969	G	$700	4/04	SEND	Twin screw
Ford	Louisville	1974	P	$1,500	7/04	NWMN	Day cab, 290 Cummins, 10 spd.
Ford	LT9000	1972	G	$7,500	7/04	NWMN	350 Cummins, 13 spd., PS, Hendrickson suspension, Catco
Ford	LT9000	1973	G	$5,200	4/04	WCMN	Dump truck
Ford	LT9000	1970	F	$8,000	3/03	ECMN	Dump truck
Ford	Model A	1930	G	$900	8/03	NCIA	
Ford	N/A	1962	F	$500	2/06	WCKS	292, V8 motor, 4 speed, 15.5' bed & hoist
Ford	N/A	1952	F	$550	5/05	NCKS	13.5' bed, hoist
Ford	N/A	1974	F	$1,650	2/05	WCOH	250-bu. truck with 5/2 spd., dual hoist w/ 16' grain bed
Ford	N/A	1975	P	$1,700	1/05	NECO	Feed truck, 82K miles, 5 spd., 390 motor
Ford	N/A	1975	G	$3,200	1/05	SCMN	Fuel truck
Ford N/A	1923	100	G	$12,500	11/04	SCCA	T-bucket street rod, 350 Chevrolet gas engine, auto trans.
Ford	N/A	1959	F	$600	7/04	NWMN	Cabover, 2 ton, 4+2 spd., 14' box, hoist
Ford	N/A	1959	F	$600	7/04	SEND	Cabover, 2t, 4+2 spd., 14' box, hoist, plumbed for drill fill
Ford	N/A	1960	F	$2,000	7/04	NWMN	Twin screw, 5+2 spd., 20' box, roll tarp
Ford	N/A	1965	F	$3,050	5/04	ECND	Super-duty twin screw, 390, V8, 5/3 spd., staked box, hoist
Ford	N/A	1967	G	$1,450	3/04	WCMN	Single axle, 12' wood box & hoist
Ford	N/A	1969	G	$1,850	3/04	SCMN	Single axle, bed, hoist
Ford	N/A	1970	P	$1,100	7/04	NWMN	Tender truck, lift tag, 10 ton, 361 V8, OH
Ford	N/A	1970	P	$1,100	7/04	SEND	Tender truck, lift tag, 10 ton, 361 V8, low miles on OH
Ford	N/A	1971	F	$5,250	1/04	NECO	47,802 miles, 18' steel box
Ford	N/A	1973	F	$3,905	2/04	NCKY	Live tandem, Detroit diesel, 18' grain dump, high miles
Ford	N/A	1974	F	$950	3/04	NWMN	Twin screw tandem dump truck
Ford	N/A	1974	G	$2,050	12/04	ECNE	10' dump truck
Ford	N/A	1960	G	$1,800	9/03	WCSD	2 ton, hoist, 14' box, single axle
Ford	N/A	1962	G	$275	5/03	WCSK	Canadian sale, 1 ton, wood box, running but no hoist
Ford	N/A	1962	F	$300	8/03	NCIA	V8, 4x2 spd., 14' steel box and good hoist
Ford	N/A	1966	P	$250	5/03	NCKS	Bought for engine, no bed, good 390 V8, near new tires
Ford	N/A	1966	G	$2,000	3/03	SENE	½-ton pickup, 90K miles, gas
Ford	N/A	1968	F	$400	2/03	NCMI	Single axle grain truck, V8 gas engine, 4x2 spd., wood box with hoist
Ford	N/A	1970	G	$2,500	2/03	WCMN	Grain truck

trucks

Make	Model	Year	Cond.	Price	Date	Area	Comments
Ford	N/A	1972	F	$900	10/03	NCOK	2-ton dump truck
Ford	N/A	1972	G	$3,600	3/03	WCMI	Tandem axle, V8, gas, twist in frame
Ford	N/A	1973	G	$2,450	5/03	SWOK	2 ton, lift, 16' grain bed
Ford	N/A	1974	G	$1,250	3/03	WCMI	Dump truck, tandem axle, V8, gas, manual trans.
Ford	N/A	1975	F	$375	7/03	ECND	Supercab, V8, auto, utility box
Ford	N600	1969	E	$4,750	4/05	NCOK	V8, 4x2 spd., 16' Mabar bed & hoist, 36" sides, poorboy rollover tarp
Freightliner FLD 120	193		G	$6,500	11/05	NECO	Detroit Series 60, 13 spd., air ride, sleeper
Freightliner FLD 120	193		G	$9,000	4/03	ECNE	48" flat top sleeper, Cummins n14 diesel, air ride suspension, 2 100-
Freightliner N/A		1974	F	$12,500	2/03	SEMN	350 hp.. Cummins, 13 spd. tandem axle, 20' steel box and hoist
Freightliner N/A		1975	P	$1,400	7/03	SEND	Cabover, 22.5 tires
GMC	350	1958	F	$500	1/04	SCIA	Obeco box
GMC	3500	1971	G	$2,500	3/03	NWIA	Dually, 350 V8, 4 spd. manual trans., PS, dual rear wheels
GMC	4000	1962	F	$900	2/03	ECNE	V6, 4x2 spd., 16' box and hoist
GMC	4000	1964	P	$275	12/03	SCIA	14' mid equipment box
GMC	5500	1971	F	$1,700	4/05	NCOK	Single rear axle, 15.5' steel bed with 40" sides, rollover tarp, 4x2 spd.
GMC	5500	1972	G	$2,200	1/06	SCNE	Grain truck, 88,500 actual miles, Omaha standard 13.5' box & hoist
GMC	5500	1968	G	$800	12/05	SEMN	Grain truck
GMC	5500	1970	G	$1,850	12/05	NCOH	14' new leader lime bed, cheater axle, 40,000 miles, 350 engine
GMC	5500	1972	F	$1,850	3/05	NECO	20' box, 5x2 spd., tag axle, 350 motor
GMC	5500	1972	G	$4,300	2/05	ECIL	Grain truck, 62,300 miles
GMC	5500	1968	G	$1,100	10/04	SEMN	V8, 5x2 spd., wood box and hoist
GMC	5500	1972	G	$2,450	2/04	NEKS	V8, 4x2 spd., 14' bed, hoist, 50" sides, rollover tarp
GMC	5500	1970	F	$1,100	3/03	SEND	Cabover, 366 engine, 2x4 spd., 16' Wilrich box, hoist
GMC	5500	1970	G	$3,750	5/03	NCKS	Wheat truck, 16' steel bed, hoist, rollover tarp, 350, V8, 4/2, 65,000 miles
GMC	5500	1972	G	$3,800	2/03	SWIN	Single axle, 14' Omaha bed, hoist, 350, 4x2 spd., stock racks, 67K miles
GMC	5500	1975	G	$4,000	2/03	SCIL	V8, 4x2 spd., PS, 14' Midwest grain bed, 36,869 miles
GMC	6000	1973	F	$1,375	9/05	SEIN	15' Omaha bed, hoist
GMC	6000	1975	G	$2,100	7/05	WCMN	Grain truck, 4x2sp, 38,482 miles, recent engine overhaul, single axle
GMC	6000	1975	P	$2,600	8/05	WCMN	Grain truck, 16' steel grain box, 31,500 actual miles
GMC	6000	1974	G	$5,350	1/05	WCIL	14' box, 350 V8 engine, 5x2 spd., 42,112 miles
GMC	6000	1974	G	$2,800	11/04	NEIA	14' Omaha standard grain box, hoist, 4x2 spd.
GMC	6000	1974	G	$5,500	3/04	WCIL	76,028 miles, 5,000 miles on engine, gas, 14.5' farm box, twin hoist
GMC	6000	1974	G	$5,600	8/04	NCIA	14' steel box with wood floor, hoist, V8, 4x2 spd., 47,470 miles
GMC	6000	1975	G	$1,050	4/04	SEND	
GMC	6000	1975	G	$2,600	7/04	NCIA	350, V8, 5/2, 16' wood box with roll tarp, hoist, new tires, 99,000 miles
GMC	6000	1966	F	$525	3/03	NWIL	V8, 4x2 spd., 13.5' metal grain box, hoist, 80K miles
GMC	6000	1973	E	$5,100	1/03	NCCO	64,700 miles, 15.5' bed
GMC	6000	1973	G	$5,100	3/03	NCCO	
GMC	6000	1974	G	$4,450	2/03	ECKS	350 V8, 4x2 spd., 41,300 miles, 16' grain bed, twin-cyl. hoist
GMC	6000	1974	G	$4,900	2/03	SWIL	Single-axle grain truck, 350 V8 eng., 81,582 miles
GMC	6000	1974	G	$5,500	8/03	SCKS	Tag axle, 18' bed, roll tarp, 5x2 spd., 76,112 miles
GMC	6000	1975	G	$1,400	3/03	ECNE	V8, gas, 5x2 trans., hyd. brakes, PS, spring suspension, 25,000-lb. GVWR, 16' flatbed with hoist
GMC	6500	1974	G	$4,300	2/06	ECKS	
GMC	6500	1975	G	$4,000	2/06	NCOH	Gas, 4x2sp, 14' grain bed, 3-stage twin cyl. hoist
GMC	6500	1974	F	$5,500	2/05	NWOH	16' grain bed and hoist, 366, 5x2 spd., roll tarp
GMC	6500	1974	G	$10,200	3/05	WCMN	Twinscrew, 366, V8, 5/4 trans., 20' box and hoist, roll tarp
GMC	6500	1975	E	$9,500	1/05	ECNE	2 ton, 427 V8, 5x2 spd., 22' box with twin-cyl. hoist, stock rack
GMC	6500	1970	F	$900	3/04	SEMN	Box & hoist

Make	Model	Year	Cond.	Price	Date	Area	Comments
GMC	6500	1972	F	$2,300	2/04	ECNE	V8, gas, 4x2 trans., PS, hyd. brakes, flip hood, 16' high-sided wood grain body, swing doors
GMC	6500	1973	G	$2,000	3/04	ECMI	Live tandem grain truck with Omaha 20' steel box and hoist
GMC	6500	1975	G	$6,000	2/04	NEKS	V8, 5x2 spd., 18' steel bed, hoist, 49" sides, 62,632 miles, rollover tarp
GMC	6500	1968	P	$1,825	2/03	SEMN	V5, 12' box and hoist, not running
GMC	6500	1973	G	$4,200	7/03	ECND	Tag axle, tandem, 19' box, hoist & roll tarp, 57,585 miles
GMC	6500	1973	G	$4,300	7/03	ECND	2-ton tag axle tandem, 366, 5/2, 93.00-20" tires, 19' box, hoist & roll tarp
GMC	6500	1974	G	$3,000	4/04	WCSK	Canadian sale, grain truck, steel box & hoist, tandem, 5+4 trans., 427
GMC	6500	1974	G	$6,600	12/03	SEND	Single axle with steerable front pusher, 366, 5x2 spd.
GMC	6500	1974	G	$11,000	2/03	WCOH	40K miles, 18' bed, roll tarp
GMC	7500	1967	F	$1,700	11/05	ECNE	20' wood box
GMC	7500	1972	E	$5,500	8/04	NEIA	9,500 miles, hoist
GMC	7500	1970	G	$1,400	11/03	ECND	3½ ton, 427 gas, auto, gravel dump body
GMC	9500	1974	F	$2,500	12/05	ECMI	20' box & hoist, tandem axle, 318 Detroit, 10 speed
GMC	9500	1972	G	$3,700	3/04	WCMI	318 Detroit wet kit, air plate, 13 spd., older but clean
GMC	9500	1969	G	$2,100	2/03	SEMN	318 Detroit, 13 spd.
GMC	Astro	1973	G	$1,300	7/03	ECND	Coe 95, 318 Detroit, Fuller 13 spd., 10.00-22.5" rear tires
GMC	Astro	1973	P	$6,300	3/03	NCCO	Mohrlang 20' spreader
GMC	Astro	1973	G	$7,300	7/03	ECND	Triaxle, 318 Detroit, 13 spd., new 13R80x20" frt.
GMC	C2500	1970	F	$525	7/04	SEND	Service truck, air compressor, fuel tank
GMC	C2500	1970	F	$525	7/04	NWMN	Service truck, single axle cab & chassis, 404 gas
GMC	C50	1971	G	$4,200	2/03	ECIL	66,676 miles, 15' bed, tag, clean
GMC	C60	1968	G	$4,900	12/03	SEND	Single axle, w/ front cheater tag, 427, 5x2 spd., Magnum 16' steel box
GMC	C600	1972	G	$2,100	12/04	SCNH	16' box, hoist
GMC	C65	1973	G	$6,900	4/03	WCSK	Canadian sale, tag axle truck, 5+2, V8, 427, hoist, tarp, radio
GMC	C65	1975	F	$3,000	7/03	WCSK	Canadian sale, 3-ton grain truck, 10:00x20" tires, 366, 5+2, 15' steel box, hoist, 50,535 miles
GMC	N/A	1962	F	$1,500	1/06	NCCO	18' bed, side hoist, tag axle
GMC	N/A	1972	G	$3,400	2/06	WCIL	Tandem grain truck, 20' bed, tag tandem, 5/2 trans, 125,000 miles
GMC	N/A	1967	F	$1,200	9/05	SEIA	1 ton, dump truck
GMC	N/A	1969	G	$15,000	10/05	SWSD	Farm truck, tag axle, 366, V8, 20' Plains box with twin cyl., 3-stage tarp
GMC	N/A	1971	G	$3,750	11/05	NCCA	2 axle
GMC	N/A	1972	F	$900	11/05	NWIL	1 ton, grain box, good tires, 100K miles
GMC	N/A	1952	P	$200	4/05	NCOK	Not running, wood bed
GMC	N/A	1953	F	$425	6/05	NEND	½ ton
GMC	N/A	1963	F	$550	6/05	NEND	Stepside, ¾ ton, V6
GMC	N/A	1969	G	$1,950	1/05	SENE	2 ton, box, hoist
GMC	N/A	1973	G	$2,800	2/05	NWKS	16' bed & hoist, 5x2 spd., roll tarp
GMC	N/A	1950	F	$400	8/04	WCIL	13' bed, hoist, 6 cyl., 4 spd., OD
GMC	N/A	1967	G	$800	5/04	WCWA	Detroit
GMC	N/A	1967	F	$3,400	3/04	SEND	Lift tag tandem, 16½' box, roll tarp, plumbed for drop deck
GMC	N/A	1968	F	$70	2/04	ECNE	4x2 trans., PS, hyd. brakes, spoke wheels, 16' high sided wood grain
GMC	N/A	1968	E	$1,050	5/04	SENE	1 ton, 12' box, hoist, gas
GMC	N/A	1969	G	$1,250	3/04	SCMN	
GMC	N/A	1970	F	$100	3/04	SEND	¾-ton pickup, utility box
GMC	N/A	1970	F	$5,250	7/04	NWMN	3.5-ton twin screw, gas, 5+4 spd, 20' box, hoist, new roll tarp, air brakes, aux trans. rebuilt
GMC	N/A	1971	F	$350	3/04	SEND	Flatbed
GMC	N/A	1971	G	$2,900	9/04	ECIA	Farm truck, box, hoist
GMC	N/A	1975	G	$1,000	9/04	SEIA	Crew cab dually pickup
GMC	N/A	1957	G	$1,500	4/03	NCND	2 ton, V8, 4x2 spd., 15' steel box floor, hoist, new tires
GMC	N/A	1964	G	$2,100	10/03	SCKS	2,000 miles on reconditioned engine, 16' bed, lift, 4x2 spd. 3/03

trucks

Make	Model	Year	Cond.	Price	Date	Area	Comments
GMC	N/A	1968	F	$450	12/03	WCMI	Tandem axle, dump, Detroit diesel, 9 spd., 5-yard box
GMC	N/A	1968	G	$1,800	4/03	WCSK	Canadian sale, 1 ton, 4 spd., wooden box & hoist, duals
GMC	N/A	1971	F	$1,800	3/03	WCMN	Twin screw, 238 Detroit, 10 spd., flatbed
GMC	N/A	1971	G	$2,750	7/03	WCMN	Metro twin screw cabover, 13 spd., Detroit diesel, 20:00-22" tires
GMC	N/A	1973	G	$2,300	3/03	WCMI	427 gas, 2 axle, air brakes
GMC	N/A	1974	F	$3,000	3/03	WCMN	Cabover, 318 Detroit, 10 spd., flatbed with hoist
GMC	N/A	1975	F	$700	9/03	NCWI	Dump truck, tandem
GMC	Sierra	1975	G	$5,800	2/06	WCIL	Grain truck, 6000 V8 engine, 4/2 trans, 13' bed, 78,172 miles
GMC	Sierra	1975	G	$15,500	7/05	ECND	Twin screw, 427, Browning 5/4, 20' Knapheide
Hendrickson	n/a	1974	G	$2,000	6/05	ECWI	Cat diesel, 13 spd.
IHC	1100	1964	F	$550	9/03	NESD	4x2 pickup, V8, 4 spd.
IHC	150	1975	F	$200	2/04	ECNE	4x4 pickup, automatic, propane, 392 engine on propane, no box
IHC	1500	1974	P	$950	4/04	NCKS	Rough, Loadstar, 2-ton feed truck, V8 engine, Allison auto
IHC	1600	1968	F	$650	2/06	SEIA	Loadstar, 4x2 spd., 302 engine, 13.5' grain bed
IHC	1600	1973	G	$2,500	2/06	ECIL	Grain truck, 13.5' bed, 5x2 spd., 93,164 miles
IHC	1600	1973	G	$3,600	2/06	NWSD	Loadstar, single axle, 16' steel comb. box, plumbed for hyd. drill fill
IHC	1600	1974	G	$7,000	2/06	ECKS	16' bed & hoist
IHC	1600	1966	G	$1,500	11/05	SCNE	72,954 miles, 4/2spd., 15½' box and hoist, kept inside
IHC	1600	1974	G	$5,100	9/05	NCND	Loadstar, 16' steel box with 48" sides and roll tarp, 4/2 spd.
IHC	1600	1975	G	$2,250	9/05	NWMO	Loadstar, 2 ton, 16' Knapheide box & hoist
IHC	1600	1975	G	$6,100	12/05	WCIL	Loadstar, 345, V8, 4/2 trans., 14' Schien bed, 40,100 miles
IHC	1600	1975	G	$7,000	10/05	NCND	Loadstar, 16' steel box and floor with steel fold down stock rack
IHC	1600	1963	F	$700	4/05	SEND	Loadstar, 15.5' steel box and floor, 4x2 trans.
IHC	1600	1963	G	$1,200	3/05	NESD	16' Flasco wood, twin-cyl. hoist, 304 eng., 4x2 trans., plumbed
IHC	1600	1964	F	$600	6/05	NEND	Loadstar, 13.5' steel box, hoist
IHC	1600	1968	P	$450	6/05	SEND	Loadstar single axle, V8, 4x2 spd., 15' box, hoist, plumbed, bad brakes
IHC	1600	1969	P	$850	4/05	NCOH	Loadstar, 12' hoist bed, V8
IHC	1600	1970	F	$900	2/05	WCIN	10 wheeler, 18' bed, hoist
IHC	1600	1971	F	$550	8/05	SWOH	Loadstar, 16' Omaha bed, 5x2 spd., 127K miles, no hoist
IHC	1600	1974	G	$3,000	2/05	SCMN	Loadstar, 1000-gal. poly tank
IHC	1600	1975	G	$2,700	3/05	NESD	16' Omaha steel box, hoist, 345 eng., 4x2 trans., silage liner
IHC	1600	1966	F	$700	2/04	ECNE	Loadstar cabover grain truck, 16' wooden box, hoist, 4 spd., 73,756 miles
IHC	1600	1966	G	$2,200	3/04	NENE	18' box, hoist
IHC	1600	1967	P	$250	2/04	ECNE	Loadstar, 4x2 spd., 14' wooden box, 345 gas engine, 8.25-20" tires
IHC	1600	1967	G	$1,200	4/04	ECNE	Loadstar, 245 V8, 4x2 trans., Budd wheels, 14' flat bed body, hyd. hoist
IHC	1600	1967	G	$4,200	11/04	NCKS	Feed truck, 4x4, 4 spd., hi/lo
IHC	1600	1967	G	$4,800	11/04	NCOH	Loadstar, 4x2 spd., 304 engine, 13' Marion metal bed
IHC	1600	1969	G	$4,300	11/04	ECND	Loadstar single axle, 304, 4/2 spd., 15½' box, hoist, roll tarp
IHC	1600	1970	G	$3,900	2/04	NEIN	Loadstar grain truck, 345 V8, 4x2 spd., hoist, 16' grain & livestock, 98,066 miles
IHC	1600	1970	G	$5,200	1/04	WCIL	2 ton, 33,610 miles, 304 V8, 4x2 spd., 16' Knapheide bed
IHC	1600	1972	F	$2,000	1/04	NCOH	Loadstar, 36K miles, V8, 4x2 spd., 14' bed w/ single-cyl. hoist, 41" sides
IHC	1600	1973	G	$2,700	4/04	NCND	Loadstar, Omaha standard box & hoist
IHC	1600	1973	G	$4,000	1/04	SCNE	Grain truck, 345, V8, 4/2 trans., 19' Omaha box, 73,684 miles
IHC	1600	1974	G	$2,000	12/04	NCOH	Loadstar, 15' bed, hoist
IHC	1600	1974	G	$4,000	7/04	SEND	Loadstar, single axle, 340, 4+2 spd., 15' box, roll tarp, aux. tank, 31,000 miles, plumbed for drill fill
IHC	1600	1975	G	$3,100	3/04	SWMN	Loadstar, single axle, 4x2 spd., Parkhurst steel 14' box, hoist
IHC	1600	1975	G	$5,400	9/04	ECND	Single axle, V8 gas eng., 4/2 spd., 16' Westgo steel box

Make	Model	Year	Cond.	Price	Date	Area	Comments
IHC	1600	1963	F	$2,050	3/03	NCCO	
IHC	1600	1964	G	$1,450	4/03	SCMN	Loadstar, single-axle truck, 14' wood box, V8, engine, 4 spd.
IHC	1600	1964	G	$14,500	11/03	NWKS	Loadstar feed truck, 350R Harsh feed box & scales, 4x4, 4x2 spd.
IHC	1600	1965	P	$300	10/03	WCSD	Loadstar, 16' comb. wood box, hoist
IHC	1600	1965	G	$2,000	7/03	ECND	Tag axle, nonlift, gas, 5/2, 16' Knapheide box & hoist
IHC	1600	1965	G	$4,500	7/03	NCND	Loadstar, 4x2 spd., 16' Westgo steel box, hoist, roll tarp, 44,052 miles
IHC	1600	1967	P	$900	7/03	SEND	Single axle, 392, 4/2 spd., 15' Frontier box, Shurlock tarp
IHC	1600	1968	G	$1,750	11/03	WCMN	15' wood box, hoist, 304 engine, 4x2 spd.
IHC	1600	1969	F	$1,500	7/03	SEND	Single axle, 345, 4/2 spd., 16' Westgo box, Shurlock tarp, spare tire
IHC	1600	1970	G	$2,350	2/03	ECNE	16' box, 345 V8, 4x2 spd., hyd. brakes, 22,000-lb. GVWR, 205" wheelbase
IHC	1600	1971	F	$800	6/03	NCIA	Loadstar, 345, 4x2 spd., hoist, 14' steel box with wood floor
IHC	1600	1971	F	$850	3/03	ECMI	Loadstar single axle grain truck, V8 gas eng., 4x2 spd. trans.
IHC	1600	1972	G	$825	7/03	NEOH	12' flatbed, single axle, Loadstar
IHC	1600	1972	G	$1,700	7/03	ECND	Tag tandem dump truck, V8, gas, hi/lo, 8-yard box, 8.25-20" tires
IHC	1600	1974	F	$3,100	4/03	ECND	Loadstar, single axle, 345, 4/2 spd., 16' box, roll tarp
IHC	1600	1975	G	$875	6/03	ECNE	345, 5x2 trans., hyd. brakes, PS, single axle, spoke wheels, 900/20
IHC	1600	1975	G	$3,650	9/03	SENE	Gas, 17' box, hoist
IHC	1600	1975	F	$4,750	12/03	WCIA	Loadstar, Obeco 16' box, cheater axle
IHC	1600	1975	G	$5,250	4/03	WCSK	Canadian sale, Loadstar grain truck, 15' steel box & hoist, roll tarp
IHC	1610A	1961	F	$2,100	12/05	NCOH	Cabover, 16' hoist bed, V8, 22,375 miles, no brakes
IHC	1700	1965	F	$700	2/05	WCOH	Cabover, 5x2 spd., dual hoist, 20' grain and livestock bed, 60,513 miles
IHC	1700	1970	G	$2,400	6/05	SEND	Loadstar, single axle, 345, 5x2 spd., 16' Omaha std. steel box
IHC	1700	1970	G	$6,800	7/05	ECND	Tag tandem, gas, 5/2, 18' grain box, 24,970 miles
IHC	1700	1972	F	$1,375	3/05	SCMI	Loadstar, single axle, gas, Kilbros 385 box & auger
IHC	1700	1972	G	$2,900	5/05	NWAB	Canadian sale, grain truck, single axle, 16' wood box
IHC	1700	1973	F	$750	3/05	ECND	Loadstar single axle, V8, 5 spd., 16' flatbed, hoist
IHC	1700	1975	G	$2,000	4/05	NWIL	Loadstar grain truck, 2 spd., 345, hyd. lift, 13' box,
IHC	1700	1962	G	$1,000	9/04	ECNE	Loadstar, 345, 5x2 spd., 18' box, twin-cyl. hoist, drag tag
IHC	1700	1970	G	$2,600	12/04	SENE	Box, hoist, gas
IHC	1700	1971	G	$550	7/04	ECND	Bulk fuel truck, V8, 5/2, 1500-gal. 5 compartment
IHC	1700	1971	G	$2,000	3/04	SWMN	Loadstar, PTO pump, no box, 392, V8, 5x2 spd.
IHC	1700	1971	G	$3,250	9/04	ECNE	Loadstar, 16' wood box, 9:00R20" tires, Eaton 2 speed axle shift, stock rack, IHC gas motor
IHC	1700	1972	G	$1,900	7/04	SEIN	Loadstar, grain truck, 16' bed & hoist
IHC	1700	1972	G	$4,100	9/04	ECND	Loadstar, single axle, 345 V8 gas eng., 4/2 spd., 16' Westgo steel box, hoist, roll tarp, 31,309 miles
IHC	1700	1973	G	$2,200	9/04	SWIA	Loadstar, gas, V8, 20' box, roll tarp, 5x2 spd.
IHC	1700	1973	G	$2,500	3/04	NEKS	Loadstar, 81K miles, 16' comb. bed & hoist
IHC	1700	1973	G	$4,750	11/04	ECND	Single axle, 392, V8, 5/2 spd., 16' Midland box, hoist, roll tarp, 153,036 miles
IHC	1700	1964	G	$2,400	3/03	ECMI	Loadstar grain truck dead axle, twin post hoist, 345 V8, 5x2 spd., 18' metal grain box
IHC	1700	1971	G	$5,600	11/03	WCMN	Tandem truck, 19' steel box, hoist, 392 engine, Allison auto, roll tarp
IHC	1700	1975	G	$1,950	3/03	NWIA	Loadstar dump truck, 345, V8, 5/2 spd., hyd. brakes, PS
IHC	1710A	1972	G	$7,300	1/05	WCIL	16' bed, 55K miles
IHC	1710B	1975	G	$2,000	5/05	SCMN	Cargostar, water truck, gas, auto, right-hand steer
IHC	1750	1974	G	$1,100	4/04	WCNE	Loadstar, diesel, Cat 3208, 5x2 spd.
IHC	1800	1973	F	$3,600	6/05	SEND	Loadstar, 392, V8, 5x2 spd., 19' Frontier box, hoist, roll tarp, 54,192 miles
IHC	1800	1975	G	$3,500	7/05	ECND	French 19' 3-in-1 boc, center-mount hoist, 40,000 miles, trans. OH
IHC	1800	1964	G	$1,100	9/04	ECNE	Loadstar, 392, 5x2 spd., 16' box, twin-cyl. hoist, cheater axle
IHC	1800	1972	G	$6,800	5/04	ECNE	Loadstar crane truck, 58' boom length
IHC	1800	1972	G	$9,500	11/04	ECND	Loadstar, twin screw, 392 V8, automatic, 19.5' Peterson box, hoist
IHC	1800	1974	P	$1,500	12/04	WCMN	Twinscrew, 18' box, hoist, roll tarp, 348, V8, 5x3 spd., rough

trucks

Make	Model	Year	Cond.	Price	Date	Area	Comments
IHC	1800	1974	G	$9,250	4/04	NCND	Loadstar, twin screw, new 18' alum, 72" high, roll tarp, Michelin tires
IHC	1800	1975	G	$5,800	10/04	SEMN	Loadstar, 446, V8, 5/4 trans., twin screw, 119,990 miles, 12,000 miles on rebuilt engine
IHC	1800	1975	G	$6,500	7/04	NWMN	Twin screw, 478 V8, 3+5 spd., 19.5' Frontier box, hoist, beet equipped
IHC	1800	1975	G	$9,000	3/04	SWMN	Loadstar twin screw, 5x3 spd., V8-392 engine, 19' steel box with twin-post hoist, rebuilt eng., clutch and rear end
IHC	1800	1975	G	$12,500	3/04	ECMI	Loadstar twin screw, 20,062 miles, 18' Midwest steel grain box
IHC	1800	1965	G	$2,000	8/03	ECNE	Loadstar tandem axle grain trailer with 20' box
IHC	1800	1966	G	$2,100	7/03	WCMN	Loadstar, single axle, steel box, hoist, roll tarp
IHC	1800	1972	G	$12,100	8/03	SWMN	Tandem axle truck, large V8, 5x3 spd. trans., 16,003 miles, 20' steel box and hoist
IHC	1800	1974	F	$1,075	12/03	SCNE	Loadstar, 18' box, hoist, tag axle
IHC	1800	1975	G	$5,800	8/03	SWMN	Loadstar, tandem axle, V8, 5x3 trans., PS, 20' steel box and hoist
IHC	1810B	1975	F	$1,550	12/04	ECNE	Cat V-8 3606 diesel engine, 5x2 trans., spring suspension
IHC	1850	1971	F	$3,250	7/03	WCSK	Canadian sale, grain truck, cargo star, diesel, cabover, air brakes
IHC	1890	1972	P	$550	4/03	NWPA	Needs motor & radiator repair, 33,000-lb. GVWR, 14' Midwest dump body
IHC	1900	1967	F	$4,250	3/04	WCMN	Twin screw, 210 hp., 15 speed, 20' Knapheide box, hoist, roll tarp
IHC	1900	1968	G	$1,600	4/03	NCWI	Cummins 250, 10 spd. trans., 10 spd. aux.
IHC	1910	1974	G	$6,700	1/04	SCNE	Tandem axle grain truck, 549, V8, Omaha standard, 18' steel box
IHC	1910A	1974	G	$5,400	3/04	WCMN	Fleetstar, twin screw, V8, 5/4 spd., 20' steel box, hoist, roll tarp
IHC	1910A	1974	G	$6,000	1/04	SCNE	Cargo star truck, 5/2 spd., 549, V8, 20' box
IHC	1910A	1970	F	$2,900	7/03	WCSK	Canadian sale, Fleetstar, gas, tandem axle, 18' box, hoist, roll tarp, 5+4
IHC	200	1968	G	$450	6/03	WCSK	Canadian sale, ¾ ton, auto, V8
IHC	2000	1966	G	$4,100	11/05	ECNE	Fleetstar, twin screw, Detroit DWL5 diesel engine, Fuller 9 speed
IHC	2000	1965	F	$1,650	3/05	NWMN	Twin screw tandem gravel truck
IHC	2000	1966	F	$600	1/04	SCNE	Semi truck, 250 Cummins, no title
IHC	2010A	1969	G	$8,500	12/05	SCMN	Twin screw, 538 eng., 5x2 spd., 19' steel box & hoist, roll tarp, air brakes
IHC	2010A	1968	P	$500	12/04	SEPA	Fleetstar, 4x2 spd., 20' Midwest grain dump, tag axle
IHC	2010A	1970	G	$4,200	3/03	WCMN	Fleetstar, heavy-duty engine, 18' alum box, auto trans.
IHC	2050A	1974	G	$6,500	6/03	ECNE	Fleetstar truck, Cat diesel, 5 spd., twin screw
IHC	2070	1975	F	$3,800	3/04	SEND	Twin screw, 671 Detroit, 5/2 spd., split, PS, PTO, 20' box capability
IHC	2070	1974	G	$3,000	3/03	WCMN	Dump truck
IHC	4070	1970	G	$1,950	3/04	NWMN	Transtar twin screw, 8v71 Detroit, 10 spd., 11-22.5" front tires, 2 tender boxes with swing-out augers, gas
IHC	4070	1972	G	$2,800	4/04	WCNE	Transtar, twin screw with air tag, Reitan 22' alum box with 6' sides, diesel
IHC	4070	1975	G	$4,250	3/04	NWIA	Transtar II, cabover, 668,883 miles, 350 Cummins, 13 speed, twin screw 3 speed, spring suspension, (2) mounted 5-ton fertilizer tenders, 16 hp. Kohler drive, twin fuel tanks
IHC	4070A	1969	G	$7,500	4/05	NENE	Transtar grain truck, 318 Detroit, twin screw, diff. lock, 13 speed, Harsh triple-stage hoist, 20' wooden box with steel floor, rear air tag axle, roll tarp
IHC	4070A	1971	F	$600	4/05	SCMI	Cabover semi tractor, Transtar, Cummins engine, 354K miles
IHC	4200	1974	G	$1,250	7/05	NCMN	Twin screw
IHC	4200	1974	G	$1,250	7/05	NCMN	Twin screw
IHC	4200	1974	G	$2,100	7/05	NCMN	Twin screw
IHC	4200	1974	G	$2,200	7/05	NCMN	Twin screw
IHC	4200	1974	G	$3,100	7/05	NCMN	Twin screw
IHC	4200	1975	F	$5,000	3/03	ECMN	Dump truck, tri-axle
IHC	4300	1975	G	$2,700	5/04	SCMN	Cummins diesel, tri-axle

Make	Model	Year	Cond.	Price	Date	Area	Comments
IHC	4300	1972	G	$9,000	3/03	NCCO	
IHC	500	1974	F	$1,600	9/03	ECND	1½-ton service truck, V8, 4/2 steel bed with large fuel tank, hyd. pump, air pump, dual gas tank, heavy-duty hitch, 32,000 miles
IHC	5000	1975	G	$9,900	12/03	NCOH	Paystar, tandem-axle truck, air brakes, 5x2 spd., 549 engine, 20' Scott bed w/ roll tarp
IHC	5070	1975	G	$900	6/05	ECPA	Dump truck
IHC	666	1974	G	$7,600	1/06	WCNE	
IHC	966	1974	P	$3,700	7/03	NWIL	Cab, 2 hyd., rough, torque out, 18.4-34"
IHC	A160	1959	G	$800	10/05	NCND	Wood box and hoist
IHC	B160	1962	G	$1,500	2/06	NWIL	13.5' farm box, 345 V8 engine
IHC	B170	1962	G	$2,100	6/03	WCSK	Canadian sale, 3-ton grain truck, 304 V8, 5+2, wooden box
IHC	BC160	1960	G	$1,400	4/05	NWOK	Steel bed, hoist, 4x2 spd., runs great!
IHC	KB6	1946	G	$700	6/05	SEND	Single axle, 4x2 spd., wood box, hoist, 88K miles
IHC	KB6	1948	G	$1,300	4/05	NWOK	Wood grain bed, grain sides, stock rack
IHC	L160	1952	F	$1,500	9/04	WCWA	2-yard dump, 6 cyl.
IHC	Loadstar	1975	G	$6,300	2/06	SCMI	Loadstar seed truck/ 390 Killbros box/seed jet, Shurlock tarp
IHC	Loadstar	1973	F	$4,000	7/04	NWMN	Lift tag, 392, 5+2 spd., 19' box & hoist, roll tarp, combo
IHC	Loadstar	1974	G	$4,000	7/04	NWMN	Single axle, 340, 4+2 spd., 15' box, roll tarp, aux tank, 31,000
IHC	Loadstar	1975	G	$10,000	8/04	WCMN	Single-axle grain truck, 4x2 spd., Loadstar
IHC	Loadstar	1974	G	$7,500	7/03	WCSK	Canadian sale, grain truck, 345 V8, 5+2, 18' wooden box
IHC	N/A	1964	F	$550	2/06	NWSD	Loadstar, box and hoist
IHC	N/A	1970	F	$800	9/05	SEIA	Grain truck
IHC	N/A	1973	F	$1,000	9/05	SCON	Dump truck
IHC	N/A	1973	G	$7,500	12/05	WCMN	Twin screw, 318 Detroit diesel, 13 speed, 22' poly-lined steel box
IHC	N/A	1926	G	$2,650	3/05	WCNE	8.5' Omaha standard wood box
IHC	N/A	1951	G	$1,475	3/05	WCIL	Dump truck, former fire truck, 18K miles
IHC	N/A	1962	P	$340	4/05	SEND	Fleetstar, 671 Detroit engine, Fleetstar
IHC	N/A	1963	P	$130	4/05	SEND	Single axle, wood box
IHC	N/A	1969	F	$950	1/05	SEMI	Twin screw, 15 speed, twin hoist
IHC	N/A	1973	G	$4,500	3/05	SWIN	Three-axle grain truck, 5x3 spd., Cat 3208 engine, Hendrickson suspension, air brakes, 20' wood floor with metal grain sides, tarp
IHC	N/A	1973	G	$6,000	3/05	ECMI	Cabover tandem axle grain truck, 18' steel grain box and hoist, V8, 5x2 spd., 24,084 miles
IHC	N/A	1953	F	$650	4/04	NCND	2 ton, 13' box & hoist
IHC	N/A	1964	F	$350	3/04	SEND	Wood grain box
IHC	N/A	1967	G	$2,200	12/04	WCMN	V8, 18' wood box and hoist, tag axle
IHC	N/A	1968	F	$600	8/04	ECKS	250 Cummins 9 spd. and twin screw
IHC	N/A	1972	G	$950	3/04	WCIL	Grain truck, 345 eng., 4/2 trans.
IHC	N/A	1972	G	$2,200	7/04	SEIN	Cargostar, grain truck, 15' bed & hoist
IHC	N/A	1972	F	$4,750	3/04	WCMN	Twin screw, V8, 5x4 spd., both rebuilt, 18½' Frontier box, hoist, roll tarp
IHC	N/A	1973	G	$7,100	3/04	SEND	Fleetstar twin screw, V8, 5x4 spd., 20' box, hoist, roll tarp, 3-pc. endgate, hyd. grain gate
IHC	N/A	1961	G	$900	3/03	SEIA	Grain truck, 345 V8, 16' box
IHC	N/A	1961	G	$2,000	9/03	WCSD	2 ton, hoist, 14' box, single axle
IHC	N/A	1966	P	$750	9/03	SEND	Cabover, 345, V8, 5/2 spd., 18' steel box, roll tarp
IHC	N/A	1967	G	$1,800	2/03	ECIA	64K miles
IHC	N/A	1968	F	$800	4/03	WCMN	16' steel box and hoist, single axle
IHC	N/A	1969	F	$300	12/03	WCMI	Tandem axle, dump, 6-cyl. gas, 5+2 spd., 5-yard box
IHC	N/A	1971	G	$2,100	11/03	WCKS	4x2 spd., V8, 16' bed, hoist
IHC	N/A	1974	G	$1,000	8/03	SENE	59K miles, ¾ ton
IHC	N/A	1975	G	$3,250	5/03	SWOK	2 ton, lift
IHC	N/A	1975	G	$4,600	6/03	SWMN	Tandem, 20' steel box & hoist, Detroit diesel, 3 spd.

trucks

Make	Model	Year	Cond.	Price	Date	Area	Comments
IHC	Paystar	1975	G	$14,000	9/04	NWSD	20-ton dump truck, 355 Cummins engine, 5-speed Allison 5000 trans., 15½-yard dump box, 44K miles, 5x2 spd., flotation tag
IHC	R190	1961	P	$50	3/03	SWWI	19' steel 500-bu. grain bed, twin hoist
IHC	S160	1956	G	$1,300	7/03	ECND	Single axle, V6, 512 trans., 14' wood box w/ steel floor & hoist, 8.25x20" tires
IHC	Transtar	1974	F	$750	6/05	SEND	318 Detroit, 13 speed, 10:00-20" rubber
IHC	Transtar	1969	F	$1,250	7/03	SEND	Cabover, 270 Cummins, 9 speed, spring suspension, tires 80%
Kenworth	K125	1971	F	$800	9/03	ECND	Cabover, 13 spd.
Kenworth	N/A	1972	G	$9,750	12/05	SWMS	Daycab, diesel
Kenworth	N/A	1974	F	$2,000	11/05	WCKS	Semi tractor, 13-speed trans.
Kenworth	N/A	1968	F	$300	3/04	NWPA	Semi tractor, cabover, 318 Detroit, no wet line
Kenworth	N/A	1974	F	$500	2/04	NEIN	Cabover
Kenworth	N/A	1974	F	$650	2/04	SENE	Cabover semi truck, 13 speed, 285/75R24.5" rubber, PS,
Kenworth	N/A	1974	G	$6,500	7/04	WCWA	10-yard dump, V8
Kenworth	N/A	1968	G	$4,400	6/03	WCSK	Canadian sale, highway tractor, 250 Cummins rebuilt eng.
Kenworth	N/A	1975	P	$800	3/03	WCMN	318 Detroit, 13 speed, twin screw, needs work on cab
Kenworth	T900	1969	G	$7,750	3/05	ECSD	Conventional, Cummins big cam 4, 13 speed, double frame
Kenworth	W900	1974	F	$5,100	3/04	SEMN	Semi tractor, 400 Cummins, 13 speed
Kenworth	W900	1975	G	$600	11/04	SCCA	Diesel, 3 axle, Cat 3306, Road Ranger trans., air sliding 5th wheel
Kenworth	W924	1974	G	$4,000	6/04	WCWA	Detroit 12-cyl. diesel, 5/2, PS, wet kit
Mack	B61	1967	E	$8,250	3/04	NWIN	Tri-axle, diesel, 3+5, 20' bed & hoist
Mack	DM600	1973	G	$2,750	6/04	ECMN	15.5' dump box, 18,000-lb. front axles, 483,798 miles
Mack	DM611S	1968	F	$1,900	4/03	NCWI	Mack 237, 5 spd., 4-spd. aux w/ Lockwood 20' belt bottom box w/ hyd. side gate
Mack	DM685S	1974	G	$7,000	6/05	ECNE	Tandem-axle dump truck, 15' steel box, 5x2 spd., Mack 300 diesel engine, Budd wheels, air endgate
Mack	DM685S	1970	G	$3,600	3/03	ECNE	Dump truck, Mack diesel, 2 stick trans., 52,000-lb. GVWR, air brakes, PS, heat, PTO, 60-gal. step fuel tank, upright exhaust, flip hood, 18' steel dump box & hoist
Mack	N/A	1974	G	$3,500	9/04	ECMN	Water truck, tri-axle, spray bars, heavy front
Mack	N/A	1964	G	$5,000	10/03	SEMN	Wrecker truck, single axle, 711 engine
Mack	N/A	1969	F	$1,400	9/03	ECND	903 Cummins, 50,000-lb. winch
Mack	N/A	1969	G	$13,000	2/03	SEMN	Tri-axle drive truck, 237-hp. Mack eng., 6-spd. trans, Crysteel steel box and Cobra hoist, roll tarp
Mack	N/A	1971	G	$6,300	5/03	NCWI	1983 cab, twin stick, tri-axle, 20' steel grain box
Mack	N/A	1972	G	$3,900	8/03	SWMN	Semi tractor, diesel, 10 speed
Mack	N/A	1975	F	$2,200	3/03	ECMI	Tandem axle cabover road tractor, 370 Cummins, 13 spd. wet kit, camel back suspension
Mack	N/A	1975	F	$6,000	3/03	ECMN	Truck tractor
Mack	R	1971	G	$2,400	3/04	SWPA	Dump truck, 237, 6 speed, 18' aluminum dump
Mack	R	1969	G	$9 500	8 03	WCMN	237 Mack 5 spd., 621,800 miles
Mack	R600	1973	G	$1,800	7/03	ECND	5 spd., 11-22.5" Dayton tires
Mack	R600	1974	G	$10,250	2/03	SEND	Gold Bulldog, 237 Mack, straight 5 spd., PS, air PTO, 20' Grainmaster box, 3-pc. endgate, roll tarp
Mack	R685LS	1972	G	$3,200	6/05	ECPA	
Mack	R685ST	1970	G	$1,500	4/03	NCWI	Mack 237, 5 spd., 10-spd. aux, wet kit, Lockwood 20' belt bottom box
Mack	RD688S	1973	F	$2,200	12/05	SWMS	Diesel, tandem axle, water truck
Mack	RL600	1973	F	$1,900	6/05	ECNE	Mack engine, 5x3 spd., PS, 2 70-gal. fuel tanks, twin screw camel back spring suspension
Mack	RS686LST	1971	G	$2,500	3/03	ECNE	Cab & chassis, Mack diesel, dual alum. fuel tanks
Oshkosh	N/A	1955	G	$3,600	4/04	WCMN	Plow truck, V plow

194

Make	Model	Year	Cond.	Price	Date	Area	Comments
Oshkosh	N/A	1959	G	$800	3/03	WCMI	Tank truck, IHC gas, 4,000-gal. tank
Oshkosh	N/A	1970	G	$4,500	12/03	SEMN	Plow truck, Cummins
Peterbilt	N/A	1974	F	$1,500	9/03	ECND	Cat 1693, 13 spd.
Peterbilt	N/A	1975	F	$5,000	3/03	ECMN	Truck tractor
REO	220	1957	F	$450	2/04	ECMI	Single axle, Pitman Unidyne hyd. stinger, great for truss setting
REO	N/A	1912	F	$1,750	7/04	NWMN	Box, running order
REO	N/A	1912	F	$1,750	7/04	SEND	Box
Studebaker	n/a	1959	G	$2,300	10/05	SWSD	18' box and hoist
Studebaker	n/a	1949	F	$175	11/04	NCKS	Restorable, 1½-ton truck, flat iron bed
Volvo	N/A	1973	G	$7,500	6/04	NWMN	3176 Cat, integral sleeper, jake brake, 9 speed, 11R:24.5" alum.
White	9000	1970	P	$1,800	2/06	NCKS	Twin screw truck, rough, Cummins 270, 13 speed, road ranger, 20' bed
White	N/A	1968	F	$600	4/05	SCMI	Straight truck, 18' box, twin-post hoist
White	N/A	1963	G	$1,250	2/04	ECNE	Compact grain truck, 16' wooden box, hoist, single axle, pushers tag
White	N/A	1970	P	$750	4/04	SEND	Day cab, 250 Cummins, 13 speed
White	N/A	1953	F	$2,000	12/03	WCMI	Construction lift truck, gas, 22' lift height
White	N/A	1970	F	$500	12/03	WCMI	Dump, tandem axle, 671 Detroit, 4WD, 15-yard box

Diamond T, Reo connection

Consolidation in the 1950s in the auto industry brought together two vaunted names in trucks that, for a short time, shared a moniker that became famous itself – Diamond-Reo.

Reo, the brainchild of Ranson E. Olds of Oldsmobile fame, was better known for cars and pickups, like the Reo Speedwagon. But the Lansing, Michigan, firm also sold a respectable line of large transport trucks, beginning in 1904.

The Diamond organization, and its Diamond T truck line, traces its roots back to 1911 and its founder, C.A. Tilt of Chicago.

In 1957, Reo was acquired by White Motor Company, which would purchase Diamond T the following year. The two divisions marketed trucks under their respective names until White Motor consolidated the two divisions in 1967, creating Diamond-Reo. Trucks were sold under that name for just seven years, until a combination of stiff competition, poor markets, and faulty management decisions inspired White to sell off the truck line.

The Diamond and Reo names would appear on other vehicles in ensuing years but finally disappeared from use sometime in the 1980s. And the organization that was once Diamond-Reo evolved over time to become Nucor Corporation, currently the largest steel manufacturer in the U.S.

For more history on Reo and Diamond T trucks, go to www.agelessiron.com.

serial numbers

Advance-Rumely serial numbers

Advance Thresher steam engines

Year	Beginning number
1885	101
1886	130
1887	231
1888	401
1889	652
1890	969
1891	1,410
1892	1,724
1893	2,151
1894	2,625
1895	2,915
1896	3,304
1897	3,707
1898	4,016
1899	4,423
1900	4,957
1901	5,512
1902	6,237
1903	6,951
1904	7,732
1905	8,463
1906	9,192
1907	9,926
1908	10,578
1909	11,134
1910	11,690
1911	12,359

1912	13,005
1913	13,466
1914	14,190
1915	14,438
1916	14,453
1917	14,638

Meinrad Rumely steam traction engines

Year	Serial number range
1895	2,600 – 2,725
1896	2,726 – 2,878
1897	2,879 – 3,049
1898	3,050 – 3,218
1899	3,219 – 3,297
1900	3,438 – 3,640
1901	3,641 – 3,855
1902	3856 – 4,136
1903	4,137 – 4,374
1904	4,375 – 4,435
1904	4,437 & 4,452
1904	4,439 – 4,444
1904	4,458 – 4,462
1904	4,466 – 4,468
1904	4,473 – 4,477
1904	4,482 – 4,483
1904	4,506 – 4,529
1904	4,532 – 4,539
1905	4,436
1905	4,445 – 4,450
1905	4,452 & 4,478
1905	4,455 – 4,457
1905	4,469 – 4,472
1905	4,480 – 4,481
1905	4,484 – 4,505
1905	4,530 – 4,531
1905	4,540 – 4,628
1906	4,438
1906	4,453 – 4,454
1906	4,463 – 4,465
1906	4,629 – 4,764
1907	4,479
1907	4,765 – 4,952
1908	4,953 – 5,184
1908	5,186 – 5,195
1909	5,185
1909	5,196 – 5,587
1910	5,588 – 5,920
1911	5,921 – 6,287
1912	6,288 – 6,588
1913	6,589 – 6,714

1914	6,715 – 7,036
1915	7,037 – 7,038
1916	7,039

Rumely and Advance-Rumely Oilpull tractors

B 25-45 Oilpull

Year	Serial number range
1910	1 - 100
1911	2,101 - 2,269
1912	2,270 - 2,936

E 30-60 Oilpull

Year	Serial number range
1910	101 – 236
1911	237 – 746
1912	747 – 1,678
1913	1,679 – 1,787
1914	None built
1915	1,819 – 2,018
1916	2,019 – 2,100
1917	2,997 – 8,724
1918	8,725 – 8,902
1919	11,500 – 11,596
1920	2,252 – 2,351
1921	2,352 – 2,402
1922	2,404 – 2,453
1923	2,454 – 2,503

F 15-30 & later (1918) 18-35 Oilpull

Year	Serial number range
1911	5,001 – 5,680
1912	5,681 – 6,738
1913	6,739 – 7,487
1914	7,500 – 7,856
1915	None built
1916	7,857 – 8,084
1917	8,085 – 8,591
1918	8,903 – 9,177

G 20-40 Oilpull

Year	Serial number range
1918	10,425 – 10,750
1919	10,751 – 15,221
1919	G741 – G948
1920	G949 – G1,727
1921	G1,728 – G2,241
1922	G2,242 – G2,689
1923	G2,690 – G3,558
1924	G3,559 – G3,894

H 16-30 & earlier (pre-1919)
14-28 Oilpull

Year	Serial number range
1917	8,627 – 8,699
1918	9,178 – 10,710
1919	10,711 – 16,284
1919	H3,751 – H4,392
1920	H4,393 – H7,239
1921	H7,240 – H7,395
1922	H7,396 – H8,645
1923	H8,646 – H9,045
1924	H9,046 – H9,645

K 12-20 Oilpull

Year	Serial number range
1918	12,000 – 12,100
1919	12,101 – 13,656
1920	13,657 – 15,100
1920	16,836 – 17,639
1921	17,640 – 18,648
1922	18,649 – 19,268
1923	19,269 – 20,510
1924	20,511 – 21,018

L 15-25 Oilpull

Year	Serial number range
1924	1 – 10
1925	11 – 1,606
1926	1,607–4,213
1927	4,214 – 4,855

M 20-35 Oilpull

Year	Serial number range
1924	1
1925	2 – 1,013
1926	1,014 – 3,084
1927	3,085 – 3,671

R 25-45 Oilpull

Year	Serial number range
1924	1
1925	2 – 138
1926	139 – 647
1927	648 – 761

S 30-60 Oilpull

Year	Serial number range
1924	1 – 4
1925	5 – 34
1926	35 – 234
1927	235 – 434
1928	435 – 514

W 20-30 Oilpull

Year	Serial number range
1928	1 – 2,128
1929	2,129 – 3,733
1930	3,734 – 3,952

X 25-40 Oilpull

Year	Serial number range
1928	X-1 – X-1,545
1929	1,546 – 2,259
1930	2,260 – 2,400

The following Model X tractors were converted from Model M 20-35 Oilpull tractors built earlier: 1-125, 757, 773, 1,616, 1,637, 1,800, 1,955-57, 1,970, 2,020–2,022, 2,040, 2,046, 2,080–2,082, 2,100, 2,150, 2,200 – 2,212, 2,220, & 2,225.

Y 30-50 Oilpull

Year	Serial number range
1929	1 – 245

Tractors Y-1 to Y-100 and Y-221 to Y-245 were converted from Model R to Model Y tractors.

Z 40-60 Oilpull

Year	Serial number range
1929	1 – 215

Tractors Z-1 to Z-62 were converted from Model S tractors to Model Z tractors, and later converted back again to Model S tractors.

Do-All Tractor

1928	501 – 700
1929	701 – 2,115
1930	2,116 – 3,513
1931	3,514 – 3,693

Rumely 6-A Tractor

Year	Serial number range
1930	501 – 502
1931	503 – 1,302

Allis-Chalmers serial numbers

The Model WC established Allis-Chalmers as a leading tractor manufacturer thanks to its feature-rich $675 asking price.

Location of serial numbers
Models 20-35, E20-35, and E25-40:
Tractor – top of transmission ahead of shift lever quadrant
Engine – left side of block

Models U, United, All-Crop, UC, and IU:
Tractor – rear axle housing near PTO
Engine – Continental, right rear of block (Model UM - right side of block)

Model A:
Tractor – rear axle housing near PTO
Engine – left side of block

Models WC (prior to serial number 74330) **and WF** (prior to serial number 1904) **and RC:**
Tractor – rear side of differential near oil filler plug
Engine – rear of engine block

Models WC (serial number 74330 and up) **and WF** (serial number 1904 and up)**:**
Tractor – rear side of differential near oil filler plug
Engine – left side of block to rear of carburetor

Models B, IB, and C:
Tractor – top of transmission case in front of gear shift lever
Engine – rear side of block or flange to clutch housing

Models WD and WD45:
Tractor – rear side of differential housing.
Engine – gas, left side of block; diesel, left side of engine

Model CA:
Tractor – top of transmission next to shift pattern
Engine – rear left side of engine

Model G:
Tractor – top of transmission
Engine – near starter

Models D14, D15, D17, D10, D12, D15 and D21:
Tractor – left front end of torque housing
Engine – left side of block

Model D19:
Tractor – top of rear main housing
Engine – top left side of block

Model ED40:
Tractor – under seat on left side of transmission
Engine – top right side of block

Models 170G, 175G, 180, 190, 190XT, 210, and 220:
Tractor – left front end of torque housing.
Engine – left side

Model 170D:
Tractor – left front of torque housing
Engine – right side of block

Model 175D:
Tractor – left front end of torque housing
Engine – some left side of block, some right side of block

Model 185 and 200:
Tractor – right front of torque housing
Engine – left side of block

Allis-Chalmers serial numbers

Model 440:
Tractor – left side of instrument panel
Engine – left front and left rear of engine block

Model 160:
Tractor – plate ahead of fuel tank
Engine – left side of block

Model 6040:
Tractor – plate ahead of fuel tank
Engine – right side of block under intake manifold

Models 5040, 5045, and 5050:
Tractor – rear of console under steering wheel
Engine – left side of block

Models 5015, 5020, and 5030:
Tractor – nameplate on rear side of steering gearbox. 5015 also has Product Identification Number (PIN). Engine – left side of block.
Transmission – right side of engine block

Models 6060, 6070, and 6080:
Tractor – right side of adapter housing.
Engine – left side of block. After 1982, PIN plate is on rear of left side frame.

Model 6140:
Tractor – Product Identification Number on plate at left side of clutch housing
Engine – left side of block

Models 7010, 7020, 7030, 7040, 7045, 7050, 7060, and 7080:
Tractor – on rear main housing near PTO.
Engine – upper left side of block

Models 7580 and 8550:
Tractor – rear of left front frame
Engine – upper left side of block

Models 8010, 8030, 8050, and 8070:
Tractor – Product Identification Number on top rear of left side frame
Engine – upper left side of block

Models 4W220 and 4W305:
Tractor – Product Identification Number on top rear of left side frame
Engine – upper left side of block

Monarch 50:
Tractor – on front of main frame and on instruction plate on dash.

Models K and KO:
Tractor – on right near top of transmission case and on instrument panel.

Models L and LO:
Tractor – on shelf that runs out to rear of transmission and on instrument panel.

Model M:
Tractor – on transmission case on right side behind clutch inspection cover.
Engine – right side of block

Models S and SO:
Tractor – Top right rear face of transmission case
Engine – lower center of left side of block

Model HD7:
Tractor – top right rear face of transmission case and on master clutch inspection cover
Engine – top front of right side of engine

Model HD10: Tractor – top right rear face of transmission case and on steering lever stop angle, which is on top of transmission

Model HD14:
Tractor – right side of shelf that runs out to rear of transmission case and on right side of front floor plate

Models WC Speed Maintainer and W Speed Patrol:
Tractor – on right differential housing
Engine – left side of block

Maintainer – plate on left drawbar member.
Patrol – plate on right front frame extension

Models 42, 54, and KO 54 Speed Patrols:

Grader - plate on front of left frame
Tractor – rear axle housing near PTO
Engine – left side of block

Models I40 and I400:

Location is the same as Models D10, I60, I600, and 600 FL

Model 500 FL:

Location same as D15

Models 190 Beachmaster and 918:

Location same as 190

Models H3 and HD3:

Location same as D15, H4, and HD4

10-18

Years	Serial number range
1914-1923	No information

6-12

Years	Serial number range
1918-1926	No information

15-30/18-30

Year	Serial number range
1918	5000 – 5005
1919	506 – 5160
1920	5161 – 6014
1921	6015 – 6160
1922	None

20-35

Year	Serial number range
1923	6161 – 6396
1924	6397 – 6754
1925	6755 – 7368
1926	7369 – 8069
1927	8070 – 9869
1928	9870 – 10000

E20-35

Year	Serial number range
1928	1201 – 17661
1929	16762 – 20250
1929	22001 – 23251
1930	23252 – 24185

E25-40

Year	Serial number range
1930	24186 – 24842
1931	24843 – 24971
1932	24972 – 25023
1933	25024 – 25061
1934	25062 – 25308
1935	25309 – 25581
1936	25582 -25611

L12-20/15-25

Year	Serial number range
1921	20001 - 20334
1922	20335 – 20497
1923	20498 – 20905
1924	20906 – 20995
1925	20996 – 21370
1926	21371 – 21681
1927	21682 – 21705

A

Year	Serial number range
1936	25701 – 25725
1937	25726 – 26304
1938	26305 – 26613
1939	26614 – 26781
1940	26782 – 26895
1941	26896 – 26914
1942	26915 – 26925

B

Year	Serial number range
1937	1 – 96
1938	97 – 11799
1939	11800 – 33501
1940	33502 – 49720
1941	49721 – 56781
1942	56782 – 61400

Allis-Chalmers serial numbers

B (125-cubic-inch engine)

Year	Serial number range
1943	64501 – 65501
1944	65502 – 70209
1945	70210 – 72264
1946	72265 – 73369
1947	73370 – 74079
1947	75080 – 80555
1948	80556 – 85883
1948	87834 – 92294
1949	92295 – 102392
1950	102393 – 103578
1950	106579 – 114526
1951	114527 – 118673
1952	118674 -122309
1953	122310 – 124200
1954	124201 – 124710
1955	124711 – 126496
1956	126497 – 127185
1957	126186 – 127461

Model IB

Year	Serial number range
1946	1001 – 102
1947	1003 – 1009
1948	1010 – 1281
1949	1282 – 1555
1950	1556 – 1878
1951	1879 – 2118
1952	2219 – 2567
1953	2570 – 2847
1954-58	INA

Model C

Year	Serial number range
1940	1 – 111
1941	112 – 12388
1942	12389 – 18781
1943	18782 – 23907
1944	23908 – 30694
1945	30695 – 36377
1946	36378 – 39167
1947	39168 – 51514
1948	51515 – 68280
1949	68281 – 80517
1950	80518 – 84030

CA

Year	Serial number range
1950	14- 321
1951	322 – 10538
1952	10539 – 22180
1953	22181 – 31423
1954	31424 – 32906
1955	32907 – 37202
1956	37203 – 38617
1957	38618 – 38976
1958	38977 – 39513

ED40

Year	Serial number range
1963-64	No info.

G

Year	Serial number range
1948	6 – 10960
1949	10961 – 23179
1950	23180 – 24005
1951	24006 - 25268
1952	25269 – 26496
1953	26497 – 28035
1954	28036 – 29035
1955	29036 – 29976

Model RC

Year	Serial number range
1939	4 – 4391
1940	4392 - 5416
1941	5417 – 5504

United U (Continental engine)

Year	Serial number range
1929	U1 – U1974
1930	U1975 – U6553
1931	U6554 – U7261
1932	U7262 – U7404

Model U (UM engine)

Year	Serial number range
1932	U7405 – U7418
933	U7419 – U7684
1934	U7685 – U8062
1935	U8063 – U9470
1936	U9471 – U9988

U (4.5-inch bore engine)

Year	Serial number range
1936	U12001 – U12821
1937	U12822 – U14854
1938	U14855 – U15586
1939	U15587 – U16077
1940	U16078 – U16721
1941	U16722 – U17136
1942	U17137 – U17469
1943	U17470 – U17801
1944	U17802 – U17819
1945-46	No info.
1947	18309 – 18612
1947	20174 – 20178
1948	18613 – 19421
1948	20179 – 20300
1948	21000 – 21035
1949	20301 – 20421
1949	21036 – 21986
1949	22018 – 22023
1950	20422 – 20512
1950	22024 – 22547
1951-52	No information

All-Crop/UC (Continental engine)

Year	Serial number range
1930	UC1 – UC38
1931	UC39 – 1099
1932	UC1100 – UC1231
1933	UC1232 – UC1268

UC (UM engine)

Year	Serial number range
1933	UC1269 – UC1293
1934	UC1294 – UC1551
1935	UC1552 – UC2000
1936	UC2001 – UC2281

UC (4.5-inch bore engine)

Year	Serial number range
1936	UC2282 – UC2770
1937	UC2771 – UC3756
1938	UC3757 – UC4546
1939	UC4547 – UC4769
1940	UC4770 – UC4971
1941	UC4972 – UC5037

Model UC Cane

Year	Serial number range
1944	5038 – 5067
1945-46	None
1947	5068 – 5267

1948	5268 – 5525
1949	5526 – 5643
1950	5644 – 5805
1951	5806 – 5938
1952	5939 - 6142
1953	6143 - 6217

WC (square radiator)

Year	Serial number range
1933	WC1 – WC28
1934	WC29 – WC3126
1935	WC3127 – WC13869
1936	WC13870 – WC31783
1937	WC31784 – WC60789
1938	WC60790 – WC74329

WC (styled)

Year	Serial number range
1938	74330 – 75215
1939	75216 – 91533
1940	91534 – 103516
1941	103517 – 114533
1942	114534 – 123170
1943	None
1944	304 – 3194
1945	3195 – 3509
1946	3510 – 3747
1947	3748 – 4110
1948	4111 – 5499
1949	5500 – 7317
1950	7318 – 8315
1951	8316 – 8353

WC Speed Maintainer

Year	Serial number range
1938	IC1 – IC150
1939	IC151 – 1C400
1940	IC401 – IC407
1941	IC408 – IC411

W Speed Patrol

Year	Serial number range
1940	IE1 – IE466
1941	IE467 – IE634
1942	IE635 – IE678
1943-44	None
1945	IE681 – IE819
1946	IF820 – IF1437
1947	IE1438 – IE2278
1948	IE2279 – IE3515
1949	IE3516 – IE3746
1950	IE3547 – IE3753

Allis-Chalmers serial numbers

WD

Year	Serial number range
1948	7-9249
1949	9250 – 35444
1950	35445 – 72327
1951	72328 – 105181
1952	105182 – 126931
1952	127007 – 131242
1953	131243 – 146606

WD45

Year	Serial number range
1953	146607 – 160385
1954	160386 – 190992
1955	190993 – 217991
1956	217992 – 230294
1957	230295 – 236958

D10

1959	1001 – 1933*

D10 (Persian Orange 2)

1960	1950 – 2702
1961	2801 – 3262

D10 (149-cubic-inch engine)

Year	Serial number range
1961	3501 – INA
1962	INA – 4511*

D10 Series II

Year	Serial number range
1963	6801 – 7674
1964	7675 – 7850

D10 Series III

Year	Serial number range
1964	9001 – 9203
1965	9204 – 9485
1966	9486 – 9794
1967	9795 – 9978
1968	9979 – 10100

D12

Year	Serial number range
1959	1001 – 1734*

D12 (Persian 2)

Year	Serial number range
1960	1950 – 2428*
1961	2801 – 2919

D12 (149-cubic-inch engine)

Year	Serial number range
1961	3001 – INA
1962	INA – 3638

D12 Series II

Year	Serial number range
1963	5501 – 6011
1964	6012 – 6144

D14

Year	Serial number range
1957	1001 – 9399
1959	9400 – 14899
1960	14900 – 18230

D14 (black bars)

Year	Serial number range
1959	19001 – 21799
1960	21800 – 24050

D15

Year	Serial number range
1960	1001 – 1899
1961	190 – 6469
1962	6470 – 8169

D15 Series II

Year	Serial number range
1963	13001 – 16927
1964	16928 – 19680
1965	19681 – 21374
1966	21375 – 23733
1967	23734 – 25126
1968	25127 – 25419

D17

Year	Serial number range
1957	1001 – 4299
1958	4300 – 16499
1959	16500 – 23363

D17 (black bars)

Year	Serial number range
1959	24001 – 28199
1960	28200 – 31625

D17 (Persian Orange 2)

Year	Serial number range
1960	32001 – 32099
1961	33100 – 38069
1962	38070 – 41540

D17 Series III

Year	Serial number range
1962	42001 – 43358
1963	65001 – 70610
1964	70611 – 72768

D17 Series IV

Year	Serial number range
1964	75001 – 77089
1965	77090 – 80532
1966	80533 – 86060
1967	86061 – 89213

D19

Year	Serial number range
1961	1001 – 1249
1962	1250 – 7331
1963	12001 – 14944
1964	14945 – 16266

D21

Year	Serial number range
1963	1001 – 1416
1964	1417 – 2078
1965	2079 – 2129

D21 Series II

Year	Serial number range
1965	2201 – 2407
1966	2408 – 2862
1967	2863 – 3776
1968	3777 – 4497
1969	4498 – 4609

One Sixty

Year	Serial number range
1969-71	No info.

160

Year	Serial number range
1972-73	No info.

One-Seventy

Year	Serial number range
1967	1005 – 2720
1968	2721 – 5373
1969	5374 – 6368
1970	6369 – 6987
1971	6988 – 7384

170 (Black hood decal)

Year	Serial number range
1971	7500 – 7796
1972	7797 – 8820
1973	8821 – 10300

175

Year	Serial number range
1970	1001 – 1476
1971	1477 – 1623
1972	1624 – 1739
1973	1740 – 2152
1974	2153 -3254
1975	3255 – 3739
1976	3740 – 4811
1977	4812 – 5662
1978	5663 – 6320
1979	6321 – 6998
1980	6999 – 7502*

One-Eighty

Year	Serial number range
1967	1007 – 2681
1968	2682 - 6093
1969	6094 – 9234
1970	9235 – 10560
1971	10561 – 11728
1972	11729 – 12446
1973	12447 – 12985

185

Year	Serial number range
1970	1001 – 1951
1971	1952 – 2934
1972	2935 – 3762
1973	3763 – 4960
1974	4961 – 6541
1975	6542 – 8366
1976	8367- 10024
1977	10025 – 11625
1978	11626 – 13159
1979	13160 – 14671
1980	14672 – 15647
1981	15648 – 15961

Allis-Chalmers serial numbers

One-Ninety and XT (bar grill)

Year	Serial number range
1964	1001 – 2484
1965	2485 – 8218
1966	8219 – 8626
1966	904 – 13272
1967	13273 – 17784

One-Ninety and XT Series II (no bars)

Year	Serial number range
1967	1901 – 19261
1968	19262 – 22153

One-Ninety and XT Series III

Year	Serial number range
1968	23001 – 23233
1969	23234 – 2590
1970	25901 – 29135
1971	29136 – 31056
1972	31057 – 31117
1973	31118 – 31140

200

Year	Serial number range
1972	1004 – 3343
1973	3344 – 3558
1973	4001 – 6293
1974	6294 – 9249
1975	9250 – 11521

Two-Ten

Year	Serial number range
1970	104 – 1106
1971	1107 – 2081
1972	2082 – 2469

Two-Twenty

Year	Serial number range
1969	1004 – 1937
1970	1938 – 2450
1971	2451 – 2625
1972	2626 – 2866

440

Year	Serial number range
1972	1001 – 1139
1973	1140 – 1339
1974	1440 – 1650
1975	1651 – INA
1976	INA – 2010

5015

Year	Serial number range
1982	1001 – 1726
1983	1727 – 3276
1984	3277 – 4231
1985	4232 – INA

5020

Year	Serial number range
1977	1001 – 2219
1978	2220 – 3090
1979	3091 – 4114
1980	4115 – 5789
1981	5790 – 7033
1982	7034 – 8387
1983	8388 – 8733
1984	8734 – 9216
1985	9217 – INA

5030

Year	Serial number range
1978	1001 – 2004
1979	2005 – 2254
1980	2255 – 2975
1981	2976-3519
1982	3520 – 4065
1983	4066 – 4213
1984	4214 – 4368
1985	4369 – INA

5040

Year	Beginning number
1976	408445 –
1977	462148 –
1978	410384 –
1979	47300 –
1980	474000 –

5045

Year	Serial number range
1981	988501

6060

Year	Serial number range
1980	1001 – 1296
1981	1297 – 2462
1982	2463 – 3893
1983	3894 – 4571
1984	4572 – 5027

5050

Year	Beginning number
1977	573461
1978	579832
1979	584000
1980	591000
1981	596014
1982	597730
1983	599290

6040

Year	Serial number range
1974	No info.

6070

Year	Serial number range
1984	1001 – 1608
1985	1609 – 1972

6080

Year	Serial number range
1980	1001 – 1151
1981	1152 – 3001
1982	3002 – 4566
1983	4567 – 5779
1984	5780 – 6852
1985	6853 – 7698

6140

Year	Serial number range
1982	1001 – 1446
1983	1447 – 1850
1984	1851 – 2710
1985	2711 – 2714
1985	3545 – 3732

7000 (maroon)

Year	Serial number range
1975	1001 – 1647
1976	1648 – 5935
1977	5036 – 6372
1978	6373 – 6760

7000 (black)

Year	Serial number range
1978	8000 – 8962
1979	8963 – 9503

7010

Year	Serial number range
1979	1001 – 1924
1980	1925 – 2805
1981	2806 – 3433

7020

Year	Serial number range
1977	1001 – 1316
1978	1317 – 2731
1979	2732 – 3841
1980	3842 - 4709
1981	4710 – 5209

7030

Year	Serial number range
1973	1001 – 2594
1974	2596 – 4398

7040

Year	Serial number range
1974	1001 – 1302
1975	1303 – 4128
1976	4129 – 6839
1977	6840 – 8250

7045

Year	Serial number range
1977	1001 – 1233
1978	1234 – 2151
1979	2152 – 3398
1980	3399 – 4224
1981	4225 – 4888

7050

Year	Serial number range
1973	1001 – 1687
1974	1688 – 3300

7060 (maroon)

Year	Serial number range
1974	1001 – 1298
1975	1299 – 2748
1976	2749 – 4581
1977	4582 – 5644

7060 (black)

Year	Serial number range
1978	6001 – 6788
1979	6789 – 7692
1980	7693 – 8441
1981	8442 – 9142

7080 (maroon)

Year	Serial number range
1974	1001 – 1006
1975	1007 – 1571
1976	1572 – 2500
1977	2501 – 2930

Allis-Chalmers serial numbers

7080 (black)

Year	Serial number range
1978	3001 – 3267
1979	3268 – 3647
1980	3648 – 3953
1981	3954 – 4225

7580 (maroon)

Year	Serial number range
1976	1001 – 1287
1977	1288 – 1604
1978	1605 only

8550

Year	Serial number range
1977	1001 – 1082
1978	1083 – 1341
1979	1342 – 1552
1980	1553 – 1722
1981	1723 – 2021

8010

Year	Serial number range
1981	1001 – 1019
1982	1020 – 1711
1983	1712 – 2265
1984	2266 – 2608
1985	2609 – 2832

8030

Year	Serial number range
1981	1001 – 1008
1982	1009 – 2092
1983	2093 – 2700
1984	2701 – 3145
1984	3146 – 3328

8050

Year	Serial number range
1981	1001 – 1015
1982	1016 – 1923
1983	1924 – 2495
1984	2496 – 3186
1985	3187 – 3336

8070

Year	Serial number range
1981	1001 – 1003
1982	1004 – 1429
1983	1430 – 2089
1984	2090 – 2902
1985	2903 – 3354

4W220

Year	Serial number range
1981	101 – 1002
1982	103 – 180
1983	1081 – 1144
1984	1145 – 1175

4W305

Year	Serial number range
1981	1001 – 1003
1982	1004 – 1111
1983	1112 – 1175
1984	1176 – 1337
1985	1338 – 1412

West Allis Industrial Tractors

140

Year	Serial number range
1964	1055 – INA
1965	INA-INA
1966	INA-1608

160

Year	Serial number range
1965	1005 – INA
1966	INA – 2340

1600

Year	Serial number range
1966	1002 – 1746
1967	1747 – 2708
1968	2709 – 3056

600 Forklift

Year	Serial number range
1968	1001 – 1114
1969	1115 – 1714

918 LBH

Year	Serial number range
1968	1001 – 1031

H3/HD3

Year	Serial number range
1960	1001 – 1195
1961	1250 – INA
1962	3199 – 4294
1963	6001 – 6944
1964	6945 – 7889
1965	7890 – 8855
1966	8856 – 9482
1967	9483 - 9699
1968	9700 – 9949

H4/HD4

Year	Serial number range
1965	1001 – 1243
1966	1244 – 2689
1967	2690 – 2937
1968	3001 – 3905
1969	3906 – 4332

Speed Patrol
H

Year	Serial number range
1932	2001 – 2049
1933	2050 only

42S*

Year	Serial number range
1933	2501 – 2643
1934	2644 – 2775
1935	2766 – 2941
1936	3031 – 3160
1937	3276 – 3325
1938	3455 – 3516
1939	3517 – 3567
1940	3568 – 3575

*42S and 42T SNs are mixed.

42T*

Year	Serial number range
1936	3161T – 3199T
1937	3200T – 3361T
1938	3362T – 3488T
1939	3489T – 3625T
1940	3636T – 3675T

*42S and 42T SNs are mixed.

54S**

Year	Serial number range
1934	6501 – 6502
1935	6503 – 6597
1936	6628 – 6763
1937	6821 – 7002

54T**

Year	Serial number range
1936	6639 – 6777
1937	6825T – 7108T
1938	7021T – 7186T
1939	7187T – 7227T
1940	7261T – 7277T

K054S**

Year	Serial number range
1937	681700 – 71270

K054T**

Year	Serial number range
1937	67780T – 69770T
1938	70530T – 71200T
1939	77280T – 72600T

TW Speed Ace (Springfield)

Year	Serial number range
1935	1 – 10
1936	13 – 37
1937	38 – 87

Monarch crawlers
Monarch F 10 Ton

Year	Serial number range
1926	10001 – 10081
1927	10082 – 10240
1928	10241 – 10250

Monarch F-75

Year	Serial number range
1928	70001 – 70207
1929	70208 – 70654
1930	70655 – 70894
1931	70895 – 71066

Monarch G 5 Ton

Year	Serial number range
1926	7001 – 7090
1927	7091 – 7117

Allis-Chalmers serial numbers

Monarch H 6-Ton

Year	Serial number range
1927	60001 – 60206
1928	60207 – 60297

Monarch H-50

Year	Serial number range
1928	60298 – 60610
1929	60611 – 61558
1930	61559 – 62146
1931	62147 – 62297

Monarch K/KO

Year	Serial number range
1929	1 – 48
1930	49 – 1372
1931	1373 – 2333
1932	2334 – 2653
1933	2654 – 3045
1934	3046 – 3593
1934	6001 – 6018
1935	3594 – 4792
1936	4793 – INA
1936	6019 – 6335
1937	6336 – 7707
1938	7708 – 8017
1939	8018 – 8522
1940	8523 – 8956
1941	8957 – 9268
1942	9269 – 9393
1943	9394 – 9468

Monarch L/LO

Year	Serial number range
1931	1 – 34
1932	35 - 498
1933	499 – 660
1934	661 – 887
1934	401 – 4021
1935	888 – 1438
1936	1439 – 2136
1937	2137 – 2705
1938	2706 – 2943
1939	2944 – 3232
1939	LD 8-17
1940	3233 – 3251
1941	3252 – 3272
1942	3273 – 3357

Monarch M

Year	Serial number range
1932	1 – 41
1933	42 – 401
1934	402 – 841
1935	842 – 1941
1936	1942 – 3841
1937	3842 – 7066
1938	7067 – 8126
1939	8127 – 9539
1940	9540 – 11379
1941	11380 – 12946
1942	12947 – 14524

Monarch S/SO

Year	Serial number range
1937	3 – 412
1938	413 – 584
1939	585 – 1084
1940	1085 – 1127
1941	1128 – 1211
1942	1212 – 1227

GM Two-Cycle Diesels HD5

Year	Serial number range
1946	1 – 6
1947	6 – 1357
1948	1358 – 4315
1949	4316 – 7498
1950	7499 – 11070
1951	11071 – 14289
1952	14290 – 17557
1953	17558 – 21836
1954	21837 – 25563
1955	25564 – 29255

HD7, HD7W, Military

Year	Serial number range
1940	3 – 502
1941	503 – 1136
1942	1137 – 2980*
1943	2977 – 5952
1944	5285 – 8948*
1945	7998 – 12090*
1946	12091 – 13077
1947	13078 – 15121*
1948	15117 – 16751
1949	16752 – 18085
1950	18086 – 18505

HD9

Year	Serial number range
1950	1
1951	2 – 737
1952	738 – 1882
1953	1883 – 3590
1954	3591 – 5208
1955	5209 – 5850

HD10, HD10W, Military

Year	Serial number range
1940	2 – 641
1941	642 – 1445
1942	1446 – 2081
1942	2452 – 2855
1943	2082 – 2338
1943	2856 – 3651
1944	2339 – 2451
1944	3652 – 4094
1944	4152 – 4336
1944	4452 – 4896
1945	4095 – 4151
1945	4337 – 4451
1945	4897 – 5963
1946	5964 – 6462
1947	6463 – 7601
1948	7602 – 8675
1949	8676 – 9630
1950	9631 – 10198

HD14/HD14C

Year	Serial number range
1939	18 – 25
1940	26 – 548
1941	549 – 1165
1942	1166 – 2112
1943	2113 – 3137
1944	3138 – 4258
1945	4259 – 5454
1946	5455 – 5814
1947	5815 – 6422

HD15

Year	Serial number range
1950	1
1951	2 – 810
1952	811 – 1857
1953	1858 – 2855
1954	2856 – 3684
1955	3685 – 3909

HD19

Year	Serial number range
1947	4 – 120
1948	121 – 1195
1949	1196 – 2001
1950	2002 – 2654

HD20

Year	Serial number range
1951	3001 – 3827
1952	3828 – 4922
1953	4923 – 5736
1954	5737 – 6100

HD3 (Springfield)

Year	Serial number range
1942	3 – 32

(No 20 or 30)

HD6, HD6G, HD6GB

Year	Serial number range
1955	101 – 1146
1956	1147 – 6465
1957	6466 – 7947
1958	7948 – 10053
1959	10054 – 12505
1960	12506 – 13776
1961	13777 – 14897
1962	14898 – 16041
1963	16042 17104
1964	17105 – 18188
1965	18189 –
1966	19401 –
1967	20201 –
1968	20809 –
1969	21432 –
1970	22272 –
1971	23355 –
1972	24012 –
1973	24672 –
1974	25012 – 25271

Allis-Chalmers serial numbers

HD11

Year	Serial number range
1955	101 – 1057
1956	1058 – 3254
1957	3255 – 4114
1958	4115 – 4767
1959	4768 – 5801
1960	5802 – 6447
1961	6448 – 6994
1962	6995 – 7869
1963	7870 – 8605
1964	8606 – 10532
1965	10533 –
1966	11451
1967	12251 –
1968	13131 –
1969	13657 –
1970	14681

HD11 Ser. B

Year	Serial number range
1971	16001 – 16615
1972	16615 – 17342
1973	17343 – 18015
1974	18016 – 18798

HD16, HD16G

Year	Serial number range
1955	101 – 1008
1956	1009 – 2462
1957	2463 – 2756
1958	2757 – 443
1959	4144 – 4725
1960	4726 – 5097
1961	5098 – 5447
1962	5448 – 5731
1963	5732 – 6269
1964	6270 – 6964
1965	6965 – 7467
1966	7468 – 8075
1967	8076 – 8424
1968	8425 – 8793
1969	8794 – 9564
1970	9565 – 9619

HD 16 Series B

Year	Serial number range
1970	10301 – 10461
1971	10462 – 11703
1972	11704 – 12698
1973	12699 – 13142
1974	13143 – 14000
1975	14001 – 14300
1976	14301 – 14911
1977	14912 – 15021
1978	15022 – 15149
1979	15150 – 15365
1980	15366 – 15439
1981	15440 – 15521

HD21, HD21G

Year	Serial number range
1954	7001 – 7012
1955	7013 – 7915
1956	7916 – 9090
1957	9091 – 9301
1958	9302 – 11028
1959	11029 – 11681
1960	11682 – 11938
1961	11939 – 12259
1962	12260 – 12456
1963	12457 – 13249
1964	12250 – 13736
1965	13737 – 14158
1966	14159 – 14604
1967	14605 – 14883
1968	14884 – 15110
1969	15511 – 15207

HD21 Series B

Year	Serial number range
1969	16001 – 16560
1970	16561 17656
1971	17657 – 18504
1972	18505 – 19113
1973	19114 – 19443
1974	19444 – 19946
1975	19947 – 21000

Aultman-Taylor serial numbers

Steam engines

Year	Serial number
1897	5148-5285
1898	5286-5492
1899	5493-5758
1900	5759-5939
1901	5940-6126
1902	6127-6347
1903	6348-6547
1904	6548-6805
1905	6806-7056
1906	7057-7373
1907	7374-7615
1908	7616-7702
1909	7703-7875
1910	7876-8123
1911	8124-8290
191	8291-8438
1913	8439-8617
1914	8618-8896
1915	8897-9089
1916	9090-9185
1917	9186

B.F. Avery serial numbers

On Models A, BF, BG, and R the serial number is on the right frame rail. On the Model V the number is located on top of the frame rail adjacent to the right-hand side of the flywheel bell housing.

B.F. Avery's Model V was ideal for small farm and truck garden markets offering a 65-cubic-inch engine and three-speed transmission.

Model A

Year	Beginning number
1945	4A786
1946	7A305
1947	9A867
1948	13A427
1949	17A456
1950	19A366

Model BF

Year	Beginning number
1950	R500
1951	R1839
1952	R4460

Model BFW

Year	Beginning number
1953	R6538

Model BFD

Year	Beginning number
1953	57700001

Model BFS

Year	Beginning number
1953	57600001

Model BFH

Year	Beginning number
1953	58000001

Model BG

Year	Beginning number
1953	57900001
1954	57900601
1955	57900769

Model V

Year	Beginning number
1946	1V5
1947	1V144
1948	2V577
1949	4V490
1950	5V501
1951	6V207
1952	6V422

Caterpillar serial numbers

Holt 2 Ton

Year	Beginning number
1925-1928	25003, 70001

Holt 5 Ton

Year	Beginning number
1919-1926	19001, 42001, 43001

Holt 10 Ton

Year	Beginning number
1925	15001, 34001

Ten

Year	Beginning number
1928-1933	PT1

Fifteen

Year	Beginning number
1929-1933	PV1
1932-1933	7G1

Fifteen-HC

Year	Beginning number
1932-1939	1D1

Twenty

Year	Beginning number
1932-1934	8C1
1927-1933	L1, PL1

Twenty-Two

Year	Beginning number
1934-1939	2F1, 1J2

Twenty-Five

Year	Beginning number
1931-1933	3C1

Twenty-Eight

Year	Beginning number
1933-1935	4F1

Thirty

Year	Beginning number
1925-1932	S1001, PS1

Thirty-R4

Year	Beginning number
1935-1944	6G1

Thirty-Five

Year	Beginning numbe
1932-1934	5C1

Thirty-Five Diesel

Year	Beginning number
1933-1934	6E1

Forty

Year	Beginning number
1934-1936	5G1

Forty Diesel

Year	Beginning number
1934-1936	3G1

Fifty

Year	Beginning number
1931-1937	5A1

Fifty Diesel

Year	Beginning number
1933-1936	1E1

Sixty

Year	Beginning number
1925-1931	101A, PA1

Sixty-Five

Year	Beginning number
1932-1933	2D1

Sixty-Five Diesel

Year	Beginning number
1931-1932	1C1

Seventy

Year	Beginning number
1933-1937	8D1

Seventy Diesel

Year	Beginning number
1933	3E1

Seventy-Five Diesel

Year	Beginning number
1933-1935	2E1

D2

Year	Beginning number
1938-1947	3J1, 5J1
1947 On	4U, 5U

D4 and RD4

Year	Beginning number
1936-1947	4G1, 2T1, 7J1, 5T1

D4

Year	Beginning number
1947 On	6U, 7U

D5NG

Year	Beginning number
1939	9M

D6 and RD6

Year	Beginning number
1935-1941	5E801, 2H1

D6

Year	Beginning number
1941-1947	4R, 5R
1947	8U, 9U

D7 and RD7

Year	Beginning number
1935-1940	5E7501, 9G1

D7

Year	Beginning number
1940 On	7M, 3T

D8 and RD8

Year	Beginning number
1935 On	5E, 1H, 8R, 2U

R-2

Year	Beginning number
1934-1937	5E3501
1938-1942	6J1, 4J1

R-3

Year	Beginning number
1934-1935	5E2501

R-5

Year	Beginning number
1934-1940	4H501, 3R1, 5E3001

The Caterpillar Model Thirty traces its roots back to 1921 when it was built by the C.L. Best Tractor Company as the Tracklayer 30. Best would later merge with Holt Mfg. to form Caterpillar.

Cletrac serial numbers

AG
Serial number is located in the upper right-hand corner of instrument panel.

Year	Beginning serial number
1939	2X0886
1940	2X1702
1941	2X2474
1942	2X3102

AG-6

Year	Beginning serial number
1944	3X0000
1945	3X1512
1946	3X3260
1947	3X4586
1948	3X6062
1949	3X7644
1950	3X8542
1951	3X8456
1952	3X8626
1953	3500000
1954	4500000
1955	4X020
1956	4X100
1957	4X216

AD
Serial number is located on the right-hand side of panel behind the engine.

Year	Beginning serial number
1939	5Z36
1940	9Z32
1941	1Z106
1942	1Z690
1943	1Z836
1944	1Z838
1945	2Z172
1946	2Z672
1947	3Z700
1948	4Z912
1949	6Z214
1950	7Z390
1951	7Z422
1952	8Z296
1953	3500000
1954	4500000
1955	8Z992
1956	9iZ128
1957	9Z178
1958	9Z212
1959	9Z225

AD2

Year	Beginning serial number
1939	4N60
1940	5N76

BD
Serial number is located on the right-hand side of panel behind the engine.

4-Cylinder

Year	Beginning serial number
1939	3D708
1940	4D206

6-Cylinder

Year	Beginning serial number
1940	5D000
1941	5D422
1942	6D032
1943	6D286
1944	6D948
1945	7D714
1946	8D474
1947	9D680
1948	11D224
1949	13D820
1950	15D658
1951	16D514
1952	18D032
1953	3500802
1954	4500758
1955	20D220

BG
Serial number is located on the upper right-hand side of panel behind the engine.

BG 4-Cylinder

Year	Beginning serial number
1939	2C578
1940	2C798

BG 6-Cylinder

Year	Beginning serial number
1940	3C00
1941	3C338
1942	3C654
1943	3C738
1944	3C976

BGS

Year	Beginning serial number
1944	6C000
1945	6C630
1946	8C370
1947	9C062
1948	10C238
1949	11C462
1950	11C950
1951	12C230
1952	12C504
1953	3500802
1954	4500937
1955	12C934

CG

Year	Beginning serial number
1939	5M260
1940	5M312
1941	5M544
1942	5M604

DD

DD serial numbers are located on the upper left-hand side of panel behind the engine.

DD 4-Cylinder

Year	Beginning serial number
1939	1L4220

DD 6-Cylinder

Year	Beginning serial number
1939	1L5000
1940	1L5222
1941	1L5644
1942	1L6332
1943	1L6560
1944	1L6820
1945	1L7422
1946	1L8012
1947	1L8792
1948	2L0194
1949	2L2142
1950	2L3528
1951	2L4130
1952	2L5350
1953	3500000
1954	4500000
1955	3L226
1956	3L404
1957	3L498
1958	3L596

DG

Serial number is located on the upper right-hand side of panel behind the engine.

DG 4-Cylinder

Year	Beginning serial number
1939	4E66

DG 6-Cylinder

Year	Beginning serial number
1939	7E00
1940	7E68
1941	1E200
1942	1E364
1943	1E392
1944	1E464
1945	1E748
1946	2E356
1947	2E620
1948	2E852
1949	3E186
1950	3E298
1951	3E362
1952	3E402
1953	3500000
1954	4500000
1955	3E502
1956	3E516
1957	3L558***
1958	3L600***

E31

Year	Beginning serial number
1939	1B816

E42

Year	Beginning serial number
1939	5H130
1940	5H428
1941	5H574

Cletrac serial numbers

ED 38 and 42

Year	Beginning serial number
1939	1AA78
1940	7AA24
1941	8AA74

ED2 42

Year	Beginning serial number
1939	5S92
1941	6S74

ED2 62, 68, and 76

Year	Beginning serial number
1939	2V28
1940	3V58

EGH 62, 68, and 76

Year	Beginning serial number
1939	5R20
1940	7R78
1941	8R18

FD

Serial number is located on the right side of panel beside the fuel tank.

Year	Beginning serial number
1939	8Y094
1940	8Y366
1941	8Y476
1942	8Y684
1943	8Y772
1944	8Y910
1945	9Y116

FDLC

Year	Beginning serial number
1941	1HA00
1942	1HA076
1943	1HA096
1944	1HA110
1945	1HA196

FDE

Year	Beginning serial number
1945	10Y000
1946	10Y200
1947	10^480
1948	10^794
1949	11Y122

1950	11Y582
1951	11Y790
1952	12Y124

FG6

Year	Beginning serial number
1939	1CA532
1940	1CA608
1941	1CA796
1942	1CA846
1943	1CA880

GG

Year	Beginning serial number
1939	1FA000
1940	5FA388
1941	1FA0086
1941	1FA1000
1942	1FA6532

HG

Serial number is located on right-hand side of engine main frame, rear of footrest (early), or front of footrest (late).

Year	Beginning serial number
1939	1GA000
1940	2GA884
1941	5GA022
1942	7GA484
1943	8GA702
1944	9GA632
1945	13GA422
1946	19GA994
1947	25GA240
1948	33GA146
1949	41GA896
1950	48GA428
1951	55GA858

HGF

Year	Beginning serial number
1947	26GA108
1948	35GA340
1949	46GA508

HGR

Year	Beginning serial number
1945	1NA000
1947	1NA050
1948	1NA706

MG1

Year	Beginning serial number
1941	1JA000
1942	1JA236
1943	7JA542
1944	12A710

MG1

Year	Beginning serial number
1942	1DA000
1943	1DA062

MG2

Year	Beginning serial number
1942	1KA000

MG3

Year	Beginning serial number
1942	1LA000

Oliver Cletrac crawlers

R

Years built	Serial number range
1916-1917	1 – 1000

H

Years built	Serial number range
1917-1919	1001 – 13755

W (W-12)

Years built	Serial number range
1919-1932	13756 – 30971

F

Years built	Serial number range
1920-1922	1 – 3000

20K

Years built	Serial number range
1925-1932	101 – 10207

30A (A30)

Years built	Serial number range
1926-1928	6 – 1421

30B (B30)

Years built	Serial number range
1929-1930	1601 – 3057

40

Years built	Serial number range
1928-1931	101 – 1833

55-40

Years built	Serial number range
1931-1932	1835 – 1889

55

Years built	Serial number range
1932-1938	1890 – 3852

100

Years built	Serial number range
1927-1930	50 – 158

15

Years built	Serial number range
1931-1933	76 – 11999

20C

Years built	Serial number range
1933-1936	12000 – 14547

AG

Years built	Serial number range
1936-1937	14548 – 20201

AG

Years built	Serial number range
1937-1942	2X0202 – 2X3398

AG-6*

Years built	Serial number range
1944-Up	3X0000 – Up

AD

Years built	Serial number range
1937-Up	1Z00 – Up

AD2

Years built	Serial number range
	5N80

BD Four Speed

Years built	Serial number range
1936-1939	1D00 – 4D236

Cletrac serial numbers

BD Six Speed
Years built	Serial number range
1939-Up	5D000 – Up

BD2
Years built	Serial number range
1937-1938	1P00 – 1P16

25
Years built	Serial number range
1932-1935	76 – 1372

30G
Years built	Serial number range
1935-1936	1C00 – 2C79

BG Four Speed
Years built	Serial number range
1937-1939	2C80 – 2C798

BG Six Speed
Years built	Serial number range
1939-Up	3C000 – Up

BGS
Years built	Serial number range
1944-Up	6C000 – Up

40-30
Years built	Serial number range
1930-1931	76 – 399

35
Years built	Serial number range
1932-1936	400 – 3835

CG
Years built	Serial number range
1936-1942	2836 5M000 – 3246 5M608

35D
Years built	Serial number range
1934-1935	10000 – 10217

40D
Years built	Serial number range
1935-1936	10218 – 10831

DD Four Speed
Years built	Serial number range
1936-1939 – 11581 1L4460	10832 1L3000

DD Six Speed
Years built	Serial number range
1939 – Up1L5000 Up	

DG Four Speed
Years built	Serial number range
1936-1939	1E00 – 5E86

DG Six Speed
Years built	Serial number range
1939 and up	7E00 and up

EN (E31)
Years built	Serial number range
1934-1939	1B00 – 1B946

E38 (pre-streamlined)
Years built	Serial number range
1934-1936	7B30 – 1B318

E38 (streamlined)
Years built	Serial number range
1936-1938	2H000 – 3H168

E42
Years built	Serial number range
1938-1942	5H000 – 5H604

E-62-68-76
Years built	Serial number range
1934-1941	1A00 – 5A330

EHG-62-68-76
Years built	Serial number range
1937-1941	1R00 – 8R52

ED-38-42
Years built	Serial number range
1938-1941	1AA00 – 9AA00

ED2-38
Years built	Serial number range
1937-1941	S00 – 1S52

ED2-42

Years built	Serial number range
1937-1941	5S00 – 6S80

ED2-62-68-76

Years built	Serial number range
1938-1941	1V00 – 4V13

80D

Years built	Serial number range
1933-1936	6000 – 6321

FD Four Speed

Years built	Serial number range
1936-1938	6322 – 6699

FD Six Speed

Years built	Serial number range
1938-Up 8Y000 – Up	

FDLC

Years built	Serial number range
1941-Up	1HA000 – Up

30-60

Years built	Serial number range
1930-1932	113 – 409

80

Years built	Serial number range
1932-1932	420 – 499

80G

Years built	Serial number range
1932-1936	500 – 846

FG Four Speed

Years built	Serial number range
1936-1938	1CA046 – 1CA054

FG Six Speed

Years built	Serial number range
1938-Up	1CA500 – Up

GG (sold as Twin Row, General, and Co-Op)

Years built	Serial number range
1939-1942	1FA000 1FA1000 – 1FA01641FA6886

HG-31-42-68

Years built	Serial number range
1939-Up	1GA000 – Up

The Model W 12-20 holds the distinction of being the first Cletrac crawler to hit the market. This crawler's manufacturer, Cleveland Tractor Company, got its start in 1917 when Roland White, head of White Motor Company, gathered investors together to form the company. The next year that firm introduced the 15½ drawbar horsepower Model W. This crawler also holds the honor of being the first crawler tractor tested at the Nebraska Tractor Test.

Cockshutt serial numbers

Serial numbers for Cockshutt Models 20, 30, 40, and 50 are found on the top of the left frame side, next to the engine. Models 35, 35L, Golden Eagle 40D4, and 40PD serial numbers are on the top of the right frame side. Serial numbers for Models 550, 560, 570, and 570 Super are on the top right of the frame side. It's on the top left frame side of the 540.

20

Year	Beginning number
1952	101
1953	1657
1954	2568
1955	10001
1956	20001
1957	30001
1958	40001

30 and Gamble's Farmcrest)

Year	Beginning number
1946	1
1947	442
1948	6705
1949	17370
1950	26417
1951	28524
1952	32389
1953	32389
1954	35974
1955	40001
1956	50001

35 Deluxe and 35L Deluxe

Year	Beginning number
1956	1001
1957	10001
1958	20001

Golden Arrow

Year	Beginning number
1957	16001

40

Year	Beginning number
1949	101
1950	194
1951	4101
1952	6901
1953	10501
1954	11401
1955	20001
1956	30001
1957	40001
1958	50001

40PD and Golden Eagle 40D4

Year	Beginning number
1955	27001
1956	30001
1957	40028
1958	50001

50

Year	Beginning number
1953	101
1954	1801
1955	10001
1956	20001
1957	30001
1958	40001

540

Year	Beginning number
1958	AM1001
1959	AN5001
1960	none built
1961	AP1001
1962	AR1001

550

Year	Beginning number
1958	BM1001
1959	BN5001
1960	BO1001
1961	BP1001
1962	BR1001

The Cockshutt Model 30 was the first tractor to feature a fully independent or "live" PTO.

560

Year	Beginning number
1958	CM1001
1959	CN5001
1960	CO7001
1961	CP1001

570

Year	Beginning number
1958	DM1001
1959	DN5001
1960	DO7001

570 Super

Year	Beginning number
1961	DP1001
1962	DR1001

18-28

Year	Serial number
1930	800 001
1931	800 460
1932	800 964
1933	800 985
1934	800 051
1935	801 241
1936	801 990
1937	802

28-44

Year	Serial number
1930	500 001
1931	503 600
1932	506 185
1933	506 212
1934	506 255
1935	506 401
1936	507 176
1937	508 016

70 RC

Year	Serial number
1935	200 001
1936	200 686
1937	208 729
1938	219 645
1939	223 255
1940	231 116
1941	236 356
1942	241 391
1943	243 640
1944	244 711

1945	250 180
1946	252 780
1947	258 140
1948	262 840

1350

Year	Beginning number
1966	28302844
1967	28303141
1968	28304546

2

Year	Beginning number
1954	2601
1955	10001
1956	20001

3

Year	Beginning number
1953	35601
1955	40001

18-28

Year	Serial number range
1930	800001-800459
1931	800460-800963
1932	800964-800984
1933	800985-801050
1934	801051-801240
1935	801241-801989
1936	801990-802937
1937	802938-803928

28-44

Year	Serial number range
1930	500001-503599
1931	503600-506184
1932	506185-506211
1933	506212-506254
1934	506255-506400
1935	506401-507175

60 Row Crop

Year	Serial number range
1940	600001-600070
1941	600071-606303
1942	606304-607394
1943	607395-608525
1944	608526-612046
1945	612047-615627
1946	615628-616706
1947	616707-620256
1948	620257-625131

Cockshutt serial numbers

60 Standard

Year	Serial number range
1942	410001-410500
1943	410501-410510
1944	410511-410616
1945	410617-410910
1946	410911-411310
1947	411311-411960
1948	411961-413605

70 Row Crop

Year	Serial number range
1935	200001-200685
1936	200686-208728
1937	208729-216925
1937	220426-220694
1938	219645-220425
1938	220695-223254
1939	223255-231115
1940	231116-236355
1941	236356-241390
1942	241391-243639
1943	243640-244710
1944	244711-250179
1945	250180-252779
1946	252780-258139
1947	258140-262839
1948	262840-267866

70 Standard

Year	Serial number range
1936	300001-300633
1937	300634-301802
1937	301803-302083
1938	302084-303464
1939	303465-305361
1940	305362-306593
1941	306594-307579
1942	307580-308187
1943	308188-308483
1944	308484-310217
1945	310218-311115
1946	311116-312689
1947	312690-314220
1948	314221-315420

80 Row Crop

Year	Serial number range
1937	109152-109166
1938	109167-109782
1939	109783-110220
1940	110221-110614
1941	110615-110944
1942	110945-111218
1943	111219-111390
1944	111391-111928
1945	111929-112878
1946	112879-114143
1947	114144-114943
1948	114944-115373

80 Standard

Year	Serial number range
1937	803929-803990
1938	803991-805376
1939	805377-806879
1940	806880-808124
1941	808125-809050
1942	809051-809990
1943	809991-810469
1944	810470-811990
1945	811991-813066
1946	813067-814563
1947	814564-815215
1948	815216-816241

90 and 99

Year	Serial number range
1937	508918-508934
1938	508935-509611
1939	509612-510067
1940	510068-510563
1941	510564-510976
1942	510977-511295
1943	511296-511473
1944	511474-512043
1945	512044-512043
1946	512821-513105
1947	513106-513855
1948	513856-514855
1949	514856-516275
1950	516276-516887
1951	516888-517873
1952	517874-518212

Co-op serial numbers

Serial numbers for Co-op Models No. 1, 2, and 3 are located on the top edge of the left frame rail near the distributor. Throughout the years of production, they are present in at least three separate forms:

A. X XXX
B. X*XXX
C. XXXX-X

One might expect this variation to denote manufacturing location. The first digit in A and B above would be model number, e.g., 1 for Model No. 1, 2 for a No. 2, and 3 for No. 3. The third example appears on the Farmers Union production models from St. Paul. Numbering on the West Virginia version is unknown because no specific tractors can be traced to the West Virginia plant.

Post-war Co-op No. 3S serial numbers are found on a plate affixed to the dash and start with 3001.

The B-2, B-3, and B-2 Jr. serial numbers are located on the right frame rail near the brake pedal.

Model C serial numbers are located on the top of the right side frame rail near the belt pulley. Two forms of numbering are known to exist:

A. C – XXX (square axle housing)
B. C XX-XXX (round axle housing)

The first 53 produced had square axles; therefore, the example in B directly above would start C54-XXX.

E-2 (Cockshutt built)

Year	Beginning number
1952	101
1953	1657
1954	2568
1955	10001
1956	20001
1957	30001
1958	40001

The 29 (drawbar) horsepower Farmers Union Co-op No. 3 boasted a Chrysler L-head, six-cylinder engine mated to a five-speed truck transmission.

E-3 (Cockshutt built)

Year	Beginning number
1946	0
1947	442
1948	6705
1949	17370
1950	26417
1951	28524
1952	32389
1953	32389
1954	35974
1955	40001
1956	50001

E-4 (Cockshutt built)

Year	Beginning number
1949	101
1950	194
1951	4101
1952	6901
1953	10501
1954	11401
1955	20001
1956	30001
1957	40001
1958	50001

E-5 (Cockshutt built)

Year	Beginning number
1953	101
1954	1801
1955	10001
1956	20001
1957	30001
1958	40001

David Brown serial numbers

VAK 1
Years	Serial numbers
1939-1944	1001-6000

VAK 1A
Years	Serial numbers
1945-1947	6351-9852

Cropmaster
Years	Serial numbers
1947-1953	P10000-44000

30C First Series
Years	Serial numbers
1953-1954	P44500-46058

30C Second Series
Years	Serial numbers
1954-1957	P/30 10001-12766

Cropmaster Diesel
Years	Serial numbers
1949-1953	PD10001-18499

30D Diesel First Series
Years	Serial numbers
1953-1954	PD18500-20797

30D Second Series
Years	Serial numbers
1954-1957	PD/30 10001-19452

Super Cropmaster
Years	Serial numbers
1950-1952	SP10001-10600

Prairie Cropmaster
Years	Serial numbers
1951-1954	SPP10001-14881

Prairie Cropmaster Diesel
Years	Serial numbers
1952-1954	PDP10001-10245

Cropmaster Vineyard
Years	Serial numbers
1947-1953	N10026-10205

Cropmaster Diesel Vineyard
Years	Serial numbers
1951-1952	ND10001-10084

50D
Years	Serial numbers
1953-1958	VAD 10001-11260

25C
Years	Serial numbers
1953-1958	P25 10001-21318

25D
Years	Serial numbers
1953-1958	PD25 10001-23424

2D
Years	Serial numbers
1957-1961	VAD12V 10001-11644

2DV
Years	Serial numbers
1957-1961	VAD12V 10001-10364

900 Petrol
Years	Serial numbers
1956-1958	900G 10001-10305

900 Kerosene
Years	Serial numbers
1956-1958	900K 10001-10265

900 Diesel
Years	Serial numbers
1956-1958	900D 10001-17437

900 J & L Series
Years	Serial numbers
1957-1958	J900G, L900G J900K, L900K J900D, L900D 50001-55445

DAVID BROWN

950
Years	Serial numbers
1958-1959	T950G, U950G
	T950K, U950K
	T950D, U950D
	57000-62934

950 Implematic First Series
Years	Serial numbers
1959-1961	V950G, W950G
	V950K, W950K
	V950D, W950D
	63000-81126

950 Implematic Second Series
Years	Serial numbers
1961-1962	950/3A, 950/3B
	4400001-401489

850 Implematic First Series
Years	Serial numbers
1960-1961	A850D, B850D
	A850G, B850G
	300001-306334

850 Implematic Second Series
Years	Serial numbers
1961-1965	850C, 850D
	850DM
	310001-317439

850 Implematic Narrow
Years	Serial numbers
1961-1965	850CV, 850DV
	N390001-390469

880 Implematic First Series
Years	Serial numbers
1961-1964	880C, 880D
	350001-362382

880 Implematic Narrow
Years	Serial numbers
1961-1965	880CV, 880DV
	N395001-395303

900 Implematic
Years	Serial numbers
1961-1965	990A, 990B
	440001-480600

880 Implematic Second Series
Years	Serial numbers
1964-1965	880E, 880F
	521001-527521

Oliver 500
Years	Serial numbers
1960-1964	100001-102000

Oliver 600
Years	Serial numbers
1961-1964	449800-453700

770 Selectamatic
Years	Serial numbers
1965-1970	580001-592375

780 Selectamatic
Years	Serial numbers
1967-1971	600001-611551

780 Selectamatic Narrow
Years	Serial numbers
1969-1971	645001-645647

880 Selectamatic
Years	Serial numbers
1965-1971	530001-563379

990 Selectamatic
Years	Serial numbers
1965-1968	482001-505286

990 Selectamatic
Years	Serial numbers
1968-1971	800001-831351

1200 Selectamatic
Years	Serial numbers
1967-1971	700001-718990

3800 Selectamatic
Years	Serial numbers
1968-1971	650001-650522

4600 Selectamatic
Years	Serial numbers
1968-1971	900001-900582

775 Synchromesh
Years	Serial numbers
1972-1976	651001-651870

David Brown serial numbers

885 Gasoline

Years	Serial numbers
1972-1976	594001-594235

885 Synchromesh

Years	Serial numbers
1971-1976	620001-640365

885 Synchromesh Narrow

Years	Serial numbers
1971-1976	64601-647360

990 Synchromesh

Years	Serial numbers
1971-1976	850001-868541

995 Synchromesh

Years	Serial numbers
1971-1976	920001-936004

996 Synchromesh

Years	Serial numbers
1971-1976	980001-989042

1210 Synchromesh

Years	Serial numbers
1971-1976	720001-731855

1212 Hydra Shift

Years	Serial numbers
1971-1976	1000001-1005283

1410 Synchromesh and 1412 Synchromesh

Years	Serial numbers
1974-1976	1050001-1051058

8 Series

Years	Serial numbers
1976-1983	11000001-11021851

9 Series

Years	Serial numbers
1976-1980	11070001-11106274

12 Series

Years	Serial numbers
1976-1980	11150001-11167079

14 Series

Years	Serial numbers
1976-1980	11200001-11206445

3800

Year	Beginning number
1968	650001
1969	650277
1970	650358

4600

Year	Beginning number
1968	900001
1969	900312
1970	900422

VAK on tracks

Year	Number produced
1940	550

DB4

Years	Number produced
1942-1949	110

Trackmaster

Years	Serial numbers
1950-1953	10001-10700

Trackmaster Diesel

Years	Serial numbers
1950-1953	10001-10500

Trackmaster 30T

Years	Serial numbers
1953-1958	10750-11153

Trackmaster 30TD

Years	Serial numbers
1953-1959	10550-11203

Trackmaster 50D

Years	Serial numbers
1952-1953	10001-10150

Trackmaster 50TD

Years	Serial numbers
1953-1956	10175-10686

30ITD

Years	Serial numbers
1953-1959	10001-10343

50ITD

Years	Serial numbers
1953-1956	10001-10298

50TD MkII

Years	Serial numbers
1957-1963	20001-20471

40TD

Years	Serial numbers
1960-1963	30001-30143

Eagle serial numbers

The Eagle 6B Universal was the last of a long line of durable tractors built by the Appleton, Wisconsin-based Eagle Manufacturing Company. The Eagle was powered by a six-cylinder Hercules OXB-5 engine that provided enough power to pull a two- to three-bottom plow. The Eagle was also offered in a standard-tread model, the 6C.

Eagle 6A

Year	Starting Number
1930	1987
1931	2226
1932	2256
1933	2283
1934	2314
1935	2354

6A, 6B and 6C

Year	Starting Number
1936	2355
1937	2392
1938	2457

Empire serial numbers

The Philadelphia, Pennsylvania-based Empire Tractor Corporation existed for a short time between 1946 and 1948 producing a no-thrills 40-hp. tractor that employed a Willys-Overland engine.

Model 88

Years	Serial numbers
10/1946 to 8/1947	#0001 - #3000 (estimate)

Model 90

Years	Serial numbers
9/1947 to 1/1948	#3001 - #6800 (estimate)

Euclid serial numbers

EUCLID

Serial numbers for all crawler tractor models

Year	Beginning number
1934	01
1935	69
1936	256
1937	481
1938	644
1939	752
1940	958
1941	1253
1942	1945
1943	2667
1944	3322
1945	3901
1946	4594
1947	5698
1948	7626
1949	9140
1950	10085
1951	11394
1952	13224
1953	15154
1954	16923
1955	18442
1956	20685
1957	23849
1958	26238
1959	27571
1960	29700
1961	30888
1962	32487
1963	34434
1964	36809
1965	39451
1966	42631
1967	48296
1968	50801
1969	60398
1970	61329
1971	61900
1972	62572
1973	63154
1974	64211
1975	65437
1976	66721
1977	67667
1978	68298
1979	69164
1980	69967
1981	70573
1982	71386
1983	71898
1984	72141
1985	72579
1986	73035
1987	73641
1988	74153
1989	74591
1990	75047
1991	75290
1992	75530
1993	75765
1994	75995

Ferguson serial numbers

Ferguson's Model TED-20 proved to be the most popular tractor among British farmers during the machine's heyday from 1946 to 1956. The tractor employed a Standard Motor Company Model VO (vaporizing oil) engine that could operate on distillate-type fuel. The TED-20 featured adjustable front and rear tread, electric starting, a three-point hitch, and a four-speed transmission.

Ferguson Model A

Year	Number range
1936 - 1938	1 - 1350

Ford-Ferguson

Year	Beginning number
1939	1
1940	14644
1941	47843
1942	92363
1943	107755
1944	131783
1945	174638
1946	204129
1947	267289
end	306221

Ferguson TE-20

Year	Beginning number
1946	1
1947	315
1948	20895
1949	77773
1950	116551
1951	167923

Ferguson TE 20-85

Year	Beginning number
1951	172588
1952	241585
1953	311009

Ferguson TE-30
The serial number is located behind the steering wheel and above the throttle.

Year	Beginning number
1950	116462
1951	167837
1952	241336
1953	310780
1954	367999

Ferguson TO-35 Gas Deluxe

Year	Beginning number
1958	178216
1959	188851

Ferguson TO-35 Gas Special

Year	Beginning number
1958	183348
1959	185504

Ferguson TO-35 Diesel

Year	Beginning number
1958 Diesel	I180742
1959 Diesel	I187719

Ferguson TO20 and TO030
The serial number is located behind the steering wheel and above the throttle.

Year	Beginning number
1948	1
1949	1808
1950	14660
1951	39163

Ferguson TO-30
The serial number is located behind the steering wheel and above the throttle.

Year	Beginning number
1951	60001
1952	72680
1953	108645
1954	125959

Ferguson TO-35
The serial number is located on the dash, a 2×3-inch plate attached with rivets.

Year	Beginning number
1954	140001
1955	140006
1956	167157
1957	171741

Ferguson 35
(also the Massey-Ferguson 35)

Year	Beginning number
1956	1001
1957	9226
1958	79553
1959	125068
1960	171471

Massey-Ferguson 65

Year	Beginning number
1958	500001
1959	510451
1960	520569
1961	533180

Ferguson 40

Year	Beginning number
1956	400001
1957	405671

Ford serial numbers

Serial number location

9N, 2N, and 8N tractors produced from 1939 to 1952

The serial number is located on the mid-left side of the engine block on an approximately ½×3-inch vertical flat. The serial number is hand-stamped onto the vertical flat, not cast into the engine block. Format is model designation before sequential production number. Serial numbers for the 9N and 2N Ford begin with the designation "9N." Serial numbers for the 8N Ford begin with the designation "8N."

Golden Jubilee and NAA tractors produced from 1953 to 1954

On early production models, before serial number NAA-22239, the serial number is located on the left front corner of the engine block, just below the manifold. On models numbered NAA-22239 and beyond, the serial number is located on the left side of the transmission housing, above and to the rear of the starter, just below a 3×6-inch horizontal flat on a ³⁄₈×3-inch semivertical surface. The serial number is hand-stamped onto the semivertical flat, not cast into the transmission housing. Format is model designation (e.g. "NAA" or "NAB") before sequential production number.

Hundred Series tractors produced from 1955 to 1962

The serial number is located on the left side of the transmission housing, above and to the rear of the starter, on a 3×6-inch horizontal flat. The serial number is hand-stamped onto the horizontal flat, not cast into the transmission housing. Format is model designation above or below sequential production number.

Hundred Series tractors produced from 1955 to 1958

Workmaster and Powermaster Ford tractors were produced from 1958 to

1962. The numerical designations 501, 600, 601, 700, 701, 800, 801, 900, and 901 represent the series designation. The serial number reflects the model designation and sequential production number, e.g., a 641 Ford tractor is series 601, Model 641.

Thousand Series tractors produced from 1962 to 1964

The serial number is located on the left side of the transmission housing, above and to the rear of the starter or directly below the starter, on a 3×6-inch horizontal flat. The serial number is hand-stamped onto the horizontal flat, not cast into the transmission housing. Format is model designation above or below sequential production number. The numerical designations 2000, 4000, 6000, etc., represent the series designation. The serial number reflects the model designation and sequential production number.

Additional designations for Ford tractors produced from 1939 to 1962

A "star" before and/or after the serial number indicates hardened steel-cylinder sleeves. Hardened steel-cylinder sleeves were used in production up to tractor serial number 8N-433578.
A "diamond" before and/or after the serial number indicates cast-iron cylinder sleeves, which are .098-inch larger in bore. Suffix-AN, e.g., "8NAN," distillate model, 1939-1952.
Suffix-B, e.g., "NAB," distillate model, 1953-1954.
Suffix-L, e.g., "640L," LP-gas model, 1955-1962.

Suffix-D, e.g., "851D," diesel model, 1958-1962.

Ford tractors have no separate engine serial number. Engine type may be determined by the casting code found on the right side of the engine. The casting code is cast into the engine block rather than hand-stamped like the serial number. Casting code EAE signifies the 134-cubic-inch Red Tiger OHV engine found on the Golden Jubilee/NAA, 600, 700, 501, 601, 701, and early, four-cylinder 2000 Series Ford tractors.

Casting code EAF signifies the 172-cubic-inch Red Tiger OHV engine found on the 800, 900, 801, 901, and early, four-cylinder 4000 Series Ford tractors.

Fordson

Year	Beginning number
1917	1
1918	255
1919	34422
1920	91712
1921	162667
1922	199448
1923	268433
1924	370331
1925	453341
1926	557509
1927	645611
1928	739583
1929	747584
1930	757265

Fordson Dexta

Year	Beginning number
1958	16066
1959	22427
1960	46216
1961	72003

Fordson Super Dexta

Year	Beginning number
1961	09A-312001-M
1962	09B-070000-A
1963	09C-731454-A
1964	09D-900000-A

Fordson Major (diesel)

Year	Beginning number
1951	1217101
1952	1217104
1953	1247381
1954	1276857
1955	1322525
1956	1371418
1957	1412409
1958	1458281

Fordson Power Major

Year	Beginning number
1958	1481091
1959	1494448
1960	1538065
1961	1583906

Fordson Super Major

Year	Beginning number
1961	08A-300001M
1962	08B-740000-A
1963	08C-781370-A
1964	08D-900000-A

9N

Year	Beginning number
1939	1
1940	10234
1941	45976
1942	88888

2N

Year	Beginning number
1942	99003
1943	105375
1944	126538
1945	169982
1946	198731
1947	258504

8N

Year	Beginning number
1947	1
1948	37908
1949	141370
1950	245637
1951	343593
1952	442035

600, 700, 800, 900

Year	Beginning number
1954	1
1955	10615
1956	77271
1957	116368

Ford serial numbers

501, 601, 701, 801, 901

Year	Beginning number
1957	1001
1958	11997
1959	58312
1960	105943
1961	131427
1962	15553

2000, 4000, 6000

Year	Beginning number
1962	1001
1963	11948
1964	38931

2000 (three-cylinder), 9000

Year	Starting number
1965	C100000
1966	C124200
1967	C161300
1968	C190200
1969	C226000
1970	C257600
1971	C292100
1972	C327200
1973	C367300
1974	C405200
1975	C450700

Hundred Series and Thousand Series

The model number consists of three digits, followed in some cases by a suffix consisting of a number and/or letter. The first digit designates the engine size and tractor type. The second digit designates the transmission type, and the third digit designates the production year range of the series.

The numerical designations 501, 600, 601, 700, 701, 800, 801, 900, and 901, represent the series designation. Hundred Series Ford tractors (Series 600, 800, 900, etc.) were produced from 1955 to 1958. Workmaster and Powermaster Series Ford tractors (Series 601, 801, 901, etc.) were produced from 1958 to 1962. The serial number reflects the series, model designation, and sequential production number, e.g., the 641 Ford tractor is Series 601, Model 641.

5** Single-row 8-inch offset tractor with 134-cubic-inch gasoline/LP-gas or 144-cubic-inch diesel engine

6** Four-wheel adjustable axle with 134-cubic-inch gasoline/LP-gas or 144-cubic-inch diesel engine

7** High-clearance row crop with 134-cubic-inch gasoline, LP-gas, or diesel engine

8** Four-wheel adjustable axle with 172-cubic-inch engine

In 1961 Ford Motor Company introduced its "Long Blue Line" of tractors, which included the Model 2000. Ford was the master of model variations offering the 2000 in at least seven different versions including four-, six-, and eight-speed tractors sold with either gas or diesel engines. The standard engine was a 158-cubic-inch power plant that generated a maximum 30½ (PTO) horsepower.

234

9** High-clearance row-crop type with 172-cubic-inch engine
1 Select-O-Speed transmission without PTO
2 Four-speed transmission without PTO or hydraulic lift
3 Four-speed transmission without PTO
4 Four-speed transmission
5 Five-speed transmission with transmission PTO
6 Five-speed transmission with live PTO
*7*Select-O-Speed transmission with single-speed PTO
*8*Select-O-Speed transmission with two-speed and ground drive

PTO
**0 Series designation, 1955 to 1958
**1 Series designation, 1958 to 1962
***-1 Tricycle type with single front wheel
***-4 High clearance, four-wheel adjustable axle type
***-D Diesel engine
***-L LP-gas engine
***-37 Equipped with Sherman Reversing Transmission
***-21 Equipped with Sherman Combination Transmission

Thousand Series Model Numbers
2***134-cubic-inch gasoline or 144-cubic-inch diesel engine
4***172-cubic-inch gasoline, LPG, or diesel engine
*0**Industrial models produced prior to 1963
*1**Industrial and agricultural models produced after 1963
**3*Utility-type tractor with nonadjustable front axle
**4*Heavy-duty industrial-type with sub frame
***1 Low center of gravity model
***1 Four-speed without PTO or hydraulic system
***2 Four-speed with hydraulic system, without PTO
***3 Four-speed with hydraulic system and PTO

Gaar-Scott serial numbers

Steam traction engine serial numbers

Year	Beginning number
1885	4,158
1886	4,331
1887	4,666
1888	4,817
1889	5,118
1890	5,519
1891	5,861
1892	6,362
1893	No data available
1894	7,233
1895	7,519
1896	7,842
1897	8,216
1898	8,568
1899	9,061
1900	9,603
1901	10,109
1902	10,775
1903	11,475
1904	11,967
1905	12,548
1906	13,071
1907	13,597
1908	14,052
1909	14,363
1910	14,738
1911	15,288
1912	15,608
1913	16,182
1914	16,544

THE GAAR-SCOTT
TIGER LINE
MANUFACTURED BY
M. RUMELY CO.
RICHMOND, IND., U.S.A.

Hart-Parr serial numbers

Little Red Devil

Year	Beginning number
1914	6219
1915	6245
1916	6244

10-20 B

Year	Beginning number
1921	35001
1922	35217

10-20 C

Year	Beginning number
1922	35501
1923	35528
1924	35761

12-24 E

Year	Beginning number
1924	36001
1925	36075
1926	36601
1927	37195
1928	38119

12-24 H

Year	Beginning number
1928	39602
1929	39687
1930	42278

12-27

Year	Beginning number
1914	5816
1915	5993

15-30

Year	Beginning number
1910	2332
1911	2353
1912	2383

15-30 A

Year	Beginning number
1918	8401
1919	9384
1921	18470
1922	18851

15-30 A

Year	Beginning number
1920	13026-17915

15-30 C

Year	Beginning number
1922	21001
1923	21393
1924	21899

16-30 E

Year	Beginning number
1924	22501
1925	22602

16-30 F

Year	Beginning number
1926	24001

17-30

Year	Beginning number
1901	1205
1902	1206
1903	1208-1219
1904	None built
1905	1346-1347
1906	1435-1454

18-30

Year	Beginning number
1903	1207 only

18-36 G

Year	Beginning number
1926	26001
1927	26360

18-36 H

Year	Beginning number
1927	28851
1928	29636
1929	24567
1929	85001
1930	89159

20-40

Year	Beginning number
1912	4112-4211
1913	4714
1914	4764

22-40

Year	Beginning number
1923	70001
1924	70021
1925	70114
1926	70251
1927	70494

22-40

Year	Beginning number
1923	70001
1924	70021
1925	70114
1926	70251
1927	70494

28-50

Year	Beginning number
1927	70501
1928	70719
1929	70968
1930	71401

40-80

Year	Beginning number
1908	2015
1909	2019
1910	2025
1911	2101
1912	2201
1913	2276
1914	2301

30-60

Year	Beginning number
1907	1605
1908	1811-2014
1909	2325-2331
1910	2432
1911	3311-3999
1912	4212-4711
1913	4814
1914	5262
1915	5441
1916	5522
1917	5552
1918	5641

60-100

Year	Beginning number
1911	4000
1912	4101

Huber serial numbers

Huber tractor models shared a unified serial number system where the year any model was made is determined by its serial number regardless of make. Huber models included the Model B, Farmers Tractor, HK 32-45, HS 27-42, K, Light Four 12-25, Light Four 20-36, Mast Four 25-50, Modern Farmer, Modern Farmer L, Modern Farmer LC, Modern Farmer SC, OB Orchard, Super Four 15-30, Super Four 18-36, Super Four 20-40, Super Four 25-50, Super Four 32-45, Supter Four 40-62, Farmer Tractor 13-22, 20-40, 30-60, and the 35-70.

Year	Number range
1911	100-181
1212	182-217
1913	218-320
1914	321-402
1915	403-511
1916	512-639
1917	640-1612
1918	1613-2179
No record of nos.	2180-4501
1919	4502-5426
1920	5427-6499
1921	6500-7029
1922	7030-7256
1923	7257-7427
1924	7428-7702
1925	7703-8023
1926	8024-8399
1927	8400-8957
1928	8958-9399
1929	9400-10187
1930	10188-10707
1931	10708-10964
1932	10965-11044
1933	11045-11077
1934	11078-11143
1935	11144-11487
1936	11488-11958
1937	11959-12845
1938	12846-13460
1939	13461-13796
1940	13797-13930
1941	13931-14018
1942	14019-14258
1943	14259-14303

International Harvester serial numbers

The numbers listed here include those for tractors built under the names of International Harvester Company, International, Farmall, McCormick, and McCormick-Deering.

Except where indicated, number nameplate is generally found on the left or right side of transmission housing or clutch housing.

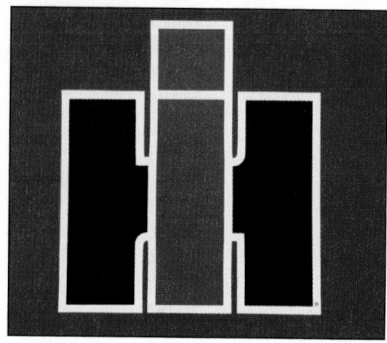

International and Farmall

8-16 Mogul

Year	Number range
1915	SB501-SB3750
1916, 1917	SB3751-SB15000

10-20 Mogul

Year	Number range
1917-1919	BC501 - ?

12-25 Mogul

Year	Number range
1913-1918	F501-F750 (flat head)
1913-1918	F751-F2100 (round)

10-20 Titan with barrel

Year	Number range
1916	TV116-TV2356
1917	TV2357-TV11397
1918	TV11398-TV29072
1919	TV29073-TV46306
1920	TV46307-TV50235
1920	TY50236-TY67810
1921	TY67811-TY75539
1922	TY75540-TY78464

I-130 and F-130

Year	Beginning number
1956	501
1957	1120
1958	8363

I-966 and F-966

Year	Beginning number
1971	7101
1972	11815
1973	17794
1974	22526
1975	28119

I-140 and F-140

Year	Beginning number
1958	501
1959	2011
1960	8082
1961	11168
1962	16637
1963	21181
1964	25387
1965	28408
1966	31285
1967	34818
1968	37352
1969	39906
1970	42300
1971	44424
1972	46605
1973	48507
1974	50720
1975	54273

I-1066 and F-1066

Year	Beginning number
1971	7101
1972	12677
1973	24205
1974	34849
1975	46855

I-1466 and F-1466

Year	Beginning number
1971	7101
1972	10408
1973	15533
1974	19746
1975	25404

I-1468 and F-1468

Year	Beginning number
1971	7201
1972	7239
1973	9109
1974	9670

I-1566 and F-1566

Year	Beginning number
1974	7101
1975	7837

I-1568 and F-1569

Year	Beginning number
1974	7201
1975	7821

10-20 Gear Drive – KC

Year	Beginning number
1923	501
1924	7641
1925	18869
1926	37728
1927	62824
1928	89470
1929	119823
1930	159111
1931	191486
1932	201213
1934	204239
1935	206179
1936	207275
1937	210235
1938	212425
1939	214886

10-20 Gear Drive – NC and NT

Year	Beginning number
1926	501
1927	649
1928	832
1929	1155
1930	1543
1931	1750
1932	1833
1933	1912
1934	1952

Cub

Number nameplate is located on the right side of the steering gear housing.

Year	Beginning number
1947	501
1948	11348
1949	57831
1950	99536
1951	121454
1952	144455
1953	162284
1954	179412
1955	186441
1956	193658
1957	198231
1958	204389
1959	211441
1960	214974
1961	217382
1962	220038
1963	221383
1964	223453
1965	225110
1966	227209
1967	229225
1968	231005
1969	232981
1970	234868
1971	238506
1973	240581
1974	242746
1975	245651

Cub Cadet

Year	Beginning number
1961	590
1962	23675
1963	49846
1964	73875
1965	104307
1966	137051
1968	225056
1969	280840
1970	322858
1971	373301
1972	417643
1973	457305
1974	495749
1975	536073

International Harvester serial numbers

Cub Lo-Boy
Number nameplate is located on the right side of the steering gear housing.

Year	Beginning number
1955	501
1956	2555
1957	3929
1958	5582
1959	10567
1960	12371
1961	13904
1962	15506
1963	16440
1964	17928
1965	19406
1966	21176
1967	23115
1968	24481

Cub 154 Lo-Boy and 185 Lo-Boy
Number nameplate is located on the top left front side of the main frame.

Cub 154 Lo-Boy

Year	Beginning number
1968	3505
1969	3773
1970	15502
1971	20332
1972	23343
1973	27538
1974	31766

Cub 185 Lo-Boy

Year	Beginning number
1974	37001
1975	37316

International B-275

Year	Beginning number
1959	501
1960	1720
1961	3415

Hydro 70

Year	Beginning number
1973	7501
1974	7570
1975	8681

Hydro 100

Year	Beginning number
1973	7501
1974	7727
1975	10915

I-6, ID-6, I-9, and ID-9
Number nameplate is located on left side of clutch compartment cover.

I-6 and ID-6

Year	Beginning number
1940	501
1941	1225
1942	3718
1943	5057
1944	6371
1945	9518
1946	14198
1947	17317
1948	24021
1949	28868
1950	35472
1951	38518
1952	44318
1953	45274

I-9 and ID-9

Year	Beginning number
1940	501
1941	578
1942	3003
1943	3651
1944	5501
1945	11459
1946	17294
1947	22715
1948	29207
1949	36350
1950	45689
1951	51739
1952	59407
1953	64014

I-100

Year	Beginning number
1954	501
1955	504
1956	575

I-240

Year	Beginning number
1958	501
1959	4835
1960	8628
1961	10079
1962	10727

I-300U

Year	Beginning number
1955	501
1956	20219

I-330

Year	Beginning number
1957	501
1958	1488

I-340

Year	Beginning number
1958	501
1959	2467
1960	5741
1961	8736
1962	11141
1963	12032

I-350

Year	Beginning number
1956	501
1957	1963
1958	15049

IW-400

Year	Beginning number
1955	501
1956	2187

I-424

Year	Beginning number
1964	501
1965	1402
1966	7841
1967	13627

I-444

Year	Beginning number
1967	501
1968	1190
1969	5720
1970	9010
1971	12357

I-404 and 2404

Year	Beginning number
1961	501
1962	1045
1963	4205
1964	6452
1965	8292
1966	9548
1967	10534
1968	11032

IW-450

1956	501
1957	568
1958	1661

I-454

Year	Beginning number
1970	501
1971	508
1972	4908
1973	8064

I-460

Year	Beginning number
1958	501
1959	2711
1960	6883
1961	9420
1962	11619
1963	11898

I-464

Year	Beginning number
1973	100003
1974	102196
1975	104775

I-544 and 2544

Year	Beginning number
1968	10250
1969	12699
1970	14589
1971	16018
1972	16838
1973	17341

International Harvester serial numbers

I-504 and 2504

Year	Beginning number
1961	501
1962	512
1963	3376
1964	6797
1965	10996
1966	14695
1967	17992
1968	20392

I-560

Year	Beginning number
1958	501
1959	1210
1960	3103
1961	4032
1962	4944
1963	5598

I-574

Year	Beginning number
1970	504
1971	650
1972	3329
1973	7074
1974	102961
1975	107880

I-600

Year	Beginning number
1956	501

I-606 and 2606

Year	Beginning number
1961	501
1962	503
1963	1702
1964	3214
1965	5041
1966	6960
1967	7922

I-650

Year	Beginning number
1956	501
1957	688
1958	11659

I-656 and 2656

Year	Beginning number
1966	7501
1967	7842
1968	9929
1969	11802
1970	13353
1971	14194
1972	14952
1973	15746

I-660

Year	Beginning number
1959	501
1960	3398
1961	4259
1962	5883
1963	6995

I-664

Year	Beginning number
1972	2501
1973	3212

I-666

Year	Beginning number
1972	7500
1973	8200
1974	11585
1975	13131

I-674

Year	Beginning number
1973	100001
1974	101862
1975	103172

I-706 and 2706

Year	Beginning number
1963	501
1964	1251
1965	3478
1966	4789
1967	5316

I-756 and 2756

Year	Beginning number
1967	7501
1968	7672

1969	8164
1970	8424
1971	8427

I-766

Year	Beginning number
1971	7101
1972	7416
1973	9611
1974	12378
1975	14360

I-806 and 2806

Year	Beginning number
1963	501
1964	1403
1965	3758
1966	5917
1967	7409

I-826 and 2826

Year	Beginning number
1969	7501
1970	7518
1971	7719

I-856 and 2856

Year	Beginning number
1967	7501
1968	7904
1969	9016
1970	9544
1971	9653

I-1026 and 21026

Year	Beginning number
1970	7501
1971	7550

I-1206 and 21206

Year	Beginning number
1965	7501
1966	7772
1967	8492

I-1256 and 21256

Year	Beginning number
1967	7501
1968	7703
1969	8444

I-1456 and 21456

Year	Beginning number
1969	10001
1970	10025
1971	10249

I-4100

Year	Beginning number
1966	8001
1967	8723
1968	8986

I-4156

Year	Beginning number
1969	9219
1970	9365

I-4166

Year	Beginning number
1972	10001
1973	10769
1974	11255
1975	11684

I-4366 and I-4568

Number nameplate is located on left side on top step.

I-4366

Year	Beginning number
1973	7501
1974	7780
1975	8616

I-4568

Year	Beginning number
1975	8001

Farmall 100

Year	Beginning number
1954	501
1955	1720
1956	12895

200

Year	Beginning number
1954	501
1955	1032
1956	10904

International Harvester serial numbers

230

Year	Beginning number
1956	501
1957	815
1958	6827

240

Year	Beginning number
1958	501
1959	1777
1960	3415
1961	3989

300

Year	Beginning number
1954	501
1955	1779
1956	23224

340

Year	Beginning number
1958	501
1959	2723
1960	5411
1961	6642
1962	7276
1963	7699

350

Year	Beginning number
1956	501
1957	1004
1958	14175

400

Year	Beginning number
1954	501
1955	2588
1956	29065

404

Year	Beginning number
1961	501
1962	826
1963	1936
1964	2259
1965	2568
1966	2790
1967	2980
1968	3170

450

Year	Beginning number
1956	501
1957	1734
1958	21871

460

Year	Beginning number
1958	501
1959	4765
1960	16902
1961	22622
1962	28029
1963	31552

504

Year	Beginning number
1961	501
1962	810
1963	5000
1964	7732
1965	10696
1966	13596
1967	15113
1968	16115

544

Year	Beginning number
1968	10253
1969	12541
1970	13585
1971	14507
1972	15262
1973	15738

560

Year	Beginning number
1958	501
1959	7341
1960	26914
1961	36125
1962	47798
1963	60278

656

Year	Beginning number
1965	8501
1966	15505
1967	24372

1968	32007
1969	38861
1970	42518
1971	45497
1972	47951

666

Year	Beginning number
1972	7500
1973	8200
1974	11585
1975	13131

706

Year	Beginning number
1963	501
1964	7073
1965	21162
1966	30288
1967	38521

756

Year	Beginning number
1967	7501
1968	9940
1969	14125
1970	17832
1971	18374

806

Year	Beginning number
1963	501
1964	4709
1965	15946
1966	24038
1967	34943

826

Year	Beginning number
1969	7501
1970	8153
1971	16352

856

Year	Beginning number
1967	7501
1968	9854
1969	19554
1970	32099
1971	32420

1026

Year	Beginning number
1970	7501
1971	9707

1206

Year	Beginning number
1965	7501
1966	8626
1967	12731

1256

Year	Beginning number
1967	7501
1968	8849
1969	13140

1456

Year	Beginning number
1969	10001
1970	10405
1971	14149

A, AV, B, and BN

Number nameplate is located on left side of seat support.

Year	Beginning number
1939	501
1940	6744
1941	41500
1942	8739
1944	96390
1945	113218
1946	146700
1947	182964

Super A

Number nameplate is located on right side of toolbox and seat support.

Year	Beginning number
1947	250001
1948	250082
1949	268196
1950	281269
1951	300126
1952	324470
1953	336880
1954	353348

International Harvester serial numbers

C

Year	Beginning number
1948	501
1949	22624
1950	47010
1951	71880

Super C

Year	Beginning number
1951	100001
1952	131157
1953	159130
1954	187788

F-12

Year	Number range
1932	501-525
1933	526-4880
1934	4881-17410
1935	17411-48659
1936	48660-81836
1937	81837-117517
1938	117518-123942

F-14

Year	Number range
1938	124000-139606
1939	139607-155902

F-20

Year	Beginning number
1932	501
1933	1251
1934	3001
1935	6382

F-30

Year	Beginning number
1931	501
1932	1184
1933	4305
1934	5526
1935	7032
1936	10407
1937	18684
1938	27186
1939	29007

H and HV

Year	Beginning number
1939	501
1940	10653
1941	52387
1942	93237
1943	122091
1944	150251
1945	186123
1946	214820
1947	241143
1948	268991
1949	300876
1950	327975
1951	351923
1952	375861
1953	390500

Super H and HV

Year	Beginning number
1953	501
1954	22202

M, MD, MDV, and M

Year	Beginning number
1939	501
1940	7240
1941	25371
1942	50988
1943	60011
1944	67424
1945	88085
1946	105564
1947	122823
1948	151708
1949	180514
1950	213579
1951	147518
1952	290923

Super M, MD, MDV, MTA, and MV

Year	Beginning number
1952	F501
1952	L500001
1953	F12516
1953	L501906
1954	F51977
1954	L600001

Regular and Fairway

Year	Beginning number
1924	501
1925	701
1926	1539
1927	5969
1928	15471
1929	40370
1930	75691
1931	117784
1932	131872

McCormick

O-4, OS-4, W-4, and Super W-4

Number nameplate is located on left side of transmission housing.

O-4, OS-4, and W-4

Year	Beginning number
1940	501
1941	943
1942	4056
1943	5693
1944	7593
1945	11171
1946	13934
1947	16022
1948	18880
1949	21912
1950	24470
1951	28167
1952	31214
1953	33067

Super W-4

Year	Beginning number
1953	501
1954	2668

O-6, OS-6, ODS-6, W-6, and WD-6

Number nameplate is located on left side of clutch compartment cover.

1940	501
1941	1225
1942	3718
1943	5057
1944	6313
1945	9396
1948	14153
1947	17792
1948	22961

1949	28704
1950	33698
1951	28518
1952	44318
1953	45274

Super W-6, W-6TA, and WD-6

Number nameplate is located on left side of transmission housing.

Year	Beginning number
1952	501
1953	2908
1954	8997

W-9, WD-9, WDR-9, and WR-9

Number nameplate is located on the right side of the fuel tank support, located above the clutch housing.

Year	Beginning number
1940	501
1941	578
1942	2993
1943	3651
1944	5394
1945	11459
1946	17289
1947	22714
1948	29207
1949	36159
1950	45551
1951	51739
1952	59407
1953	64014

WR-9-S

Year	Beginning number
1953	501
1954	550
1955	722
1956	755

W-30

Year	Beginning number
1932	50
1933	522
1934	548
1935	3182
1936	9723
1937	15095
1938	23834
1939	29922
1940	32482

International Harvester serial numbers

McCormick-Deering

O-12, O-14, and Fairway 12 & 14
Year	Beginning number
1934	512
1935	1092
1936	1626
1937	2277
1938	3261
1939	3882

W-12
Year	Beginning number
1934	503
1935	1356
1936	2031
1937	2768
1938	3799

W-14
Year	Beginning number
1938	4134
1939	4610

W-40, WD-40, and WK-40
Year	Beginning number
1935	501
1936	1441
1937	5120
1938	7665
1939	9756
1940	10323

International Crawlers

100 Series C
Year	Beginning number
1970	501
1971	599
1972	946
1973	1152
1974	1473

100 Series E
Year	Beginning number
1974	4001
1975	4287

125 Series C
Year	Beginning number
1970	501
1971	647
1972	1077
1973	1427
1974	1854

125 Series E
Year	Beginning number
1974	6001
1975	6384

500
Year	Beginning number
1965	501
1966	891
1967	2501
1968	3544
1969	4065

500C
Year	Beginning number
1970	1377
1971	2577
1972	3189
1973	4018
1974	4961

500E
Year	Beginning number
1974	5501
1975	6103

T-6 and TD-6
Year	Beginning number
1940	?
1941	17373
1949	21146
1950	24862
1951	27692
1952	31056
1953	33157
1954	35746
1955	37570
1956	38706
1956 TD-61	38951
1957	39817
1958	40822

Year	Beginning number
1959	41448
1959 TD-62	501
1960	1063
1961	1629
1962	2056
1963	2404
1964	2758
1965	3177
1966	3631
1967	3991
1968	4221
1969	4424

T-20

Year	Beginning number
1931	501
1932	551
1933	2051
1934	2528
1935	3276
1936	5387
1937	8501
1938	12519
1939	14550

TD-7 Series C

Year	Beginning number
1979	501
1971	694
1972	1040
1973	1471
1974	2007

TD-7 Series E

Year	Beginning number
1974	3001
1975	3379

TD-8 Series C

Year	Beginning number
1970	501
1971	704
1972	1023
1973	459
1974	1912

TD-8 Series E

Year	Beginning number
1974	5001
1975	5521

Unless otherwise indicated, tractor number is stamped on the instrument panel nameplate.

T-9

Year	Beginning number
1940	Begin?
1948	29519
1949	32978
1950	36927
1951	40465
1952	44710
1953	47855
1954	52600
1955	56276
1956	58819

TD-9

Year	Beginning number
1940	Begin?
1948	29512
1949	32973
1950	36963
1951	40400
1952	44710
1953	48848
1954	52599
1955	56208
1956	56436
1956 TD-91	60301
1957	63946
1958	65802
1959	57290
1959 TD-92	201
1960	3353
1961	5895
1962	6090
1962 TD-9B	7502
1963	6455
1964	8898
1965	10446
1966	11685
1970	51530
1971	15965
1972	16243
1973	16499
1974	16732

International Harvester serial numbers

TD-14 and TD-14A

Year	Beginning number
1939	501
1940	575
1941	2045
1942	3856
1943	5380
1944	7451
1945	10728
1946	12704
1947	14437
1948	21027
1949	26001
1950	27082
1951	29361
1952	32427
1953	34525
1954	37344
1955	39061
1956 TD-141	39301
1956	40862
1956 TD-142	41551
1957	43968

TD-15

Year	Beginning number
1958	501
1959	577
1960 TD-150	2456
1961	3501
1961 TD-151	4001
1962	4680
1963 TD-15B	6001
1964	7100
1965	8935
1966	20377

TD-15C

Year	Beginning number
1972	501
1973	1130
1974	1849
1975	2750

TD-18

Year	Beginning number
1939	520
1940	1240

1941	2292
1942	3607
1943	5804
1944	6899
1945	9011
1946	11092
1947	12644
1948	14626
1949	16708

TD-18A

Year	Beginning number
1939	520
1940	1240
1941	2292
1942	3607
1943	5804
1944	6899
1945	9011
1946	11092
1947	12644
1948	14626
1949	16708

TD-24

Year	Beginning number
1947	506
1948	515
1949	1501
1950	1967
1951	2915
1952	4120
1953	5075
1954	6049
1955	6556

TD-241

Year	Beginning number
1955	8001
1956	8793
1957	9655
1958	10330
1959	10631

TD-24 – 241 Series

Year	Beginning number
1955	601
1956	826
1957	1249
1958	1420
1959	1598

TD-40

Year	Beginning number
1934	2501
1935	2785
1936	4393
1938	7719
1939	8599

TD-340

Year	Beginning number
1960	1979
1961	5370
1962	6169
1963	6397
1964	7338
1965	8525

Stationary engines

IHC Type M
1½ hp., 650 rpm, kerosene

Year	Beginning number
1917	A101
1918	A1970
1919	A19492
1920	A42765
1921	A70745
1922	A82430
1923	A91826

IHC Type M
1½ hp., 500 rpm, gasoline

1923	Ab101
1924	AB153
1925	AB1061
1926	AB1786
1927	AB1880
1928	AB1923
1929	AB2006
1930	AB2031
1931	AB2039
1932	AB2046

IHC Type M
1½ hp., 500 rpm, kerosene

Year	Beginning number
1924	AX101
1925	AX530–
1926	AX3407
1927	AX5344
1928	AX7452
1929	AX10274
1930	AX13178
1931	AX16092
1932	AX16333
1933	AX16474

IHC Type M
3 hp., kerosene

Year	Beginning number
1918	B101
1919	B3038
1920	B15813
1921	B35786
1922	B42783
1922	B45951
1923	B49813
1924	B59660
1925	B64819
1926	B65032
1927	B65294
1928	B65322
1929	B65362
1930	B65381
1931	B65386
1932	B65392

IHC Type M
6 hp., kerosene

Year	Beginning number
1925	CW101
1926	CW2297
1927	CW7201
1928	CW11202
1929	CW14401
1930	CW17972
1931	CW19989
1932	CW20623
1933	CW21203
1934	CW21222
1935	CW21471
1936	CW21783
1937	CW21855

International Harvester serial numbers

IHC Type M
6 hp., kerosene

Year	Beginning number
1918	C101
1919	C752
1920	C6873
1921	C16143
1922	C20458
1922	C22211
1923	C25768
1924	C31469
1924	C34575
1925	C34730
1926	C34824
1927	C34971
1928	C34994
1929	C35026
1930	C35044
1931	C35058
1932	C35068
1934	C35073

IHC Type M
10 hp., kerosene

Year	Beginning number
1920	D101
1921	D1390
1922	D2749
1922	D3076
1923	D3350
1924	D3930
1925	D3955
1926	D4228
1927	D4680
1928	D4783
1929	D4862
1930	D4981
1931	D5052
1932	D5069
1933	D5082

IHC Type M
10 hp., kerosene

Year	Beginning number
1927	DW157
1928	DW672
1929	DW848
1930	DW1184
1931	DW1331
1932	DW1402

IHC Type L
1½ hp.

Year	Beginning number
1929	EW101

McCormick Deering Type LA
1½ - 2½ hp.

Year	Beginning number
1934	LA101
1935	LA133
1936	LA14655
1936	LAA17853
1937	LAA29505
1938	LAA41947

McCormick Deering Type LA
3 to 5 hp.

Year	Beginning number
1935	LA501
1936	LA981
1936	LAB1726
1937	LAB4471
1938	LAB9030

McCormick Deering Type LB
1½ - 2½ hp.

Year	Beginning number
1941	62614
1942	66394
1943	72944
1944	76061
1945	86648
1946	100999
1947	114788
1948	130394

McCormick Deering Type LB
3 to 5 hp.

Year	Beginning number
1941	22287
1942	25274
1943	30923
1944	33509
1945	40101
1946	48767
1947	56536
1948	63626

J.I. Case serial numbers

For all J.I. Case, except for the Models 70, 90, 94, and 96 Series, serial numbers can be found stamped on the nameplate fastened to the instrument panel. Serial numbers can also be found on the toolbox.

B, C, CC, CI, CO, R, RC, D, DC, DI, DO, LA, LAI, S, SC, SI, SO, V, VC, VI, VO, VAC, VAH, VAI, VAO, and W

Year	Beginning number
1929	300201
1930	300301
1931	300401
1932	300501
1933	300601
1934	300701
1935	300801
1936	300901
1937	301001
1938	4200001
1939	4300001
1940	4400001
1941	4500001
1942	4600001
1943	4700001
1944	4800001
1945	4900001
1946	5000001
1947	5100001
1948	5200001
1949	5300001
1950	5400001
1951	5500001
1952	5600001
1953	5700001
1954	5800001
1955	5900001
1956	6000001

9-18

Year	Beginning Number
1912	100
1913	891
1914	2496
1915	2842
1916	3691
1917	7492
1918	13285

10-18

Year	Beginning number
1918	13285
1919	22223
1920	32841
1921	42256
1922	43943

10-20

Year	Beginning number
1915	2842
1916	3691
1917	7492
1918	13285

12-20

Year	Beginning number
1921	42256
1922	43943
1923	45281
1924	48227
1925	48402
1926	55919
1927	62409

12-25

Year	Beginning number
1914	2496
1915	2842
1916	3691
1917	7492
1918	13285

J.I. Case serial numbers

15-27

Year	Beginning number
1919	22223
1920	42435
1921	42835
1922	42852
1923	43435
1924	48413

18-32

Year	Beginning number
1925	51678
1926	55919
1927	62409

20-40

Year	Beginning number
1912	100
1913	691
1914	2496
1915	2842
1916	3691
1917	7492
1918	13285
1919	22223

22-40

Year	Beginning number
1919	22223
1920	32841
1921	42256
1922	43943
1923	45281
1924	48413
1925	51678

30-60

Year	Beginning number
1912	100
1913	691
1914	2496
1915	2842
1916	3691

40-72

Year	Beginning number
1921	40256
1922	43943
1923	45281

40-80

Year	Beginning number
1915	2842

200B and 210B

Year	Beginning number
1958	6095001
1959	6120001

211B, 311B, 411B, 511B, and 611B

Year	Beginning number
1958	5095001
1959	6120001

300 and 320

Year	Beginning number
1956	605000301
1957	6075001

300B, 310B, and 320B

Year	Beginning number
1958	6095001
1959	6120001

300 and 400

Year	Beginning number
1957	3000001

320

Year	Beginning number
1956	6050301
1957	6075001
1958	6095001
1959	6120001

400

Year	Beginning number
1955	8060001
1956	8080001
1957	8100001

400B

Year	Beginning number
1958	6095001
1959	6120001

420B

Year	Beginning number
1958	6095001
1959	6120001

Models 430 and 530 Utility

Year	Beginning number
1960	3012275

Models 430 and 530

Year	Beginning number
Utility	1961

Models 430, 530, 530B, 630, 730, 830, 930, and 1030

Year	Beginning number
1960	8160001
1961	8168801
1962	8190001
1963	8208001
1964	8229001
1965	8253501
1966	8279001
1967	8306501
1968	8332101
1969	8356251

Models 470, 570, 590B, 770, 870, 970, 1070, 1090, and 1170

Year	Beginning number
1970	8650001
1971	8674001
1972	8693001
1973	8712001
1974	8736601
1975	8770001

For Case 70 Series tractors, the serial number is stamped just above the platform floor and next to the steering wheel on the left-hand side of the tractor.

500

Year	Beginning number
1953	5700001
1954	8035001
1955	8060001
1956	8080001
1957	8100001

500B and 600B

Year	Beginning number
1958	6095001
1959	6120001

600

Year	Beginning number
1957	8100001

680C

Year	Beginning number
1969	9103226
1970	9104651
1971	9106001

700 and 800

Year	Beginning number
1958	8120001
1959	8140001

900

Year	Beginning number
1957	8100001
1958	8120001
1959	8140001

1031 and 1032

Year	Beginning number
1966	8279001
1967	8306501
1968	8332101
1969	8356251

1175, 1270, and 1370

Year	Beginning number
1972	8693001
1973	8712001
1974	8736601
1975	8770001

1200TK

Year	Beginning number
1966	9802101
1967	9806101
1968	9808000
1969	9808276

1470TK

Year	Beginning number
1969	9810000
1970	9811301
1971	8674001
1972	8691901

J. I. Case serial numbers

2470 and 2670

Year	Beginning number
1971	8674001
1972	8692381
1973	8712001
1974	8762001
1975	8767001

A, AE, and AI

Year	Beginning number
1928	69004
1929	69803

B

Year	Beginning number
1928	69004

D and LA

Year	Beginning number
1953	5700001
1954	5800001

K

Year	Beginning number
1928	69004
1929	69803

L and LI

Year	Beginning number
1929	303201
1930	303301
1931	303401
1932	303501
1933	303601
1934	303701
1935	303801
1936	303901
1937	304001
1938	4200001
1939	4300001
1940	4400001

S

Year	Beginning number
1953	5700001
1954	8035001

T and TE

Year	Beginning number
1928	69004
1929	69803

VA

Year	Beginning number
1953	5750001
1954	6011001
1955	6038001

At the beginning of the 1960s, J.I. Case introduced a new series of workhorses referred to as the 30 Series tractors. The big brother of that line, the Model 930, was powered by a Case-built 401-cubic-inch, six-cylinder diesel rated at 1,600 rpm. At the Nebraska Tractor Test the 930 generated 71.9 drawbar horsepower. Power was transferred through a six-speed transmission. Other 930 features included a chain final drive and oil-lubricated hand clutch. The 930 would stay in production until 1969.

Making of a Deere expert

By Roger Welsch

I gave a John Deere B to wife Linda for Christmas one year – an improvement, she said, over the time I bought her a shotgun. But not much of one.

Any any rate, now that we've had this malicious beast for a while, I'm pretty much an expert on this model of John Deere, about the same as I am an expert on the Allis-Chalmers Model WC, in fact. I even got it started once.

There are signs this tractor was not reassembled with total care and precision, but I hope to work some of those problems out – if I ever get it started again. For one thing, the clutch doesn't work worth a darn; I don't know how many times and how hard I pushed on that blasted pedal and still couldn't get it in gear without a terrible grinding of gears. My left foot is still sore.

Moreover, I think I've figured out why it won't start, let alone run. Dick Day, my buddy who restored the tractor and sold it to me (he should run for Congress; he has all the qualifications), was either in too much of a hurry or maybe thought he could scrounge enough parts to make two tractors out of one. Thing is, when he reassembled this machine, he left off two of the cylinders. Unless they're somewhere else, because all I can find is two.

And even then, I tried to check the ignition setup, but Dick just hung up on me when I asked him what the firing order is. Maybe one of you readers who knows something abut green machines can give me some help on this.

The John Deere is going to take some getting used to, no doubt about it. I tried to use it with my buzzsaw but had a heck of a time getting my big old Allis belt to fit on that skinny little belt pulley. And who designed these things anyway? You can't get at the starter switch or choke when the belt is on the pulley!

My John Deere pals up in town have been very helpful. More helpful than usual, in fact. They usually just give me a bad time whenever I ask them about my tractor problems, but this time when I described my woes at getting the thing running, they showered me with good advice.

Kenny Porath pointed out one possible problem: The gas line had been mistakenly hooked up from the carburetor to the gas tank rather than from the gas tank to the carburetor. He said he could fix that up for me, but he'd have to charge for two hours labor, no cost on the parts. What a guy!

Dennis Adams suggested that I dismantle the fuel pump and put a rebuild kit in it, which I am going to try this very weekend. He even had a spare fuel pump kit that he very reluctantly let me have for $40.

Dan Selden chimed in that his dad had pretty much the same problem with a John Deere B but, in his case, the problem turned out to be the water pump. And darned if he didn't have a complete (and very rare, he says) overhaul kit for a John Deere B water pump, which he let me have for another $40.

Melvin Nelson got to looking around Linda's tractor and happened to notice it was missing its crank. Well, soon he was looking through the drawers in his shop and just happened to find a like-new John Deere B crank, which he dang near gave me for, well – $40. Funny how that works out, huh?

You're a Deere man and want to get started with Allis WCs like mine? No problem at all. All you need is a set of Allis socket wrenches. I'm sure Dennis or Dan can help you out with a little thing like that. And if you're missing something, just ask around town. You're certain to find some good buddy who's ready and willing to help you out. And, in all probability, it won't cost you much more than, well, uh – $40.

Speak of the devil, here's Al Schmitt coming into my drive this very minute with that muffler oil he said he'd round up. And he said he could get it for me at a good price. With pals like mine, it doesn't take long to get an old tractor up and running darn near like new. And I'm willing to bet that given half a chance, they'd do the same for you.

Mine a treasure trove of Roger Welsch's musings and talk to the master of tractor mayhem in person at agelessiron.com.

John Deere serial numbers

Years are product years (usually August 1 of the preceding calendar year to the following July 31) unless noted as follows: *Calendar Year; **Fiscal Year (November 1 to October 31).
Tractors are listed alphabetically and numerically, rather than chronologically.

A

Year	Beginning number
1934	410 000
1935	412 869
1936	424 025
1937	442 151
1938	466 787
1939	477 000
1940	488 000
1941	499 000
1942	514 127
1943	523 133
1944	528 778
1945	548 352
1946	555 334
1947	578 516
1948	594 433
1949	620 843
1950	648 000
1951	667 390
1952	689 880

AO and AR

Year	Beginning number
1936	250 000
1937	253 521
1938	255 416
1939	257 004
1940	258 045
1941	260 000
1942	261 558
1943	262 243
1944	263 223
1945	264 738
1946	265 870
1947	267 082
1948	268 877
1949	270 646
1950	272 985
1951	276 078
1952	279 770
1953	282 551

AO (Styled)

Year	Beginning number
1937	AO-1000
1938	AO-1539
1939	AO-1725
1940	AO-1801

B

Year	Beginning number
1935	1 000
1936	12 012
1937	27 389
1938	46 175
1939	60 000
1940	81 600
1941	96 000
1942	126 345
1943	143 420
1944	152 862
1945	173 179
1946	183 673
1947	199 744
1948	209 295
1949	237 346
1950	258 205
1951	276 557
1952	299 175

BO and BR

Year	Beginning number
1936	325 000
1937	326 655
1938	328 111
1939	329 000
1940	330 633
1941	332 039
1942	332 427
1943	332 780
1944	333 156
1945	334 219
1946	335 641
1947	336 746

BO (Lindeman) Crawler

Year	Beginning number
1943	332 901
1944	333 110
1945	333 666
1946	335 361
1947	336 441

D

Year	Beginning number
1924	30 401
1925	31 280
1926	35 309
1927	43 410
1928	54 554
1929	71 561
1930	95 367
1931	109 944
1932	115 477
1933	115 665
1934	116 273
1935	119 100
1936	125 430
1937	130 700
1938	138 413
1939	143 800
1940	146 566
1941	149 500
1942	152 840
1943	155 005
1944	155 426
1945	159 888
1946	162 598
1947	167 250
1948	174 879
1949	183 516
1950	188 420
1951	189 701
1952	191 180
1953	191 439

G/GM/G

Year	Beginning number
1938	1 000
1939	7 734
1940	9 321
1941	10 489
1942	12 069
1943	12 941
1944	13 748
1945	13 905
1946	16 94
1947	20 527
1948	28 127
1949	34 587
1950	40 761
1951	47 194
1952	56 510
1953	63 489

GP Standard

Year	Beginning number
1928	200 111
1929	202 566
1930	216 139
1931	224 321
1932	228 666
1933	229 051
1934	229 216
1935	230 515

GP – Wide Tread

Year	Beginning number
1929	400 000
1930	400 936
1931	402 741
1932	404 770
1933	405 110

GP-O

Year	Beginning number
1931	15 000
1932	15 226
1933	15 387
1934	15 412
1935	15 589

John Deere's Model 430C traces its roots back to the Lindeman Brothers of Yakima, Washington, who added tracks to a Model GP Deere to create the GPO crawler. John Deere bought out the Lindeman operation in 1946 subsequently making their own crawlers. Introduced in 1958, the 430C was offered in gasoline, distillate, and LP-gas versions.

John Deere serial numbers

H

Year	Beginning number
1939	1 000
1940	10 780
1941	23 654
1942	40 995
1943	44 755
1944	47 796
1945	48 392
1946	55 956
1947	60 107

L

Year	Beginning number
1937	621 000
1938	621 079
1939	626 265
1940	630 160
1941	634 191
1942	640 000
1943	640 738
1944	641 038
1945	641 538
1946	641 958

LA

Year	Beginning number
1941	1 001
1942	5 361
1943	6 029
1944	6 159
1945	9 732
1946	11 529

M

Year	Beginning number
1947	10 001
1948	13 734
1949	25 604
1950	35 659
1951	43 525
1952	50 580

MC Crawler

Year	Beginning number
1949	10 001
1950	11 630
1951	13 630
1952	16 309

MT

Year	Beginning number
1949	10 001
1950	18 544
1951	26 203
1952	35 845

R

Year	Beginning number
1949	1 000
1950	3 541
1951	6 368
1952	9 293
1953	15 720
1954	19 485

Waterloo Boy L and LA

Year	Beginning number
1914	1 000

Waterloo Boy N

Year	Beginning number
1917	10 020
1918	10 221
1919	13 461
1920	18 924
1921	27 026
1922	27 812
1923	28 119
1924	29 520

Waterloo Boy R

Year	Beginning number
1915	1 026
1916	1 401
1917	3 556
1918	6 982
1919	9 056

40 Hi-Crop

Year	Beginning number
1954	60 001
1955	60 060

40 Special

Year	Beginning number
1955	60 001

40 Standard

Year	Beginning number
1953	60 001
1954	67 359
1955	69 474

40 Tricycle

Year	Beginning number
1953	60 0
1954	72 167
1955	75 531

40 2-Row Utility

Year	Beginning number
1955	60 001

40 Utility

Year	Beginning number
1953	60 001
1954	60 202
1955	63 140

40C Crawler

Year	Beginning number
1953	60 001
1954	63 358
1955	66 894

50

Year	Beginning number
1952	5 000 001
1953	5 01 254
1954	5 016 041
1955	5 021 977
1956	5 030 600

60

Year	Beginning number
1952	6 000 001
1953	6 007 694
1954	6 027 995
1955	6 042 500
1956	6 057 650

70

Year	Beginning number
1953	7 000 001
1954	7 005 692
1955	7 017 501
1956	7 034 950

80

Year	Beginning number
1955	8 000 001
1956	8 000 755

320

Year	Beginning number
1956	320 001
1957	321 220
1958*	325 127

330

Year	Beginning number
1958	330 001
1959	330 171
1960	330 935

420

Year	Beginning number
1956	30 001
1957	107 813
1958	127 782

420C Crawler

Year	Beginning number
1956	80 001
1957	107 813
1958*	127 782

430

Year	Beginning number
1958	140 001
1959	142 671
1960	158 632

430C Crawler

1958	140 001
1959	142 671
1960	158 632

435

Year	Beginning number
1959	435 001
1960	437 655

520

Year	Beginning number
1956	5 200 000
1957	5 202 982
1958	5 209 029

John Deere serial numbers

530
Year	Beginning number
1958	5 300 000
1959	5 301 671
1960	5 307 749

620
Year	Beginning number
1956	6 200 000
1957	6 203 778
1958	6 215 048

630
Year	Beginning number
1958	6 300 000
1959	6 302 749
1960	6 314 381

650
Year	Beginning number
1981	1 000
1982	3 539
1983	6 250
1984	10 543
1985	15 001
1986	19 001
1987	22 501

655
Year	Beginning number
1986	360 001
1987	420 001

720
Year	Beginning number
1956	7 200 000
1957	7 203 420
1958	7 217 368

730
Year	Beginning number
1958	7 300 000
1959	7 303 761
1960	7 322 075
1961	7 328 801

750
Year	Beginning number
1981	1 000
1982	3 448
1983	5 613
1984	8 597
1985	13 001
1986	18 501
1987	22 601

755
Year	Beginning number
1986	360 001
1987	420 001

820 (two-cylinder)
Year	Beginning number
1956	8 000 000
1957	8 200 565
1958	8 203 850

820 (three-cylinder)
Year	Beginning number
1968	10 000
1969	23 100
1970	36 000
1971	54 000
1972	71 850
1973	90 200

830 (two-cylinder)
Year	Beginning number
1958	8300 000
1959	8 300 727
1960	8 305 301
1961	8 306 892

830 (three-cylinder)
Year	Beginning number
1974	108 507
1975	155 914

850

Year	Beginning number
1978	1 024
1979	3 859
1980	7 389
1981	11 338
1982	12 481
1983	14 183
1984	16 006
1985	18 001
1986	22 001
1987	25 501

855

Year	Beginning number
1986	360 001
1987	420 001

900 HC

Year	Beginning number
1986	1 001
1987	1 701

950

Year	Beginning number
1978	1 024
1979	5 229
1980	10 453
1981	14 893
1982	16 204
1983	18 204
1984	20 007
1985	23 001
1986	26 001
1987	28 501

1010

Year	Beginning number
1961	10 001
1962	23 630
1963	32 188
1964	43 900
1965	53 722

1010C Crawler

Year	Beginning number
1960	10 001
1961	13 692
1962	23 630
1963	32 188
1964	43 900
1965	52 722

1020**

Year	Beginning number
1965	14 501
1966	14 682
1967	42 715
1968	65 184
1969	82 409
1970	102 039
1971	117 500
1972	134 700
1973	157 109

1050

Year	Beginning number
1980	1 000
1981	5 280
1982	6 572
1983	9 001
1984	11 006
1985	14 001
1986	17 001
1987	19 501

1250

Year	Beginning number
1982	1 001
1983	1 256
1984	3 001
1985	4 001
1986	5 001
1987	5 501

1450

Year	Beginning number
1984	1 020
1985	2 201
1986	3 001
1987	3 501

1520**

Year	Beginning number
1968	76 112
1969	82 405
1970	102 061
1971	117 500
1972	134 700
1973	157 109

1530

1974	108 811L
	176 601T
1975	145 500L

John Deere serial numbers

1650

Year	Beginning number
1984	1 021
1985	2 401
1986	3 001
1987	3 501

2010

Year	Beginning number
1961	10 001
1962	21 087
1963	31 250
1964	44 036
1965	58 186

2010C Crawler

Year	Beginning number
1960	10 001
1961	10 999
1962	21 087
1963	31 250
1964	44 036
1965	58 186

2020**

Year	Beginning number
1965	14 502
1966	14 680
1967	42 721
1968	65 176
1969	82 404
1970	102 032
1971	117 500

2030

Year	Beginning number
1972	134 700T
1973	157 109T
1974	140 000L
	187 301T
1975	145 500L
	213 350T

2040

Year	Beginning number
1976	179 963
1977	221 555
1978	266 057
1979	304 165
1980	336 935
1981	392 026
1982	419 145

2150

Year	Beginning number
1983	433 467
1984	505 001
1985	532 000
1986	562 001

2155

Year	Beginning number
1987	600 000

2240

Year	Beginning number
1976	179 298
1977	221 716
1978	277 267
1979	305 307
1980	337 767
1981	392 292
1982	418 608

2255

Year	Beginning number
1983	468 228
1984	505 001
1985	532 000
1986	562 001

2350

Year	Beginning number
1983	433 474
1984	505 001
1985	532 000
1986	562 001

2355

Year	Beginning number
1987	600 000

2355N

Year	Beginning number
1987	600 000

2440

Year	Beginning number
1976	235 210
1977	258 106
1978	280 789
1979	305 501
1980	335 625
1981	362 173
1982	376 746

2510

Year	Beginning number
1966	1 000
1967	8 958
1968	14 291

2520

Year	Beginning number
1969	17 000
1970	19 416
1971	22 000
1972	22 911
1973	23 865

2550

Year	Beginning number
1983	433 480
1984	505 001
1985	532 000
1986	562 001

2555

Year	Beginning number
1987	600 000

2630

Year	Beginning number
1974	188 601
1975	213 360

2640

Year	Beginning number
1976	235 313
1977	258 106
1978	280 789
1979	305 505
1980	335 628
1981	362 175
1982	376 744
1983	388 347

2750

Year	Beginning number
1983	433 494
1984	505 001
1985	523 000
1986	562 001

2755

Year	Beginning number
1987	600 000

2840

Year	Beginning number
1977	214 909
1978	264 711
1979	304 654

2855N

Year	Beginning number
1987	600 000

2940

Year	Beginning number
1980	350 586
1981	390 496
1982	418 953

2950

Year	Beginning number
1983	433 508
1984	505 001
1985	532 000
1986	562 001

2955

Year	Beginning number
1987	600 000

John Deere serial numbers

3010

Year	Beginning number
1961	1 000
1962	10 801
1963	32 400

3020

Year	Beginning number
1964	50 000
1965	68 000
1966	84 000
1967	97 286
1968	112 933
1969	123 000
1970	129 897
1971	150 000
1972	154 197

3150

Year	Beginning number
1985	532 000
1986	562 001
1987	587 950

4000

Year	Beginning number
1969	211 422
1970	222 143
1971	250 000
1972	260 791

4010

Year	Beginning number
1961	1 000
1962	20 201
1963	38 200

4020

Year	Beginning number
1964	65 000
1965	91 000
1966	119 000
1967	145 660
1968	173 982
1969	201 000
1970	222 143
1971	250 000
1972	260 791

4030

Year	Beginning number
1973	1 000
1974	6 700
1975	10 153
1976	13 022
1977	15 417

4040

Year	Beginning number
1978	1 000
1979	3 199
1980	6 033
1981	8 707
1982	11 727

4050

Year	Beginning number
1983	1 000
1984	3 501
1985	5 001
1986	6 501
1987	7 001

4230

Year	Beginning number
1973	1 000
1974	13 000
1975	22 074
1976	28 957
1977	35 588

4240

Year	Beginning number
1978	1 000
1979	7 434
1980	14 394
1981	20 186
1982	25 670

4250

Year	Beginning number
1983	1 000
1984	6 001
1985	9 001
1986	11 001
1987	12 501

4320

Year	Beginning number
1971	6 000
1972	17 031

4430

Year	Beginning number
1973	1 000
1974	17 500
1975	33 050
1976	47 222
1977	62 960

4440

Year	Beginning number
1978	1 000
1979	14 820
1980	29 539
1981	42 665
1982	56 346

4450

Year	Beginning number
1983	1 000
1984	11 001
1985	18 001
1986	22 001
1987	24 001

4520

Year	Beginning number
1969	1 000
1970	7 005

4620

Year	Beginning number
1971	10 000
1972	13 692

4630

Year	Beginning number
1973	1 000
1974	7 022
1975	11 717
1976	18 392
1977	25 794

4640

Year	Beginning number
1978	1 000
1979	7 422
1980	13 860
1981	19 459

4650

Year	Beginning number
1983	1 000
1984	7 001
1985	10 001
1986	12 501
1987	14 001

4840

Year	Beginning number
1978	1 000
1979	4 233
1980	7 539
1981	11 042
1982	4 933

4850

Year	Beginning number
1983	1 000
1984	5 001
1985	8 001
1986	10 001
1987	11 001

5010

Year	Beginning number
1963	1 000
1964	4 500
1965	8 000

5020

Year	Beginning number
1966	12 000
1967	15 650
1968	20 399
1969	24 038
1970	26 624
1971	30 000
1972	30 608

6030

Year	Beginning number
1972	33 000
1973	33 550
1974	34 586
1975	35 400
1976	36 014
1977	36 577

John Deere serial numbers

7020

Year	Beginning number
1971	1 000
1972	2 006
1973	2 700
1974	3 156
1975	3 579

7520

Year	Beginning number
1972	1 000
1973	1 600
1974	3 054
1975	4 945

8010

Year	Beginning number
1960	1 000

8020

Year	Beginning number
1964	1 000

8430

Year	Beginning number
1975	1 000
1976	1 690
1977	3 962
1978	5 323

8450

Year	Beginning number
1982	1 000
1983	2 000
1984	3 501
1985	5 001
1986	5 501
1987	6 001

8440

Year	Beginning number
1979	1 001
1980	2 266
1981	3 758
1982	5 235

8630

Year	Beginning number
1975	1 000
1976	2 382
1977	5 222
1978	7 626

8640

Year	Beginning number
1979	1 500
1980	3 198
1981	5 704
1982	7 960

8650

Year	Beginning number
1982	1 500
1983	3 000
1984	5 001
1985	7 001
1986	8 001
1987	8 501

8850

Year	Beginning number
1982	2 000
1983	4 000
1984	5 101
1985	6 001
1986	6 501
1987	7 001

In 1960 Deere & Company ended over 40 years of use of two-cylinder engines with the introduction of their "new generation" of tractors. The Models 3010 and 4010 (at right) were powered with six-cylinder power plants. The 302-cubic-inch gasoline unit in the 4010 generated 71 drawbar and 81 PTO horsepower.

Massey-Harris-Ferguson serial numbers

Introduced in 1930, Massey-Harris's Model 15-22 General Purpose featured an innovative four-wheel-drive system. The tractor first used Hercules and then later Waukesha four-cylinder engines. You could also choose different tread widths that ranged from 48 to 76 inches.

Serial number locations

Massey-Harris 20: Numbers are located on plate on left side of main frame and stamped on frame on top of transmission cover.

Colt, Mustang, 22, 30, 33, 44-4, 44-6, and 55: Numbers are located rear left-hand side of tractor frame just forward of the transmission case.

333, 444, and 555: Numbers are located rear left-hand side of tractor frame just forward of the transmission case.

35 through 204 Industrial: Unless otherwise indicated, numbers are stamped on instrument panel nameplate.

MH-50: Numbers are stamped on instrument panel nameplate.

230, 235, 245, 255, 265, 275, and 285: Numbers are located on left-hand side of tractor, just forward of transmission.

1100 and 1130: Numbers are located on left-hand side of tractor, just forward of transmission.

1085, 1105, 1135, and 1155: Numbers are on left-hand side just ahead of instrument panel.

20 R.C.

Year	Beginning number
1946	1001
1947	1580
1948	3584

20 Standard

Year	Beginning number
1946	1001
1947	1002
1948	2230

20K R.C.

Year	Beginning number
1947	1001
1948	1354

20K Standard

Year	Beginning number
1947	1001
1948	1819

21-Colt

Year	Beginning number
1952	1001
1953	1417

22 R.C.

Year	Beginning number
1948	1001
1949	2096
1950	4580
1951	7624
1952	10145
1952	20046
1953	20585

22 Standard

Year	Beginning number
1948	1001
1949	1542
1950	3208
1951	4532
1952	5717
1952	20046
1953	20585

Massey-Harris-Ferguson serial numbers

22K R.C.

Year	Beginning number
1948	1001
1949	1154
1950	1336
1951	1558
1952	1776
1952	20046
1953	20585

22K Standard

Year	Beginning number
1948	1001
1949	1317
1950	1488
1951	1570
1952	1748
1952	20046
1953	20585

23 – Mustang

Year	Beginning number
1952	1001
1953	1666
1954	4346
1955	4553
1956	4773

25

Year	Beginning number
1932-35	69001
1936	69970
1937	71045
1938 A Gears	73112
1938 B Gears	85001

25 Industrial

Year	Beginning number
1937	90001

30K R.C.

Year	Beginning number
1947	1001
1948	1225
1949	2010
1950	2393
1951	2731
1952	30001
1953	30596

30 R.C.

Year	Beginning number
1946	1001
1947	1002
1948	3386
1949	6825
1950	9345
1951	13816
1952	17934
1952	30001
1953	30596

30 Standard

Year	Beginning number
1946	1001
1947	1002
1948	2120
1949	3194
1950	5567
1951	7491
1952	8696
1952	30001
1953	30596

30K Standard

Year	Beginning number
1947	1001
1948	1894
1949	3251
1950	3531
1951	3861
1952	30001
1953	30596

33

Year	Beginning number
1952	1001
1953	2055
1954	6617
1955	9782

44 R.C.

Year	Beginning number
1946	1001
1947	1002
1948	2048
1949	5318
1950	13822
1951	21815

1952	31275
1952	40001
1953	43700
1954	51364
1955	58067

44 Standard

Year	Beginning number
1946	1001
1947	1141
1948	1871
1949	4528
1950	9581
1951	13726
1952	17059
1952	40001
1953	43700
1954	51364
1955	58067

44D Orchard

Year	Beginning number
1950	1001
1951	1002

44D R.C.

Year	Beginning number
1949	1001
1950	1004
1951	2483
1952	4704
1952	40001
1953	43700
1954	51364
1955	58067

44D Standard

Year	Beginning number
1948	1001
1949	1023
1950	2180
1951	3989
1952	5639
1952	40001
1953	43700
1954	51364
1955	58067

44 GRA (high altitude, R.C.)

Year	Beginning number
1951	1001
1952	1164

44 GSA (high altitude, Standard)

Year	Beginning number
1951	1001
1952	1055

44 Orchard

Year	Beginning number
1950	1001
1951	1101
1952	40001
1953	43700

44 Special G & D

Year	Beginning number
1953	50001
1954	51364
1955	58067

44 Vineyard

Year	Beginning number
1950	101
1951	1031
1952	40001
1953	43700

44K R.C.

Year	Beginning number
1947	1001
1948	1079
1949	1856
1950	2599
1951	3329
1952	40001
1953	43700
1954	51364
1955	58067

44 – LP R.C.

Year	Beginning number
1952	1001

44 – LP Standard

Year	Beginning number
1952	1001

Massey-Harris-Ferguson serial numbers

44K Standard

Year	Beginning number
1946	1001
1947	1011
1948	1441
1949	3598
1950	4827
1951	6019
1952	6787
1952	40001
1953	43700
1954	51364
1955	58067

44-6 R.C.

Year	Beginning number
1946	1001
1947	1002
1948	2983
1949	4755
1950	5255
1951	5509

44-6 Standard

Year	Beginning number
1947	1001
1948	2001
1950	2601

55

Year	Beginning number
1946	1001
1947	1116
1948	2132
1949	3581
1950	5468
1951	6399
1952	10001
1953	13017
1954	15299
1955	17059

55D Standard

Year	Beginning number
1949	1001
1950	1022
1951	2058
1952	2822
1953	10001
1954	13017
1954	15299
1955	17059

55D Riceland & Hillside

Year	Beginning number
1950	1001
1951	1152
1952	1452
1952	10001
1953	13017
1954	15299
1955	17059

55 DISH – DSW (diesel Western)

Year	Beginning number
1951	1001
1952	1190
1952	10001
1953	13017
1954	15299

55 – GISH - GSW (gas Western)

Year	Beginning number
1951	1002
1952	1083
1952	10001
1953	13017
1954	15299

55 – GSA, GSWA, & GSHA (high altitude)

Year	Beginning number
1951	1001
1952 GSWA	1025
1952	10001
1953	13017
1954	15299

55 – GSH & GIWH Riceland & Hillside

Year	Beginning number
1949	1001
1950	1035
1951	1216
1952	10001
1953	13017
1954	15299
1955	17059

272

55K Standard

Year	Beginning number
1946	1001
1947	1013
1948	1554
1949	3033
1950	4078
1951	4808
1952	5503
1952	10001
1953	13017
1954	15299
1955	17059

55K Standard - Riceland & Hillside

Year	Beginning number
1949	1001
1950	1013
1951	1110
1952	10001
1953	13017
1954	15299
1955	17059
1956	20001
1957	22649

81 R.C.

Year	Beginning number
1941	400001
1942	403168
1944	403354
1945	403364
1946	404664

81 Standard

Year	Beginning number
1941	425001
1942	425678
1944	425757
1945	425780
1946	426803

82 R.C.

Year	Beginning number
1941	420001
1942	420055
1945	420274
1946	420307

82 Standard

Year	Beginning number
1941	435001
1942	435279
1943	435452
1945	435458
1946	435738

101 Jr. R.C.

Year	Beginning number
1939	375001
1940	37618
1941	395570
1942	397637
1943	398596
1944	500003
1945	502434
1946	503779

101 Jr. Standard

Year	Beginning number
1939	377001
1940	377928
1941	379550
1942	379815
1943	379855
1944	380641
1945	382569
1946	384298

101 Senior R.C.

Year	Beginning number
1938	255001
1939	256085
1940	257281
1941	258769
1942	259762
1943	260430
1944	260796
1945	263020
1946	270145

101 Senior Standard

Year	Beginning number
1938	355001
1939	355603
1940	356792
1941	358188
1942	358869
1943	358975
1944	359457
1945	360927
1946	362520

Massey-Harris-Ferguson serial numbers

102 Junior R.C.
Year	Beginning number
1939	387001
1940	37031
1941	387127
1942	387419
1943	387601
1944	387844
1945	388240
1946	388995

102 Junior Standard
Year	Beginning number
1939	385001
1940	385204
1941	385450
1942	36099
1943	386662
1944	390008
1945	390994
1946	391913

102 Senior R.C.
Year	Beginning number
1942	265001
1943	265044
1944	265078

102 Senior Standard
Year	Beginning number
1941	365001
1942	365202
1943	366062
1944	366183
1945	367353

201
Year	Beginning number
1940	91201
1941	91541
1942	91691
1943	98674
1944	98807
1946	99689
1947	100120

201 – Diesel
Year	Beginning number
1940	99501

202
Year	Beginning number
1940	95001
1941	95002
1942	95182

203
Year	Beginning number
1944	95223
1945	
1946	95295
1947	95338

203 – Diesel
Year	Beginning number
1940	98001
1941	98028
1942	98364
1943	98674
1944	98807
1945	n/a
1946	99689
1947	100120

303 – Industrial
Year	Beginning number
1956	1001
1957	1076
1958	1194

333
Year	Beginning number
1956	20001
1957	22649

404 – Industrial
Year	Beginning number
1956	1001
1957	1051

444
Year	Beginning number
1956	70001
1957	73989
1958	77000

555

Year	Beginning number
1955	20001
1956	20133
1957	21133
1958	22950

744 – Great Britain

Year	Beginning number
1948	201
1949	401
1950	1401

(After 1950, year is indicated by a letter, e.g., F=1951, G=1952, etc.

Challenger

Year	Beginning number
1936-37	130001

Challenger Distillate

Year	Beginning number
1936	140001

Challenger Twin Power Gas

Year	Beginning number
1938	133367

GP 4WD

Year	Beginning number
1930-35	300001
1936-38	303001

I-162

Year	Beginning number
1953	1001

FSI-244 (USAF w/ PTO)

Year	Beginning number
1955	2001
1956	2219

I-244 (no PTO)

Year	Beginning number
1955 Navy	1001
1956 Navy	1020
1956 USAF	3001
1957 USAF	3181

I-330 (Navy)

Year	Beginning number
1954	1001

MH-50

Year	Beginning number
1955	500001
1956	500473
1957	510764

Pacemaker

Year	Beginning number
1936-37	107001

Pacemaker Distillate

Year	Beginning number
1936	120001

Pacemaker Distillate OPA

Year	Beginning number
1936	204001

Pacemaker Distillate VPA

Year	Beginning number
1936	201501

Pacemaker Twin Power Gas

Year	Beginning number
1938	109838

Pacemaker Twin Power OPA Gas

Year	Beginning number
1938	200403

Pacemaker Twin Power VPA Gas

Year	Beginning number
1938	201042

Pacer – 16

Year	Beginning number
1954	50001
1955	51613
1956	52771

Pony – 11 & 14

Year	Beginning number
1947	PGS 1001
1948	PGS 1321
1949	PGA 1571A
1950	PGA 10817A
1951	PGA 13726
1952	PGA 18225
1953	PGA 22007
1954	PGA 22669

Massey-Harris-Ferguson serial numbers

Model 35

Year	Beginning number
1960	204181
1961	211071
1962	222207
1963	235123
1964	247605

50

Year	Beginning number
1956	500001
1957	510764
1958	515708
1959	522693
1960	528163
1961	528419
1962	529821
1963	533422
1964	536063

65

Year	Beginning number
1957	650001
1958	650024
1959	661164
1960	671379
1961	680210
1962	685370
1963	693040
1964	701057
1965	710788

85

Year	Beginning number
1958	800001
1959	800048
1960	804355
1961	807750
1962	808564

88

Year	Beginning number
1959	880001
1960	881453
1961	882229
1962	882496

90 and Super

Year	Beginning number
1962	810000
1963	813170
1964	816113
1965	819342

90WR and Super

Year	Beginning number
1961	885000
1962	885010
1963	885870
1964	886829
1965	888238

97D

Year	Beginning number
19i62	25200001
1963	25200506
1964	25202005
1965	25203504

97 LPG

Year	Beginning number
1962	25300001
1963	25300096
1964	25300397
1965	25300399

135

Year	Beginning number
1964	641000001
1965	641001909
1966	641014871
1967	9A10001
1968	9A39386
1969	9A63158
1970	9A87325
1971	9A107519
1972	9A128141
1973	9A152025
1974	9A182761
1975	9A207681

150

Year	Beginning number
1964	642000001
1965	642000015
1966	642000505
1967	9A10001
1968	9A39836
1969	9A63158
1970	9A87325
1971	9A107519
1972	9A128141
1973	9A152025
1974	9A182761
1975	9A207681

165

Year	Beginning number
1964	643000001
1965	643000003
1966	643000149
1967	9A10001
1968	9A39836
1969	9A63158
1970	9A87325
1971	9A107519
1972	9A128141
1973	9A152025
1974	9A182761
1975	9A207681

175

Year	Beginning number
1965	644000001
1966	644000004
1967	644000214
1967	9A10001
1968	9A39836
1969	9A6158
1970	9187325
1971	9A107519
1972	9A128141
1973	9A152025
1974	9A182761
1975	9A207681

230, 235, 245, 255, 265, 275, and 285

Year	Beginning number
1975	9A182761
1975	9A207681

180

Year	Beginning number
1964	645000001
1965	645000002
1966	645000047
1967	9A10001
1968	9A39836
1969	9A63158
1970	9A87325
1971	9A107519
1972	9A128141
1973	9A152025
1974	9A182761
1975	9A207681

202 Industrial

Year	Beginning number
1958	301172
1959	303158
1960	305108
1961	30619
1962	306779
1963	307923
1964	309222
1965	310067
1966	311084

203 Industrial

Year	Beginning number
1961	659000001
1962	659000681
1963	659001379
1964	659001767
1965	659002054
1966	659002667

204 Industrial

Year	Beginning number
1959	340001
1960	341381
1961	341986
1962	342648
1963	343182
1964	343836
1965	344309
1966	345103

1080

Year	Beginning number
1969	9B18673
1970	9B23486
1971	9B28227
1972	9B31958

Massey-Harris-Ferguson serial numbers

1100

Year	Beginning number
1964	650000001
1965	650000003
1966	650000831
1967	9B10001
1968	9B14693
1969	9B18673
1970	9B23486
1971	9B28227
1972	9B31958

1130

Year	Beginning number
1964	651500001
1965	651500004
1966	651500049
1967	9B10001
1968	9B14693
1969	9B13673
1970	9B23486
1971	9B28227
1972	9B31958

1085, 1105, 1135, and 1155

Year	Beginning number
1972	9B36563
1973	9B36841
1974	9B43432
1975	9B50494
1976	9B58735

1500 and 1800

Year	Beginning number
1971	9C1007
1972	9C1912
1973	9C2462
1974	9C3184

1505 and 1805

Year	Beginning number
1974	9C003184
1975	9C004227
1976	9C006086
1945	388240
1946	388995

102 Junior Standard

Year	Beginning number
1939	385001
1940	385204
1941	385450
1942	36099
1943	386662
1944	390008
1945	390994
1946	391913

102 Senior R.C.

Year	Beginning number
1942	265001
1943	265044
1944	265078

102 Senior Standard

Year	Beginning number
1941	365001
1942	365202
1943	366062
1944	366183
1945	367353

201

Year	Beginning number
1940	91201
1941	91541
1942	91691
1943	98674
1944	98807
1946	99689
1947	100120

201 – Diesel

Year	Beginning number
1940	99501

202

Year	Beginning number
1940	95001
1941	95002
1942	95182

203

Year	Beginning number
1944	95223
1946	95295
1947	95338

203 – Diesel

Year	Beginning number
1940	98001
1941	98028
1942	98364
1943	98674
1944	98807
1945	n/a
1946	99689
1947	100120

303 – Industrial

Year	Beginning number
1956	1001
1957	1076
1958	1194

333

Year	Beginning number
1956	20001
1957	22649

404 – Industrial

Year	Beginning number
1956	1001
1957	1051

444

Year	Beginning number
1956	70001
1957	73989
1958	77000

555

Year	Beginning number
1955	20001
1956	20133
1957	21133
1958	22950

744 – Great Britain

Year	Beginning number
1948	201
1949	401

Minneapolis-Moline serial numbers

Twin City tractors

Twin City 16-30

Year	Number range
1936	5501 - 6203

Twin City 17-28 TY

Year	Number range
1930	30104 - 30281
1931	30282 - 30298
1932	30299 - 30309
1933	30310 - 30333
1934	30334 - 30762
1935	30763 - 30808

TC 17-28 Industrial

Year	Beginning number
1934	43001

Twin City 27-44 AT

Year	Number range
1926 - 1928	May fall within TC 2-35
1929	250001 - 250730
1930	250731 - 250796
1931	250797- 250799
1932	None produced
1933	None produced
1934	250800 - 250805
1935	250806 - 250839

Twin City 21-32

Year	Number range
1926 - 1928	150001 - 150302

Twin City KT Orchard

Year	Number range
1931	301863 - 301890

Twin City 21-32 FT

Year	Number range
Pre-1930	150303 - 151796
1930	151797 - 154073
1931	154074 - 154123
1932	154124 - 154129
1934	154130 - 154275

Minneapolis-Moline serial numbers

Twin City 21-32 FTA

Year	Number range
1935	154300 - 155381
1936	154382 - 156247
1937	156124 - 154129
1938	156909 - 154275

Twin City FT Industrial

Year	Number range
1932	46001 - 46004
1934	46005 - 46029

Twin City FTA Industrial

Year	Number range
1935	46030
1936	46031 - 46046
1937	46047 - 46074

Twin City KT

Year	Number range
1929	300001 - 300079
1930	300080 - 301583
1931	301584 - 301862
	301865 - 301866
	301882
1932	301 957 - 301 981
1933	301 982 - 201 987
1934	301 988 - 302 078

Twin City KT Industrial

Year	Number range
1932	40001 only
1933	40002 - 40004
1934	40005 - 40008
1935	40009 only

Twin City LT

Year	Number range
1934	500,001 - 500,010

Twin City KTA

Year	Number range
1934	302 200 - 302 371
1935	302 372 - 303 825
1936	303 826 - 304 701
1937	304 702 - 306 281
1938	306 282 - 306 751

Twin City MT

Year	Number range
1930	525 001 - 525 020
1931	525 021 - 526 118
1932	526 096 - 525 334
1933	525 335 - 525 345
1934	525 346 - 525 420

Twin City Universal MTA

Year	Number range
1934	525 421 - 525 490
1935	525 491 - 526 118
1936	526 119 - 526 960
1937	526 961 - 528 049
1938	528 050 - 528 645

Twin City Universal JT

Year	Number range
1934	550 001 - 550 025
1935	550 026 - 551 762
1936	551 763 - 554 554
1937	554 555 - 556 244

Minneapolis-Moline's innovative Model UDLX embodied all the benefits of a modern car built into a tractor. Creature comforts included a radio, heater with defrost, windshield wiper, and a second seat for passengers. When introduced in 1938 the UDLX sold for a then princely sum of $1,900.

Twin City JT Standard

Year	Number range
1936	600 001 - 600 322
1937	600 323 - 600 469

Twin City JT Orchard

Year	Number range
1936	625 001 - 625 103
1937	625 104 - 625 156

Twin City LT

Year	Number range
1930	500 001 - 500 010

Minneapolis-Moline tractors

GT (GE or 403 engine)

Year	Number range
1938	160 001 - 160 076
1936	160 077 - 160 545
1940	160 546 - 160 878
1941	160 879 - 161 253

GTA (LE engine)

Year	Number range
1942	162 001 - 162 300
1943	162 301 - 162 302
1944	162 303 - 162 659
1945	162 660 - 162 869
1946	162 870 - 163 219
1947	163 220 - 163 610

GTB (403 engine)

Year	Number range
1947	164 001 - 164 178
1948	164 179 - 164 214 Early
1948	016 480 0001 - 016480 0600 Late
1949	016 490 0001 - 016 490 1205
1950	016 500 0001 - 016 501 863
1951	01601864 - 01603396
1952	01603397 - 01604889
1953	01604890 - 01605972
1954	01605973 - 01606289

GTB-D   D425-6

Year	Number range
1953	06800001 only
1954	06800002 - 06800850

GTC   340-4

Year	Number range
1951	04700001 - 04700018
1952	04700019 - 04700676
1953	04700677 - 0470110

GB   403 C - 4

Year	Number range
1955	08900001 - 0890150
1956	08901501 - 08902601
1957	08902602 - 08903401
1958	08903402 - 08904251
1959	08904252 - 08904442

GB-D

Year	Number range
1955	09000001 - 09000850
1956	09000851 - 09001525
1957	09001526 - 09002145
1958	09002146 - 0900265
1959	09002656 - 09002790

RT

Year	Number range
1939	400 001 - 402 200
1940	402 201 - 405 575
1941	405 576 - 407 950
1942	407 951 - 408 825
1943	408 826 - 409 357
1944	409 358 - 410 747
1945	410 748 - 413 754
1946	413 755 - 416 544
1947	416 545 - 422 057

RTE

Year	Number range
1948	0044800001 - 0044800501
1949	0044900001 - 0044900315
1950	0045000001 - 0045000204
1951	00400202 - 00400281
1952	00400282 only
1953	00400283 - 00400287

RTN

Year	Number range
1948	0034800001 - 0034800100
1949	0034900001 - 0034900200
1950	0035000001 - 0035000093
1951	00300094 - 00300173

RTI

Year	Number range
1948	0054800001 - 0054800700
1949	0054900001 - 0054900450
1950	0055000001 - 0055000115
1951	00500116 - 00500598
1952	00500599 - 00501000
1953	00501001 - 00501311

Minneapolis-Moline serial numbers

1954	00501312 - 00501511
1955	00501512 - 00501579

RTS

Year	Number range
1949	0024900001 - 0024900375
1950	0025000001` - 0025000300
1951	00200301 - 00200401
1952	00200402 - 00200551
1953	00300552 - 00200701

RTU

Year	Number range
1948	0014800001 - 0014802402
1949	0014900001 - 0014903039
1950	0015000001 - 0015002155
1951	00102156 - 00103972
1952	00103973 - 00104823
1953	
1954	00104824 - 00104831

RTI-M

Year	Number range
1953	05500001 - 0550249

U

Year	Number range
1938	310 026 - 310 645
1939	310 646 - 312 450
1940	312 451 - 314 892
1941	314 893 - 316 500
1942	316 501 - 317 701
1943	317 702 - 318 162
1944	318 163 - 321 101
1945	321 102 - 325 231
1946	325 231 - 329 751
1947	329 752 - 337 412
1948	337 418 - 339 682

UDLX

Year	Number range
1938	310 001 - 310 025 (early)
1938	310 501 - 310 625 (late)

UTC (w/ 6-volt ignition)

Year	Number range
1948	0154800001 - 0154800300
1949	0154900001 - 0154900100
1951	01500101 - 01500180
1952	01500181 - 01500265

1954	01500266 - 01500271

UTC (w/ 12-volt ignition)

Year	Number range
1954	08800001 - 08800060
1955	08800061 - 08800110

UTE

Year	Number range
1951	04300001 - 04300111
1952	04300112 - 04300261
1953	04300262 - 04300264
1954	04300265 - only

UTN

Year	Number range
1950	0385000001 - 0385000101
1951	03800102 - 03800204
1952	03800205 - 03800354

UTS

Year	Number range
1948	0124800001 - 0124802276
1949	0124900001 - 0124903901
1950	0125000001 - 01203850
1951	01203851 - 01207138
1952	01207139 - 01210570
1953	01210571 - 01213219
1954	01213220 - 01213325
1955	01213326 - 01214125
1956	01214126 - 01215100
1957	01215101 - 01215150

UTU

Year	Number range
1948	0114800001 - 0114802053
1949	0114900001 - 0114905000
1950	0115000001 - 01105383
1951	01105384 - 01110117
1952	01110118 - 01113449
1954	01113450 - 01113453
1955	01113454 - 01113456

UDU

Year	Number range
1952	04900001 only
1953	04900002 - 04900030

UTS-D

Year	Number range
1952	05000001 - 05000018

1954	05000019 - 05000755
1955	05000955 - 05001154
1956	05002105 - 05002404

UDS-M
Year	Number range
1954	05000756 - 05000954
1955	05001155 - 05002104

UBU
Year	Number range
1953	05800001 - 05802912
1954	05802913 - 05804002
1955	05804003 - 05805077

UBE
Year	Number range
1953	05900001 - 05900896
1954	05900897 - 05901068
1955	05901069 - 05901421

UBN
Year	Number range
1953	06000001 - 06000202
1954	06000203 - 06000207
1955	0600208 - 06000241

UBU Diesel
Year	Number range
1954	07800001 - 07800746
1955	07800747 - 07801041

UBE Diesel
Year	Number range
1954	07000001 - 07000231
1955	07000232 - 07000362

UBN Diesel
Year	Number range
1954	06900001 – 06900048

UB Special
Year	Number range
1955	09700001 - 09701475

UB Special - Diesel
Year	Number range
1955	09800001 - 09800300
1956	09800301 - 09800464
1957	09800465 - 09800520

ZTI
Year	Number range
1936	599 001 - 599 003

1937	599 004 - 599 016
1936	599 017 - 599 018
1936	559 019 - 559 022

ZTU - ZTN
Year	Number range
1936	560 001 - 560 037
1937	560 038 - 562 974
1938	562 975 - 565 406
1939	565 407 - 567 154
1940	567 155 - 568 754
1941	568 755 - 570 821
1942	570 822 - 571 421
1943	571 422 - 572 967
1944	572 968 - 575 712
1945	575 713 - 576 813
1445	572 713 - 576 813
1946	576 814 - 578 013
1947	578 041 - 581 814
1948	581 815 - 585 817

ZTS
Year	Number range
1937	610 001 - 610 035
1938	610 036 - 610 388
1939	610 389 - 610 684
1940	610 685 - 611 087
1941	611 088 - 611 342
1942	611 343 - 611 446
1943	611 447 - 611 965
1944	611 966 - 612 485
1945	612 486 - 612 885
1946	612 886 - 613 085
1947	613 086 - 613 490

ZAU
Year	Number range
1949	0064900001 - 0064903013
1950	0065000001 - 00605435
1951	00605436 - 00609939
1952	00609940 - 00614658

ZAS
Year	Number range
1949	0074900001 - 0074900150
1950	0075000001 - 00700480
1951	00700481 - 00701285
1952	00701286 - 00701910
1953	00701911 - 00702610

ZAN
Year	Number range
1949	0084900001 - 0084900150

Minneapolis-Moline serial numbers

Year	Number range
1950	0085000001 - 00800238
1951	00800239 - 00800442
1952	00800443 - 00800618
1953	00800619 - 00800620

ZAE

Year	Number range
1949	094900001 - 0094900301
1950	0095000001 - 00900373
1951	00900374 - 0000576
1952	00900577 - 0900997
1953	00900998 - 00901122

ZBE

Year	Number range
1953	06300001 - 06300075
1954	06300076 - 06300306
1955	06300307 - 06300501

ZBN

Year	Number range
1953	06300001 - 0630075
1954	06300076 - 06300306
1955	06300307 - 06300501

ZBN

Year	Number range
1954	06400001 - 06400072
1955	06400073 - 06400106

ZBA

Year	Number range
1953	06200001 - 06200957
1954	06200958 - 06202479
1955	06202480 - 06203059

335 Utility

Year	Number range
1956	10400001 - 10400101
1957	10400102 - 10402087
1958	10402088 - 10402336
1959	10402337 - 10402439
1960	10402440 - 10402489
1961	10402490 - 10402539

335 Universal

Year	Number range
1957	11600001 - 11600301
1958	11600302 - 11600305
1959	11600306 - 11600334

335 Industrial

Year	Number range
1957	11300001 - 11300440
1958	11300441 - 11300521
1959	11300522 - 11300596
1960	11300597 - 11300746

445 Universal

Year	Number range
1956	10100001 - 10102854
1957	10102855 - 10104125
1958	10104126 - 10104804
1959	10104805 - 10104847

445 Utility

Year	Number range
1956	10200001 - 10201445
1957	10201446 - 10202101
1958	10202102 - 10202242
1959	10202243 - 10202249

445 Utility (diesel)

Year	Number range
1959	15400001 - 15400018

445 Industrial

Year	Number range
1956	11100001 - 11100075
1957	11100076 - 11100388
1958	11100389 - 11100645

445 Industrial (diesel)

Year	Number range
1958	15200001 - 15200025

445 (military)

Year	Number range
1958	15700001 - 15700074

445 Universal (diesel)

Year	Number range
1958	15200001 - 15200190

Big Mo 400 (gas)

Year	Number range
1961	16700001 - 16700100
1962	16700101 - 16700210
1963	16700211 - 16700360
1963	16700361 - 16700410

Big Mo 400 (military)

Year	Number range
1959	17000001 - 17000356
1960	17000357 - 17000632
1961	17000633 - 17000648
1962	17000649 - 17000652
1963	17000653 - 17000757

Big Mo 500 (gas)

Year	Number range
1960	16800001 - 16800160
1961	16800161 - 16800391
1962	16800392 - 16800606
1963	16800607 - 16800681
1964	16800682 - 16800746
1965	16800747 - 16800866
1966	16800867 - 16800881

Big Mo 500 (diesel)

Year	Number range
1960	17800001 - 17800065
1963	17800066 - 1780090
1964	16800091 - 17800115
1965	17800116 - 17800145

Big Mo 600

Year	Number range
1960	18400001 - 18400060

4 Star Series (gas)

Year	Number range
1959	16600001 - 16600890
1960	11600891 - 16601685
1961	16601686 - 16601860
1962	16601861 - 16602407
1963	16602408 - 16602537

4 Star Series (diesel)

Year	Number range
1960	18200001 - 18200050
1961	18200051 - 18200072
1962	18200073 - 18200097

5 Star Universal (gas)

Year	Number range
1957	11000001 - 11001057
1958	11001058 - 11002067
1959	11002068 - 11002914

5 Star Universal (diesel)

Year	Number range
1957	14400001 - 14400203
1958	14400204 - 14400785

1959	11400786 - 14401295

5 Star Standard (gas)

1958	11200001 - 11200380

5 Star Industrial (diesel)

Year	Number range
1958	14500001 - 14500165
1959	14500166 - 14500188

5 Star Industrial (gas)

Year	Number range
1957	11700002 - 11700006
1958	11700007 - 11700025
1959	11700026 - 11700084

5 Star Industrial (diesel)

Year	Number range
1958	14600001 - 14600010
1959	14600011 - 14600028
1960	14600029 - 14600060

2 Star Crawler

Year	Number range
1958	12000001 - 12000051

Motrac Crawler (gas)

Year	Number range
1960	18500001 - 18500030
1961	18500031 - 18500038

Motrac Crawler (diesel)

Year	Number range
1960	18600001 - 18600160
1961	18600161 only

Jet Star 2 (gas)

Year	Number range
1963	25800001 - 25801100

Jet Star (gas)

Year	Number range
1959	16500001 - 16500284
1960	16500285 - 16500834
1961	16500835 - 16501701
1962	16501702 - 16502439

Jet Star (diesel)

Year	Number range
1960	17500001 - 17500060
1961	17500061 - 17500135
1962	17500136 - 17500196

Minneapolis-Moline serial numbers

Jet Star 2 (diesel)
Year	Number range
1963	25700001 - 25700113

Jet Star 3 (gas)
Year	Number range
1963	28300001 - 28301000
1964	28301001 - 28301984

Jet Star 3 Super (gas)
Year	Number range
1965	28301985 - 28302055
1966	28302056 - 28302843
1967	28302844 - 28303565
1968	28303566 - 28304800
1969	28304801 - 28305085
1970	28305086 - 28305335

Jet Star 3 (diesel)
Year	Number range
1964	28400001 - 28400050
1965	28400051 - 28400200
1966	28400201 - 28400385
1967	28400386 - 28400466
1968	28400467 - 28400526
1969	28400527 - 28400601
1970	28400602 - 28400711

Jet Star Orchard (gas)
Year	Number range
1965	30700001 - 30700050
1966	30700051 - -
1967	30700052 - 30700070

Jet Star Orchard (diesel)
Year	Number range
1967	34400001 - 34400020

Jet Star 3 (LP gas)
Year	Number range
1970	36000001 - 36000010

Jet Star 3 Industrial (diesel)
Year	Number range
1966	30900001 - 30900050

U302 (gas)
Year	Number range
1964	27600001 - 27601000
1965	27601001 - 27601300

U302 Super (gas)
Year	Number range
1966	27601301 - 27602300
1967	27602301 - 27602425
1968	27602426 - 27602759
1969	27602760 - 27602859
1970	27602860 - 27602969

U302 Super (diesel)
Year	Number range
1967	27700001 - 27700100
1968	27700101 - 27700150
1969	27700151 - 27700164
1970	27700165 - 27700190

U302 Super (LP gas)
Year	Number range
1969	36100001 - 36100025
1970	36100026 - 36100050

M5 (gas)
Year	Number range
1960	17100001 - 17101535
1961	17101536 - 17103495
1962	17103496 - 17104707
1963	17104708 - 17105157

M5 (diesel)
Year	Number range
1960	17200001 - 17201040
1961	17201041 - 17201000
1962	17202000 - 17202506
1963	17202507 - 17202656

M504 4-Wheel Drive (gas)
Year	Number range
1962	24300001 - 24300010

M504 4-Wheel Drive (diesel)
Year	Number range
1962	24200001 - 24300010

M602 (gas)
Year	Number range
1963	26600001 - 26601275
1964	26601276 - 26602957

M602 (diesel)
Year	Number range
1963	26700001 - 26700742

1964   26700743 - 26701772

M604 4-Wheel Drive (gas)
Year	Number range
1963	26800001 - 26800050
1964	26800051 - 26800053

M604 4-Wheel Drive (diesel)
Year	Number range
1963	26900001 - 26900050
1964	26900051 - 26900099

M670 (gas)
Year	Number range
1964	29900001 - 29900006
1965	29900007 - 29901891

M670 (diesel)
Year	Number range
1964	30000001 - 30000004
1965	30000005 - 30000819

M670 Super (gas)
Year	Number range
1966	29901892 - 29903579
1967	29903580 - 29904454
1968	29904455 - 29904594
1969	29904595 - 29905004
1970	29905005 - 29905104

M670 Super (gas)
Year	Number range
1966	29901892 - 29903579

M670 Super (diesel)
Year	Number range
1966	30000820 - 30001634
1967	30001635 - 30002309
1968	30002310 - 30002569
1969	30002570 - 30002860
1970	30002861 - 30003085M670

Super (LP gas)
Year	Number range
1970	36200001 - 36200075

G VI (gas)
Year	Number range
1959	16000001 - 16000876
1960	16000877 - 16001675
1961	16001676 - 16002032
1962	16002033 - 16002352

G VI (diesel)
Year	Number range
1956	16200001 - 16200805
1960	16200806 - 16201890
1961	16201891 - 16202960
1962	16202961 - 16203235

G704 (LP gas)
Year	Number range
1962	23400001 - 23400081

G704 (diesel) L
1962	23500001 - 23500123

G705 (LP gas)
Year	Number range
1962	23800001 - 23800078
1963	23800079 - 23800590
1964	23800591 - 23801092
1965	23801093 - 23801223

G705 (diesel)
Year	Number range
1962	23900001 - 23900050
1963	23900051 - 23900898
1964	23900899 - 23901868
1965	23901869 - 23902094

G706 (LP gas)
Year	Number range
1962	24000001 - 24000072
1963	24000073 - 24000305
1964	24000306 - 24000350
1965	24000351 - 24000370

G706 (diesel)
Year	Number range
1962	24100001 - 24100106
1963	24100107 - 24100549
1964	24100550 - 24100795
1965	24100796 - 24100821

G707 (LP gas)
Year	Number range
1965	31200001 - 31200283

G707 (diesel)
Year	Number range
1965	31300001 - 31300415

G708 (LP gas)
Year	Number range
1965	31400001 - 31400031

Minneapolis-Moline serial numbers

G708 (diesel)

Year	Number range
1965	31500001 - 31500075

G900 (LP gas)

Year	Number range
1967	33000001 - 33000110
1968	33000111 - 33000550
1969	3300551 - 33000670

G900 (LP gas)

Year	Number range
1969	36300001 - 36300160

G900 (diesel)

Year	Number range
1967	33100001 - 33100316
1968	33100317 - 33101376
1969	33101377 - 33101946

G950 (LP gas)

Year	Number range
1969	43500001 - 43500060
1970	43500061 - 43500085
1971	43500086 - 43500186

G950 (diesel)

Year	Number range
1969	43600001 - 43600210
1970	43600211 - 43600415
1971	43600416 - 43600829
1972	43600830 - 43600834

G955

Year	Number range
1973	239825 - 243262
1974	244559 - 251357

G1000 Row Crop (gas, LP gas)

Year	Number range
1965	30500001 - 30500450
1966	30500451 - 30500926
1967	30500927 - 30501041
1968	30501042 - 30501051

G1000 Row Crop (diesel)

Year	Number range
1965	30600001 - 30600500
1966	30600501 - 3060112
1967	30601126 - 30601285
1968	30601289 - 30601300

G1000 Wheatland (LP gas)

Year	Number range
1966	32600001 - 32600515
1967	32600516 - 32600650
1968	32600651 - 32600652
1969	32600653 - 32600822

G1000 Wheatland (diesel)

Year	Number range
1966	32700001 - 32700796
1967	32700797 - 32701450
1968	32701451 - 32701774
1969	32701775 - 32702050

G1000 Vista (LP gas)

Year	Number range
1967	34500001 - 34500290
1968	34500291 - 34300390
1969	34500391 - 34500564

G1000 Vista (diesel)

Year	Number range
Year	Number range
1967	34600001 - 34600735
1968	34600736 - 34601185
1969	34601186 - 34601610

G1050 (LP gas)

Year	Number range
1969	43000001 - 43000040
1970	43000041 - 43000060
1971	43000061 - 43000105
1972	43000106 - 43000111

G1050 (diesel)

Year	Number range
1969	43100001 - 43100285
1970	43100286 - 43100415
1971	43100544 - 43100544

G1350 Row Crop (LP gas)

Year	Number range
1969	43200001 - 43200022
1970	43255523 - 43200044
1971	43200045 - 43200097
1972	43200098 - 43200108

G1350 Row Crop (diesel)

Year	Number range
1970	43300001 - 43300042
1971	43300043 - 43300253
1972	43300254 - 43300322

G1350 Wheatland (LP gas)

Year	Number range
1969	45300001 - 45300005

G1355

Year	Number range
1973	236440 - 244184
1974	245258 - 252710

A4T-1400 (diesel)

Year	Number range
1969	43600001 - 43900102
1970	43900103 - 43900247

A4T-1600 (diesel)

Year	Number range
1970	45600001 - 45600187
1971	45600188 - 45600700
1972	45600701 - 45601190

A4T-1600 (LP gas)

Year	Number range
1970	45700001 - 45700126
1971	45700127 - 45700197
1972	45700198 - 45700257

Uni-Tractor

Year	Number range
1951	75700001 - 75700254
1952	75700255 - 75701070
1953	75701071 - 75703118
1954	75703119 - 75704118
1955	08704119 - 08705418
1956	08705419 - 08706418
1957	08706419 - 08707687
1958	08707688 - 08708062
1959	08708063 - 08708488
1960	42200001 - 42200637
1961	42200638 - 42201134
1962	42201135 - 42201637

Minneapolis Steel & Threshing serial numbers

Joy-McVicker 50-140

Year	Serial number
1911	NA

Twin City 40-65A

Year	Serial number range
1910 - 1915	NA
1916-1924	1001 - 1820

Twin City 40-65B

Year	Serial number range
NA	1821 - 1825

Twin City 24-45

Model	Serial number range
Model A	2501 - 2646
Model B	2647 - 2673
Model C	2701 - 2797
Model D	2801 - 2815
Model E	2816 - 3126

Twin City 15-30

Years	Serial number range
1913 - 1917	50001 - 5478

Twentieth Century

Years	Serial number range
1914 - ?	50001 - 5478

Twin City 16-30

Year	Serial number range
1917	5501 - 6203
1918	6201 - 6503
1919-1920	NA

Twin City 12-20

Years	Serial number range
1919-1926	10201 - 19903

Twin City 20-35

Years	Serial number range
1920-1926	2101 - 4097

Oliver serial numbers

18-27 Row Crop (single front wheel)
Year	Number range
1930	100001-102468
1931	102649-103300

18-27 (dual front wheels)
Year	Number range
1931	103301-103318
1932	103319-103617
1933	103618-104038
1934	104039-104850
1935	104851-107311
1936	107312-108573
1937	108574-109151

18-28
Year	Number range
1930	800001-800459
1931	800460-800963
1932	800964-800984
1933	800985-801050
1934	801051-801240
1935	801241-801989
1936	801990-802937
1937	802938-803928

28-44
Year	Number range
1930	500001-503599
1931	503600-506184
1932	506185-506211
1933	506212-506254
1934	506255-506400
1935	506401-507175

28-44 & High-Compression Special
Year	Number range
1936	507176-508015
1937	508016-508917

18 Industrial
Year	Number range
1931	900001-900005

28 Industrial
Year	Number range
1932	900006-900018
1933	900019-900021
1934	900022-900036
1935	900037-900072
1936	900073-900078
1937	900079-900086
1938	900087-900102
1939	900103-900112

HP 70 Row Crop
Tag located on left side of engine.
Year	Number range
1935	200001-200685
1936	200686-208728
1937	208729-216925

HP 70 Standard
Tag located on left side of engine.
Year	Number range
1936	300001-300633
1937	300634-301802

70 Row Crop
Tag located on left side of engine.
Year	Number range
1937	216926-219644
1937	220426-220694
1938	219645-220425
1938	220695-223254
1939	223255-231115
1940	231116-236355
1941	236356-241390
1942	241391-243639
1943	243640-244710
1944	244711-250179
1945	250180-252779
1946	252780-258139
1947	258140-262839
1948	262840-267866

Oliver set an industry standard when it introduced the streamlined styling of the Model 70 in 1935.

70 Standard
Tag located on left side of engine.

Year	Number range
1937	301803-302083
1938	302084-303464
1939	303465-305361
1940	305362-306593
1941	306594-307579
1942	307580-308187
1943	308188-308483
1944	308484-310217
1945	310218-311115
1946	311116-312689
1947	312690-314220
1948	314221-315420

Hart-Parr Oliver 25 Industrial
Tag located on left side of engine.

Year	Number range
1937	400001-400002

25 Industrial
Tag located on left side of engine.

Year	Number range
1938	400003-400008
1939	400009-400016
1940	400017-400021
1941	400022-400047
1942	400048-400067
1943	400068-400096
1944	400097-400181

35 Industrial
Tag located on left side of engine.

Year	Number range
1939	900113-900127
1940	900128-900229
1941	900230-900315
1942	900316-900327
1943	900328-900339
1944	900340-900395
1945	900396-900440

Industrial 80
Tag located on left side of engine.

Year	Number range
1945	900441-900633
1946	900634-900816
1947	900817-901124

44 Industrial
Tag located on left side of engine.

Year	Number range
1932	700001-700004
1933	700005-700033
1934	700034-700141
1935	700142-700239
1936	700240-700295
1937	700296-700326
1938	700327-700359
1939	700360-700367

50 Industrial

Year	Number range
1939	700368-700421
1940	700422-700604
1941	700605-700777
1942	700778-701001
1943	701002-701147
1944	701148-701163

80 Row Crop
Tag located on left side of engine.

Year	Number range
1937	109152-109166
1938	109167-109782
1939	109783-110220
1940	110221-110614
1941	110615-110944
1942	110945-111218
1943	111219-111390
1944	111391-111928
1945	111929-112878
1946	112879-114143
1947	114144-114943
1948	114944-115373

80 Standard
Tag located on left side of engine.

Year	Number range
1937	803929-803990
1938	803991-805376
1939	805377-806879
1940	806880-808124
1941	808125-809050
1942	809051-809990
1943	809991-810469
1944	810470-811990
1945	811991-813066
1946	813067-814563
1947	814564-815215
1948	815216-816241

Oliver serial numbers

90-99
Tag located on left side of engine.

Year	Number range
1937	508918-508934
1938	508935-509611
1939	509612-510067
1940	510068-510563
1941	510564-510976
1942	510977-511295
1943	511296-511473
1944	511474-512043
1945	512044-512043
1946	512821-513105
1947	513106-513855
1948	513856-514855
1949	514856-516275
1950	516276-516887
1951	516888-517873
1952	517874-518212

99 Industrial
Tag located on left side of engine.

Year	Number range
1945	701164-701225
1946	701226-701265
1947	701266-701287

900 Industrial

Year	Number range
1946	710001-710077
1947	710078-710134
1948	710135-710227
1949	710228-710256
1950	710257-710281

60 Row Crop
Tag located on left side of engine.

Year	Number range
1940	600001-600070
1941	600071-606303
1942	606304-607394
1943	607395-608525
1944	608526-612046
1945	612047-615627
1946	615628-616706
1947	616707-620256
1948	620257-625131

60 Standard
Tag located on left side of engine.

Year	Number range
1942	410001-410500
1943	410501-410510
1944	410511-410616
1945	410617-410910
1946	410911-411310
1947	411311-411960
1948	411961-413605

66 Row Crop
Tag is located on the right side of the transmission housing. In 1951 the tag moved to the lower left side of dash panel.

Year	Number range
1949	420001-423100
1950	423101-426010
1951	426011-429770
1952	429771-431472
1953	3503990-3510962
1954	4500309-4503563

66 Standard
Tag is located on the right side of the transmission housing. In 1951 the tag moved to the lower left side of dash panel.

Year	Number range
1949	470001-471050
1950	471051-472390
1951	472391-474232
1952	474233-476408
1953	3504001-3511337
1954	4501624-4504476

77 Row Crop
Tag is located on the right side of the transmission. In 1951 the tag was moved to the lower left side of the dash panel.

Year	Number range
1948	320001-320240
1949	320241-327900
1950	327901-337242
1951	337243-347903
1952	347904-354447
1953	3500001-3510830
1954	4501301-4504470

77 Standard

Tag is located on the right side of the transmission housing. In 1951 the tag moved to the lower left side of dash panel.

Year	Number range
1948	269001-269940
1949	269941-271266
1950	271267-272465
1951	272466-273375
1952	273376-274051

88 Row Crop (old style)

Year	Number range
1947	120001-120352
1948	120353-121300

88 Standard (old style)

Year	Number range
1947	820001-820136
1948	820136-820485

88 Row Crop

Tag is located on the right side of the transmission housing. In 1951 the tag moved to the lower left side of dash panel.

Year	Number range
1948	121301-123300
1949	123301-128652
1950	128653-132862
1951	132863-138183
1952	138184-143232
1953	3500977-3511566
1954	4500076-4505123

88 Standard

Tag is located on the right side of the transmission housing. In 1951 the tag moved to the lower left side of dash panel.

Year	Number range
1948	820486-821085
1949	821086-824240
1950	824241-825810
1951	825811-826916
1952	826917-827966
1953	3501813-3511484
1954	4500080-4505081

99 (6-cylinder Fleetline)

Year	Number range
1953	518300-519244
1954	519245-519299

Super 44

Tag located on clutch shaft cover behind battery.

Year	Number range
1957	1001-1550
1958	1551-1775

Super 55

Tag located on the left side of the center frame.

Year	Number range
1954	6001-8290
1955	11837-31370
1956	35001-43647
1957	43916-56036
1958	56501-59033

Super 66

Tag is on lower left side of the dash panel.

Year	Number range
1954	7085-7284
1955	14099-27842
1956	39371-42430
1957	45846-55800
1958	57858-72824

Super 77

Tag is on lower left side of the dash panel.

Year	Number range
1954	8303-8988
1955	10001-29842
1956	38500-43637
1957	44167-55955
1958	56917-59008

Super 88

Tag is on lower left side of the dash panel.

Year	Number range
1954	6503-8302
1955	10075-29347
1956	36774-43715
1957	43901-55607
1958	56580-59001

Super 99

Tag is on left side of clutch cover.

Year	Number range
1954	519300-519675
1955	519676-520455
1956	520456-520943
1957	520944-521612
1958	521613-521635

Oliver serial numbers

OC-3

Year	Beginning Number
1951	1WH000
1952	3WH712
1953	350000
1954	450000
1955	11WH760
1956	15WH306
1957	19WH090

OC-4

Year	Beginning Number
1956	1TG002
1957	1TG004
1958	4TG077

OC-4-3-D

Year	Beginning Number
1957	1WD002
1958	1WD120
1959	1WD950
1960	2WD824
1961	3WD594
1962	800270
1963	800431
1964	801280
1965	801795

OC-4-3-G

Year	Beginning Number
1958	1WR002
1959	1WR542
1960	4WR958
1961	6WR746
1962	800001000
1963	800431436
1964	801280
1965	801795

OC-6-D

Year	Beginning Number
1953	3500000
1954	4500000
1955	1RC468
1956	1RC632
1957	1RC876
1958	2RC262
1959	2RC366
1960	2RC458

OC-6-G

Year	Beginning Number
1953	3500000
1954	4500000
1955	1RM182
1956	1RM314
1957	1RM504
1958	1RM808
1959	2RM004
1960	2RM126

OC-9

Year	Beginning Number
1959	1MA001
1960	1MA182

OC-96

Year	Beginning Number
1959	1MB001
1960	1MB168
1961	2MB020
1962	800-270
1963	800431
1964	801-277
1965	801-856

OC-12-D

Year	Beginning Number
1954	1JX001
1955	1JX042
1956	2JX350
1957	3JX636
1958	4JX652
1959	5JX140
1960	5JX506
1961	5JX828

OC-12-G

Year	Beginning Number
1954	1JR001
1955	1JR002
1956	1JR062
1957	1JR178
1958	1JR202
1959	1JR21
1960	1JR228

Sears Handiman serial numbers

Year	Serial or Type numbers
1931	SR8355
1932	SR32538 - SR32251
1933	Type #60209. Two models: Heavy-Duty and Model A
1934	1424
1935	Type #60500. Two models: C-35 and B-35
1936	Type #60754. Three models: Z-36, C-36, and B-36
1937	Type #60754. Three models: Z-37, C-37, and B-37
1938	Model #917.5047, Type #20407. Three models: Z-38, C-38, and B-38
1938-1939	Model #917.5032, Type #20430. Three models: Z-38, C-38, and B-38
1939	Model #917.5044, Type #25862. Three models: Z-38, C-38, and B-38
1939	Model #917.5161
194 ?	Model #917.60754, Series 291
1940	No data. Three models: Z-40, C-40, and B-40
1941	No data. Three models: Z-41, C-41, and B-41
1942	No data. One model available.

Handiman Junior

Year	Serial or Type numbers
1938	917.5032
1940	917.50321
1941	917.503281 and 503282

Handiman R/T

Year	Serial or Type numbers
1939	917.5151, 917.5154
1940	917.5155
Late '50s	917.60120 and 21
Early '60s	917.60124 and 25

Oliver's Model 990 was the most powerful tractor of its time when introduced in 1958. The tractor's 213-cubic-inch General Motors diesel turned out 62 (drawbar) horsepower.

Silver King
serial numbers

Serial numbers for all models

Year	Starting number
1934	0
1935	326
1936	1001
1937	1986
1938	3025
1939	3876
1940	4245
1941	4906
1942	5256
1943	5594
1944	5710
1945	6161
1946	6449
1947	6947
1948	7475
1949	8245
1950	8395
1951	8545
1952	8627
1953	8708
1954	8717

Wallis
serial numbers

Bear

Year	Beginning number
1912	201-INA
1913	INA-210

Cub Models C & D

Year	Number range
1913 to 1917	1001-1660

Cub Model J

Year	Beginning number
1915	10001
1916	13505

Cub Model K

Year	Beginning number
1916	14001-INA
1916	OMA
1917	INA
1918	INA
1919	INA
1920	INA
1921	INA
1922	23156

Cub Model OKO

Year	Number range
1922	23200 to 23156
1926	40001 to 50000

Cub Certified Standard

Year	Number range
1926	25645 to 40000

The Wallis Cub Junior Model 13-25 featured the one-piece frame construction innovated by its predecessor, the Wallis Cub. Introduced in 1918, the 13-25 was powered by a four-cylinder engine capable of pulling a two- to three-bottom plow. Wallis Trctor Company became part of J.I. Case Plow Co. in 1919.

White serial numbers

Abbreviation guide:
2WD = two-wheel drive
FWD = front-wheel drive

2-50

Year	Number range
1976 (2WD)	516 625 – 518 781
1976 (FWD)	516 898 – 518 993
1977 (2WD)	518 782 – 520 783
1977 (FWD)	518 994 – 521 634
1978 (2WD)	520 784 – 525 267
1978 (FWD)	521 635 – 525 238
1979 (2WD)	525 268 – 525 725
1979 (FWD)	525 290 – 527 580
1980 (2WD)	525 726 – 527 626
1980 (FWD)	527 581 – 527 687

2-60

Year	Number range
1976 (2WD)	780 725 – 790 272
1976 (FWD)	782 037 – 790 272
1977 (2WD)	790 273 – 944 701
1977 (FWD)	790 273 – 946 284
1978 (2WD)	9i44 702 – 959 279
1978 (FWD)	946 285 – 959 302
1979 (2WD)	959 280 – 959 999
	480 187 – 491 334
1979 (FWD)	959 303 – 959 999
	480 307 - 486 531

2-70

Year	Number range
1976	266 173 – 273 088
1977	274 543 – 281 876
1978	283 917 – 284 276
1979	287 528 – 292 563
1980	293 819 – 294 062
1981	296 246 – 298 946
1982	299 887 – 300 091

2-85

Year	Number range
1975	263 341 – 265 402
1976	268 142 – 273 315
1977	274 287 – 281 504
1978	282 339 – 287 196
1979	287 469 - 293 408
1980	294 063 – 295 791
1981	297 751 – 299 123
1982	300 092 – 300 158

2-105

Year	Number range
1974	255 216 – 255 537
1975	255 538 – 265 927
1976	265 928 – 273 619
1977	273 760 – 280 588
1978	282 102 – 287 189
1979	287 197 – 293 357
1980	294 109 – 295 781
1981	296 878 – 299 731
1982	300 779 – 300 782

2-135

Year	Number range
1976	272 663 – 273 628
1977	273 629 – 282 078
1978	282 825 – 286 928
1979	288 201 – 293 818
1980	294 330 – 296 128
1981	296 611 – 299 632
1982	300 380 – 300 693

2-150

Year	Number range
1975	257 899 – 265 201
1976	266 783 – 271 312

2-155

Year	Number range
1976	272 595 – 272 812
1977	276 055 – 281 209
1978	282 280 – 286 929
1979	287 812 – 293 708
1980	296 160 – 296 244
1981	297 134 – 299 365
1982	300 259 – 300 429

2-180

Year	Number range
1977	281 993 – 282 087
1978	282 088 – 286 004
1979	289 447 – 292 891
1980	294 655 – 294 821
1981	296 571 – 299 002
1982	300 159 – 300 258

White serial numbers

4-150
Year	Number range
1974	246 001 – 246 849
1975	246 871 – 262 243
1976	262 244 - 267 958
1977	275 051 – 275 405
1978	275 406 – 275 571

4-175
Year	Number range
1979	292 187 – 292 334
1980	295 808 – 295 900
1981	297 293 – 299 848
1982	299 849 – 299 886

4-180
Year	Number range
1975	256 587 – 262 099
1976	262 524 – 268 111
1977	268 112 – 275 396
1978	275 450 – 275 502

4-210
Year	Number range
1978	275 572 – 275 943
1979	275 944 – 292 368
1980	295 391 – 296 205
1981	296 471 – 299 826
1982	300 694 - 300 778

2-30
Year	Number range
1979-84	001 418 – 101 461

2-32
Year	Number range
1985-86	000 007 – 000 315

2-35
Year	Number range
1979-84	05 822 – 004 001

2-45
Year	Number range
1979-81	000 001 – 000 548

2-55
Year	Number range
1982-87	000 097 – 000 807

2-62
Year	Number range
1979-81	000 001 – 001 143

2-65
Year	Number range
1982-87	000 099 – 001 202

2-75
1982-87	000 177 – 000 955

2-88
Year	Number range
1982	301 457 – 301 717
1983	None built
1984	302 464 – 302 599
1985	None built
1986	400 001 – 400 599
1987	400 734 – 400 762

2-110
Year	Number range
1982	300 783 – 301 965
1983	301 998 – 302 158
1984	302 334 – 303 551
1985	303 552 – 303 614
1986	400 231 – 400 690
1987	400 764 – 401 005

2-135 Series 3
Year	Number range
1982	301 116 – 301 811
1983	302 159 – 302 233
1984	302 715 – 303 289
1985	None built
1986	400 167 – 400 733
1987	400 831 – 400 880

2-155 Series 3
Year	Number range
1982	300 928 – 301 921
1983	None built
1984	302 791 – 303 344
1985	None built
1986	400 107 – 400 718

2-180 Series 3
Year	Number range
1982	301 922 – 310 963
1983	301 966 – 301 997
1984	302 951 – 302 990
1985	None built
1986	400 082 – 400 230

4-225

Year	Number range
1983	302 234 – 302 273
1984	302 620 – 303 468
1985	None built
1986	400 344
1987	400 901 – 400 921

4-270

Year	Number range
1983	302 274 – 302 333
1984	302 655 – 303 423
1985	None built
1986	400 639 – 400 658
1987	400 922 – 400 941
1988	401 411 – 401 435

FB 16

Year	Number range
1986-89 (2WD)	02 314 – 02 811
1986-89 (FWD)	14 422 – 16 865

FB 21

Year	Number range
1986-89 (2WD)	00 595 – 01 181
1986-89 (FWD))	02 879 – 04 844

FB 31

Year	Number range
1986-89 (2WD)	00 126 – 01 981
1986-89 (FWD)	00 028 – 01 061

FB 37

Year	Number range
1986-89 (2WD)	00 083 – 00 315
1986-89 (FWD)	00 679 – 01 339

FB 43

Year	Number range
1986-89 (2WD)	00 060 – 00 156
1986-89 (FWD)	00 322 – 00 499

American 60

Year	Number range
1989	402 965 – 403 164
1990	404 299 – 404 454
1991	405 028 – 405 047

American 80

Year	Number range
1989	402 590 – 403 464
1990	404 266 – 404 541
1991	405 048 – 405 052

100

Year	Number range
1987	401 236 – 401 260
1988	401 361 – 401 970
1989	402 661 – 403 764

120

Year	Number range
1987	401 121 – 401 235
1988	401 296 – 402 520
1989	402 521 – 403 839

125

Year	Number range
1990	404 066 – 404 165
1991	404 601 – 404 969

140

Year	Number range
1987	401 151 – 401 200
1988	401 326 – 402 440
1989	402 736 – 404 064

145

Year	Number range
1991	404 671 – 404 923

160

Year	Number range
1987	401 096 – 401 120
1988	401 261 – 402 220
1989	403 640 – 404 024

170

Year	Number range
1990	404 228 – 404 265
1991	404 766 – 405 207

185

Year	Number range
1986 (FB 185)	400 659 – 400 708
1987	400 881 – 401 095
1988	401 579 – 402 050
1989	402 761 – 404 014

195

Year	Number range
1990	404 166 – 404 227
1991	404 826 – 404 995

The Nebraska Tractor Test's original self-contained "mobile" laboratory is seen above in a photograph taken in 1937. This vehicle rode on its own wheels and was loaded with what seemed at that time like a wealth of testing equipment. Over the years, this sleek-styled vehicle evaluated more than 1,500 tractors at the Nebraska Tractor Test's $\frac{1}{3}$-mile long track located on the University of Nebraska's East Campus in Lincoln, Nebraska. Numerous upgrades were made to the mobile laboratory over the years with the latest design update occuring in 1963. The vehicle was retired in 2004 but can still be seen at the Nebraska Tractor Test museum. For more information, contact the museum at 402/472-8389 or go to www.tractormuseum.unl.edu.

tractor test results

advance-rumely test results

Year tested	Name	Model	Company	Rated belt hp.	Drawbar hp.	Rated PTO hp.
1920	Rumely Oil Pull	E, 30-60	Advance-Rumely	75	49	
1920	Rumely Oil Pull	H, 16-30	Advance-Rumely	33	22	
1920	Rumely Oil Pull	K, 12-20	Advance-Rumely	25	15	
1920	Rumely Oil Pull	G, 30-40	Advance-Rumely	46	30	
1924	Rumely Oil Pull	S, 30-60	Advance Rumely Thresher Co.	70	40	
1925	Rumely Oil Pull	M, 20-35	Advance Rumely Thresher Co.	43	27	
1925	Rumely Oil Pull	L, 15-25	Advance Rumely Thresher Co.	30	19	
1925	Rumely Oil Pull	R, 25-45	Advance Rumely Thresher Co.	50	35	
1927	Rumely Oil Pull	W, 20-30	Advance Rumely	35	26	
1927	Rumely Oil Pull	X, 25-40	Advance Rumely	50	38	
1927	Rumely Oil Pull	Y, 30-50	Advance Rumely	63	47	
1928	Rumely	DO-All	Advance Rumely Thresher Co.	21	16	
1931	Rumely	6A	Advance Rumely Thresher Co.	48	33	

allis-chalmers test results

Year tested	Name	Model	Company	Rated belt hp.	Drawbar hp.	Rated PTO hp.
1920	Allis Chalmers	6-12	Allis-Chalmers	12	6	
1920	Allis Chalmers	18-30	Allis-Chalmers	33	20	
1921	Allis Chalmers	15-27	Allis-Chalmers	33	21	
1921	Allis Chalmers	12-20	Allis-Chalmers	33	21	
1921	Allis Chalmers	18-30	Allis-Chalmers	43	25	
1921	Allis Chalmers	22-38	Allis-Chalmers	43	25	
1928	Allis Chalmers	20-35 (A)	Allis-Chalmers	44	33	
1928	Allis Chalmers	20-35 (E)	Allis-Chalmers	44	33	
1929	Allis-Chalmers	U United	Allis-Chalmers	35	25	
1929	Monarch	35-30	Allis-Chalmers		40	
1930	Monarch	50	Allis-Chalmers	62	53	
1931	Allis-Chalmers	UC All Crop	Allis-Chalmers	36	24	
1931	Allis-Chalmers	EK	Allis-Chalmers	47	33	
1932	Allis-Chalmers	L	Allis-Chalmers	91	76	
1933	Allis-Chalmers	Special K	Allis-Chalmers	55	47	
1933	Allis-Chalmers	M	Allis-Chalmers	35	29	
1934	Allis-Chalmers	WC	Allis-Chalmers	21	Steel - 14 Rubber - 19	
1935	Allis-Chalmers	U	Allis-Chalmers	34	Steel - 23 Rubber - 30	
1935	Allis-Chalmers	UC	Allis-Chalmers	34	Steel - 24 Rubber - 28	
1935	Allis-Chalmers	M	Allis-Chalmers	35	28	
1937	Allis-Chalmers	WK-0	Allis-Chalmers	59	50	
1937	Allis-Chalmers	S-0	Allis-Chalmers	74	62	
1937	Allis-Chalmers	L-0	Allis-Chalmers	91	76	
1938	Allis-Chalmers	B	Allis-Chalmers	15	13	
1938	Allis-Chalmers	WC	Allis-Chalmers	25	Steel - 18 Rubber - 20	
1938	Allis-Chalmers	WC	Allis-Chalmers	29	Steel - 22 Rubber - 24	
1939	Allis-Chalmers	RC	Allis-Chalmers	18	15	
1939	Allis-Chalmers	WK	Allis-Chalmers	62	53	
1939	Allis-Chalmers	WS	Allis-Chalmers	84	68	
1939	Allis-Chalmers	L	Allis-Chalmers	108	91	
1940	Allis-Chalmers	HD-7W	Allis-Chalmers	68	57	
1940	Allis-Chalmers	HD-10W	Allis-Chalmers	98	82	
1940	Allis-Chalmers	HD-14	Allis-Chalmers	145	126	
1940	Allis-Chalmers	C	Allis-Chalmers	19	16	
1940	Allis-Chalmers	C	Allis-Chalmers	23	18	
1948	Allis-Chalmers	HD-5B	Allis-Chalmers	47	38	
1948	Allis-Chalmers	HD-19	Allis-Chalmers	129	110	
1948	Allis-Chalmers	G	Allis-Chalmers	10	9	
1948	Allis-Chalmers	WD	Allis-Chalmers	26	24	
1950	Allis-Chalmers	B	Allis-Chalmers	22	19	
1950	Allis-Chalmers	WD	Allis-Chalmers	34	30	
1950	Allis-Chalmers	CA	Allis-Chalmers	25	22	

allis-chalmers test results

Year tested	Name	Model	Company	Rated belt hp.	Drawbar hp.	Rated PTO hp.
1951	Allis-Chalmers	HD-9	Allis-Chalmers	79	67	
1951	Allis-Chalmers	HD-15	Allis-Chalmers	117	105	
1951	Allis-Chalmers	HD-20	Allis-Chalmers		116	
1953	Allis-Chalmers	WD-45	Allis-Chalmers	43	37	
1953	Allis-Chalmers	WD-45	Allis-Chalmers	33	29	
1953	Allis-Chalmers	WD-45	Allis-Chalmers	44	38	
1955	Allis-Chalmers	HD-21 AC	Allis-Chalmers		135	
1955	Allis-Chalmers	HD-16 AC	Allis-Chalmers		104	
1955	Allis-Chalmers	HD-16A	Allis-Chalmers	133	118	
1955	Allis-Chalmers	WD-45	Allis-Chalmers	43	39	
1956	Allis-Chalmers	HD-6B	Allis-Chalmers	60	49	
1956	Allis-Chalmers	HD-11B	Allis-Chalmers	89	73	
1957	Allis-Chalmers	D-14	Allis-Chalmers	34	30	
1957	Allis-Chalmers	D-17	Allis-Chalmers	52	48	
1957	Allis-Chalmers	D-17	Allis-Chalmers	51	46	
1958	Allis-Chalmers	D-17	Allis-Chalmers	50	46	
1958	Allis-Chalmers	D-14	Allis-Chalmers	31	28	
1958	Allis-Chalmers	HD-21A	Allis-Chalmers		147	
1959	Allis-Chalmers	D-12	Allis-Chalmers		24	28
1959	Allis-Chalmers	D-10	Allis-Chalmers		25	28
1961	Allis-Chalmers	H-3	Allis-Chalmers		27	32
1961	Allis-Chalmers	HD-3	Allis-Chalmers		27	32
1961	Allis-Chalmers	D-15	Allis-Chalmers		35	40
1961	Allis-Chalmers	D-15	Allis-Chalmers		33	36
1961	Allis-Chalmers	D-15	Allis-Chalmers		34	37
1962	Allis-Chalmers	D-19	Allis-Chalmers		63	71
1962	Allis-Chalmers	D-19	Allis-Chalmers		62	66
1962	Allis-Chalmers	D-10	Allis-Chalmers		29	33
1962	Allis-Chalmers	I-40	Allis-Chalmers		29	33
1962	Allis-Chalmers	D-12	Allis-Chalmers		29	33
1962	Allis-Chalmers	D-19	Allis-Chalmers		59	66
1963	Allis-Chalmers	D-15 Series II	Allis-Chalmers		39	46
1963	Allis-Chalmers	D-15 Series II	Allis-Chalmers		37	43
1963	Allis-Chalmers	D-21	Allis-Chalmers		95	103
1965	Allis-Chalmers	190	Allis-Chalmers		67	77
1965	Allis-Chalmers	200	Allis-Chalmers		84	93
1965	Allis-Chalmers	190XT	Allis-Chalmers		84	93
1965	Allis-Chalmers	D-21 Series II	Allis-Chalmers		117	127
1965	Allis-Chalmers	190XT	Allis-Chalmers		77	85
1965	Allis-Chalmers	190	Allis-Chalmers		65	75
1965	Allis-Chalmers	190XT	Allis-Chalmers		81	89
1967	Allis-Chalmers	180	Allis-Chalmers		56	64
1967	Allis-Chalmers	170	Allis-Chalmers		48	54
1967	Allis-Chalmers	170	Allis-Chalmers		48	54
1969	Allis-Chalmers	180	Allis-Chalmers		57	65
1969	Allis-Chalmers	220	Allis-Chalmers		121	135
1969	Allis-Chalmers	6040	Allis-Chalmers		38	40
1969	Allis-Chalmers	160	Allis-Chalmers		38	40

aultman-taylor test results

Year tested	Name	Model	Company	Rated belt hp.	Drawbar hp.	Rated PTO hp.
1920	Aultman-Taylor	30-60	Aultman-Taylor	75	55	
1920	Aultman-Taylor	30-60	Aultman-Taylor	80	58	
1920	Aultman-Taylor	15-30	Aultman-Taylor	34	21	
1920	Aultman-Taylor	22-45	Aultman-Taylor	46	28	

b.f. avery test results

Year tested	Name	Model	Company	Rated belt hp.	Drawbar hp.	Rated PTO hp.
1920	Avery	7-14, C	Avery	14	8	
1920	Avery	8-15	Avery	15	8	
1920	Avery	12-20	Avery	24	17	
1920	Avery	14-28	Avery	31	21	
1920	Avery	25-50	Avery	56	32	
1920	Avery	40-80	Avery	69	49	
1920	Avery	5-10	Avery	11	6	
1920	Avery	18-36	Avery	44	27	
1921	Avery	12-25	Avery	25	13	
1921	Avery	8-16	Avery	16	9	
1923	Avery	15-25 Track Runner	Avery	29	20	
1923	Avery	20-35	Avery	37	22	

c.l. best test results

Year tested	Name	Model	Company	Rated belt hp.	Drawbar hp.	Rated PTO hp.
1921	Best	60, 35-55	CL Best	56	50	
1921	Best	30, 18-30	CL Best	30	24	
1923	Best	60, 40-60	CL Best	65	56	
1923	Best	30, 20-30	Best Tractor Co.	32	25	
1924	Best	S30, 25-30	CL Best	37	33	
1924	Best	A60, 50-60	CL Best	72	61	

caterpillar tractor test results

Year tested	Name	Model	Company	Rated belt hp.	Drawbar hp.	Rated PTO hp.
1928	Caterpillar	20, 20-25	Caterpillar	29	26	
1929	Caterpillar	15, 15-20	Caterpillar	24	21	
1929	Caterpillar	10, 10-15	Caterpillar	18	14	
1932	Caterpillar	25	Caterpillar	32	27	
1932	Caterpillar	50	Caterpillar	56	49	
1932	Caterpillar	20	Caterpillar	27	22	
1932	Caterpillar	35	Caterpillar	43	36	
1932	Caterpillar	15	Caterpillar	20	16	
1932	Caterpillar	60	Caterpillar	77	65	
1932	Caterpillar	65	Caterpillar	78	67	
1933	Caterpillar	70	Caterpillar	82	72	
1933	Caterpillar	50	Caterpillar	61	52	
1933	Caterpillar	35	Caterpillar	44	39	
1933	Caterpillar	75	Caterpillar	92	80	
1934	Caterpillar	R-5	Caterpillar	58	49	
1934	Caterpillar	R-2	Caterpillar	32	27	
1934	Caterpillar	22	Caterpillar	29	23	
1934	Caterpillar	R-3	Caterpillar	41	34	
1934	Caterpillar	22	Caterpillar	30	25	
1935	Caterpillar	50	Caterpillar	61	52	
1935	Caterpillar	50	Caterpillar	71	64	
1935	Caterpillar	40	Caterpillar	56	50	
1935	Caterpillar	RD-6	Caterpillar	48	42	
1935	Caterpillar	40	Caterpillar	48	42	
1935	Caterpillar	40	Caterpillar	48	41	
1935	Caterpillar	40	Caterpillar	56	48	
1936	Caterpillar	RD-7	Caterpillar	68	60	
1936	Caterpillar	RD-7	Caterpillar	77	65	
1936	Caterpillar	RD-7	Caterpillar	95	78	
1936	Caterpillar	RD-8	Caterpillar	103	91	
1936	Caterpillar	D-8	Caterpillar	103	91	
1936	Caterpillar	RD-8	Caterpillar	118	103	
1936	Caterpillar	D-8	Caterpillar	118	103	
1936	Caterpillar	30	Caterpillar	36	30	
1936	Caterpillar	R-4	Caterpillar	36	30	
1936	Caterpillar	R-4	Caterpillar	39	35	
1936	Caterpillar	30	Caterpillar	39	35	
1936	Caterpillar	D-4	Caterpillar	40	35	
1936	Caterpillar	RD-4	Caterpillar	40	35	
1938	Caterpillar	D-8	Caterpillar	109	96	
1939	Caterpillar	R-2	Caterpillar	29	23	
1939	Caterpillar	R-2	Caterpillar	28	22	
1939	Caterpillar	D-2	Caterpillar	29	25	
1940	Caterpillar	D-8	Caterpillar	127	110	
1940	Caterpillar	D-7	Caterpillar	89	78	
1941	Caterpillar	D-6	Caterpillar	78	63	
1949	Caterpillar	D-8	Caterpillar		123	
1949	Caterpillar	D-6	Caterpillar	76	61	

Year tested	Name	Model	Company	Rated belt hp.	Drawbar hp.	Rated PTO hp.
1949	Caterpillar	D-4	Caterpillar	51	41	
1949	Caterpillar	D-2	Caterpillar	36	30	
1955	Caterpillar	D-2	Caterpillar	41	36	
1955	Caterpillar	D-4	Caterpillar	58	48	
1955	Caterpillar	D-6	Caterpillar	92	73	
1956	Caterpillar	D-7	Caterpillar	121	103	
1956	Caterpillar	D-8	Caterpillar		157	
1956	Caterpillar	D-9	Caterpillar		252	
1959	Caterpillar	D-7	Caterpillar		115	
1959	Caterpillar	D-8	Caterpillar		177	
1960	Caterpillar	D-4	Caterpillar	56	50	
1960	Caterpillar	D-6	Caterpillar		75	

cletrac tractor test results

Year tested	Name	Model	Company	Rated belt hp.	Drawbar hp.	Rated PTO hp.
1920	Cletrac	W, 12-20	Cleveland Tractor	24	15	
1922	Cletrac	F, 9-16	Cleveland Tractor	19	13	
1926	Cletrac	K, 15-25	Cleveland Tractor	28	23	
1926	Cletrac	K, 15-25	Cleveland Tractor	30	24	
1926	Cletrac	20-27	Cleveland Tractor	30	24	
1926	Cletrac	A, 30-45	Cleveland Tractor	48	38	
1928	Cletrac	40, 40-55	Cleveland Tractor	63	55	
1928	Cletrac	55	Cleveland Tractor	63	55	
1930	Cletrac	80-60	Cleveland Tractor	90	83	
1931	Cletrac	35	Cleveland Tractor	45	40	
1931	Cletrac	40-30	Cleveland Tractor	45	40	
1931	Cletrac	15	Cleveland Tractor	25	18	
1932	Cletrac	25	Cleveland Tractor	33	26	
1932	Cletrac	15	Cleveland Tractor	26	22	
1935	Cletrac	DD	Cleveland Tractor	63	57	
1935	Cletrac	40	Cleveland Tractor	63	57	
1936	Cletrac	CG	Cleveland Tractor	51	40	
1936	Cletrac	BG	Cleveland Tractor	39	28	
1936	Cletrac	AG	Cleveland Tractor	30	24	
1936	Cletrac	EG	Cleveland Tractor	28	20	
1936	Cletrac	FG	Cleveland Tractor	104	87	
1936	Cletrac	FD	Cleveland Tractor	100	86	
1937	Cletrac	BD	Cleveland Tractor	41	34	
1937	Cletrac	CG	Cleveland Tractor	52	45	
1939	Cletrac	G General	Cleveland Tractor	19	14	
1939	Cletrac	HG	Cleveland Tractor	19	14	
1939	Cletrac	BD	Cleveland Tractor	45	36	
1939	Cletrac	FD	Cleveland Tractor	107	91	

cockshutt tractor test results

Year tested	Name	Model	Company	Rated belt hp.	Drawbar hp.	Rated PTO hp.
1947	Co-op	E3	Cockshutt	31	27	
1947	Cockshutt	30	Cockshutt	31	27	
1947	Farmcrest	30	Cockshutt	31	27	
1950	Co-op	E4	Cockshutt	43	37	
1950	Cockshutt	40	Cockshutt	43	37	
1952	Co-op	E2	Cockshutt	28	25	
1952	Cockshutt	20	Cockshutt	28	25	
1952	Co-op	E5	Cockshutt	51	46	
1952	Cockshutt	50	Cockshutt	51	46	
1952	Co-op	E5	Cockshutt	55	51	
1952	Cockshutt	50	Cockshutt	55	51	
1958	Cockshutt	550	Cockshutt	38	34	
1958	Cockshutt	560	Cockshutt	48	45	
1958	Cockshutt	570	Cockshutt	60	52	

The literally thousands of garden tractor models like the Ottawa Mule Team 15 (left) that were built over the last 100 years had a huge impact on agriculture as well as consumer life. Oftentimes the firms that built these tractors, like the Mule Team's Ottawa Manufacturing of Ottawa, Kansas, were in existence for a few years and then ceased building garden tractors or failed entirely, never to be heard from again.

david brown tractor test results

Year tested	Name	Model	Company	Rated belt hp.	Drawbar hp.	Rated PTO hp.
1954	David Brown	25	David Brown		34	26
1959	David Brown	950	David Brown		36	39
1960	David Brown	850	David Brown		31	33
1960	David Brown	850	David Brown		28	32
1965	David Brown	880	David Brown		35	40
1965	David Brown	990	David Brown		45	51
1966	David Brown	770	David Brown		28	32
1966	David Brown	880	David Brown		36	42
1968	David Brown	1200	David Brown		56	65
1968	David Brown	990	David Brown		44	52
1969	David Brown	3800	David Brown		34	39
1969	David Brown	4600	David Brown		39	46

ford tractor test results

Year tested	Name	Model	Company	Rated belt hp.	Drawbar hp.	Rated PTO hp.
1920	Fordson	Fordson	Ford Motor Co.	19	9	
1926	Fordson	Fordson	Ford Motor Co.	22	12	
1930	Fordson	F	Ford Motor Co.	23	13	
1930	Fordson	F	Ford Motor Co.	29	18	
1937	Fordson	All-Around	Ford Motor Co.	22	Steel - 14 Rubber - 18	
1938	Fordson	All-Around	Ford Motor Co.	28	Steel - 19 Rubber - 21	
1940	Ford-Ferguson	9N	Ferguson-Sherman	23	17	
1940	Ford-Ferguson	2N	Ferguson-Sherman	23	17	
1947	Ford	8N	Ford Motor Co.	21	17	
1948	Ford	8N	Ford Motor Co.	25	21	
1950	Ford	8N	Ford Motor Co.	26	21	
1950	Ford	8NAN	Ford Motor Co.	21	18	
1953	Ford	Jubilee	Ford Motor Co.	31	25	
1953	Ford	NAA	Ford Motor Co.	31	25	
1953	New Fordson	Major	Ford Motor Co.	38	35	
1953	New Fordson	Major	Ford Motor Co.	33	30	
1955	Ford	640	Ford Motor Co.	31	28	
1955	Ford	660	Ford Motor Co.	34	28	
1955	Ford	860	Ford Motor Co.	45	39	
1955	Ford	960	Ford Motor Co.	46	38	
1955	Ford	740	Ford Motor Co.	31	28	
1957	Ford	850	Ford Motor Co.	39	35	
1957	Ford	541	Ford Motor Co.	28	27	
1957	Ford	640	Ford Motor Co.	28	27	
1958	Ford	841	Ford Motor Co.	41	40	
1958	Ford	851	Ford Motor Co.	48	41	
1958	Ford	841	Ford Motor Co.	44	41	
1958	Ford	641	Ford Motor Co.	33	29	
1958	Ford	541	Ford Motor Co.	33	29	
1958	Ford	661	Ford Motor Co.	35	29	
1958	Ford	651	Ford Motor Co.	35	29	
1958	Ford	861	Ford Motor Co.	48	41	
1958	Ford	841	Ford Motor Co.	39	36	
1958	Ford	861	Ford Motor Co.	41	36	
1958	Ford	851	Ford Motor Co.	41	36	
1959	Fordson	Dexta	Ford Motor Co.		27	31
1959	Fordson	Power Major	Ford Motor Co.	47	43	
1959	Ford	741	Ford Motor Co.	31	29	
1959	Ford	641	Ford Motor Co.	31	29	
1959	Ford	631	Ford Motor Co.	31	29	
1959	Ford	621	Ford Motor Co	31	29	
1959	Ford	541	Ford Motor Co.	31	29	
1959	Ford	881	Ford Motor Co.		37	46
1959	Ford	811	Ford Motor Co.		37	46
1959	Ford	681	Ford Motor Co.		27	34
1959	Ford	671	Ford Motor Co		27	34

ford tractor test results

Year tested	Name	Model	Company	Rated belt hp.	Drawbar hp.	Rated PTO hp.
1959	Ford	771	Ford Motor Co.		27	34
1959	Ford	611	Ford Motor Co.		27	34
1959	Ford	881	Ford Motor Co.		34	43
1959	Ford	871	Ford Motor Co.		34	43
1959	Ford	971	Ford Motor Co.		34	43
1959	Ford	811	Ford Motor Co.		34	43
1959	Ford	981	Ford Motor Co		34	43
1959	Ford	671	Ford Motor Co		26	32
1959	Ford	611	Ford Motor Co.		26	32
1959	Ford	771	Ford Motor Co.		26	32
1959	Ford	681	Ford Motor Co.		26	32
1959	Ford	881	Ford Motor Co.		33	41
1959	Ford	981	Ford Motor Co		33	41
1959	Ford	971	Ford Motor Co.		33	41
1959	Ford	811	Ford Motor Co.		33	41
1959	Ford	871	Ford Motor Co.		33	41
1959	Ford	771	Ford Motor Co		25	31
1959	Ford	671	Ford Motor Co.		25	31
1959	Ford	681	Ford Motor Co.		25	31
1959	Ford	611	Ford Motor Co.		25	31
1961	Ford	6000	Ford Motor Co.		61	66
1961	Ford	6000	Ford Motor Co.		61	66
1963	Ford	6000	Ford Motor Co.		53	62
1963	Ford	6000	Ford Motor Co.		54	62
1963	Ford	2000 Super Dexta	Ford Motor Co.		33	38
1963	Ford	5000	Ford Motor Co.		41	47
1965	Ford	6000	Ford Motor Co.		58	66
1965	Ford	6000	Ford Motor Co.		63	66
1965	Ford	5000	Ford Motor Co.		49	55
1965	Ford	5000	Ford Motor Co.		45	54
1965	Ford	3000	Ford Motor Co.		36	39
1965	Ford	3000	Ford Motor Co.		33	38
1965	Ford	3000	Ford Motor Co.		36	39
1965	Ford	2000	Ford Motor Co.		27	30
1965	Ford	3000	Ford Motor Co.		30	36
1965	Ford	3000	Ford Motor Co.		33	37
1965	Ford	3000	Ford Motor Co.		34	39
1965	Ford	4000	Ford Motor Co.		39	45
1965	Ford	4000	Ford Motor Co.		41	46
1965	Ford	4000	Ford Motor Co.		39	45
1965	Ford	4000	Ford Motor Co.		42	46
1965	Ford	2000	Ford Motor Co.		27	30
1966	Ford	5000	Ford Motor Co.		53	60
1966	Ford	5000	Ford Motor Co.		50	58
1967	Ford	2000	Ford Motor Co.		28	32
1967	Ford	2000	Ford Motor Co.		28	31
1968	Ford	8000	Ford Motor Co.		91	105

Year tested	Name	Model	Company	Rated belt hp.	Drawbar hp.	Rated PTO hp.
1968	Ford	4000	Ford Motor Co.		47	52
1968	Ford	4000	Ford Motor Co.		46	51
1968	Ford	5000	Ford Motor Co.		60	67
1968	Ford	5000	Ford Motor Co.		54	65
1968	Ford	6600	Ford Motor Co.		57	67
1968	Ford	5000	Ford Motor Co.		57	67
1968	Ford	4000	Ford Motor Co.		42	50
1968	Ford	5000	Ford Motor Co.		58	66
1968	Ford	4600 (8x2)	Ford Motor Co.		44	52
1968	Ford	4610 (8x2)	Ford Motor Co.		44	52
1968	Ford	4000 (8x2)	Ford Motor Co.		44	52
1969	Ford	8000	Ford Motor Co.		94	105
1969	Ford	9000	Ford Motor Co.		117	131

hart-parr tractor test results

Year tested	Name	Model	Company	Rated belt hp.	Drawbar hp.	Rated PTO hp.
1920	Hart-Parr	30, 15-30	Hart-Parr	31	19	
1921	Hart-Parr	20, 11-20	Hart-Parr	23	14	
1923	Hart-Parr	40, 20-40	Hart-Parr	46	28	
1924	Hart-Parr	E, 16-30	Hart-Parr	37	24	
1924	Hart-Parr	E, 12-24	Hart-Parr	26	17	
1926	Hart-Parr	18-36	Hart-Parr	42	32	
1926	Hart-Parr	H,12-24	Hart-Parr	31	21	
1927	Hart-Parr	28-50	Hart-Parr	64	46	

huber tractor test results

Year tested	Name	Model	Company	Rated belt hp.	Drawbar hp.	Rated PTO hp.
1920	Huber	12-25	Huber	25	16	
1921	Huber	Super 4	Huber	39	26	
1926	Huber	18-36	Huber	43	30	
1926	Huber	20-40	Huber	50	40	
1927	Huber	40-62	Huber	69	50	
1929	Huber	20-36	Huber	42	29	
1937	Huber	LC	Huber	43	Steel - 30 Rubber - 31	
1937	Huber	B	Huber	27	Steel - 20 Rubber - 22	
1949	Global	B	Huber	42	37	
1949	Huber	B	Huber	42	37	

ihc tractor test results

Year tested	Name	Model	Company	Rated belt hp.	Drawbar hp.	Rated PTO hp.
1920	International	10-20 Titan	International	28	15	
1920	International	15-30	International	36	25	
1920	International	8-16	International	18	11	
1922	McCormick-Deering	15-30	International	32	20	
1923	McCormick-Deering	10-20	International	21	15	
1925	McCormick-Deering	Farmall	International	20	13	
1926	McCormick-Deering	15-30	International	34	26	
1927	McCormick-Deering	10-20	International	24	19	
1929	McCormick-Deering	22-36	International	40	30	
1929	McCormick-Deering	15-30	International	40	30	
1931	McCormick-Deering	20 Industrial	International	29	23	
1931	McCormick-Deering	F-30 Farmall	International	32	24	
1931	McCormick-Deering	T-20 Tractractor	International	26	23	
1932	McCormick-Deering	W-30	International	33	24	
1932	McCormick-Deering	T-40 Tractractor	International	46	42	
1933	McCormick-Deering	F-12 Farmall	International	16	12	
1933	McCormick-Deering	F-12 Farmall	International	14	11	
1934	McCormick-Deering	F-20 Farmall	International	23	15	
1934	McCormick-Deering	W-12	International	15	12	
1934	McCormick-Deering	T-40 Tractractor	International	48	43	
1934	McCormick-Deering	W-12	International	17	13	
1935	McCormick-Deering	WD-40	International	48	37	
1936	McCormick-Deering	F-20 Farmall	International	27	20	
1936	McCormick-Deering	WK-40	International	45	31	
1936	McCormick-Deering	WK-40	International	49	35	
1936	McCormick-Deering	F-20 Farmall	International	27	20	
1937	McCormick-Deering	TD-35 Tractractor	International	42	37	
1937	McCormick-Deering	T-35 Tractractor	International	42	35	
1937	McCormick-Deering	T-35 Tractractor	International	44	36	
1937	McCormick-Deering	T-40 Tractractor	International	49	42	
1937	McCormick-Deering	T-40 Tractractor	International	51	44	
1938	McCormick-Deering	F-14 Farmall	International	17	14	
1938	McCormick-Deering	TD-40 Tractractor	International	53	48	
1939	International	TD-18 Tractractor	International	80	72	
1939	McCormick-Deering	M Farmall	International	34	30	
1939	McCormick-Deering	M Farmall	International	36	33	
1939	McCormick-Deering	A Farmall	International	18	16	
1939	McCormick-Deering	A Super Farmall	International	18	16	

Year tested	Name	Model	Company	Rated belt hp.	Drawbar hp.	Rated PTO hp.
1939	McCormick-Deering	A Farmall	International	16	15	
1939	McCormick-Deering	A Super Farmall	International	16	15	
1939	McCormick-Deering	B Farmall	International	18	16	
1939	McCormick-Deering	B Super Farmall	International	18	16	
1939	McCormick-Deering	B Farmall	International	16	14	
1939	McCormick-Deering	B Super Farmall	International	16	14	
1939	McCormick-Deering	H Farmall	International	26	24	
1939	McCormick-Deering	H Farmall	International	23	21	
1940	McCormick-Deering	W-4	International	23	21	
1940	International	TD-14 Tractractor	International	61	51	
1940	International	TD- Tractractor	International	43	37	
1940	International	TD-6 Tractractor	International	34	28	
1940	International	T-6 Tractractor	International	36	30	
1940	International	T-6 Tractractor	International	34	29	
1940	McCormick-Deering	W-4	International	26	23	
1940	McCormick-Deering	W-6	International	34	31	
1940	McCormick-Deering	W-6	International	36	32	
1940	McCormick-Deering	WD-6	International	34	31	
1941	McCormick-Deering	MD Farmall	International	35	31	
1941	McCormick-Deering	W-9	International	49	44	
1941	McCormick-Deering	WD-9	International	46	42	
1941	McCormick-Deering	W-9	International	46	42	
1941	International	T-9 Tractractor	International	46	40	
1947	McCormick-Deering	Ccub Farmall	International	9	8	
1948	McCormick-Deering	C Farmall	International	21	18	
1950	McCormick-Deering	WD-9	International	51	46	
1950	International	TD-14A	International	71	62	
1950	International	TD-18A	International	97	85	
1950	International	TD-24	International		142	
1951	McCormick-Farmall	C Super	International	23	20	
1951	McCormick-Deering	WD-6	International	37	33	
1951	McCormick-Farmall	MD	International	38	34	
1951	International	TD-9	International	46	39	
1951	International	TD-6	International	38	31	
1952	McCormick-Farmall	M Super	International	46	41	
1952	McCormick-Deering	W-6 Super	International	46	41	
1952	McCormick-Farmall	MD Super	International	46	42	
1952	McCormick-Deering	WD-6 Super	International	46	41	
1952	McCormick-Farmall	M Super	International	47	44	
1952	McCormick-Deering	W-6 Super	International	47	42	
1953	McCormick-Deering	W-4 Super	International	33	29	
1953	McCormick-Farmall	H Super	International	33	30	

ihc tractor test results

Year tested	Name	Model	Company	Rated belt hp.	Drawbar hp.	Rated PTO hp.
1954	McCormick-Farmall	600	International	65	57	
1954	McCormick-Farmall	650	International	65	57	
1954	McCormick-Deering	WD-9 Super	International	65	57	
1954	International	TD-24	International		154	
1954	McCormick-Farmall	400	International	50	45	
1954	International	W-450	International	52	45	
1954	International	W-400	International	51	45	
1955	McCormick-Farmall	400	International	46	42	
1955	International	W-400	International	46	43	
1955	International	W-450	International	46	43	
1955	McCormick-Farmall	200	International	24	20	
1955	McCormick-Farmall	100	International	20	17	
1955	McCormick-Farmall	300	International	38	33	
1955	IHC	300 Utility	International	41	37	
1956	McCormick-Farmall	Cub	International	10	9	
1956	McCormick-Farmall	400	International	52	48	
1956	International	W-400	International	50	47	
1956	International	W-450	International	50	47	
1956	McCormick-Farmall	300	International	38	35	
1956	IHC	300 Utility	International	42	38	
1956	International	TD-14	International	91	76	
1956	International	TD-9	International	62	52	
1956	International	TD-6	International	48	39	
1956	International	TD-18	International	121	100	
1956	International	T-6	International	48	39	
1957	McCormick-Farmall	450	International	48	45	
1957	McCormick-Farmall	350	International	38	36	
1957	IHC	350 Utility	International	42	40	
1957	McCormick-Farmall	350	International	40	37	
1957	McCormick-Farmall	450	International	55	51	
1957	IHC	350 Utility	International	43	39	
1957	McCormick-Farmall	230	International	28	25	
1957	McCormick-Farmall	130	International	22	19	
1957	IHC	650	International	62	56	
1957	IHC	350 Utility	International	45	41	
1957	McCormick-Farmall	450	International	54	49	
1957	IHC	650	International	63	58	
1957	McCormick-Farmall	350	International	41	38	
1957	International	TD-18	International		106	
1957	International	TD-24	International		168	
1957	IHC	330 Utility	International	34	31	
1957	IHC	340 Utility	International	34	31	
1958	IHC	340 Farmall	International	34	31	
1958	McCormick-Farmall	340	International	34	31	
1958	IHC	140	International	23	31	
1958	McCormick-Farmall	140	International	23	21	
1958	McCormick-Farmall	240	International	30	27	
1958	IHC	240 Utility	International	30	28	

312

Year tested	Name	Model	Company	Rated belt hp.	Drawbar hp.	Rated PTO hp.
1958	International	240	International	30	28	
1958	IHC	560	International	59	54	
1958	McCormick-Farmall	560	International	59	54	
1958	IHC	460	International	49	45	
1958	IHC	560	International	63	58	
1958	McCormick-Farmall	560	International	63	58	
1958	IHC	460	International	50	46	
1958	IHC	460 Utility	International	50	45	
1958	IHC	460 Utility	International	49	45	
1958	IHC	560	International	60	55	
1958	McCormick-Farmall	560	International	60	55	
1958	IHC	460	International	49	46	
1958	IHC	460 Utility	International	48	45	
1959	IHC	660	International		71	78
1959	IHC	660	International		71	81
1959	IHC	660	International		71	80
1959	International	T-340	International		31	36
1960	IHC	354	International		30	32
1960	International	TD-15	International		84	
1960	International	TD-9	International		57	69
1960	International	TD-25	International		188	
1960	International	T-5	International		29	36
1960	International	T-4	International		27	32
1960	International	TD-5	International		30	35
1960	IHC	340 Farmall	International		36	38
1960	McCormick-Farmall	340	International		36	38
1960	International	TD-340	International		32	39
1960	IHC	B275	International UK		30	32
1961	International	TD-20	International		115	
1962	IHC	B414	International UK		32	35
1962	IHC	4300	Frank G. Hough Co.		214	
1962	IHC	B414	International UK		31	36
1962	IHC	504	International		40	45
1962	IHC	404 I	International		33	36
1962	IHC	504	International		41	46
1962	IHC	504	International		41	44
1962	IHC	I2606	International		46	53
1962	IHC	606	International		46	53
1962	IHC	606	International		48	54
1962	IHC	I2606	International		48	54
1963	IHC	706 Farmall	International		67	72
1963	International	706	International		67	72
1963	IHC	806 Farmall	International		86	94
1963	International	806	International		86	94
1963	IHC	706 Farmall	International		66	73
1963	International	706	International		66	73
1963	IHC	856	International		81	93
1963	IHC	806 Farmall	International		81	93
1963	International	806	International		81	93
1963	IHC	706 Farmall	International		67	73
1963	International	706	International		67	73

ihc tractor test results

Year tested	Name	Model	Company	Rated belt hp.	Drawbar hp.	Rated PTO hp.
1963	IHC	856	International		84	93
1963	IHC	806 Farmall	International		84	93
1963	International	806	International		84	93
1965	IHC	424	International		32	36
1965	IHC	656 Farmall	International		54	63
1965	IHC	1206	International		99	112
1965	IHC	444	International		32	36
1965	IHC	424	International		32	36
1965	IHC	656 Farmall	International		54	61
1965	IHC	4100	International		116	
1966	IHC	706 Farmall	International		69	76
1966	IHC	756	International		69	76
1966	IHC	706	International		68	76
1966	IHC	756	International		68	76
1966	IHC	756	International		68	76
1966	IHC	706	International		68	76
1966	International	500	International Canada		31	37
1966	International	500	International Canada		31	36
1967	IHC	656 Farmall	International		52	66
1967	IHC	656 Farmall	International		51	65
1968	IHC	856	International		90	100
1968	IHC	1256 Farmall	International		105	116
1968	IHC	544	International		45	52
1968	IHC	544	International		45	52
1968	IHC	444	International		33	38
1969	IHC	2544	International		42	53
1969	IHC	544	International		42	53
1969	IHC	544	International		42	55
1969	IHC	2544	International		42	55

The Model M stands as the pinnacle of success for the famous Farmall line although it was outsold by its little brother, the Model H. Yet the powerful M was a favorite of heartland farmers and grew to become one of the most famous tractors in agriculture. The three-plow tractor offered optional gas-distillate, high-compression gas or diesel (Model MD) four-cylinder International-built engines. Power was put to work through a five- (forward) gear transmission with speeds ranging from 2½ to 16³/₈ mph.

j.i. case tractor test results

Year tested	Name	Model	Company	Rated belt hp.	Drawbar hp.	Rated PTO hp.
1920	Case	10-18	J.I. Case	18	11	
1920	Case	15-27	J.I. Case	31	21	
1920	Case	22-40	J.I. Case	49	31	
1920	Case	10-20	J.I. Case	22	15	
1920	Case	20-40	J.I. Case	42	24	
1920	Wallis	15-25	J.I. Case	29		
1920	Wallis	15-25	J.I. Case	27	18	
1922	Case	12-20	J.I. Case	22	13	
1923	Case	40-72	J.I. Case	91	55	
1923	Case	12-20	J.I. Case	25	17	
1923	Wallis	OK,15-27	J.I. Case	28	18	
1924	Case	K, 18-32	J.I. Case	36	24	
1924	Case	25-45	J.I. Case	52	34	
1929	Case	L, 26-40	J.I. Case	44	30	
1929	Case	C, 17-27	J.I. Case	29	21	
1929	Case	CC	J.I. Case	28	22	
1936	Case	RC	J.I. Case	19	14	
1938	Case	R	J.I. Case	20	18	
1938	Case	L	J.I. Case	47	Steel - 31	
					Rubber - 40	
1940	Case	DC	J.I. Case	37	33	
1940	Case	VC	J.I. Case	24	18	
1940	Case	D	J.I. Case	35	30	
1941	Case	SC	J.I. Case	22	19	
1949	Case	VAC	J.I. Case	17	15	
1949	Case	VAC	J.I. Case	21	19	
1952	Case	LA	J.I. Case	58	51	
1952	Case	LA	J.I. Case	48	44	
1952	Case	LA	J.I. Case	59	51	
1953	Case	SC	J.I. Case	31	27	
1953	Case	SC	J.I. Case	24	23	
1953	Case	500	J.I. Case	63	56	
1955	Case	401	J.I. Case	49	43	
1955	Case	411	J.I. Case	53	44	
1957	Case	311	J.I. Case	33	29	
1957	Case	301	J.I. Case	30	28	
1957	Case	300B	J.I. Case	30	28	
1958	Case	511B	J.I. Case	45	39	
1958	Case	711B	J.I. Case	52	46	
1958	Case	811B	J.I. Case	53	49	
1958	Case	811B (TC)	J.I. Case	53	43	
1958	Case	801B	J.I. Case	54	51	
1958	Case	801B (TC)	J.I. Case	54	46	
1959	Case	611B	J.I. Case		37	44
1959	Case	611B (TC)	J.I. Case		32	44
1959	Case	211B	J.I. Case		26	30
1959	Case	411B	J.I. Case		31	37
1959	Case	411B (TC)	J.I. Case		27	37

j.i. case test results

Year tested	Name	Model	Company	Rated belt hp.	Drawbar hp.	Rated PTO hp.
1959	Case	900B	J.I. Case		66	70
1959	Case	701B	J.I. Case		47	51
1959	Case	711B	J.I. Case		48	53
1959	Case	811B (TC)	J.I. Case		46	55
1959	Case	811B	J.I. Case		50	55
1959	Case	940	J.I. Case		62	71
1959	Case	910B	J.I. Case		62	71
1959	Case	310C	J.I. Case		27	33
1959	Case	1010	J.I. Case		55	
1959	Case	810	J.I. Case		40	
1959	Case	610	J.I. Case		33	38
1960	Case	831C (TC)	J.I. Case		52	63
1960	Case	831C	J.I. Case		58	63
1960	Case	831	J.I. Case		55	63
1960	Case	841	J.I. Case		53	64
1960	Case	940	J.I. Case		71	79
1960	Case	841	J.I. Case		54	63
1960	Case	930	J.I. Case		71	80
1960	Case	731C (TC)	J.I. Case		44	56
1960	Case	731C	J.I. Case		50	56
1960	Case	731	J.I. Case		48	56
1960	Case	541C (TC)	J.I. Case		33	41
1960	Case	541C	J.I. Case		37	41
1960	Case	640C (TC)	J.I. Case		39	49
1960	Case	640C	J.I. Case		43	49
1960	Case	541	J.I. Case		33	39
1960	Case	570	J.I. Case		33	39
1960	Case	531	J.I. Case		37	41
1960	Case	570	J.I. Case		37	41
1960	Case	640	J.I. Case		42	50
1960	Case	470	J.I. Case		29	33
1960	Case	441	J.I. Case		29	33
1960	Case	841C (TC)	J.I. Case		54	65
1960	Case	841C	J.I. Case		59	65
1960	Case	741C (TC)	J.I. Case		45	57
1960	Case	741C	J.I. Case		50	57
1960	Case	741	J.I. Case		51	57
1960	Case	841C	J.I. Case		57	65
1960	Case	841C (TC)	J.I. Case		53	65
1960	Case	741C	J.I. Case		52	57
1960	Case	741C (TC)	J.I. Case		46	57
1960	Case	741	J.I. Case		52	57
1961	Case	470	J.I. Case		31	34
1961	Case	431	J.I. Case		31	34
1961	Case	531C	J.I. Case		36	40
1961	Case	531C (TC)	J.I. Case		32	40
1961	Case	630C (TC)	J.I. Case		40	48
1961	Case	630C	J.I. Case		45	48

Year tested	Name	Model	Company	Rated belt hp.	Drawbar hp.	Rated PTO hp.
1961	Case	630	J.I. Case		40	48
1961	Case	310E	J.I. Case		31	36
1964	Case	750	J.I. Case		38	
1964	Case	1200	J.I. Case		106	119
1965	Case	831 CK	J.I. Case		58	64
1965	Case	931 GP	J.I. Case		76	85
1965	Case	841 CK	J.I. Case		59	65
1965	Case	941 GP	J.I. Case		72	86
1965	Case	841 CK	J.I. Case		59	64
1965	Case	941 GP	J.I. Case		75	85
1966	Case	1030	J.I. Case		92	101
1969	Case	1470	J.I. Case		132	144
1969	Case	870	J.I. Case		64	70
1969	Case	870	J.I. Case		63	70
1969	Case	770	J.I. Case		48	53
1969	Case	770	J.I. Case		50	56

Test yourself on tractor trivia

Can you name the first tractor or most popular model ever built? How about reciting at least three European firms who have sold tractors in the United States? Here's your chance to test yourself on tractor trivia, but don't peek before answering. Here are the test questions:

● *What was the first tractor built?*

Answer: In 1890 George Taylor patented a walking-type motor using a "petroleum engine," marking it as one of the first gas tractors built.

● *Who coined the term "tractor"?*

Answer: It is claimed that W.H. Williams, who worked for the Hart-Parr Company of Charles City, Iowa, coined the term "tractor" in 1906 for use in advertisements promoting the firm's machines. Prior to that tractors were referred to as "gasoline traction engines."

● *What was the most popular tractor ever built?*

Answer: Henry Ford's introduction of the Fordson in 1915, priced to sell at $495, ushered in an era of affordable horsepower. During its 10-year production run over 700,000 Fordsons were built, making it the most popular tractor ever built. Interest in the machine was so strong that in 1925, at the height of its popularity, approximately 75% of all tractors sold in the U.S. were Fordsons. Firms like John Deere and International Harvester even built implements for use behind Fordsons.

● *Besides Ford, what other automobile manufacturer built and sold a tractor?*

Answer: General Motors was in the tractor business for a brief time selling a tractor called the Samson. Sales of the Samson, which launched in 1918, were sluggish at best, causing GMC to discontinue making tractors in 1922. The plant used to manufacture Samson tractors was later converted to make Chevy cars.

● *What tractor company is credited with creating the Jeep?*

Answer: The idea behind the Jeep goes to Minneapolis-Moline, who made innovative use of a tractor to create an artillery mover used by the Minnesota National Guard in 1938.

● *Name three European-built tractors that were sold in the United States.*

Answer: That list includes Mercedes-Benz, Porsche and Deutz from Germany, Someca from France, Volvo from Sweden, David Brown and Nuffield from England, Lamborghini and Same from Italy, Belarus from Russia, Long from Romania, Ursus from Poland, and Zetor from Czechoslovakia.

john deere tractor test results

Year tested	Name	Model	Company	Rated belt hp.	Drawbar hp.	Rated PTO hp.
1924	John Deere	D, 15-27	Waterloo Gas Engine Co.	30	22	
1927	John Deere	D, 15-27	John Deere	36	28	
1928	John Deere	10-20, GP	John Deere	24	17	
1931	John Deere	GP	John Deere	25	18	
1934	John Deere	A, GP	John Deere	24	18	
1935	John Deere	B, GP	John Deere	16	11	
1935	John Deere	D	John Deere	41	30	
1937	John Deere	G	John Deere	35	27	
1938	John Deere	B	John Deere	18	Steel - 14 Rubber - 16	
1938	John Deere	H	John Deere	14	12	
1938	John Deere	L	John Deere	10	9	
1939	John Deere	A	John Deere	29	26	
1940	John Deere	D	John Deere	42	38	
1941	John Deere	B	John Deere	20	18	
1941	John Deere	LA	John Deere	14	13	
1941	John Deere	2WD	John Deere	30	26	
1947	John Deere	B	John Deere	27	24	
1947	John Deere	B	John Deere	23	21	
1947	John Deere	G	John Deere	38	34	
1947	John Deere	A	John Deere	38	34	
1947	John Deere	330	John Deere	20	18	
1947	John Deere	320	John Deere	20	18	
1947	John Deere	M	John Deere	20	18	
1949	John Deere	R	John Deere	48	43	
1949	John Deere	MT	John Deere	20	18	
1949	John Deere	AR	John Deere	37	34	
1950	John Deere	MC	John Deere	21	17	
1952	John Deere	60	John Deere	40	35	
1952	John Deere	50	John Deere	30	27	
1953	John Deere	60	John Deere	32	29	
1953	John Deere	70	John Deere	48	42	
1953	John Deere	40	John Deere	24	21	
1953	John Deere	40S	John Deere	23	21	
1953	John Deere	40C	John Deere	24	19	
1953	John Deere	70	John Deere	43	39	
1953	John Deere	50	John Deere	24	22	
1953	John Deere	60	John Deere	41	37	
1953	John Deere	70	John Deere	50	45	
1954	John Deere	70	John Deere	50	45	
1955	John Deere	50	John Deere	31	28	
1955	John Deere	40S	John Deere	20	18	
1955	John Deere	80	John Deere	65	60	
1956	John Deere	520	John Deere	37	33	
1956	John Deere	530	John Deere	37	33	
1956	John Deere	620	John Deere	49	44	
1956	John Deere	630	John Deere	49	44	
1956	John Deere	520	John Deere	25	23	

Year tested	Name	Model	Company	Rated belt hp.	Drawbar hp.	Rated PTO hp.
1956	John Deere	530	John Deere	25	23	
1956	John Deere	730	John Deere	57	52	
1956	John Deere	720	John Deere	57	52	
1956	John Deere	730	John Deere	56	51	
1956	John Deere	720	John Deere	56	51	
1956	John Deere	530	John Deere	37	33	
1956	John Deere	520	John Deere	37	33	
1956	John Deere	620	John Deere	46	42	
1956	John Deere	630	John Deere	46	42	
1956	John Deere	430W	John Deere	28	26	
1956	John Deere	420W	John Deere	28	26	
1956	John Deere	430S	John Deere	22	21	
1956	John Deere	420S	John Deere	22	21	
1956	John Deere	420C	John Deere	28	23	
1956	John Deere	430C	John Deere	28	23	
1956	John Deere	630	John Deere	34	32	
1956	John Deere	620	John Deere	34	32	
1956	John Deere	720	John Deere	57	53	
1956	John Deere	730	John Deere	57	53	
1956	John Deere	720	John Deere	44	40	
1956	John Deere	730	John Deere	44	40	
1957	John Deere	820	John Deere	72	67	
1957	John Deere	830	John Deere	72	67	
1959	John Deere	435	John Deere		28	32
1959	John Deere	440ID	John Deere		27	32
1959	John Deere	440I	John Deere		26	31
1959	John Deere	440ICD	John Deere		26	32
1959	John Deere	440IC	John Deere		24	31
1960	John Deere	4010	John Deere		72	80
1960	John Deere	4010	John Deere		72	80
1960	John Deere	4010	John Deere		73	84
1960	John Deere	3010	John Deere		54	59
1960	John Deere	3010	John Deere		52	55
1960	John Deere	3010	John Deere		50	55
1961	John Deere	1010C	John Deere		29	36
1961	John Deere	2010RU	John Deere		41	46
1961	John Deere	2010RU	John Deere		40	46
1961	John Deere	1010C	John Deere		28	35
1961	John Deere	1010RU	John Deere		30	36
1961	John Deere	1010RU	John Deere		30	35
1962	John Deere	5010	John Deere		108	121
1962	John Deere	2010C	John Deere		39	47
1962	John Deere	2010C	John Deere		39	47
1963	John Deere	500	John Deere		57	65
1963	John Deere	3020	John Deere		57	65
1963	John Deere	4020	John Deere		78	91
1963	John Deere	600	John Deere		78	91
1963	John Deere	4020	John Deere		75	88
1963	John Deere	600	John Deere		75	88
1963	John Deere	500	John Deere		55	64
1963	John Deere	3020	John Deere		55	64

john deere tractor test results

Year tested	Name	Model	Company	Rated belt hp.	Drawbar hp.	Rated PTO hp.
1963	John Deere	3020	John Deere		56	64
1963	John Deere	4020	John Deere		79	90
1965	John Deere	2510	John Deere		42	49
1965	John Deere	2510	John Deere		46	53
1965	John Deere	2510	John Deere		45	50
1965	John Deere	2510	John Deere		48	54
1965	John Deere	4020	John Deere		85	94
1966	John Deere	4020	John Deere		86	94
1966	John Deere	1020	John Deere		32	38
1966	John Deere	2020	John Deere		44	53
1966	John Deere	1020	John Deere		32	38
1966	John Deere	2020	John Deere		47	54
1966	John Deere	4020	John Deere		84	95
1966	John Deere	3020	John Deere		63	71
1966	John Deere	3020	John Deere		63	70
1966	John Deere	3020	John Deere		64	70
1966	John Deere	5020	John Deere		116	133
1968	John Deere	1520	John Deere		38	46
1968	John Deere	2520	John Deere		54	61
1968	John Deere	2520	John Deere		47	56
1969	John Deere	2520	John Deere		48	56
1969	John Deere	2520	John Deere		55	60
1969	John Deere	1520	John Deere		38	47
1969	John Deere	3020	John Deere		58	67
1969	John Deere	3020	John Deere		63	71
1969	John Deere	4020	John Deere		84	95
1969	John Deere	4020	John Deere		87	96
1969	John Deere	4520	John Deere		111	122
1969	John Deere	4520	John Deere		112	123
1969	John Deere	4000	John Deere		85	96
1969	John Deere	4020	John Deere		84	95
1969	John Deere	5020	John Deere		126	141

As with other Deere models built during this time, the Model B came in a wide variety of styles including the single-front wheel BN, wide-front axle BW, high-crop BNH, and BWN. The original B's had the traditional Deere two-cylinder engine with a 4¼×5¼-inch bore-and-stroke engine rated at 1,150 rpm.

massey-harris-ferguson test results

Year tested	Name	Model	Company	Rated belt hp.	Drawbar hp.	Rated PTO hp.
1929	Massey-Harris	12	Massey-Harris	24	18	
1929	Wallis	12-20	Massey-Harris	24	18	
1930	Massey-Harris	Gen. Purp.	Massey-Harris	24	19	
1931	Massey-Harris	Gen. Purp.	Massey-Harris	22	16	
1933	Massey-Harris	3-4 Plow	Massey-Harris	44	33	
1936	Massey-Harris	Challenger	Massey-Harris	28	20	
1936	Massey-Harris	Pacemaker	Massey-Harris	29	19	
1937	Massey-Harris	Challenger Twin Power	Massey-Harris	34	Steel - 25 Rubber - 29	
1937	Massey-Harris	Pacemaker Twin Power	Massey-Harris	36	Steel - 26 Rubber - 30	
1938	Massey-Harris	101S	Massey-Harris	35	Steel - 23 Rubber - 30	
1938	Massey-Harris	101R	Massey-Harris	35	Steel - 25 Rubber - 31	
1939	Massey-Harris	101R Junior	Massey-Harris	26	20	
1940	Massey-Harris	20	Massey-Harris	30	24	
1940	Massey-Harris	101R Junior	Massey-Harris	30	24	
1941	Massey-Harris	81R	Massey-Harris	27	20	
1941	Massey-Harris	20	Massey-Harris	27	20	
1941	Massey-Harris	Colt	Massey-Harris	27	20	
1941	Massey-Harris	101R	Massey-Harris	46	34	
1947	Massey-Harris	44RT	Massey-Harris	45	39	
1948	Massey-Harris	55	Massey-Harris	58	52	
1948	Massey-Harris	16	Massey-Harris	11	10	
1948	Massey-Harris	Pony	Massey-Harris	11	10	
1948	Massey-Harris	22RT	Massey-Harris	31	22	
1948	Massey-Harris	Mustang	Massey-Harris	31	22	
1949	Massey-Harris	30RT	Massey-Harris	34	26	
1949	Massey-Harris	44	Massey-Harris	41	37	
1949	Massey-Harris	44K	Massey-Harris	38	35	
1949	Massey-Harris	55K	Massey-Harris	52	47	
1950	Massey-Harris	555	Massey-Harris	59	52	
1950	Massey-Harris	55	Massey-Harris	59	52	
1951	Massey-Harris	55	Massey-Harris	66	57	
1951	Massey-Harris	555	Massey-Harris	66	57	
1953	Massey-Harris	33RT	Massey-Harris	39	35	
1953	Massey-Harris	44 Special	Massey-Harris	48	43	
1954	Massey-Harris	Pacer, 16	Massey-Harris-Ferguson	18	17	
1955	Ferguson	TO-35	Massey-Harris-Ferguson	33	30	
1955	Massey Ferguson	35	Massey-Harris-Ferguson	33	30	
1956	Massey-Harris	444	Massey-Harris-Ferguson	48	44	
1956	Massey-Harris	333	Massey-Harris-Ferguson	37	33	
1956	Massey-Harris	50	Massey-Harris-Ferguson	32	30	
1956	Ferguson	40	Massey-Harris-Ferguson	32	30	
1956	Massey Ferguson	50	Massey-Harris-Ferguson	32	30	
1956	Massey-Harris	444	Massey-Harris-Ferguson	49	45	
1956	Massey-Harris	333	Massey-Harris-Ferguson	41	37	
1958	Massey Ferguson	65	Massey-Ferguson	42	38	
1958	Massey Ferguson	50	Massey-Ferguson	32	29	

massey-harris-ferguson test results

1958	Massey Ferguson	50	Massey-Ferguson	32	29	
1958	Massey Ferguson	65	Massey-Ferguson	46	41	
1959	Massey Ferguson	TO-35	Massey-Ferguson		30	32
1959	Massey Ferguson	85	Massey-Ferguson		52	61
1959	Massey Ferguson	90	Massey-Ferguson		52	61
1959	Massey Ferguson	85	Massey-Ferguson		56	62
1959	Massey Ferguson	90	Massey-Ferguson		56	62
1960	Massey Ferguson	35	Massey-Ferguson		33	37
1960	Massey Ferguson	65	Massey-Ferguson		42	48
1960	Massey Ferguson	88	Massey-Ferguson		55	63
1960	Massey Ferguson	85	Massey-Ferguson		55	63
1961	Massey Ferguson	90 Super	Motec Industries		68	78
1961	Massey Ferguson	50	Massey-Ferguson		34	38
1961	Massey Ferguson	65	Massey-Ferguson		45	50
1962	Massey Ferguson	90 Super	Massey-Ferguson		61	68
1963	Massey Ferguson	25	Massey-Ferguson		20	24
1965	Massey Ferguson	135	Massey-Ferguson		33	37
1965	Massey Ferguson	165	Massey-Ferguson		46	52
1965	Massey Ferguson	175	Massey-Ferguson		55	63
1965	Massey Ferguson	165	Massey-Ferguson		41	46
1965	Massey Ferguson	135	Massey-Ferguson		30	35
1965	Massey Ferguson	180	Massey-Ferguson		54	63
1965	Massey Ferguson	150	Massey-Ferguson		33	37
1965	Massey Ferguson	1100	Massey-Ferguson		85	93
1966	Massey Ferguson	1130	Massey-Ferguson		109	120
1966	Massey Ferguson	130	Massey-Ferguson		23	26
1967	Massey Ferguson	1100	Massey-Ferguson		76	90
1969	Massey Ferguson	165	Massey-Ferguson		45	51
1969	Massey Ferguson	30 IND	Massey-Ferguson		45	51
1969	Massey Ferguson	150	Massey-Ferguson		32	37
1969	Massey Ferguson	135	Massey-Ferguson		32	37
1969	Massey Ferguson	175	Massey-Ferguson		51	61
1969	Massey Ferguson	180	Massey-Ferguson		54	62
1969	Massey Ferguson	1080	Massey-Ferguson		73	81

This upgraded version of the Massey-Harris Model 33 was offered in gasoline, distillate, LP gas, and diesel models. When tested in 1956 the Model 333 (at left) delivered over 37 belt horsepower thanks to a Massey-built 208-cubic-inch, four-cylinder engine. Power was transferred through a transmission that offered high and low ranges producing a total of 10 forward speeds. The 333 was in production for one year beginning in 1956.

minneapolis-moline test results

Year tested	Name	Model	Company	Rated belt hp.	Drawbar hp.	Rated PTO hp.
1920	Minneapolis-Moline	D 9-18 Universal	Moline Plow	27	17	
1920	M-M Twin City	40-65	Minneapolis Steel & Mach.	65	49	
1920	M-M Twin City	20-35	Minneapolis Steel & Mach.	46	34	
1920	M-M Twin City	12-20	Minneapolis Steel & Mach.	27	18	
1926	M-M Twin City	TY, 17-28	Minneapolis Steel & Mach. Co.	30	22	
1926	M-M Twin City	AT, 27-44	Minneapolis Steel & Mach. Co.	49	34	
1926	M-M Twin City	FT, 21-32	Minneapolis Steel & Machinery Co.		35	31
1928	M-M Twin City	FT, 21-32	Minneapolis Steel & Machinery Co.		39	30
1930	M-M Twin City	KT, 11-20	Minneapolis-Moline	25	18	
1931	Minneapolis-Moline	MT Universal	Minneapolis-Moline	26	18	
1935	M-M Twin City	JT	Minneapolis-Moline	24	17	
1935	M-M Twin City	KTA	Minneapolis-Moline	33	24	
1935	M-M Twin City	MTA	Minneapolis-Moline	33	24	
1936	M-M Twin City	KTA	Minneapolis-Moline	41	Steel - 30 Rubber - 25	
1936	M-M Twin City	FTA	Minneapolis-Moline	44	35	
1937	M-M Twin City	ZT	Minneapolis-Moline	26	20	
1938	M-M Twin City	UTS	Minneapolis-Moline	42	39	
1938	M-M Twin City	UTS	Minneapolis-Moline	36	33	
1939	M-M Twin City	GTA	Minneapolis-Moline	55	47	
1939	M-M Twin City	GT	Minneapolis-Moline	55	47	
1939	M-M Twin City	GTB	Minneapolis-Moline	55	47	
1939	M-M Twin City	UTU	Minneapolis-Moline	42	36	
1940	M-M Twin City	RTU	Minneapolis-Moline	23	20	
1940	M-M Twin City	ZTU	Minneapolis-Moline	31	26	
1949	Minneapolis-Moline	U Standard	Minneapolis-Moline	46	41	
1950	Minneapolis-Moline	G	Minneapolis-Moline	58	49	
1950	Minneapolis-Moline	Z	Minneapolis-Moline	36	32	
1951	Minneapolis-Moline	R	Minneapolis-Moline	27	23	
1951	Avery	BF	Minneapolis-Moline	27	24	
1951	Minneapolis-Moline	BF	Minneapolis-Moline	27	24	
1954	Minneapolis-Moline	UB	Minneapolis-Moline	48	42	
1954	Minneapolis-Moline	U	Minneapolis-Moline	37	33	
1954	Minneapolis-Moline	UB	Minneapolis-Moline	51	44	
1955	Minneapolis-Moline	GB	Minneapolis-Moline	70	62	
1955	Minneapolis-Moline	GB	Minneapolis-Moline	65	59	
1955	Minneapolis-Moline	GB	Minneapolis-Moline	62	55	
1956	Minneapolis-Moline	445 Universal	Minneapolis-Moline	41	38	
1956	Minneapolis-Moline	445 Utility	Minneapolis-Moline	41	38	
1957	Minneapolis-Moline	335	Minneapolis-Moline	33	29	
1958	Minneapolis-Moline	5 Star	Minneapolis-Moline	54	49	
1958	Minneapolis-Moline	5 Star	Minneapolis-Moline	54	49	
1960	Minneapolis-Moline	M602	Minneapolis-Moline		54	61
1960	Minneapolis-Moline	M5	Minneapolis-Moline		54	61
1960	Minneapolis-Moline	M5	Minneapolis-Moline		54	61
1960	Minneapolis-Moline	M602	Minneapolis-Moline		54	61

minneapolis-moline test results

Year tested	Name	Model	Company	Rated belt hp.	Drawbar hp.	Rated PTO hp.
1960	Minneapolis-Moline	M5	Minneapolis-Moline		51	58
1960	Minneapolis-Moline	M602	Minneapolis-Moline		51	58
1961	Minneapolis-Moline	4 Star	Motec Industries		39	44
1961	Minneapolis-Moline	Jet Star 3	Motec Industries		39	44
1961	Minneapolis-Moline	Jet Star 3	Motec Industries		41	45
1961	Minneapolis-Moline	4 Star	Motec Industries		41	45
1961	Massey Ferguson	90 Super	Motec Industries		71	78
1961	Minneapolis-Moline	Gvi	Motec Industries		71	78
1961	Minneapolis-Moline	Gvi	Motec Industries		68	78
1963	Massey Ferguson	97	Minneapolis Moline		89	101
1963	Minneapolis-Moline	G706	Minneapolis-Moline		89	101
1963	Massey Ferguson	97	Minneapolis-Moline		90	101
1963	Minneapolis-Moline	G706	Minneapolis-Moline		90	101
1963	Massey Ferguson	97	Minneapolis-Moline		93	101
1963	Minneapolis-Moline	G705	Minneapolis-Moline		93	101
1963	Massey Ferguson	97	Minneapolis-Moline		92	101
1963	Minneapolis-Moline	G705	Minneapolis-Moline		92	101
1964	Minneapolis-Moline	U302	Minneapolis-Moline		49	55
1964	Minneapolis-Moline	U302	Minneapolis-Moline		49	55
1965	Minneapolis-Moline	M670 Super	Minneapolis-Moline		64	74
1965	Minneapolis-Moline	M670	Minneapolis-Moline		64	74
1965	Minneapolis-Moline	M670 Super	Minneapolis-Moline		64	73
1965	Minneapolis-Moline	M670	Minneapoli`s-Moline		64	73
1965	Minneapolis-Moline	M670	Minneapolis-Moline		64	71
1965	Minneapolis-Moline	M670 Super	Minneapolis-Moline		64	71
1966	Minneapolis-Moline	G1050	Minneapolis-Moline		110	102
1966	Minneapolis-Moline	G1000	Minneapolis-Moline		110	102
1966	Oliver	2055	Minneapolis-Moline		102	110
1966	Minneapolis-Moline	G1050	Minneapolis-Moline		99	110
1966	Minneapolis-Moline	G1000	Minneapolis-Moline		99	110
1966	Oliver	2055	Minneapolis-Moline		99	110
1968	Minneapolis-Moline	G1000 Vista	Minneapolis-Moline		100	111
1968	Minneapolis-Moline	G1000 Vista	Minneapolis-Moline		99	110
1968	Minneapolis-Moline	G950	Minneapolis-Moline		88	97
1968	Minneapolis-Moline	G900	Minneapolis-Moline		88	97
1968	Oliver	1865	Minneapolis-Moline		88	97
1968	Minneapolis-Moline	G950	Minneapolis-Moline		86	97
1968	Minneapolis-Moline	G900	Minneapolis-Moline		86	97
1968	Oliver	1865	Minneapolis-Moline		86	97
1968	Minneapolis-Moline	G900	Minneapolis-Moline		89	97
1968	Minneapolis-Moline	G950	Minneapolis-Moline		89	97

oliver tractor test results

Year tested	Name	Model	Company	Rated belt hp.	Drawbar hp.	Rated PTO hp.
1930	Hart-Parr	18-27	Oliver	29	24	
1930	Hart-Parr	18-28	Oliver	30	23	
1930	Hart-Parr	28-44	Oliver	49	34	
1930	Oliver	90	Oliver	49	34	
1936	Oliver-Hart-Parr	70 HC Row Crop	Oliver	28	21	
1936	Oliver-Hart-Parr	70 KD Row Crop	Oliver	27	20	
1937	Oliver-Hart-Parr	70 HC Standard	Oliver	27	19	
1937	Oliver-Hart-Parr	70 KD Standard	Oliver	26	19	
1938	Oliver	80 KD Row Crop	Oliver	38	29	
1938	Oliver	80 KD Standard	Oliver	39	28	
1940	Oliver	70 HC Row Crop	Oliver	31	28	
1941	Oliver	80 HC Standard	Oliver	41	35	
1941	Oliver	60 HC Row Crop	Oliver	18	16	
1947	Oliver	88 HC Row Crop	Oliver	41	36	
1947	Oliver	88 HC Standard Standard		Oliver	43	37
1948	Oliver	77 HC Row Crop	Oliver	33	28	
1948	Oliver	77 HC Standard	Oliver	33	28	
1949	Oliver	66 HC Row Crop	Oliver	24	21	
1949	Oliver	66 HC Standard	Oliver	24	21	
1949	Oliver	77 HC Row Crop	Oliver	37	32	
1949	Oliver	HG	Oliver	25	21	
1949	Oliver	DG	Oliver	69	59	
1949	Oliver	DD	Oliver	73	58	
1949	Oliver	OC-3	Oliver	25	21	
1950	Oliver	88 Row Crop	Oliver	43	38	
1950	Oliver	99	Oliver	62	52	
1951	Oliver	77 Row Crop	Oliver	35	31	
1951	Oliver	66 Row Crop	Oliver	25	22	
1952	Oliver	77 Row Crop	Oliver	36	32	
1952	Oliver	OC-18	Oliver		128	
1953	Oliver	OC-6	Oliver		31	
1953	Oliver	OC-6	Oliver		33	

oliver test results

Year tested	Name	Model	Company	Rated belt hp.	Drawbar hp.	Rated PTO hp.
1954	Oliver	55 HC Super	Oliver	34	29	
1954	Oliver	88 HC Super	Oliver	55	47	
1954	Oliver	55 Super	Oliver	33	27	
1954	Oliver	88 Super	Oliver	54	49	
1955	Oliver	66 HC Super	Oliver	33	27	
1955	Oliver	77 HC Super	Oliver	43	37	
1955	Oliver	77 Super	Oliver	44	38	
1955	Oliver	66 Super	Oliver	33	27	
1955	Oliver	OC-12	Oliver	57	50	
1955	Oliver	OC-12	Oliver	56	50	
1955	Oliver	99 GM Super	Oliver	78	73	
1955	Oliver	99 Super	Oliver	62	58	
1957	Oliver	OC-15	Oliver	101	91	
1958	Oliver	880	Oliver	61	54	
1958	Oliver	770	Oliver	50	42	
1958	Oliver	770	Oliver	48	44	
1958	Oliver	880	Oliver	59	52	
1958	Oliver	OC-4	Oliver	26	24	
1958	Oliver	OC-4	Oliver	25	23	
1958	Oliver	950	Oliver	67	61	
1958	Massey Ferguson	98	Oliver	84	77	
1958	Oliver	990 GM	Oliver	84	77	
1958	Oliver	995 GM Lugamatic	Oliver	85	71	
1959	Oliver	550	Oliver		35	41
1959	Oliver	550	Oliver		35	39
1960	Oliver	1800	Oliver		63	73
1960	Oliver	1800	Oliver		62	70
1960	Oliver	1900	Oliver		82	89
1962	Cockshutt	1900	Oliver		86	98
1962	Oliver	1900	Oliver		86	98
1962	Cockshutt	1800	Oliver		67	77
1962	Oliver	1800	Oliver		67	77
1962	Oliver	1800	Oliver		62	76
1962	Oliver	1800	Oliver		64	76
1963	Cockshutt	1800	Oliver		70	80
1963	Oliver	1800	Oliver		70	80
1963	Oliver	1600	Oliver		48	57
1963	Oliver	1600	Oliver		48	56
1963	Oliver	1800	Oliver		69	80
1963	Oliver	1900	Oliver		90	100
1964	Oliver	1850	Oliver		84	92
1964	Oliver	1850	Oliver		81	92
1964	Oliver	1950	Oliver		99	105
1964	Oliver	1950	Oliver		97	105
1964	Oliver	1650	Oliver		57	66
1964	Oliver	1650	Oliver		59	66
1964	Oliver	1855	Oliver		77	92
1964	Oliver	1850	Oliver		77	92

Year tested	Name	Model	Company	Rated belt hp.	Drawbar hp.	Rated PTO hp.
1964	Oliver	1850	Oliver		86	92
1966	Minneapolis-Moline	G550	Oliver		45	53
1966	Oliver	1550	Oliver		45	53
1966	Oliver	1555	Oliver		45	53
1966	Minneapolis-Moline	G550	Oliver		46	53
1966	Oliver	1555	Oliver		46	53
1966	Oliver	1550	Oliver		46	53
1967	Oliver	1750	Oliver		68	80
1967	Oliver	1750	Oliver		68	80
1967	Oliver	1950T	Oliver		93	105
1968	Oliver	1950T	Oliver		91	105
1968	Oliver	2150	Oliver		114	131
1968	Oliver	2050	Oliver		104	118

The United States certainly wasn't the only nation to build tractors. For example, the Stock Motor Plough (above) was built in 1909 by Stock Fabrication of Germany. This motor plow design was popular in Europe for several decades, although the approach found limited success in North America in the early 1910s. The Stock featured three plowshares mounted on the tractor's chassis.

sears-david bradley tractor test results

Year tested	Name	Model	Company	Rated belt hp.	Drawbar hp.	Rated PTO hp
1951	David Bradley	Garden Tractor	David Bradley	1	1	
1953	David Bradley	Super Power	David Bradley	2	1	
1959	David Bradley	Suburban	David Bradley	3	2	
1959	David Bradley	575 Super	David Bradley	3	3	
1959	David Bradley	300 Super	David Bradley	1	1	
1959	David Bradley	Handiman	David Bradley	2	0.6	

lesser known classic test results

Year tested	Name	Model	Company	Rated belt hp.	Drawbar hp.	Rated PTO hp.
			A			
1920	Allwork	14-28	Electric Wheel Co.	28	19	
			B			
1931	Bradley	Gen. Purp.	Bradley	24	20	
1920	Bates	Steel Mule "D"	Bates	24	20	
1920	Bates	Steel Mule F, 15-22	Bates	29	23	
1931	Bates	35 Steel Mule	Foote Bros.	52	43	
1931	Bates	45 Steel Mule	Foote Bros.	66	54	
1923	Bear	B, 25-35	Bear	49	35	
1924	Bear	B, 25-35	Bear	55	44	
1920	Beeman	G	Beeman	2	1	
1952	Bolens	12BB	Bolens	1	1	
1929	Baker	43-67	A.D. Baker Co.	75	55	
			C			
1948	Centaur	KV-48	LeRoi	24	20	
1950	Choremaster	B	The Lodge & Shipley Co.	1	.7	
1920	Coleman	B, 16-30	Coleman	30	15	
1927	Continental Cultor	32	Continental Cultor		8	
1936	Co-op	#3	Duplex Machinery	42	37	
1936	Co-op	#2	Duplex Machinery	33	29	
1949	Corbitt	G-50	Corbitt	34	30	

Year tested	Name	Model	Company	Rated belt hp.	Drawbar hp.	Rated PTO hp.

D

| 1950 | Dodge | T137 Power Wagon | Chrysler | 42 | 40 | |

E

1921	Eagle	H, 16-30	Eagle	31	19	
1921	Eagle	F, 12-22 HP	Eagle	23	14	
1930	Eagle	6A	Eagle	40	29	
1952	Economy	Special	Engineering Products	6	5	
1957	Eimco	105	Eimco		72	
1946	Ellinwood	3000-1 Bear Cat	Ellinwood	2	Steel - 1 Rubber - 1	
1947	Ellinwood	Tiger Cat	Ellinwood	4	2	
1920	Emerson-Brantingham	12-20	Emerson-Brantingham	25	17	

F

1949	Farmaster	FD-33	Farmaster	23	21	
1949	Farmaster	FG-33	Farmaster	28	25	
1953	Federal	DF	Intercontinental	33	31	
1948	Ferguson	TE-20	Harry-Ferguson	25	20	
1948	Ferguson	TO-20	Harry-Ferguson	25	20	
1951	Ferguson	TO-30	Harry-Ferguson	29	24	
1959	Fiat	411-R	Fiat		33	36
1959	Fiat	411-C	Fiat		29	37
1920	Flour City	18-35	Kinnard & Sons	35	19	
1920	Flour City	40-70	Kinnard & Sons	72	52	
1929	Four Drive	E, 15-25	Four Drive Tractor	28	18	

lesser known classic test results

Year tested	Name	Model	Company	Rated belt hp.	Drawbar hp.	Rated PTO hp.
			G			
1949	Gibson	H	Gibson	24	22	
1949	Gibson	I	Gibson	41	36	
1938	Graham-Bradley	503.103	Graham-Paige Motors Corp.	30	25	
1920	Gray	18-36	Gray	32	19	
			H			
1952	Harris	PH-53	Harris		50	
1954	Harris	FDW-C	Harris		43	
1954	Harris	FDW-C	Harris		42	
1920	Heider	C, 12-20	Rock Island	24	13	
1920	Heider	D, 9-16	Rock Island	19	11	
1925	Heider	15-27	Rock Island	30	21	
1920	Holt	T-11, 25-40	Holt	35	33	
1920	Holt	T-16, 40-60	Holt	57	51	
1922	Holt	T-35, 15-25	Holt	25	18	
			I			
1920	Indiana	5-10	Indiana Silo & Tractor	11	5	
1948	Intercontinental	C-26	Intercontinental	29	25	
1949	Intercontinental	D-26 / DE	Intercontinental	28	26	
1953	Intercontinental	DF	Intercontinental	33	31	
			K			
1962	Kramer	KL400	Kramer-Werke		28	32
1965	Kubota	RV	Kubota	8	6	
			L			
1920	La Crosse	G, 12-24	La Crosse	24	17	
1960	Land-Rover	88	Rover Co., Ltd.		29	30
1920	Lauson	15-30	John Lauson Mfg.	32	26	
1921	Lauson	12-25	John Lauson Mfg.	37	20	
1927	Lauson	16-32	John Lauson Mfg.	36	28	

Year tested	Name	Model	Company	Rated belt hp.	Drawbar hp.	Rated PTO hp.

L

Year tested	Name	Model	Company	Rated belt hp.	Drawbar hp.	Rated PTO hp.
1927	Lauson	20-40	John Lauson Mfg.	41	32	
1928	Lauson	20-35,S12	John Lauson Mfg.	40	29	
1949	Long	A	Long	31	28	

M

1949	Mercer	30BD	Farmaster	23	21	
1949	Mercer	30CK	Farmaster	28	25	
1920	Minneapolis	12-25	Minneapolis Threshing Co	26	16	
1920	Minneapolis	22-44	Minneapolis Threshing Co	46	33	
1920	Minneapolis	35-70	Minneapolis Threshing Co	74	52	
1921	Minneapolis	A ,17-30	Minneapolis Threshing Co	31	19	
1925	Minneapolis	B, 17-30	Minneapolis Threshing Co	34	23	
1929	Minneapolis	27-42	Minneapolis Threshing Co.	48	34	
1929	Minneapolis	39-57	Minneapolis Threshing Co.	64	47	
1920	Monarch	18-30	Monarch	31	21	
1924	Monarch	D, 6-60	Monarch	70	53	
1925	Monarch	C, 25-35	Monarch	43	37	
1927	Monarch	F, 10 Ton	Monarch		78	
1927	Monarch	6 Ton	Monarch		50	

N

1958	Nuffield	3 Universal	Morris Motors	34	31	
1955	Nuffield	DM-4 Universal		Morris Motors	45	41
1955	Nuffield	PM-4 Universal	Morris Motors	38	34	
1962	Nuffield	460	Morris Motors		50	54
1965	Nuffield	10/42	British Motor Co.		33	39
1965	Nuffield	10/60	British Motor Co.		47	55

P

1920	Parrett	K, 15-30	Parrett Tractor Co.	31	20	
1935	Planet	Planet Jr. Garden Tractor	S.L. Allen & Co.	2	1	
1959	Porsche	L108 Junior	Porsche		9	11
1959	Porsche	L318 Super	Porsche		33	37
1920	Port Huron	12-25	Port Huron	28	20	

lesser known classic test results

Year tested	Name	Model	Company	Rated belt hp.	Drawbar hp.	Rated PTO hp.
			R			
1927	Rock Island	18-35	Rock Island	36	30	
1929	Rock Island	G2, 15-25	Rock Island	29	22	
1929	Rock Island	G2, 18-30	Rock Island	35	25	
1922	Rogers	Rogers	Rogers Tractor & Trailer Co.	63	38	
1921	Russell	30-60 Giant	Russell & Co.	66	43	
1923	Russell	C,15-30	Russell & Co.	33	24	
1923	Russell	C, 20-40	Russell & Co.	43	32	
			S			
1920	Samson	M	Samson	19	11	
1927	Shaw	T-25	Shaw	1	.7	
1927	Shaw	T-45	Shaw	1	.7	
1921	Shawnee	Power Patrol		7		
1925	Shawnee	30	Shaw-Enochs		13	
1936	Silver King	3 wheel R-66	Fate-Root-Heath	19	Steel - 13 Rubber - 16	
1949	Silver King	3 wheel (370) Row Crop	Fate-Root-Heath	33	28	
41953	Someca	DA 50	Someca	38	33	
1957	Someca	45 Som	Someca	40	37	
1920	Square Turn	18-35	Square Turn	36		
1920	Square Turn	18-35	Square Turn	32	23	
			T			
1952	Terratrac	GT-30	American Tractor	30	25	
1920	Toro	6-10	Toro	13	9	
1920	Townsend	15-30	Townsend	29	17	

U

Year tested	Name	Model	Company	Rated belt hp.	Drawbar hp.	Rated PTO hp.
1920	Uncle Sam	20-30	U.S. Tractor	32	22	
1957	Unimog	30	Daimler-Benz	28	25	
1961	Ursus	C-325	Zaklady Mechaniczne		22	24
1968	Ursus	C-335	Zaklady Mechaniczne		26	29
1968	Ursus	C-350	Zaklady Mechaniczne		37	43
1949	USTRAC	10-A	U.S. Tractor Corp.	21	15	
1958	Volvo	T425	A-B Bolinder-Munktell	23	22	
1958	Volvo	T55	A-B Bolinder-Munktell	63	59	
1957	Wagner	TR- 9	Wagner		87	
1959	Wagner	TR-14A	Wagner		155	
1964	Wagner	WA-4	FWD Wagner		97	
1927	Wallis	20-30	Wallis	35	27	
1920	Waterloo Boy	N, 12-25	Waterloo Gas Engine Co.	25	15	
1921	Wetmore	12-25	H.A. Wetmore	27	16	
1949	Jeep CJ-3A	Willys Overland Motors Universal		28	25	
1953	Willys	Farm Jeep	Willys Motors, Inc.	35	27	
1920	Wisconsin	E, 16-30	Wisconsin	31	22	

Z

Year tested	Name	Model	Company	Rated belt hp.	Drawbar hp.	Rated PTO hp.
1960	Zetor	50 Super	Zavody Jana Svermy		44	49
1962	Zetor	3011	ZKL-BRNO		27	33
1964	Zetor	2011	ZKL-BRNO		19	21
1964	Zetor	4011	ZKL-BRNO		41	48
1967	Zetor	5511	ZKL-BRNO		45	50

In the 1950s the Swedish tractor manufacturer A-B Bolinder-Munktell tested the American market by selling its Volvo Model T425 in this country. The 17 (drawbar) horsepower tractor employed a 97.6-cubic-inch, four-cylinder engine paired up with a four-speed transmission. Other Volvo features included hydraulics and a three-point hitch. A larger (44 drawbar horsepower) Volvo tractor, the Model T55, was also sold in the U.S. in 1958.

cross reference

A

Adapto-Tractor	Geneva Tractor Company
Advance	Henry, Millard & Henry Company
Ace	Horace Keane Aeroplanes, Inc.
Akron	Wellman-Seaver-Morgan Company
Albaugh-Dover	Square Turn Tractor Company
Allaround	Ford Motor Company
Allen A	Community Manufacturing Company
All-In-One	Pacific Power Implement Company
	Stroud Motor Manufacturing Company
All Purpose	Advance-Rumely Thresher Company
AllSteel	Bates Tractor Company
Allwork	Electric Wheel Company
American	Russell and Company
Americo	American Tractor & Foundry Company
Angleworm	Badley Tractor Company
Atlas	Lyons-Atlas

Auto Cat	A.J. Erstead
Autoplow	Hackney Manufacturing Company
Autopow	Autopower Company
Autotractor	Eason-Wysong Company
Auto Tractor	Hackney Manufacturing Company
Auto Tractor-Truck	Lombard Auto Tractor-Truck Corporation
Auto Tiller	World Harvester Corporation

B

Baby Creeper	Bullock Tractor Company
Baby Savidge	Backus Tractor Company
Ball Tread	Yuba Manufacturing Company
Bates	Foote Bros. Gear & Machine Company
Bear	J.I. Case Plow Works
	Mead-Morrison Manufacturing Company

Bear Cat	Ellinwood Industries
Belt-Rail	Beltrail Tractor Company
Beaver	Goold, Shapley and Muir Company
Big Boss	Russell and Company
Big Bull	Bull Tractor Company
Big Chief	Waterloo Foundry Company
Big 4	Gas Traction Company
	Emerson-Brantingham Implement Co.
Big Mo	Minneapolis-Moline Company
Biltwell	Velie Motors Corporation
Blue	John Blue Company
Blue J	Dart Truck and Tractor Company
Bower City	Townsend Manufacturing Company
Boyer Four	Huron Tractor Company
Bulldog	Avery Company
	Heinrich Lanz

C

Cameco	Cane Machinery & Engineering Company
Canadian	Alberta Foundry & Machinery Company
Canadian Special	Gray Tractor Company
Capital	C.A. Dissinger and Brothers Company
The Cat	Four-Drive Tractor Company
Caterpillar	Holt Tractor Company
	Caterpillar Company
Centaur	Le Roi Company
	Central Tractor Company
Centiped	Phoenix Manufacturing Company
Chain Tread	Buckeye Manufacturing Company
Challenge	Challenge Tractor Company
Challenger	Massey-Harris Company
Champion	Chamberlain Industries Ltd.
Clarkat	Clark Tructractor Company
Cletrac	Cleveland Tractor Company
Cliff	John Minor Kroyer
Colby Plow Boy	Jones Manufacturing Company
Coleman	Winslow Manufacturing Company
	Coleman Tractor Corporation
Colt	Massey-Harris Company
Co-op	Farmers' Union Central Exchange Inc.
Corn Belt	Southern Corn Belts Tractor Company
Crawlerize	Hadfield-Penfield Steel Company
Creeping Grip	Bullock Tractor Company
Crop Maker	Hart-Parr Company
Cropmaster	David Brown
Cub	Wallis Tractor Company
	J.I. Case Plow Works
	International Harvester Company
Cub Jr.	J.I. Case Plow Works
Cultiplow	H.L. Hurst Manufacturing Company

Cultrac	Intercontinental Manufacturing Company
Cultractor	Baines Engineering Company
Cultitractor	United Tractors Corporation
Cultor	Continental Cultor Company
Custom	Custom Tractor Manufacturing Company
	Harry A. Lowther Company

D

Dakota	G.W. Elliot & Company
	Pope Manufacturing Company
Deering	International Harvester Company
Dixieland	Dixieland Motor Truck Company
DoAll	Advance-Rumely Thresher Company
Dreadnought Guide	Charles S. Whitworth
Du-All	Shaw Manufacturing Company
Duat	Clark Tructractor Company

E

Eagle	Eagle Manufacturing Company
Earthmaster	Aerco Corporation
Eclipse	Frick Company
Economy	Engineering Products Company
Espe	C.O.D. Tractor Company
EWC	Electric Wheel Company
E-Z Built	S. McChesney Company

F

Fair-Mor	Fairbanks, Morse & Company
Fairway	International Harvester Company
Farm Dozer	Isaacson Iron Works
Farm Horse	Farm Horse Traction Works
Farmco	Farm & Home Machinery Company
Farmer Boy	Columbus Tractor Company
	McIntyre Manufacturing Company
Farmall	International Harvester Company
Farmcrest	Gamble-Skogmo Incorporated
Farmers Tractor	Huber Manufacturing
	Sageng Threshing Machinery Company
Farmford	Detroit Harvester Company
Farmmaster	Jensen Tractor Manufacturing Company
Farmobile	William Galloway Company
Field Marshall	Marshall & Sons Company
Fitch Four Wheel Drive	Four-Drive Tractor Company
4-Pull	John Minor Kroyer
	Wizard Tractor Corporation
4-Star	Minneapolis-Moline Company
5-Star	Minneapolis-Moline Company

cross reference

F

Flexible	Franklin TractorCompany
Flex-Tred	Vaughn Motor Works, Inc.
Flour City	Kinnard-Haines Company
Fordson	Ford Motor Company
Four In One	Kardell Tractor & Truck Company
Four-Plow	Kinnard-Haines Company
Four Wheel Drive	Leonard Tractor Company
Fox	Fox River Tractor Company
Fuel-Master	M.A.N.

G

G, S & M	Goold, Shapley & Muir Company
Garner	William Galloway Company
Gas Pull	Advance-Rumely Company
Gearless	Union Iron Works
Geiser	Emerson-Brantingham Company
General	Cleveland Tractor Company
Giant	Russell and Company
	International Harvester Company
Giant Baby	Buckeye Manufacturing Company
G-O Tractor	General Ordnance Company
Golden West	Muscatine Motor Company
Graham-Bradley	Graham-Paige Motors Company

H

Heider	Rock Island Plow Company
H.M. & H.	Henry, Millard & Henry Company
Happy Farmer	LaCrosse Tractor Company
Hartsough	Gas Traction Company
Helping Henry	Auto Power Compnay
Heinze 4-Wheel	Traction Engine Company
Hoosier	Loe Rumely Tractor Company
Hudson	Evans Manufacturing Company

I

Ideal	Goold, Shapley and Muir Company
Imperial	Valentine Manufacturing Company
Imperial Super-Drive	Robert Bell Engine & Threshing Illinois Tractor Company
Ingeco	International Gas Engine Company
	Worthington Pump Company
International	International Harvester Company

Iron Horse	Samson Tractor Company
	General Motors Corporation
	Sweeney Tractor Company

J

Jerry	G.F.H. Corporation
Jet Star	Minneapolis-Moline Company
Jim Dandy	General Motors Company
Joy-McVicker	McVicker Engineering Company
Junior	Holt Tractor Company
	Pioneer Tractor Company
	Kinnard-Haines Company
	Nilson Tractor Company
	Russell & Company
	Porsche
	Buckeye Manufacturing Company

K

K.C.	Square Turn Tractor Company
K-C	Kansas City Hay Press Company
Kay-Gee	Keck-Gonnerman Company
Kerosene Annie	Advance-Rumely Thresher Company
Kingwood	Knickerbocker Motors Incorporated
Kinross American	American Tractor Corporation
Klear-View	Centaur Tractor Corporation
Klumb	Dubuque Truck & Tractor Company
Knapp Farm Locomotive	Gray Tractor Company
Knickerbocker	Knickerbocker Motors, Inc.

L

Leader	Dayton-Dick Company
	Leader Tractor Company
Le Percheron	Societe Nationale de Construction Aeronautique du Centre
Liberty	Emerson-Brantingham Company
Lightfoot	Monarch Tractor Corporation
Light Four	Huber Manufacturing Company
Lindeman	Deere & Company
Line Drive	Line Drive Tractor Inc.
Lion	Lion Tractor Company
Little Bear	L.A. Auto Tractor Company
Little Boss	Russell and Company
Little Bull	Bull Tractor Company
Little Chief	Farm Engineering Company

Little Farmer — Will-Burt Company
Little Giant — Holmes Manufacturing Company
— Mayer Brothers Company
— Little Giant Company
Little Oak — Humber-Anderson Manufacturing Company
— Willmar Tractor & Manufacturing Company
Little Pet — Flinchbaugh Manufacturing Company
Little Red Devil — Hart-Parr Company
Little Traction — Adams Husker Company
Louisville Motor Plow — B.F. Avery & Sons Company

M

M.P.M. — Farmers Tractor Corporation
Macultivator — American Swiss Magneto Company
Macdonald — Cusman Motor Works
Major — Ford Motor Company
Master Four — Huber Manufacturing Company
Master Huffman — Huffman Traction Engine Company
McCormick — International Harvester Company
McCormick Deering — International Harvester Company
Merry Garden — Atlantic Machiney & Manufacturing Co.
Midget — Shaw-Enochs Tractor Company
Midwest — Wichita Tractor Company
Mid-West — Agrimotor Tractor Company
Mighty Man — Winter Manufacturing Company
Minnesota — Minnesota Tractor Company
Modern Farmer — Huber Manufacturing Company
Modern Four — Huber Manufacturing Company
Mogul — International Harvester Company
Mohawk — United Tractors Corporation
Montana — Montana Tractor Company
Morton Traction — TruckLambert Gas Engine Company
— Ohio Manufacturing Company
— Pennsylvania Tractor Company
MotoRower — Hume-Love Company
Motox — Plano Tractor Company
— Wabash Tractor Company
Motrac — Minneapolis-Moline Corporation
Muley — C.L. Best Traction Company
Multipedal — F.C. Austin Company
— Austin Drainage Excavator Company
Multivator — Paul Hainke Manufacturing Company
Mustang — Massey-Harris Company

N

National — Denning Motor Company
— General Ordnance Company
— National Tractor Company

Neverslip — Commonwealth Tractor Company
— Monarch Tractor Company
New Elgin — Puritan Machinery Company
New Way — New Way Motor Company
Nu-Horse — William Stimson Barne

O

Oil King — Hart-Parr Company
Oil Pull — Advance-Rumely Threshing Company
Old Reliable — Hart-Parr Company

P

Pacemaker — Massey-Harris Company
Pacer — Massey-Harris Company
Paramount — National Pulley & Manufacturing
Pathmaker — Moon Tractor Company
Patriot — Hebb Motor Company
Peerless — Emerson-Brantingham Company
Planet Jr. — S.L. Allen Company
Platypus — Rotary Hoe Cultivators Ltd.
Plow Boy — Interstate Engine & Tractor Company
Plow Man — Interstate Engine & Tractor Company
— Plowman Tractor Company
Plymouth — Fate-Root-Heath Company
Pony — Pioneer Tractor Company
— Massey-Harris Company
— C.L. Best Gas Tractor Company
Powerbilt — General Tractor Corporation
Power Horse — Harris Manufacturing Company
— National Implement Company
Power-Horse — EIMCO Corporation
Power Ox — Equipment Corporation of America
PowerRower — Hume-Love Company
Prairie Dog — Kansas City Hay Press Company
Princess Pat — Scientific Farming Machinery Company

Q

Quadpull — Antigo Tractor Corporation
Quincy All Purpose — Electric Wheel Company

R

Ranger — Southern Motor Manfacturing
Red-E — M.B.M. Manufacturing Company
Reeves — Emerson-Brantingham Company
Rex — Leader Tractor Manufacturing Company
Rigid Rail — Henneuse Tractor Company
— Hadfield-Penfield Steel Company

cross reference

Road Hog	Hadfield-Penfield Steel Company
	W.A. Riddell Company
Road Layer	La Plant-Choate Manufacturing
Roadless	Richard Garrett Engineering Works Ltd.
Road King	Hart-Parr Company
Rototiller	Rototiller Inc.
Ro-Trac	Avery Company
Rumely	Advance-Rumely Threshing Company

S

Samson	General Motors Corporation
Sandusky	Dauch Manufacturing Company
Savidge	Backus Tractor Company
Seager	Olds Gas Power Company
Senior	Nilson Tractor Company
Shawnee	Shaw-Enochs Tractor Company
Shop Mule	Marsh-Capron Manufacturing
Sieve Grip	Samson Iron Works
Silver King	Fate-Root-Heath Company
	Mountain State Fabricating Company
Simplicity	Turner Manfacturing Company
Simpson Jumbo	Jumbo Steel Products
Skibo	Minneapolis Threshing Machine
	Union Iron Works
Special	Pioneer Tractor Manufacturing
Speedex	The Pond Company
Speedpull	Le Tourneau-Westinghouse Company
Square Turn	Albaugh-Dover Company
Steady Pull	Blumberg Motor Manfacturing Company
Steel-Clad	Denning Motor Company
Steel Hoof	Lambert Gas Engine Company
Steel King	Hart-Parr Company
Steel Mule	Bates Machine and Tractor Company
	Joliet Oil Tractor Company
Sterling	J.A. Hockett Company
Strait's	Killen-Walsh Company
Sunflower	Locomotive Finished Material Company
Sunshine	Sunshine Harvester Works
Super	International Harvester Company
	Oliver Corporation
	Vendeuvre Company
Super Drive	Illinois Tractor Company
Super Four	Huber Manufacturing Company
Super 4 Drive	Four Wheel Traction Company
Super Major	Ford Motor Company
Sure-Grip	Union Tool Company

T

T-C	Minneapolis Steel & Machinery Company
Tank-Tread X	Scientific Farming Machinery Company
Tank-Tread	Pan Motor Company
Terratrac	American Tractor Corporation
Thorobred	Allen-Burbank Motor Company
Tilsoil	Farm Motors Company
Tiger	Inexco Tractor Corporation
Tiger Pull	Gaar, Scott & Company
Titan	International Harvester Company
Toe Hold	Advance-Rumely Thresher Company
Tonford	Detroit Truck Company
Toro	Toro Motor Company
	Advance-Rumely Threshing Company
Tournapull	Le Tourneau-Westinghouse Company
Townmotor	The Townmotor Company
Tracford	Standard-Detroit Tractor Company
Tracklayer	C.L. Best Traction Company
Trackpull	Belle City Manufacturing
	Bean Sprayer Pump Company
Track Runner	Avery Company
Trackson	Geo. H. Smith Steel Casting Company
Tractair	Centaur Tractor Company
TractorRower	Hume-Love Company
Tractractor	International Harvester Company
TracTred	Miller Traction Tread Company
Tru-Draft	B.F. Avery & Sons Company
Trundaar	Buckeye Manufacturing Company
Tructractor	Clark Tructractor Company
Twentieth Century	Minneapolis Steel & Machinery Company
Twin City	Minneapolis Steel & Machinery Company
	Minneapolis-Moline Company
2-Star	Minneapolis-Moline Company

U

Ultimate	Plantation Equipment Company
Uncle Sam	U.S. Tractor & Machinery Company
United	Allis-Chalmers Company
Unimog	Daimler-Benz
Uni-Tractor	Minneapolis-Moline Company
Universal	Advance-Rumely Threshing Company
	Elderfields Mechanics Company
	Lawter Tractor Company
	Minneapolis-Moline Company
	Moline Plow Company
	Northwest Thresher Company

Universal Farm	American-Abell Engine & Threshing Company
Ustrac	Federal Machine & Welder Company
Utilitor	Midwest Engine Company

V

Rotary Plow	W.S. Jardine Company
Vaughn Gearless	Eaton Gas Engine Company

W

Wadsworth	Detroit Engine Works
Wallis	J.I. Case Plow Works
Waterloo Boy	Waterloo Gasoline Engine Co. Deere & Company
Weber	American Gas Engine Company
Webfoot	Blewett Tractor Company
Wellington	Sterling Manufacturing Company
Westrak	General Tractor Company
Wheat	Hession Tiller & Tractor Company Wheat Tractor & Tiller Company
Whitney	Ohio Manufacturing Company
Winona Special	Pioneer Tractor Manufacturing Company
Wisconsin	McFarland & Westmont Tractor Company
Wizard 4-Pull	Kroyer Motors Company
Wolf	Star Tractor Company
Wolverine	Ypsilanti Hay Press Company
Wonder-Boy	Simplicity Manufacturing Company

X, Y & Z

Yankee	American Tractor Corporation
York	Flinchbaugh Manufacturing

OTHERS

King of diesels – and also of beer

The mainstay of current tractor horsepower, the diesel engine, traces it roots back to Rudolph Diesel and his then revolutionary compression-ignition engine.

The German scientist first patented his concept in 1892. At first Diesel's engine operated on coal dust. This useless by-product of mining was in ample supply in Germany at that time. But the days of coal dust were numbered after it caused a serious explosion during experiments.

Diesel cast around for a substitute and found it in fuel oil, which eventually was refined into the low-grade distillate that today we call diesel fuel. And that, you might say, is the rest of the story.

But you'd be wrong. You see, Diesel's invention caught the eye of an American innovator. That entrepreneur went on to purchase the first license to sell diesels in the U.S. in 1896. The engine he sold was a two-cylinder, 60-hp. unit that weighed about 400 pounds per horsepower output.

That's some big engine! But doing things big was not new for this businessman. You see, prior to getting into diesel engines, Adolphus Busch of St. Louis, Missouri, was big into beer.

You heard right – Adolphus Busch of Anheuser-Busch – the maker of Budweiser beer.

clubs & publications

ADVANCE-RUMELY
Rumely Collector's News
12109 Mennonite Church Rd.
Tremont, IL 61568
Telephone: 309/925-3925
Web: www.rumely.com

Rumely Product Collector's, Inc.
N9596 Howard Rd.
Whitewater, WI 53190
E-mail: jamiehome@idcnet.com
Web: www.rumelycollectors.com

ALLIS-CHALMERS
Old Allis News
10925 Love Rd.
Bellevue, MI 49021-9250
Telephone: 269/763-9770
Fax: 616/763-9770
E-mail: Allisnews@aol.com

Allis Connection
7011 E. Bethel Rd.
Elizabeth, IL 61028
Telephone: 815/598-3329
E-mail: allisacres@blkhawk.net

340

Allis-Chalmers and Simplicity Garden Tractors
Kent Thomas
29 Mount Pleasant St.
North Brookfield, MA 01535
E-mail: kent@simpletractors.com
Web: www.simpletractors.com

B.F. AVERY
B.F. Avery Collectors & Associates
Avery - Wards - General - M-M Avery
Connie Lemmon
14651 S. Edon Rd.
Camden, MI 49232
Telephone: 517/368-5595

BRISTOL CRAWLER
Graham and Jean Smith
98 York Road
Connah's Quay, Deeside
Flintshire, North Wales CH5 4YF
United Kingdom
Telephone: 01244 818918
E-mail: smithbristol@bristol10tractors.
fsnet.co.uk
Web: http://home.hccnet.nl/m.hooijberg/
bristol.html

BUNGARTZ
E-mail: michiel@bungartz.nl
Web: www.bungartz.nl

BUSH HOG
Bush Hog Tractors newsletter
E-mail: bushhoggardentractors
@yahoogroups.com
Web: www.bushhogtractors.info

CATERPILLAR
Antique Caterpillar Machinery Club
P.O. Box 2220
East Peoria, IL 61611
309/694-0664
Fax: 309/694-6180
E-mail: cat@acmoc.org
Web: www.acmoc.org

CENTAUR
John Plotz
11299 Cardwell
Livonia, MI 48150
Telephone: 734/425-5323

CHAMBERLAIN
RMD 2123 Wunkar Via Loxton
South Australia 5333
Australia
Telephone: 08 8587 6223
Web: www.gibbstractorcollection.com.
au/home.htm

CLETRAC
Blake Malkamaki
21092 N. Norrisville Rd.
Conneautville, PA 16406
Telephone: 814/587-2256
E-mail: blake@cletrac.org
Web: www.cletrac.org

COCKSHUTT
International Cockshutt Club, Inc.
Cockshutt Quarterly
Lynn Harold Vernon
168 Garland Line Rd.
Dover-Foxcroft, ME 04426
Telephone: 207/564-7001
E-mail: lvernon@midmaine.com
Web: www.cockshutt.com

Cockshutt
Keith McClure
Telephone: 330/567-3951
E-mail: ckp@valkyrie.net
Web: www.valkyrie.net

CUB CADET
Cadet Connection
Brian Sell
P.O. Box 1827
Butler, PA 16003-1827
Telephone: 724/283-7595
E-mail: lhcubbin@aol.com
Web: www.cadetconnection.com/
pages/543267/index.htm

clubs & publications

CUSHMAN
Cushman Club of America
Tom O'Hara
P.O. Box 661
Union Springs, AL 36089
Telephone: 334/738-3874
E-mail: ccoa@ustconline.net
Web: www.cushmanclubofamerica.com

CUSTOM
Custom Club International News
Chris Proeschel
3516 Hamburg Rd.
Eldorado, OH 45321
Telephone: 937/273-5692

DAVID BRADLEY
David Bradley Newsletter
Terry E. Strasser
Rt. 1, Box 280
Hedgesville, WV 25427
Telephone: 304/274-1725
Web: www.davidbradley.net

DAVID BROWN
David Brown Tractor Club, Ltd.
P.O. Box 990, Holmfirth
Huddersfield, West Yorkshire HD9 1YH
United Kingdom
E-mail: darrelclegg@yahoo.co.uk
Web: www.davidbrowntractorclub.com

EAGLE
Randy Reysen
E-mail: Shemp@execpc.com
Web: http://my.execpc.com/40/56/
shemp/index.html

EMERSON-BRANTINGHAM
John Brantingham
White Lake, MI
E-mail: john.r.brantingham@delphi.com
Web: http://members.aol.com/wb8jca/
ebhome.htm

EMPIRE
Empire Tractor Club
Carl Hering
5862 State Route 90 N.
Cayuga, NY 13034
Telephone: 315/253-8151
E-mail: hering@dreamscape.com
Web: www.empiretractor.net

FERGUSON
The Ferguson Club and Journal
The Old Coach House
Bell Horse Lane, Lees Moor
Hainworth, Keighley BD21 5QF
United Kingdom
Telephone: 01535 642411
Web: www.fergusonclub.com

Ferguson Enthusiasts of North America
Eugene Kruse
850 Adams St.
Lincoln, NE 68521
Telephone: 402/476-2818
E-mail: fergusonguy@aol.com

FORD
Ford/Fordson Collectors Assn., Inc.
645 Loveland-Miamiville Rd.
Loveland, OH 45140
E-mail: info@ford-fordson.org
Web: www.ford-fordson.org

9N-2N-8N-NAA Newsletter
Rob Rinaldi
P.O. Box 275
East Corinth, VT 05040-0275
Telephone: 802/439-6054
E-mail: infon@n-news.com
Web: www.n-news.com

FRICK
Frick Engine Club
P.O. Box 220 - 9161 NC Hwy #22
Climax, NC 27233
Telephone: 336/685-4253

GIBSON

Gibson Tractor Club and *ADEHI News*
Dave Baas
4200 Winwood Ct.
Floyds Knobs, IN 47119-9225
Telephone: 812/923-5822
E-mail: dbaas_59@hotmail.com

GRAVELY

Gravely Tractor Club of America
The Gravely Gazette
2201 Rt. 302
Lisbon, NH 03585
Telephone: 603/838-5589
E-mail: pbrick@net1plus.com

Gravelys Forever
7092 Hunters Ridge Dr.
Plainfield, IN 46168
Telephone: 317/839-6869

INTERNATIONAL HARVESTER

IH Collectors Association
Al Dummler
310 Busse Hwy., PMB 250
Park Ridge, IL 60068-3251
Telephone: 847/823-8612
E-mail: ihcclub@aol.com
Web: www.ihcollectors.org

Red Power Magazine
Dennis and Sallie Miesner
P.O. Box 245
Ida Grove, IA 51445-0245
Telephone: 712/364-2131
E-mail: miesner@pionet.net
Web: www.redpowermagazine.com

Harvester Highlights
Darrell Darst
1857 W. Outer Hwy. 61
Moscow Mills, MO 63362
Telephone: 636/356-4764
E-mail: buzzys@nothnbut.net
Web: www.ihcollectors.org

HART-PARR / OLIVER / CLETRAC

The Hart-Parr Oliver Collector
Association
Hart-Parr Oliver Collector
P.O. Box 500
Missouri City, TX 77459
Web: www.hartparroliver.org

HASS

1909 County Road 1700 E.
Roanoke, IL 61561
E-mail: haastractorclub@yahoo.com.
Web site: www.geocities.com/
  haastractorclub/

J.I. CASE

J.I. Case Collectors' Assn.
Old Abe's News
P.O. Box 638
Bleecher, IL 60401
E-mail: kwin3@earthlink.net
Web: www.jicca.org

J.I. Case Heritage Foundation
Heritage Eagle
P.O. Box 081156
Racine, WI 53408-1156
Telephone: 414/554-5205
E-mail: caseheritage@aol.com
Web: www.caseheritage.org

KECK-GONNERMAN

Keck-Gonnerman Antique Machinery
  Assn.
Don Julian
5005 N. Ford Rd.
Mt. Vernon, IN 47620
Telephone: 812/985-7578
E-mail: jdjulian@evansville.net

JOHN DEERE

The Green Magazine
2652 Davey Road
Bee, NE 68314
Telephone: 402/643-6269
Fax 402/643-3912
E-mail: info@greenmagazine.com
Web: www.GreenMagazine.com

clubs & publications

JOHN DEERE (continued)
Two-Cylinder
P.O. Box 430
Grundy Center, IA 50638-0010
Telephone: 319/345-6060
Fax: 319/345-2662
E-mail: twocyl@iowatelecom.net
Web: www.two-cylinder.com

LANZ
Lanz Bulldog Owners Register
A.M. Watson
Willow Corner, Main Street, Marston
Grantham, Lincolnshire NG32 2HH
United Kingdom
Telephone: 0044 01400 250840
E-mail: amwatson@btinternet.com

LEADER
Leader Tractor Club
Henry Hahn
7606 Highway J
Perryville, MO 63775
Telephone: 573/547-8693
E-mail: hehahn@onemain.com

LONG
Long Model A Registry
Rt. 4, Box 90A
Shelbyville, IL 62565
Telephone: 217/246-3199

M.A.N.
E-mail: andreas.mehrmann@t-online.de
Web: http://mitglied.lycos.de/
    MehrmannSite/seeite2neu.htm

**MASSEY-HARRIS-FERGUSON /
WALLIS**
Massey Collectors Association
30700 E. Rt. 2
Harrisonville, MO 64701
Telephone: 816/331-5525
Web: www.masseycollectors.org/

Massey Collectors News
Wild Harvest
Keith Oltrogge
P.O. Box 529
Denver, IA 50622
Telephone: 319/984-5292

Twin Power Heritage Association, Inc.
Massey-Harris/Ferguson Collectors
Bev Hughes
Rt. 3
Ilderton, Ontario N0M 2A0
Canada
Telephone: 519/666-0452

Friends of Massey Club
Sandy Kessel
2850 Old Carlisle Rd.
Gardners, PA 17324
Telephone: 717/677-7350
E-mail: skessel@blazenet.net
Web: www.friendsofmassey.com

MINNEAPOLIS-MOLINE
The Minneapolis-Moline Collectors, Inc.
Mike Verhulst
17766 Eddyville Rd.
Ottumwa, IA 52501
Telephone: 641/682-7754
E-mail: verhulstmike@aol.com
Web: www.minneapolismoline
    collectors.org

MM Corresponder
3693 M Avenue
Vail, IA 51465
Telephone: 712/677-2491
Web: www.minneapolismolinecollectors.
    org/magazine/corresponder.asp

Prairie Gold Rush
Ken and Cheryl Delap
17390 S. State Rd. 58
Seymour, IN 47274
Telephone: 812/342-3608
E-mail: kdelapmm@hsonline.net
Web: www.prairiegoldrush.com

PANZER
Panzer Tractor Owners Club
Michael Heller
P.O. Box 2601
Manassas, VA 20108
Telephone: 703/335-5219
E-mail: panzerclub@geocities.com
Web: www.panzertractors.com

RUSSELL
National Russell Collectors
561 29th St. N.W.
Massillon, OH 44647
Telephone: 330/833-6493

SEARS HANDIMAN
Sears Handiman Garden Tractors
E-mail: dellsasser@handimantractor.
   com
Web: www.handimantractor.com

SHAW
Shaw Du-All Registry
22 Nesenkeag Dr.
Litchfield, NH 03051

SHEPPARD
Sheppard Diesel Club
John Tichenor
RR 4, Box 90-A
Shelbyville, IN 62565
Telephone: 217/246-3199

SILVER KING
Silver Kings of Yesteryear Tractor Club
Sky Writer newsletter
Richard Lyman
4235 County 20
Mt. Gilead, OH 43338
Telephone: 419/946-6932

SIMPLICITY
Kevin Williard
8868 T.R. 508
Big Prairie, OH 44611
Telephone: 330/496-3382

Simplicity and Allis-Chalmers Garden
   Tractors
Simple Tractors
Kent Thomas
29 Mount Pleasant St.
North Brookfield, MA 01535
E-mail: kent@simpletractors.com
Web: www.simpletractors.com

SPEEDEX
Speedex Tractor Club
www.SpeedexTractorInformation.com

STANDARD TWIN
E-mail: tractors@standardtwin.com
Web: www.standardtwin.com

VIERZON
Societe Francaise de Vierzon
Tracto-Retro du Rhin
3, Rue du Houblon
67170 Kriegsheim, France
Telephone: 03 88 51 18 70
E-mail: vierzon@club-internet.fr
Web: www.chez.com/sfv/accueil.htm

WHEELHORSE
Wheel Horse Collectors Club
Don Kane
551 Nawakwa Rd.
Biglerville, PA 17307
717/677-6004
E-mail: raisingcane@blazenet.com
Web: www.wheelhorsecollectors.com

ZETOR
Steernbos, Dalfsen
The Netherlands
E-mail: webmaster@zetorworld.com
Web: www.zetorworld.com

clubs & publications

GENERAL GARDEN TRACTOR CLUBS

National Garden Tractor Pulling
  Association
NQS Puller
1323 4th Ave.
DeWitt, IA 52742
Telephone: 563/659-5276
E-mail: supercub@clinton.net
Web: www.nqspulling.com

Little G Lawn & Garden Tractor
Collector's Club
13306 Black Hills Rd.
Dyersville, IA 52040

Vintage Garden Tractor Club of America
Jim Cunzenheim Jr.
412 W. Chestnut
Pardeeville, WI 53954
E-mail: towrpowr27@yahoo.com
Web: www.vgtcoa.com

GENERAL MAGAZINES

Antique Power
Patrick Ertel
Box 838
Yellow Springs, OH 45387
Telephone: 800/767-5828
E-mail: antique@antiquepower.com
Web: www.antiquepower.com

Belt Pulley
20114 Illinois Rt. 16
Nokomis, IL 62075
Telephone: 217/563-2612
Fax: 217/563-2111
E-mail: beltpulley@mcleodusa.net
Web: www.beltpulley.com

Engineers and Engines Magazine
Don Knowles
2240 Oak Leaf St., P.O. Box 2757
Joliet, IL 60434-2757
Telephone: 815/741-2240

Farm Collector News
Gas Engine Magazine
1503 SW 42nd St.
Topeka, KS 66609
Telephone: 800/678-4883
Fax: 785/274-4305
E-mail: farmcollector@jnetworks.com
Web: www.farmcollector.com

Polk's Magazine
Dennis Polk
72435 State Rd. 15
New Paris, IN 46553
Telephone: 219/831-3555
E-mail: DPE@Skyenet.net

Tractor Classics CTM
Box 489
Rocanville, Saskatchewan S0A 3L0
Canada
Telephone: 306/645-4566
Fax: 306/645-4376

ANTIQUE TRACTOR PULLING

The Hook
Box 16
Marshfield, MO 65706
Telephone: 417/468-7000
Fax: 417/859-6075
E-mail: thehook@pcis.net
Web: www.hookmagazine.com

National Antique Tractor Pullers Assn.
Ed Epperson
5070 Weaver Rd.
Germantown, OH 45327
Telephone: 937/855-4326
Web: www.natpa@eppersontire.com

CONSTRUCTION EQUIPMENT

Historic Construction Equipment Assn.
Equipment Echoes
16623 Liberty Hi Road
Bowling Green, OH 43402
Telephone: 419/352-5616
Fax: 419/352-6068
Web: www.hcea.net

STEAM TRACTION ENGINES
Steam Traction
1503 S.W. 42nd St.
Topeka, KS 66609-1265
Telephone: 800/682-4704
Fax: 785/274-4305
E-mail: lschuetz@ogdenpubs.com
Web: www.steamtraction.com

Live Steam
2779 Aero Park Dr.
Traverse City, MI 49686

ENGINES
Antique Small Engine Collectors Club
7609 State Rd. 58 E.
Heltonville, IN 47436-8772
E-mail: dale@asecc.com
Web: www.asecc.com.

Briggs-Straton Club
Jim Miller
Box 465
Conover, OH 45317

Maytag Collectors Club
960 Reynolds Ave.
Ripon, CA 95366
Telephone: 209/599-5933
Web: www.maytagclub.com/

TRUCKS
American Truck Historical Society
Wheels of Time
Larry Scheef
P.O. Box 531168
Birmingham, AL 35253-1168
Telephone: 205/870-0566
Fax: 205/870-3069
E-mail: aths@mindspring.com
Web: www.aths.org

The Antique Truck Club of America
Double Clutch
P.O. Box 91
Ingomar, PA 15127
Telephone: 412/366-0392
Web: www.antiquetruckclubofamerica.
  org

Power Wagon Advertiser
Dept SL
3090 Benton Iowa Rd.
Norway, IA 52318

The Scout and International Motor Truck
  Assn.
P.O. Box 313
New Palestine, IN 46163
Telephone: 765/763-8736
E-mail: ihsimta@aol.com

Vintage Power Wagons
302 S. 7th St.
Fairfield, IA 52556
641/472-4665
Fax: 641/472-4824
E-mail: dodge@vintagepowerwagons.
  com
Web: www.vintagepowerwagons.com

The Willys Club
795 N. Evans St.
Pottstown, PA 19464
Web: www.off-road.com/jeep/willys/
  index.htm

OTHER AGRICULTURAL
COLLECTIBLES

CAST IRON SEATS
Cast Iron Seat Collectors Association
Charolette Traxler
RR 2, Box 38
Le Center, MN 56057-9610
Telephone: 507/357-6142
Fax: 507/357-6378
E-mail: gctrax@frontiernet.net

Cast Iron Seat Society
David Cook
Harrowdene Paddock
Felmersham, Bedford MK43 7HL
United Kingdom
E-mail: janet-david@harpadfel.fsnet.
  co.uk

clubs & publications

OTHER AGRICULTURAL COLLECTIBLES

CORN ITEMS
Corn Item Collectors Assn.
The Band Board newsletter
Robert Chamberlain
9288 Poland Rd.
Warrensburg, IL 62573
Telephone: 217/674-3337
E-mail: bob@burrusseed.com

DAIRY
Cream Separator & Dairy Newsletter
W20772 State Rd. 95
Arcadia, WI 54612

The National Assn. of Milk Bottle
    Collectors
The Milk Route newsletter
Box 105
Blooming Grove, NY 10914
Telephone: 845/496-6841
E-mail: moto2@frontiernet.net

North American Dairy Association
P.O. Box 32
Arcadia, WI 54612

HOG ITEMS
The Happy Pig Collector Club
4542 N. Western Ave.
Chicago, IL 60625
E-mail: pignutz@earthlink.net
Web: http://members.iquest.net/~drdan/
    index.html

LITERATURE
Farm Machinery Advertising Collectors
FMAC Newsletter
David Schnakenberg
10108 Tamarack Dr.
Vienna, VA 22182
Telephone: 703/938-8606
E-mail: schnakenbergdd@erols.com
Web: www.farmmachineryadvertise.com

TOOLS
Mid-West Tool Collectors Association
The Gristmill
William Rigler
Rt. 2, Box 152
Wartrace, TN 37183
Telephone: 615/455-1935
Fax: 615/455-0029
E-mail: billybob@edge.net
Web: www.mwtca.org

Missouri Valley Wrench Club &
Newsletter
Virgil Saak
403 Polk
Baxter, IA 50028-1019
Telephone: 515/227-3193

SPARK PLUGS
Spark Plug Collectors
The Ignitor Magazine
Chad Windham
3401 N.E. Riverside
Pendleton, OR 97801-3431
Telephone: 541/276-4069
Fax: 541/278-6169
E-mail: sparkycush@aol.com

WINDMILLS
Windmillers Gazette
T. Lindsay Baker
P.O. Box 507
Rio Vista, TX 76093

STOCKYARD ITEMS
Stockyard Collectors Club
The Stockyard Collector
Mitchell McKay
5 Seneca West
Hawthorn Woods, IL 60047
Telephone: 847/566-5914

INTERNATIONAL CLUBS & PUBLICATIONS

AUSTRALIA

Vintage Tractor & Machinery Association of Western Australia
Lesley Smith
Box 3
Mukinbudin
Western Australia 6479
Australia
Telephone: 08 9685 1261
Fax: 08 9685 1359
E-mail: John.LesleySmith@bigpond.com

Tracmach newsletter
Pat & Vern Whitney
8 Reserve St.
Toodyay
Western Australia 6566
Australia
Telephone: 08 9574 4507

The Olde Machinery Magazine
PO Box 1200
Port Macquarie
New South Wales 2444
Australia
Telephone: 02 658 50055
E-mail: tomm_magazine@hotmail.com

ENGLAND

Tractor & Machinery
Kelsey Publishing Ltd.
Cudham Tithe Barn, Berry's Hill
Cudham, Kent TN16 3AG
United Kingdom
Telephone: 01959 541444
Fax: 01959 541400
E-mail: info@kelsey.co.uk
Web: www.tractor-and-machinery.com/

Vintage Tractor
Allan T. Condie Publications
40 Main Street
Carlton, Warwickshire, CV13 0RG
United Kingdom

Vaporiser Magazine
National Vintage Tractor and Engine Club
1 Hall Farm Cottages, Church Lane
Swarkestone, Derby, DE73 1JB
United Kingdom

The National Vintage Tractor Engine Club
Jim Albert
1 Evenden Road
Meopham, Kent DA13 0HA
United Kingdom

GERMANY

Der Schlepper im Ruckblick
Kurt Hafner
Kaiserbacher StraBe 34
71540 Murrhardt
Germany

Der Schlepperfreund Magazine
Bulldog-und Schlepperfreunde
Würrttemburg e.V. Maiser 5
71735 Eberdingen
Germany

Schlepper Post Magazine
Klaus Rabe
Postfach 25 04 28
50520 Köln
Germany
Web: www.verlagrabe.de/sp/sp.html

ISRAEL

Crawl Track Club Isreal
Web: www.ctc.gbrener.org.il/

NEW ZEALAND

Vintage Farming Magazine
Michael J. Hanrahan
78 Oxford St.
Ashburton
New Zealand

Waikato Vintage Tractor & Machinery Club, Inc.
Paul Houghton
503C Gordonton Rd., RD 1
Hamilton
New Zealand
Telephone: 07-824 3210
Fax: 07-824 3213

clubs & publications

INTERNATIONAL CLUBS & PUBLICATIONS

SOUTH AFRICA
Vintage Tractor & Engine Club of South
   Africa
The Veteran Farmer Magazine
The Editor
P.O. Box 8667
Centurion
Pretoria 0046
Republic of South Africa
Telephone: 0334-71405

SWITZERLAND
D'Fettpress Magazine
Freunde alter Landmaschinen Der
Schweiz-Fals
Paul Muri
Blumenweg 4
CH-5722 Granischen
Switzerland
Telephone: 0041-62-8421064

D'Fettpress
Zeitschrift des Verbandes Freunde alter
   Landmaschinen Schweiz Fals
Paul Müri
Blumenweg 4
CH-5722 Gränichen
Switzerland
Telephone: 0041-62-855 86 55
Fax: 0041-62-855 86 90
E-Mail: paul.mueri@ag.ch

OTHERS

_____

_____

_____

_____

_____

_____

_____

_____

_____

_____

_____

_____

_____

_____

_____

_____

_____

_____

_____

_____

_____

_____

_____

_____

_____

_____

_____

_____

_____

_____

_____

_____

_____

_____

_____